The Path of a Reluctant Metaphysician

Stories and Practices for Troubled Times

by

MICHAEL MAYER, PH.D.

The Path of a Reluctant Metaphysician: Stories and Practices for Troubled Times
by Michael Mayer, Ph.D.

Cover Design by Karin Kinsey of Dolphin Press.
Book Design by Karin Kinsey of Dolphin Press, CA, and Natasha Fischl.

First American Edition
Printed in the United States of America

———————————————————————

Library of Congress Cataloguing-in-Publication Data

Mayer, Michael, 1947-
    The path of a reluctant metaphysician : stories and practices for troubled times / by Michael Mayer. — 1st American ed.
    p. cm.
    Includes bibliographical references and index.
    ISBN 978-0-9839665-0-0

    1. Mind and body. 2. Holistic medicine. 3. Health. 4. Mayer, Michael, 1947-
I. Title.

BF161.M39 2012   158.1
QBI12-600112

This book is dedicated to my son Joab, my Godson Alexander,
And to humanities' children's, children's children.

May the world have a clean, sacredly held, sustainable environment.
And may the elders also pass on to the next generation
a Pathway to live a meaningful, sacredly held, and soulful life.

TABLE OF CONTENTS

Contents

Contents

Contents

LIST OF ILLUSTRATIONS

Chapter 1

Figure 1: The Helping Hand of the Tree of Life

Chapter 10

Figure 2: Wang Xiangzhai Standing—Holding Ball of Energy

Chapter 11

Figure 3: Wuji Standing Meditation

Figure 4: The Circle That Arises from Stillness

Figure 5: Puppet Dangling from Heaven

Figure 6: Holding Golden Balls in the Waters of Life

Figure 7: Developing the Golden Ball of the Heart and the Sphere of the Self

Figure 8: Dispersing Stagnant Qi Posture

Figure 9: Taoist Immortal Paints a Heavenly Rainbow

Chapter 12

Figure 10: Deer Looks Backward

Figure 11: Deer Rutting

Chapter 13

Figure 12: Ornithoid Android Figure Treating a Kneeling Patient

Figure 13: Crane Flying

Figure 14: Bear Pouncing

Figure 15: Bear Pushes Tree

Chapter 14

Figure 16: Cave of the Oracle of Delphi. Appreciation goes to The Philosophical Research Society, Inc. Los Angeles, CA., who published the book, The Secret Teachings of All Ages, *1971, P. LX.*

Chapter 16

Figure 17: Using The Astrological Mandala as a Psychotherapeutic Meta-system

Chapter 19

Figures 18 and 19: Master Fong Ha doing Tai Chi Joining Hands Practice with the Author

Figure 20: Master Fong Ha bouncing the author with fajing

Figure 21: After I strike at Master Tam, he yields maintaining his central equilibrium, as I lose mine. He follows my spiraling force until I fall into the trap of emptiness.

Figure 22: Master Tam yields, not using any apparent force of his own, as I begin to recoil backwards.

Figure 23: Notice the blurriness of the picture of me, showing the speed at which I am recoiling backwards, and Master Tam's stillness.

Figure 24: I am beginning to be uprooted by Master Tam's use of my force to discharge me; and I push off his expanding sphere to maintain the cohesiveness of my sphere.

Figure 25: I am fully uprooted from the power of the "no force" method.

Figure 26: I begin to land.

Figure 27: I land with a fair degree of cohesiveness of my Qi Ball, after an experience that felt like being shot out of a cannon. It is not unusual to end up 10 to 15 feet from the point of discharge by the master of the art.

Figures 21–27: Master Tam, illustrating empty force and fajing. With permission from Master Tam and Jan Diepersloot. Pictures taken of Grandmaster Sam Tam and author doing fajing practice by Sandy Rosenberg and Jan Diepersloot. Thanks to Jan Diepersloot for the time spent downloading them from his computer.

Chapter 22

Figure 28: Pelican Sinks its Qi

Chapter 23

ACKNOWLEDGMENTS

For one who has practiced Standing Meditation Qigong (called Standing Like a Tree Qigong, or in Chinese *Zhan Zhuang*) for three decades, I must say that writing a book is like a growing tree. The tree is still growing, and this book is just a snapshot of it at a given moment. Likewise, no one creates his or her own tree. It grows through the help of nature, the light of the universe, and sometimes human gardeners.

In this later context I would like to thank those remarkable people who I have mentioned in Chapter Ten, and others who I may be forgetting, who helped to sow the seeds of my ideas. As well, much appreciation goes to my friends and support system who helped to tend the garden of my writing process: Mark Fromm, Jean Hayek, Gareth Hill, Sean Kelly, Sandy Rosenberg, and David Weinstein. Deep appreciation goes to my parents, Abraham and Freda Mayer, from whose loving kindness and fertile soil I grew.

Heartfelt appreciation goes to Karin Kinsey of Dolphin Press for her sense of creative aesthetics, meticulous attention to detail, and her dedication in designing this book. Much thanks goes to Natasha Fischl who assisted in the book designing process and added a valuable ingredient with her Master's degree in computer science. Also, much appreciation goes to Paul Samberg of Mountain Lake Indexing for his adept work and conscientiousness in indexing this book.

For the book cover, much appreciation goes to the 14th World Qigong conference and Sifu Justin Ngui whose logo synchronistically was part of the inspiration process leading to the creation of the cover of this book. Right when I was meditating on the cover design and I wanted to have a figure sharing his heart with the world, a symbol of the Tao, an astrological zodiac, and a path, I saw their design which had a few of these elements creatively expressed. I synthesized my idea with theirs into this cover. Ah, the beauty of synchronicity and the generosity of others.

To the metaphysically inclined, appreciation and awe must be expressed to some force in the universe…some light that, in a process more mysterious than photosynthesis, helps us to grow. At the time of the Spring Equinox of 2010, I was ready to write my sixth book on another topic; but instead this one took over the writer's garden. Each morning the tree grew (some call this "channeling") as new buds shot forth and blossomed. Some source of light from some divine source that joins heaven and earth inspired me with what I was supposed to write as I woke every morning until the Winter Solstice of 2011. Rolling over in bed, I scribbled down the ideas that came to me every morning; my job was to find a time to write the given material down in the midst of my patient schedule and workshop planning. So, greatest acknowledgement must be given to the light that came from the "muses of the celestial spheres," and helped this tree to grow.

In the old days it was more obvious that when we wrote with pencils we were taking pieces of trees that joined heaven and earth, and by adding a little lead (symbol of incarnating into matter) or ink (colorful ways of expressing that came from the plant kingdom), writers were able to manifest an idea. Those who are metaphysically inclined have always known that ideas come down from the creative forces of the universe through the element of air, and manifest in the branches of human knowledge to produce a new oxygenating life-form that can add to the ground of our existence. It is no less so in our computer age...just a little less organically obvious how our everyday life needs to be thankful to the Tree of Life, the light and energy of the universe, and the forces of the natural world that give our books, and us, Life.

AUTHOR'S NOTE

The practices, ideas, and suggestions in this book are not intended as a substitute for medical attention. When considering applying any practices mentioned in this book to various health related issues, please consult with your medical doctor and/or other appropriate health professionals. Though benefit can be gained by reading about the integrated solutions to bodymind health issues included in this book, due caution should be exercised in undertaking the inward journeys suggested here. Such inner exploration is best done with a licensed mental health professional. For lay readers, please discuss these methods with your current health professionals to see whether, or how, they can be incorporated in your treatment. For more information on trainings in your area, or finding a therapist trained in, or certified in, these methods please see www.reluctantmetaphysician.com.

PREFACE

A Life Shaped by Stories

Let me tell you a story:
About my life, and yours, and my generation;
About the Cave of Creation, where you may go after death;
About what's behind life, how to heal your Self,
how to participate in the healing of our planet,
And about a few other little things.

—the Genii of this book's intention

My Parents, Scheherazade, and Other Master Storytellers:

One of my earliest memories is being a young child excitedly waiting for my father to tell me a story before I went to sleep each night. I still remember ones from the *Arabian Nights*, like the story of "Ali Baba and the Forty Thieves," and how my father would intone the phrase "open sesame." I learned that those like Ali Baba, who knew secret phrases, could open the hidden door to a cave of treasures, and that the tone of a storyteller's voice could open a door to a child's imagination. Just as strongly I remember how my father, who won various prizes for his storytelling ability, would tell the story of Scheherazade who, as a master storyteller, won over the evil King who had killed all his previous one-night lovers. By keeping him in suspense, due to not finishing the story each night, he eventually grew to love her, spared her life, and the kingdom was healed.

The Stories That Shape Our Lives

This was long before I knew that I would walk a path that was paved by myths and stories, and I certainly did not know how much they would play a significant part in my life as a psychotherapist and author. But nonetheless, as a child I was fascinated by how secret words could have the power to open a cave to a secret place, and how a story could even transform a King's self-centeredness. Yes, I was mesmerized by the power of a story to create love where there was narcissistic self-indulgence, and I saw that ideally a story could transform a kingdom.

Also, the stories that my mother told me captivated me as much as a call from a friend to go out and play baseball. I lived in a sheltered, well-to-do suburban community in New Jersey when my mother told me of how in her childhood, as a recent Jewish immigrant from Russia, her mother (my grandmother) brought up five children in a single room. My mother told me about how she and her siblings had to walk to the dangerous shared community outhouse in her backyard to go to the bathroom, afraid of who might be waiting out there in the darkness. Further emphasizing their poverty, my mother told me the story of how her clothes were washed in kerosene onetime when they didn't have enough soap, and when the teacher in her grammar school smelled the kerosene and asked from where it came, my mother suffered in silence as the teacher passed by her sniffing. A glance was shared, and my mother knew that the teacher knew about her poverty but was not going to reveal it to the class. From hearing my mother's tale I learned not only about the power of a story to teach me gratitude for my suburban circumstances, but also about the value of the kindness and mercy of a teacher.

Speaking of gratitude for economic circumstances, when I was five years old my mother wanted to teach me to appreciate my suburban life. So, she took me back to our old hometown, Newark, where I lived for the first five years of my life before we moved to suburban West Orange. As we drove down into the worst slums of Newark where she had lived in her childhood, she pointed out the horrible poverty in her neighborhood, "See that oil-stained vacant lot where kids are playing marbles around broken concrete, and that rusty old can where we played "kick the can?" That's where I had to play as a child. We didn't have toys like you have, or a nice front lawn." The way my mom tells the story, she looked over to me and a tear was rolling down my cheek, and she said, "What's the matter, Michael." My mother says that I replied in a quivering voice, "Sure, sure…you had a happy childhood. Look at all those kids playing over there. I wish I had so many kids to play with." In our relatively isolated suburban neighborhood I often had a hard time finding other children with whom I could to play. This story reveals many deep teachings, including an early sense in my life that there were deeper values than material comfort.

Stories of all kinds permeated my early upbringing. Mythic stories at bedtime, stories around the kitchen table of my father's cases as an attorney, stories of my mother's encounters with everyday people, and stories of the adventures of our lives. These were the emotional foods that gave nutrition to my soul throughout my childhood.

Maybe it was the stories that my father and mother told me that initiated my interest in studying mythology, and later in my life to develop a storytelling process to help my patients. I will tell you about this method later (The Mythic Journey Process) and about the book I wrote (*Trials of the Heart*) that describes how stories and myths can help to heal our relationships with others.

Or, maybe there are much larger forces at work that lead each of us to choose our life path; and perhaps these forces are as powerful, or more so, than the traditional psychological belief that it is our parents' influence on us that is the major ruler our future destiny.

What is it that forms each of our life's direction? Each of us has key experiences that change the direction of our lives. Throughout this book you will see how it was from inner dreams, outer visions, meeting with remarkable people and places, and a mysterious ingredient that may be called "our soul's purpose," that my destiny took form. As you read this book I trust that you will get more in touch with the potential of those same forces to change your life's path.

INTRODUCTION

My Religion is to live and die without regret.

—Milarepa

Difficulties in Life: A Calling to the Path of the Reluctant Metaphysician

As any of us tune into the changes that are prevalent in the social, political, philosophical, and economic atmosphere of this second decade of the third millennium we cannot help but wonder what is stirring? Are we in the midst of a revolutionary change that is as big as the change that took place at the time that a heliocentric view of the universe replaced the geocentric one? Or, is this just an inflated notion coming from one who wants to magnify his or her own moment in history?

Whether it is in our personal lives, or in our collective society, when change comes it is a natural, fundamental human tendency to attempt to make sense of the changes and to search for how to best cope with them. We have all fantasized about the how to cope with "the end times," whether it is the dissolution of a relationship, the termination of a job, a change of career, the end of a stable economic life, or death itself. How do we prepare for such times?

The great philosopher Michel de Montaigne suggested that to begin to deprive death of its advantage over us we should practice the art of dying. But how does one do this? The great philosopher Plato said, "Death is the great initiation." But, how does one learn the initiatory secrets to handle the mini-deaths of life as well as "the big one?"

Here in the early years of the 21st century, the death of ideals, climate change, environmental disasters, and economic turmoil seem to pervade the atmosphere. People are praying for rebirth no less than a Neolithic hunter in years of old would look at an eclipse and wonder if the sun would ever shine again. As polarizing forces are fighting in the current dark times of the American political climate, and creating economic uncertainty, many are wondering how to cope with the dismantling of our culture. Even traditional financial columnists like Suze Orman are saying that "The American dream as we knew it is dead" (Orman, 2012).

As I write this introduction, synchronicity is at work as I happen to turn on a *60 Minutes* show (March 6, 2011) that reports that 25% of the children in our supposedly richest country in the world go hungry. Middle class students are shown living in their parents vans and going to school after washing up at the local Wal-Mart bathroom.[1] I turn the channel and the Middle East is erupting with revolution in the streets. On another TV station a battle takes place in Wisconsin between the forces of democracy and governmental officials such as Governor Scott Walker who tries to stop workers' bargaining rights as he follows like a puppet the wishes of wealthy puppeteers like the Koch brothers. It does seem that we are in a time of economic, political and environmental upheaval (which I will talk more about in the last three chapters). Such circumstances calls each of us to find our stance towards an end of the world we knew.

What are those factors in personal of social history that create a powerful personal dream or a social revolution to take place and transform an established order? More importantly, how can any of us participate in creating a new world that is in tune with our, and our world's, highest good?

This book is not about any particular sphere of dissolution but about how the process of my life introduced me to stories and practices to cope with such changes in various spheres: philosophical, psychological, spiritual, and cultural. I call it the path of the Reluctant Metaphysician, because the complacent part of me (and for most of us) does not want to face the death of a world. Yet in doing so, guidance from the world behind the world is revealed—if we learn to listen and read the signs.

Difficulties in any sphere of life activate the calling of the Reluctant Metaphysician— they set the ball a-rolling. In this book I will use my story to talk about the evolutionary changes in my life and how they mirror changes in the wider scheme of things. As I reflect back on my own radical change, my early life was lit by the intellect; it was the star around which my early life revolved. At that stage of my life I would have agreed with Descartes' dictum, "I think therefore I am." Being brought up in a household where my father was an attorney, my psyche was cast by a philosophy that said the mind was the center of universe. However, then my culture and I were opened to a larger universe of meaning.

So, this book is not just about how to deal with the deaths of life, but it is about a Way to deal with life itself. The path of the Reluctant Metaphysician is to bring meaning and transformation to various spheres of life by connecting to the wider whole of which we are a part.

There has been a Western philosophical movement prevalent since the Age of Enlightenment age that, with all its benefits in moving from the superstition of the dark ages, has a shadow side—the desacralization of the world. We human beings have become separated and alienated from the cosmos (Weber, 1993; Schiller, 1993; Tarnas, 2007). My life journey serves as an attempt to resacralize my life, and to join others who are doing the same for their lives and our culture.

Every facet of life is a mythogem, and if we look at it with metaphysical eyes a treasure house opens. Each of our unique identities can become connected to sacred purpose, the people we meet become part of a transformative mythic journey, and nature and the cosmos itself become living symbols and messengers of an *anima mundi*—an ensouled world.

What is a Reluctant Metaphysician?

This book is about is about the path of the Reluctant Metaphysician, the path that I reluctantly was drawn to follow. I did not want to follow this path, I wanted to follow the well-worn road, the route that all of my youth I was sure I would follow—being an attorney. But other forces of destiny pulled me in another direction. I hope this book will serve to help other Reluctant Metaphysicians to listen to the calling of "the world behind the world" to find your path.

I use the term "reluctant" because from the perspective of the ego, one often experiences certain events, philosophies, or callings of life as a stretch to which the complacent part of us unwillingly, yet dharmically, feels compelled to listen. The stretching process can "shape-shift" us into a new, more expansive life-form. According to the Online Etymological Dictionary, the etymology of the word "reluctance" means "unwillingness" (first attested to in the 1660s). A still earlier definition from the 1520s is the Latin term *reluctari,* "the act of struggling or rebelling against." When I join the terms "reluctant" and "metaphysician" I am making the statement that when the world behind the world calls us, the ensuing hero's quest can be a struggle. Yet like in the Jewish tradition (which by definition is a God-wrestling path), a struggle with the divine source of creation can create increased knowledge and bring us closer to the source of wisdom and love in the universe. And so it is that I have reluctantly wrestled with spiritual philosophies, entrenched beliefs, astrological theories, the origins and practices of psychotherapy, the nature of our true identities, the political/economic/cultural dimensions of modern America, and with my own calling. From the struggle was born the knowledge, adventures, and practices of this book.[2]

There are philosophers who have been referred to as "Reluctant Metaphysicians" such as John Locke, (Tsanoff, 1942; Pasnau, 2011), John Dewy (Hickman, 1998), and Ludwig Wittgenstein (Brommage, 2008). But no one, to my knowledge has tried to answer the question, "What is the philosophy of a reluctant metaphysician?"

One can argue that each Reluctant Metaphysician will define this realm in their unique way, based upon their essential nature. In modern scholarship we can go back as far as Plato and Aristotle to find discussions about the field of metaphysics. However, it can be imagined that long before Plato and Aristotle developed their metaphysics that the world of the Reluctant Metaphysician began. The earliest humans, in moments of difficulty, quested to establish a connection with the world behind the world to heal and transform the difficulties they faced in life.

In the following chapters you will see how stories and various spiritual practices have been metaphysical tools that have helped my patients, my students, and myself to transform our lives. No less than Persephone's abduction created a journey to the underworld and a rebirth into a new life stance (Queen of the Underworld), so can each of our worlds be transformed at such times. Just as a treasure house opened for Ali Baba because he had the right approach (in his case saying "open sesame"), today for us metaphysical doorways can open to those who have the keys:

1. When psychological imbalances occur in our lives, and we go deeply into ourselves to find a way of healing and discover new stances toward life we become Reluctant Metaphysicians. In Chapter 18 you will discover integrative psychological methods to find a new life stance.

2. When a relationship unwantingly breaks up and we reluctantly look deeply into the world behind the world we may wonder, "What can I learn from this experience so it is never repeated again?" At that moment we become Reluctant Metaphysicians. You will discover how, at a moment of emotional difficulty in your life or in a relationship, you can use the Mythic Journey Process to make a connection between your bodymind and the mythic world to heal and transform (see Chapter 15). You will be introduced to the River of Life guided meditation where the connection with your inner sanctuary can help you to connect to the source of healing (see Chapter 11).

3. When ordinary life creates obstacles so solid that we are hitting our heads into walls, and a dream, a visionary experience, a person we synchronistically meet, or a message from nature opens a door to a new life direction we become Reluctant Metaphysicians. In gratitude, we bow to the world behind the world that has healed and transformed us at such times. Throughout this book you will see how my students, my patients, and I have been reluctantly and gratefully been abducted into the journey of the Reluctant Metaphysician.

4. Throughout the ages, at a moment of physical difficulty when illness or injury struck, people in pain looked up to the moon and wondered "why and wherefore?" In bygone times, our ancestors who were connected with the night sky may have spontaneously felt impelled to bring its light down to heal the darkness of their life with gestures, movements, and stories that made a connection with the world behind the world. Throughout this book you will hear about how postures, gestures, movements and experiences of connecting with the natural world can revitalize us and lead to a new life direction. As our ancestors were healed by a story around the campfire when they were suffering, so can we be today. For example, you will hear the story of the "Buddha and Sickness Demon," and how our illnesses make our eyes turn heavenward, and we become Reluctant Metaphysicians (see Chapter 15).

5. At a painful moment of emotional difficulty, early humans said, "Why me?" He or she looked up to the heavens and saw a celestial constellation and configuration. Astrology was born as meaning came into his or her world—whether we want to say that celestial synchronicities are projected or metaphysically real. In

this book, without needing to believe in astrology, you will hear about a way that you can use the metaphors of the celestial sphere to contextualize your difficulties in a sphere of new and wider meaning.

6.   Songs, meditation postures, sacred movements, storytelling, visualization methods, dream-work, and vision questing are some of the primordial ways that the Reluctant Metaphysician taps into the world behind the world for healing and restoring vital energy.

7.   When our culture destroys the middle class, pollutes our environment, and values profits over our children we may look deeply into the world behind the world to pray for change. Then we may become Reluctant Metaphysicians searching for ways from the depths of us to change the world. You will be shown ways to find new life stances and to draw from the unique talents you have that are part of your destiny (see Chapter 18).

Speaking of Ali Baba's use of the words "open sesame," the power of words has always fascinated me. However, since I am a sceptic by nature, I looked at esotericists' claims as, at best, an interesting experiment to verify. For example, one day in 1972 I read in Manly Hall's book, *The Secret Teachings of All Ages* (1962) that by repeating the name *abracadabra,* a person could have wishes come true. I thought this was nonsense, but I decided to try it one day. I knocked on a redwood tree while saying abracadabra three times, and I wished for a woman with whom I could have a child. That evening I synchronistically met a woman named Tree-la. (Remember these were the hippie days, and naming yourself after elements of nature, such as trees, was common). From our lovemaking that night my son Joab was born.

My testing the world behind the world has been a never-ending quest. One day I got a terrible case of poison oak for which my calamine lotion was not helping. I went to the health food store, and while walking down the aisle saw an advertisement for a homeopathic remedy called *Technu Extreme: Medicated Poison Ivy Scrub*. On the package is says, "Works in 15 seconds." Normally, I would not buy such a hyped-up product; but I bought it so that I could prove that the claim was false. I couldn't wait to write a letter to this company and tell them that they shouldn't advertise in such a deceptive way. However, the product gave me major relief in fifteen seconds and after a few more applications that day the poison oak no longer bothered me. Since I was highly allergic to poison oak, usually the irritation lasted for weeks, or even a month.

I should say that I have had poison oak other times since then, and this product did not work as well. As is true with many medications, it seems that the first time trying some medications they may work best. A most important point is that just because some connection with another realm (be it prayer, metaphysical incantations, or healing substances) does not work every time, does not disprove its efficacy.

One problem with the scientific method is that it rests on a particular rule of the game that does not always fit all games of life. The scientific axiom says that the effect on a dependent variable by an independent variable must reoccur regularly as the independent variable is applied in order for the phenomena under consideration to be deemed reliable and valid. Speaking as one who has written three peer reviewed scientific research articles, I must say that the scientific method has its limitations in certain fields.

In the realm of metaphysics, which most directly involves a quantum not a Newtonian reality, occurrences often take place in a non-linear, anomalous, acausal manner (Bohm, 1989; Chopra, 1990; Krippner et. al., 2000). My son's birth and various anomalous happenings open the eyes of the sceptic who must reluctantly admit that, "There's something happening here; what it is ain't exactly clear" (as the Buffalo Springfield song says).

I never said the abracadabra word before this incidence, and when I have said it since, this incantation has not worked to fulfill my wishes. However, such statistical failures in repeated experiments do not invalidate the reality of the world behind the world. In quantum physics the appearance of elementary particles of physical matter is known to be related to anomalous patterns involving energy and mind; and various building blocks of physical matter such a quarks and leptons often appear in their own time-frame in time and space, according to the laws of probability, not the laws of reliability (Ford, 2005).

There may be a consciousness behind the matter of the universe, but it does not always seem to operate according to Newton's laws. Therefore, when we follow the academic need to solely measure synchronistic and other metaphysical occurrences by the laws and science of Newton, we are succumbing to a seduction to play by the rules of a Newtonian game. Certainly "scientific research," the way it is normally construed, is important for some games; but many researchers argue that it has limited efficacy for measuring various phenomena of metaphysical life (Bohm, 1989; Wayne & Kaptchuk, 2008; Krippner et. al., 2010).

Towards a Holistic Model of Human Spirituality

Many people have attempted to create a holistic model of human spirituality. Hollick (2006) concludes that such an endeavor should "draw upon the ancient wisdom of the shamanic, polytheistic, monotheistic, and transcendent religious traditions; welcome the devotional, intellectual detached, engaged solitary, social, exoteric, esoteric, transcendent, immanent and other spiritual paths; and embrace the co-creative participatory view of our relationship with spirit (pp. 352–353). Daniels (2009) suggests that beyond the standard "ascending" (geared to other-worldly transcendence, and "descending" (geared to this-worldly immanence) there should be included a third vector, which he calls "extending." Daniels says that within the descending traditions there has been a conflation of two distinct perspectives: the depth psychological that focuses upon the exploration and integration of unconscious material, and relational/participatory perspectives, which stresses the spiritual connection with others and the world. He wrote that such relational/participatory thinking is "exemplified in indigenous spiritualities, feminist spirituality (e.g. the connected self), transpersonal ecology and ecocentrism), relational spiritualities, and Ferrer's (2002) participatory vision (emancipation form self-centeredness, co-creative participation). Daniels (2009) makes the case for an "all vector transpersonal theory and practice."

In a co-authored essay, Ferrer, Romero & Albareda (2005) introduce a pedagogical vision in which "all human dimensions (body, heart, vital energy, mind, and consciousness) co-creatively participate at all stages of the learning process in interaction with the generative power of life of the spirit.

My current book is one metaphysician's attempt to put forth an approach to such an integrative "spiritual path." The cobblestones of this pathway are paved from my thirty years as a licensed psychologist in private practice, and from many other traditions such as: astrology, cross-cultural mythology, symbolic process traditions, internal martial arts, politics, ecology, and from various Eastern and Western spiritual traditions. My aim is not to put forth an academic, philosophic treatise, but rather to put forth a type of guidebook that will inspire readers to develop their own unique amalgam of spiritual paths and practices. In this regard, I show how and why I developed my particular approach.

For those who are interested in a more traditional academic approach to integrative spirituality, one good source is Ferrer's (2011) update of his perspective on integrative models. As well, Ken Wilber's works (2006, 2007) are an important part of the literature on integrative spiritual models. It is not my purpose in this book to compare and contrast my approach to such authors, though in a later chapter I do touch on my difference with Wilber's hierarchical viewpoint. However, rather than engage in an academic discussion of this, I present the difference of viewpoints through a playful story.

My book is meant to be more experiential, trickster-like, and mythopoetic—to take you the reader on an odyssey that has a holistic spiritual/metaphysical philosophy in the background, and an emphasis on an experiential journey in the foreground. So, though there are academic discussions of distinctions between spiritual and metaphysical pathways, and theoretical discussions of various philosophical viewpoints, in the main this book is experientially based and practice oriented.

The Tapestry of This Book

This book is meant to open doors to the felt experience and awesome nature of the world behind the world through stories and practices to guide our lives, particularly during troubled times. You will see how stories lead to metaphysical practices, and how metaphysical practices lead to make your life into an interesting story. Through all these chapters, I weave together stories of my own life with stories from the collective tales of humankind. A tapestry is created.

In Chapter 1, I will introduce three frame stories that are woven throughout the book. First, you will hear about "The Old Woman in the Cave" who teaches how to remain calm in the midst of the unraveling of her life, and from this story we learn how a divine purpose weaves the threads of our unique ways. Secondly, the old tale of the bird-being "Icanchu" from South America teaches about what to do when devastation strikes your life. Thirdly, the Old Testament story of "Joseph and His Coat of Many Colors" serves as a teaching story about the threads of destiny that we carry from past generations, and how the path of our wounding leads us to our destiny.

When I describe the emotional wounds and healing of some of my patients in later sections of the book, I change some details about their lives to protect their identities. I owe a great debt of gratitude to them for their inner journeys, and how that inner work has influenced my path, professionally and personally.

The Structure of This Book

This book could be called a hodgepodge...defined as a heterogeneous mixture, a jumble. According to dictionary.com the origin of the term hodgepodge from "hotch-potch" is a thick soup or stew of vegetable or meat often thickened with barley, so it is this mixing of different substances that adds substance and nourishment to the mixture. In this spirit we will be mixing stories of my life with cross-cultural myths; and we will stir all of this into a soup that incorporates practices from indigenous, Eastern and Western metaphysical traditions.

So, my dear fellow travelers on the path, I hope this book is as enlightening and nourishing to you, as the experiences in it were for me. I hope you will absorb it as food for thought, to empower you on your life journey, and to inspire you to forge your unique path through uncharted territories.

I hope that you too may remain open to being abducted by the metaphysical world lying just behind everyday life. This was the deeper gift from those of my generation who went to Woodstock, imbibed psychedelics, and were infused by initiatory experiences from various cross-cultural traditions Timeless treasures of the inner world were opened then and are accessible now (without drugs). When John Lennon sang, "You say you want a revolution, well you better free your mind instead," I was one of those young hippies who was moved to explore the inner side of that cultural revolution.[3]

This revolution led me to explore Eastern spiritual traditions such as Tai Chi, and the Western mystery traditions—particularly symbolic process traditions. The music of the 1960s led me on a quest to the West to California, and as you will see to Esalen Institute. Esalen Institute was, and is, a seeding ground for seekers in the human growth and potential movement, a sacred place on the West Coast of the United States where East meets West—not just geographically, but philosophically. In the following pages you will see how Esalen Institute and other sacred places helped to activate the visionary experiences that lit my life path and helped me to find my way. I hope that you will become inspired in reading this book to find the places in your everyday life that will do the same for you. When you are searching for your way in life, or are dealing with troubled times, perhaps you too will become an initiate who is abducted by metaphysical experiences that open a door to the treasure house of your destiny.

A few details: I try as best as I can to tell my story in a chronological fashion beginning with some experiences of my childhood and moving on through my school years and my professional work as a psychologist; however there are times that my past and future experiences interweave with the current story. Like life, Time is fluid; so I hope that you as a reader will be able to appreciate what the past and future adds to my life story and yours.

Another editorial item: You will notice that sometimes I capitalize letters of certain words such as "Time" and certain psychological states, such as Envy and Doubt. This stems from the influence of psychologist James Hillman and archetypal psychology on my self-expression (Hillman, 1975). Capitalizing letters is an aspect of the personification of language, which stems from an earlier psychology that makes a word into an entity—even a divine entity. I will tell you more about why I do this, as part of the "reanimification" of language (see Chapter 10). Also, in this book you will notice that there are references in American Psychological Association referencing style that tell you where to find more information on the issues I am touching upon. This is not usually considered appropriate for a book that is trying to reach a popular audience. However, I hope you will appreciate seeing the sources from which my understanding is drawn.

Also, I must apologize at the outset to all who read this book. In the appendixes, in particular and throughout the book, I reluctantly have mentioned some of my accomplishments in a way that exceeds my own comfort level. The endeavor of writing a book about my path as a reluctant metaphysician, and mentioning the contributions which I hope to leave in my wake, reminds me of a story that I, and I hope you, will keep in mind.

> *Once there was a Rabbi who advised a member of his congregation to keep two pieces of paper, one in each of his pockets to have a balanced perspective on life. One said, "The Universe was created for me and I am the center of it." In the other pocket it said, "I am but a speck of dust in the universe, and I am here for a passing moment in the sea of time."*

As you read this book, I hope you can see the fullness and humbleness of my desire to reach you with what has gratefully been given to me to transmit…

Mount Analogue

Finally, I read a book a long time ago at the beginning of my spiritual odyssey called Mount Analogue (Daumal, 1952, 1992). Daumal cautions us that one that walks a spiritual path should be careful in telling his stories. If you are in the snow in the mountains and you walk up to a cliff's edge, those footprints may lead someone to walk over the precipice. So, any storyteller needs to take care in sharing where his path has led, lest it lead to dangerous territory for others. In sharing with you the stories of my life, and stories from the lives of storytellers over time, my blessings are with you that they will lead you further on your path up the sacred mountain. On any journey, falls can happen, and "demons" are met. As a matter of fact, it is from falling on the path and meeting the demons of our own inner worlds there that the deepest stories are made...and "soul" is born. I hope that any steps you take on a path opened by this book may lead you to greater heights, and safe, gentle falls.

CHAPTER 1:

Stories That Reveal and Heal

It has always been the prime function of mythology and rite to supply the symbols that move the human spirit forward.

—Joseph Campbell
Hero with a Thousand Faces

Myth is the secret opening through which the inexhaustible energies of the cosmos pour into human cultural manifestations.

—Joseph Campbell

Stories: The Spiritual Bones of Our Lives

"We make our destinies by our choice of Gods," said Virgil in his book the *Aeneid*. I think, just as truthfully it could be said that we make our destinies by our choice of stories. Whether we are conscious of it or not, stories are often the guiding lights of our lives—as much as our chosen religion. Stories can lead us into darkness, or light, or other realms formed by their making. Whether it's a religious story of "original sin," a belief we have about our worth, a message from a parent about what we deserve to have in life, an unconscious story we tell ourselves about the opposite sex, or a dream that guides us, stories often are the behind the scenes directors of our lives. The storyteller in us can tap on a divine power that can lead to a purpose-filled life, shape-shift us into another story that will better serve humanity, or change a difficult circumstance into an opportunity to create a better life.

Human beings are story-making animals. We each have our life story, or many stories. They are the spiritual bones of our lives. When we depart, most importantly, it will not be our bones that will remain, it will be our stories. They are our link to immortality. Yet the importance of stories and myths have not been integrated as a formal part of our education. We are told stories by our parents and teachers, but we are not trained in their deeper mysteries: the ability to soothe the soul, transform, awaken, and heal us.

In this book you will hear stories about my life, my dreams, my experiences and how they have influenced my life's journey. But actually this book is a story about your life too. As Upanishads its says, "By seeing all Beings in your Self, and yourself in all Beings, enlightenment is found." Thus, my autobiographical tales are your tales, and yours are mine. That is why hearing others' stories fascinates all of us humans—they open us to our common humanity. This is the deeper reason why people go to the movies or watch a stage-play; the characters with whom we identify are us. The stories and characters in these mediums help us to open a window to a fresh new way of solving one of our issues in the great mystery play of life.

Put Stories in Your Disaster Relief Kit

The kiss from eternity heals the wounds of Time.

—Michael Meade
The Roots of Time and the Roots of Eternity

"Every family should have a disaster relief kit in their homes," the common aphorism tells us. In it should be water, a supply of food that can last for at least three days, and so forth. I believe it is just as important to have our disaster kit filled with stories to help us in troubled times.

A variety of types of stories should be stored there. One type of story helps you to put your self back together when it feels like your life is destroyed. Do not put Humpty Dumpty's story in your disaster relief kit. It will tell you that "all the king's horses and all the king's men couldn't put Humpty together again," and is a story line that paves a road to the Land of Depression rather than to disaster relief.

Following are four stories to put in your disaster kit for difficult times. Let's begin with one that tells us how to put our lives back together when disaster strikes.

1. WHAT TO DO WHEN THE (YOUR) WORLD IS DESTROYED?

The master storyteller Michael Meade tells this South American tale about one of the times that the world was destroyed.

There was a time when the world has burned up and all is in ashes. Two bird-people, Icanchu and Chuna, have been away in the Otherworld, and so missed being burned in this incredible catastrophe. When they return to the world, they have no idea how to find home. After all, everything—everything—is incinerated. The Trickster appears and tells them to point their index fingers out as they fly, and when their index fingers point down—like dowsing sticks—then that would indicate they are home. They do so, flying along with fingers pointed out, and the time comes that their fingers point down, and they know they need travel no further. The place they seek is below, even if unrecognizable.

So, the two bird-people, settle down on the ashes. Nothing, and no one remains. In the midst of despair Icanchu picks up a chunk of charcoal. It reminds him of a drum, so he starts drumming on it. And after awhile, he sings as he drums, and then he dances.

All of a sudden, a tree sprouts from the ashes! Icanchu keeps drumming, singing, and dancing, and this tree grows and grows. It sprouts branches and leaves. Then Icanchu is filled with a kind wild, joyful craziness, an abandon. Finding some rocks he hurls them at the tree, breaking off each and every branch. That's quite an action to take when the first growing thing emerges in a totally destroyed world!

Surprisingly, as each branch hits the ground, it roots, and grows, and each branch grows into a completely different species of tree. And in time, all the trees that ever had been in the world before are growing again. And at the center, where the first tree had grown emerges a new tree—or the old tree—reborn. And this Tree is large, and abundant, and filled with the Medicine of the World. This source Tree is strong and sturdy, and it roots deeply, and as it does so, the forests return, and the birds, and animals, and even the humans, and the whole world repopulates and is reborn. This center Tree—this reborn Tree—is the Tree Of Life, the Shaman's Tree, the Buddha's Tree, the Tree of Life and the Knowledge of Good and Evil—all of those singular, mythic source trees at the heart of our human spirit and imagination.

Such a story helps me, and you, and my patients to reestablish a connection with our deepest selves after a devastating time of burn out, or destruction of an old way of living life. But first, the story challenges us to decipher the meaning of the symbols, and like the two birds rebirth our worlds?" Each of us has our own interpretations of a story; there is no "right" interpretation. The symbols of the story have meanings that serve to fuel the ship that leads us on the odyssey of our lives and to find our lost selves when all seems destroyed.

Some stories tell us how to deal with the destruction of the world (our inner world) by fire or water. How do we survive devastating losses? This story of Icanchu and Chuna first tells us that all we need to do is follow our pointer fingers. This is the finger in Chinese Medicine that has to do with the Large Intestine Meridian that has to do with letting go. It's not so easy to let go of the past—a lost love, or a job to which we were attached. However, if we could just be forward looking and see that there is purpose in the loss, we might become alive again when we feel dead. The pointer finger is also associated with intention and pointing to the direction that we want to go. The story tells us that at a key moment we need to follow the turned pointer finger, and go down. Why not up? The way of the "soul's journey" is down into our depths. When we point downward, we emphasize through this mudra that the direction that we need to go is down. We need to be right here in the present, not up ahead or in some idealized world of the future. This is the direction of non-transcendence—birds though we may be. The tale tells us that we must travel down into the ashes, the direction of delving into meaning, the direction where we penetrate into what past patterns created the loss. When devastating times come, whether it is an environmental catastrophe like an oil spill or our own losses, then a new world (a new way of living life) can be created by pointing downward and getting in touch with the earth element in ourselves.

What is the "charcoal" in the midst of the devastation, and what is the story telling when it talks about its turning it into a drum? Many of my patients find a rhythm or a song emerging at a moment of personal loss. One patient who lost everything in her life due to a painful breakup with her boyfriend, in the midst of her depression found help from singing, Tom Petty's "I'm free falling." The song said to her that a new life was beginning if she could let go and turn her loss into a song. This is the same place from which "soul music" is born. This is the process of turning dead places into song.

For me also it is true that songs, like stories, help me to recover my soul at the end of everyday life. Later I will tell you how specifically the psycho-spiritual, self-cultivation, energy psychology system I have developed includes chanting and music as central notes of its scale (see Chapter 11). Since, this metaphysical pathway I have walked is about returning to our primordial selves, song (the human activity which existed before language) must be a part of it. In cross-cultural mythology it is said that one key to life and healing is to be found in "returning to the origin of things" (Eliade, 1954). Since a mother's humming, her heartbeat, or a sound of emotional expression precedes more complex verbalization, such sounds return us to our roots from which new saplings of life emerge. The story of Icanchu tells us that such an ability to turn tragedy into song creates a new sapling, and then a new tree.

Why does the story tell us to throw rocks at a tree? The transcendent spiritual part of us says, "Throwing rocks doesn't sound very nice, or helpful." But the wisdom of the story lets us know that real emotion knocks down many different branches of the tree, and each becomes a whole new species. The mythic concept of "the one becoming the many" in psychological terms represents giving birth to differentiated emotions—aliveness comes down to earth. New ways of being emerge from being in touch with our multifaceted feelings. The Western psychology tradition, one of whose roots is in alchemy (Edinger, 1985)), teaches us that by differentiating our feelings and naming them that new creation emerges. Each is like a new species. There is a difference between saying that I hate my old boyfriend or girlfriend versus saying I'm "angry" and "disappointed in myself" that I made the choice that I did.

So, this tale inspires us at a difficult time to point down, and go beneath the ashes into our dark places. The usual tendency of many of us is to dissociate and escape from the difficulties and losses of life. But the story tells us that it is from the dark charcoal, and the process of exploring, singing, differentiating, and enacting deep feelings that new ways of being will sprout. The story reassures us that following this pathway we can find a new mythic center of our world where a new Tree of Life can grow.

Figure 1: The Helping Hand of the Tree of Life

Gratefully, while I am writing this book, I am looking out of my window into the back yard of my house where an oak tree grows that is shaped like a hand. I imagine it is sending healing energy out to me, to help me move through writing blocks I have when I am feeling burned out. Synchronistically, the name of the plot on the deed of my house, which describes the housing development where I live, is called "the Garden of Eden." But, any place can become the Tree of Life in the Garden of your Eden. Such is the power of imagination to recreate a world—that feels like heaven on earth.

The cross-cultural metaphysical perspective is that this experience of "oneness with all of life" gives birth to all religions, and that all religious pathways are routes to this divine place. The Waters of Life, the Tree of Life, and the Sea of Elixir symbolize it—the creative source of life and love in the universe. This path of pathways opened for my generation through psychedelic plant medicines, spiritual practices from the East, and then through indigenous traditions.

It has been said that there are many pathways to this place of unity with the divine as there are hearts of people. Throughout this book, I will tell you about some of these pathways I have walked. For example, I will share with you how my Standing Meditation practice of "Standing like a Tree" (called *Zhan Zhuang Qigong* in Chinese) helped me to find the Tree of Life, and I'll describe how to do this practice (see Chapter 11). It has served at many times to help my students, my patients, and me to find stillness in the center of the world. So, this book is not just about stories that lead us to recovering our lost souls, but also it contains practices that help us in this process.

2. STORIES THAT HELP US APPRECIATE OUR UNIQUENESS

Another type of story that you might do well to have in your disaster relief kit are those that help you to stay true to your life purpose so that you can add your special something to the fabric of life. These types of stories help to heal the wounds to our uniqueness; and they help us to remember that our unique ways of being, strange though they may be, have their own purpose.

For example, when we felt inadequate as children because of our differences we may have been told the story of the"Ugly Duckling" who also felt inadequate. After the King chose him over the other ducks that did not look the same as he did, he learned that he was a swan. Not only was he saved from his feelings of inadequacy; but also we, who listen to the tale, are transformed as we appreciate our swan-like differences from others. We wonder whether our differences too will lead us to a regal path. Such is the power of story to help us to discover our common humanity with all other human creatures, and even our animal brethren.

3. THE COAT OF MANY COLORS WE EACH WEAR—THE BIBLICAL STORY OF JOSEPH

Indeed, we each have our unique journeys and stories. Each of our lives is a weaving together of outer experiences, relationships with others, dreams, spiritual practices, and our way of living out collective myths (of which we are often unconscious).

In the Hebrew Bible, Joseph was given the "Coat of Many Colors" (*Kethoneth passim*) by his father, Jacob. The many rich colors and the many stripes of Joseph's coat are symbolic of the wealth of attributes that we have. This gift was symbolic of his father's special love for Joseph, and the blessings bestowed upon us to carry our ancestral lineage. But, true to life, it became the envy of his brothers. Buried in layers of the story's symbolic meanings, we are told that our special ways of Being are given by our heritage; on another level we get our colorful ways of Being from the father in us. So, we can creatively say, "Our Great Father whose art it is to help us to connect with heaven" gives each of us our own unique gifts.

However, the story warns us that each person's uniqueness and special ways can bring problems. When Joseph was sold into slavery by his jealous brothers, the brothers dipped this coat into goat's blood and showed it to their father saying that Joseph had been torn apart by wild beasts. Similarly, as each of us follows the path of our own uniqueness, (the ways we stand out from our brothers) we may be torn apart by the jealousy of others and the beasts of the world. Sometimes it is not until we are wounded and suffer the wounds of the brothers (and sisters) of our lives that our deeper journey begins, and the path of our destiny emerges precisely from this wounding.

It is interesting that Joseph's brothers soaked the coat of many colors in goat blood after they betrayed him. The goat is an archetypal representation of Capricorn, an astrological earth sign ruled by the Greek God Saturn, also called Cronus. According to Greek mythology, Cronus tried to swallow up his children so they would never overthrow him. So, Cronus is a symbolic representation of the realities of life that can swallow us up and can thwart our individuation process. Sometimes these antagonistic impediments on life's path come from our fellow human beings, or they can come from siblings who may be jealous of our special gifts as the tale of Joseph tells.

The quest of the hero (Campbell, 1972) is to find the path to our destinies as we overcome the obstacles of life. Sometimes we may need help from "divine forces." These forces and mythic struggles are symbolized in myths and stories. For example, Rhea, the Great Earth Goddess, tricked Cronus by giving him a stone to swallow, instead of the infant Zeus. This allowed Zeus some time to grow up in the Dikteon Cave and finally become the being of shining light that was his destiny. Similarly, Joseph suffered the pain of betrayal by his family, which resulted in his finding the path a new life. When he was reluctantly abducted to Egypt, a new life unfolded. Wounds and betrayals lead to healing pathways that are illuminated by such symbolic stories, which function as teaching tales.

Each soul's purpose is to take the joyful and painful stories of our lives, and from those experiences to weave a "coat of many colors" that will be passed on to our children or future generations. Each of us weaves together our unique quilt from the threads of various spiritual traditions we have explored (blue threads), the light hearted moments we have experienced (golden threads), the wounds we have suffered (red threads), the places in nature that have become our sanctuaries (green threads), the people we have met (uniquely colored threads), and from our dreams and visions (purple threads).

In the following chapters of this book, one metaphysician's coat will be passed on to you the reader to help facilitate your journey through the seasons of your life. But my greatest hope is that from listening to my story, you will learn how to better weave your own unique coat of many colors to pass on to posterity. Like Joseph, none of us wants to be sold into the slavery of life or suffer betrayal due to the way of being in which we are cloaked, but from such experiences the fabric of each Reluctant Metaphysician's life is woven.

4. THE OLD WOMAN IN THE CAVE—A FRAME STORY FOR THIS BOOK

How do we find our way through life? How do we deal with its difficulties? Answers to such questions are discovered through becoming an initiate in the art of deciphering cross-cultural teaching stories. So, even if we are not encouraged to forge the path to our unique destinies by our natural mothers and fathers, the archetypal stories handed down from one generation to another serve to mentor us. These are the Great Mothers and Great Fathers hidden in myths, fairytales, and stories. Each of them is a teacher and a jewel in humanities' treasure chest…if we just open the lid.

This next story is a major "frame story" for this book—because my hope is that in reading about my life's journey you will be led into the cave of your own creation, be inspired to weave the unique garment of your life, and find the way to your destiny. This story about "The Old Woman in the Cave" is another one that Michael Meade (2008) is fond of telling.

> Inside of a cave lives an old woman who remains unaffected by the strife of daily life. She spends most of her time weaving, and for a long time she has been in the process of creating a beautiful garment (In some versions of the story, it is a tapestry, or a carpet.) She is in the process of making the fringe of the garment and weaving it with porcupine quills, and stops her work to stir the soup that simmers in a great cauldron over a fire at the back of the cave. As she walks to the back of the cave and leaves her exquisite garment, a black dog who was lying on the floor of the cave picks up a loose thread. With its teeth the dog begins to pull on it and the whole elegant garment becomes undone. When the old woman returns she finds her creation turned into a chaotic mess.

> The old woman stands quietly and looks at her once beautiful design. She ignores the presence of the black dog and stares intently at the tangle of the undone threads and distorted patterns. After a while she picks up a loose thread and carefully begins to weave the whole thing again, creating a new beautiful garment. New designs begin to appear created from her old hands. Soon she has forgotten what she wove before as she concentrates on making this the most beautiful garment in the world.

After hearing the myths, folktales, or stories told in this book it is important to sit with them and experience what is stirred in your inner pot. It is from this inner stirring, that a new world is created for you.

It is probably easy for any of us to identify with the Black Dogs in life that destroy our inner peace and unravel our well layed-out plans. The coping skills exhibited by this Old Woman evokes in us an admiration for such a person who doesn't miss a beat when her life's efforts are destroyed. The story may make us wonder, "What practices did this Old Woman do, what abilities did this old woman have that enabled her to stay centered, relaxed, and accepting when the Black Dog came and pulled apart her garment? Where do I go to learn such a way of Being?

Spiritual Practices: Pathway to Stillness at the Center of the World

Throughout psycho-mythological history, caves been used to symbolize the place of spiritual retreat. Here we can find an inner place of stillness away from the hustle and bustle of everyday life. Whether the cave is in a field or in an opening in the depth of a mountain, these sacred openings into the depths of the Earth have served as an entryway into the source of creation—a place to go to renew our life energy.

The Old Testament and The Zohar tell us that the Cave of Patriarchs (The Dual Cave of *Machpelah*) was located in a field in Hebron. It was a special place where Abraham prayed daily. Emanating from this cave he saw light and perceived a sublime fragrance.

Abraham bought the land that contained this cave from Ephron, the Hittite owner of the cave, because he felt that it was a part of his destiny, and that it was a special place that represented how the other world is represented in this world. Abraham said, "The blessed Holy One has formed everything so this world corresponds to the pattern above" (Matt, 2004, p. 225). Abraham chose this cave as the place where he and his wife Sarah were buried (Matt, 2004, 2007).

This image of this dual chambered cave has been used throughout the ages as an initiatory chamber where the *tzaddik* (wise person) imaginally travels. He or she leaves the body like a corpse in one chamber of the cave, as an ascent takes place to a higher realm (the second cave). Then the tzaddik returns to the body with a new infusion of divine love (Kraseen & Aharon, 2011, p. 1).[1]

It is not so easy to keep in touch with those relaxed spiritual places of depth and equanimity as the forces of life disrupt our peace. So, how does a person keep the thread of life connected to the Cave of Creation, and to its stillness and transformative potential? How does a person develop the centered quality of the Old Woman in the Cave so that we can remain centered when the disruptions and disasters of life ruin our beautiful creation?

Many people are able to find stillness from tapping into the depths of their chosen spiritual practice. Maybe your sitting meditation practices, or your prayers, are the threads that help you to "stay connected." Throughout this book I will share with you the practices that have helped me to enter into "a zone," and experience what many mythologists call "a stillness the center of the world." Psycho-mythology often gives us symbols that allude to this place so that the searching mind can travel to these places as Icanchu did when he recreated the Tree of Life from dark charcoal. When the classical mythologist Mircea Eliade (1954) speaks of "the myth of the eternal return," and those places of stillness symbolized by the Tree of Life growing at the center of the world, these are not just academic concepts; they are also inductions to find these places in our inner terrain. Likewise, symbols such as the fountain at the center of the Garden of Eden, the Cave of the Patriarchs, and the Cave of Creation that is invoked in the story of the Woman in the Cave can become sanctuaries in our inner geography.

Keeping Connected to the Cave of Creation through the Threads of Our Lives

Every tradition has their symbols and rituals for finding the thread that connects to their pathway to "God." *Tzitzit* are the blue colored fringes on the *tallis*, the Jewish prayer shawl, which connect the practicing Jew to the divine source of life. Jewish *daveners* twirl their fingers around these blue threads as they chant various songs that bring them back to a connection with the divine source.

One way that many modern people stay connected to the cave of their life energy is through physical exercise. Whether we use exercise machines, jog, or go to various classes (such as Palates or Feldenkrais), physical exercise is one important thread for finding the equanimity of the Old Woman in the Cave. The fact that exercise is an important ingredient in healing depression is documented by modern psychological research.[2] So when many modern people say that what keeps them sane in an insane world are those daily trips to the gym, it is true that exercise is an important ingredient in a holistic approach to depression—but it is not "the whole enchilada."

Ancient Greeks believed that mind, body, and spirit were all part of the equation of making a more whole person. When combined with an integrative approach, spiritual traditions are time tested pathways in the thick woods of life that lead not only to mountain caves, but to the state of mind that is manifested by the Old Woman in the Cave. A person who follows a spiritual path often says that the practice of these traditions is what is most essential to be woven into their lives. Our spiritual practices form some of the most essential threads of our lives.

Right now, in our culture in the 21st century we are bearing witness to the fraying of the fabric of our American culture. The social safety net is being cut apart and the threads of values in the economic, political, social, and ecological tapestry of our culture have been torn asunder. Many of our individual lives have been torn apart by the Black Dogs of corporate and government influence that, in times past, doggedly served us; but now in a seeming sneak attack they have torn our lives apart. How do we keep the perspective of the Old Woman in the Cave at such times? (In the last three chapters of this book, I will address how a Reluctant Metaphysician can use the unraveling of the fabric of life by the Black Dogs of predatory capitalism as an opportunity to recreate a new and better quilt that can be rewoven with stories, spiritual practices, and political actions.)

Tai Chi: Its Unique Ability to Keep us Connected to the Threads of Creation

In later chapters of this book, I will show you more specifically the methods that I discovered that have helped my patients, students, and myself to stay connected to the "cave of creative, healing energy." For example, Tai Chi is oriented to help practitioners to stay centered when everyday life's crosscurrents knock us off balance. From a cross-cultural mythology perspective, Tai Chi has a practice that weaves imaginary threads to connect the practitioner back to the metaphorical Cave of Creation. It is called "Reeling Silk;" and the initiate in this tradition first accesses this altered state, "a stillness at the center of the world," through static postures (Mayer 2004). Then, the practitioner begins to move through various postures in the Tai Chi Chuan set while attempting to stay connected to this sense of stillness and openhearted oneness with life. The key to Reeling Silk and "cultivating qi" is to synchronize breath and movement, as an imaginary thread is drawn from the place of stillness into each movement and then back to stillness.[3]

The Metaphysical Path: Non-Sectarian Threads

My generation revered "the pathless path" (Osho, 2002), finding non-sectarian ways of connecting with the spiritual "center of the world" (Eliade, 1963). This non-attachment to specific forms of religion, which leads to the source of all religions, has been called "the mystical or spiritual path."

I prefer to call the path I am walking, "the metaphysical path." I'll tell you why. James Hillman (1975) taught my generation that the word "spirit" is connected with the word "pneuma," which means traditions that are transcendent—traditions of the mountaintop where one rises up above the circumstances of life. The term "soulful" resonates with the Greek word "psyche." Hillman teaches that soul traditions involve disciplines that emphasize the transmuting, alchemical processes of life that bring us down into the emotions…the wet places in the valleys of life.

I view the metaphysical (beyond, behind, and through the physical) path as one that contains both spiritual and soulful pathways. The Greek tradition contains gods and goddesses of the heavens (which I view as symbolic of transcendent pathways), gods and goddesses of the earth (symbolic of reverence for our planet), and gods and goddesses of the underworld (representing the opening to emotional, soulful, and transformative realms).

I am re-visioning the term "metaphysical" to convey that everyday life and the Black Dogs that tear our carefully constructed world apart, call us to journey to three realms for healing: 1.) to spiritually rise above dire circumstances (as Friedrich Nietzsche said, "That which does not kill us makes us stronger"), 2.) to appreciate the healing powers of the earth, and 3.) to embark on a journey to soulful, transformative pathways. If we want to be colorful about it, the threads of the garment that we weave from our encounters with life has blue (spiritual), brown (earthy), and green (soulful, planted in the underworld and growing through our encounters with life) threads.

So, even though the words "spiritual" and "metaphysical" are often used interchangeably, if we follow Hillman's insight, we can say that "spiritual traditions" are inherently associated with the transcendent elements. One of his contributions to psychology is to function as a gadfly (as Socrates did) counterbalancing the dissociated spirituality that he saw in our culture. The metaphysical pathway, on the other hand, includes spiritual, earthy, and soulful threads, weaving them together into our unique creative mix.

One place that was, and still is, a symbol of this type of multifaceted spirituality (including traditions of the heavens, earth and underworld) is Esalen Institute, though Esalen does not specifically call its type of spirituality, metaphysical. Jeffrey Kripal wrote about this multidimensional spiritualty in his book *Esalen: America and the Religion of No Religion* (Kripal, 2007). At Esalen Institute and other leading edge workshop venues (such as Omega Institute, Kripalu Center, and Mount Madonna) Eastern and Western practices join, and spiritual and soulful are integrated. Body, mind, and spirit are stirred in the cauldron of the "spirituality" at such workshop locations and in the "soulful quest" of my generation.

This "religion of no religion," this pathless path values each individual way that leads to the source of creation. The pathless path means that we do not literalize that ours is the best or only way to get to the source. From the perspective of cross-cultural approaches to religion, and the "religion of symbolic process traditions," we can imagine that all of life is a garment. The threads of all metaphysical pathways and all of our unique ways of being are threads that lead back to the center of the mandala, where sits the Great Goddess (the source of the threads). The further we get away from the cave the more important our differences are; as we get the closer to the place where all threads meet in the center, we recognize that we are all connected to the source of creation.

Different Versions of the Story of the Goddess who Weaves our Destiny

In different versions of the story, the object of the weaving of the Great Goddess can be a blanket, a tapestry, a carpet, or even the very fabric of life itself. Remember the baby blanket that you may have had a child that gave you comfort and a sense of warm connectedness with your parents? The threads of that blanket connected you back to the warm, cuddling, comforting function of the Great Goddess of Creation. At times when a person's feelings of entitlements get gnarled at, or our connection with life gets torn apart, we have to reweave the threads of that blanket.

Or, have you ever had an intricately woven tapestry from another culture up on one of your walls, maybe one that has a mandala at its center? As you walk by the tapestry, you may have a feeling of being more connected to yourself. Similarly, a focus upon the threads of the woven tapestry of our lives helps us to center ourselves on each of our life's purpose; and it helps us to realize that the threads of our lives connect us to a beautiful center. However, real life often takes us away from any ideal view of centeredness. Thus the Tibetan and Navajo practice of making beautiful sand-painting mandalas, and then they destroy them to learn the lesson of non-attachment to the ideal and perfect.

Poignantly true…the carefully woven garment, blanket, tapestry, or carpet of our lives is often pulled apart by the Black Dogs of everyday reality—doubts, judgments, insecurities, stresses, and blindsided attacks. However, if we view our process from the perspective of our deepest self, found in the depths of the Cave of our Being, we can use the unraveling that comes from life's crises as an opportunity to weave an even better garment. The threads of our lives come together in our unique Coat of Many Colors, and the weaving becomes a sacred garment that covers our vulnerable places with soft texture and radiant color. Such a weaving can become a blanket to give us comfort, a tapestry that we can view that helps to center us, or it can become a carpet of meaning that we can stand on to find our life stances.[4]

When we cover ourselves with this sacred garment it serves to give us solace in difficult times. Perhaps that is one reason why I like to call myself a "re-covered psychologist." In the chapters that follow I'll tell you how by re-covering myself with the woven cloth of the dreams, visionary experiences, and synchronistic experiences of my life journey I have created a Coat of Many Colors to center myself in difficult times. I hope as you read about my journey you will be inspired to weave your own garment and "re-cover your-self" (*double entendre* intended).

In Greek mythology the very fates of humans and the Gods lives were said to be subject to the power of *Moirae* (the three fates),) who were the weavers of destiny. The Gods themselves feared the Moirae.

In any era, it is the initiates' task is to find the way to deal with the fateful forces and Black Dogs of life. Our life stories are our meetings with such "demons." Can we do as well as the Old Woman in the Cave (who secretly is the Great Goddess of Creation)?

As I meet with young students in these troubled times of excess student debt I am moved by how the Black Dog of predatory capitalism and student loans have torn apart their lives. Modern students are being called to stay committed to their destinies, despite the unraveling that has happened along the way. Each student is challenged to find a sense of equanimity, and to reweave the garment of his or her destiny.[5]

Messages from the Cave of the Goddess

How does one hear the call of Destiny and stay on purpose? Messages are sent from the Cave of Creation throughout our lives. Our "inner voice" speaks to us from our internal mythic landscape as we listen to stories, myths, and folktales—and the way we identify with the characters in them. Also, our dreams, our spiritual practices, and even everyday events can remind us of "our mission."

A secret that all who study stories know, is that each symbol in a story is a part of our Selves. Each of us is the Great Goddess in the Cave of Creation; each of us weaves our own multi-threaded garment. We must continually stir the soup of life as we add in new ingredients and stir in new morsels of truth that are digested from our work, interpersonal relationships, and from life in general. From the experiences of stirring the soup, and from our own reflections in the cave of our inner world, we create threads of meaning.

As in this story, on many days, Black Dogs unravel our lives. We suffer losses, our world unravels, and the complexes of our psyches bite us. Our sense of equanimity is tested. Our task, like the Old Woman's, is to reweave the garment of our lives even when the Black Dogs of Life tear it apart. At the end of our lives, maybe we have a few good stories about how we were torn apart, and how we put ourselves back together. Hopefully, our stories will be remembered and put into the great quilt of humanities' teaching stories.

Porcupine Quills

When the fabric of our lives is torn apart by Black Dogs, the story tells us, we can re-knit it with porcupine quills. Why porcupine quills? Don't they hurt, and not heal? The wisdom of this tale here invokes the myth of the Wounded Healer (Halifax, 1988), which teaches how we can develop healing ways, or further cultivate our spiritual depth, from the way that we deal with the wounds of life. Porcupines protect themselves with their quills, and help the Old Woman in the Cave to reknit the tapestry of life. So, we can take the story to mean that our wounds, and the ways we defend ourselves from the assaults of others and from life, are an important part of weaving each of our life stories.

Amplifying the meaning of the symbol of porcupine quills further, Native Americans have used rose thorns to release energy blocks similar to the way Chinese medical doctors use acupuncture needles. One can wonder whether porcupine needles functioned the same way. Perhaps the symbol of weaving the garment of life with a porcupine quill in the Cave of the Great Goddess of Creation is telling us that the tool that helps in the weaving of the garment of our lives is connected with that which wounds and sticks us. Maybe the symbol is telling us that by "handling" that which wounds us that we too will be able to learn the skills of a weaver and artfully work with the healing energies of life.

Unique Twists—Twists of Fate

Each of our unique life stories is born from dealing with the wounds of our lives, whether we want to frame our story in terms of coping with the Black Dogs of life, or the journey opened by the Coat of Many Colors and the betrayal of Joseph by his brothers. These wounds create red threads from the blood of difficult and traumatic encounters. Our stories and our red threads can come from Fate taking us down a path different from the mainstream.

So, it is not just Joseph who is abducted by the forces of Fate and taken to a foreign land. The twists of fate in all of our lives help us to form our identities. Throughout this book I'll tell you about the twists of fate in my life that have led me in a new direction. Each of us responds to these twists of fate differently at different times—through humor (as Seinfeld does), or with love and compassion (as the Dalai Lama does). Each of these different approaches, our unique twists on the ways we meet the dramas of life, adds something back to the woven garment in the Cave of the Great Goddess, the quilt of humanity.

A metaphysical secret is contained in the story of The Great Goddess who gives each thread of the garment a unique twist. Since each part of the story is a symbol of us, the story tells us that the Goddess has given us each of us our unique twist. We are threads in the fabric of life.

If we are each a single thread in the tapestry of creation, how do we go about discovering the nature of our own unique twist? Throughout this book, I will tell you more about various metaphysical pathways that have helped my patients, students and me to discover the nature of our unique twists in the fabric of life. For example, one such art is using astrological metaphors to meditate upon how one's life fits into the cosmos (Tarnas, 1993, 2007; Rudhyar, 1970; Mayer, 1983). Interpreting the experiences that come from a vision quest, is another.

The unique twists that are given to each of us by the mythic Great Creation Goddess may give us inclinations to walk our life paths in particular ways. But when the Black Dogs of life come and unravel us, we are the ones who choose our way of reweaving ourselves. Then we become the weavers of our own destinies by: dealing with our wounds, discovering spiritual practices, meeting with remarkable people and traditions, interpreting our dreams, learning from the happenstances of everyday life—and making them all into interesting stories.

Exercising Our Story Muscles

Through our awareness of life as a story we exercise our "story muscles." A metaphysician believes that fine-tuning our awareness of the stories that construct our world, and exercising our story muscles thereby, is as important as a trip to the gym to exercise our physical muscles. A metaphysician does not believe that it is an exaggeration to say that such awareness is a key to humanities' survival, a key to going to war or finding peace, and an essential tool in each of our survival kits.

For example, the false story of Jews being responsible for Jesus' death was a major factor in killing countless Jewish people in the Christian inquisition and throughout the ages (Greenberg, 2007; Wilford, 2006). Our Bible's story that women were born from Adam's rib is a hypnotic induction into the belief that women are an appendage to men— whereas many cross-cultural mythologies see The Great Goddess as the Creator (Von Franz, 2001). Stories of the United States' "manifest destiny" allowed the self-righteous slaughtering of Native Americans. The Spanish version of manifest destiny that school kids are told about the great hero Columbus discovering America, doesn't tell the rest of the story. Columbus and his men raped, tortured, enslaved, and committed genocide on the indigenous people of Hispaniola (Hartmann, 2004).

The metaphysician looks behind the holidays that others take for granted. For example, did you know that the Christmas holiday has roots in the shamanistic traditions of the tribal peoples of pre-Christian Northern Europe? According to various scholars (Arthur, 2000; Larsen, 2003), most of the major elements of the modern Christmas celebration, such as Santa Claus's red and white garb, magical reindeer, pine Christmas trees, socks hung by the chimney, and the giving of gifts, are originally based upon the traditions surrounding the harvest and consumption of psychedelic mushrooms.

When you look at the red and white outfit that Santa Claus wears, it is interesting to know that the sacred mushroom of these people was the red and white *Amanita Muscaria* mushroom. Reindeer were the sacred animals of these semi-nomadic people, as the reindeer provided food, shelter, clothing; and they are also fond of eating the Amanita mushrooms that often grow under pine trees. Reindeer will seek out these mushrooms, and then prance about while under their influence. Shamans would consume the urine of the reindeer for its psychedelic effects, since the deer's digestion system helped eliminate toxic compounds. After gathering the mushrooms from under the sacred trees, the shamans would fill their sacks and return home. Climbing down the chimney-entrances in their yurts, they would share their mushroom's gifts. The effects of the Amanita mushroom usually include sensations of size distortion and flying. This feeling of flying could account for the legends of flying reindeer, and legends of shamanic journeys that included stories of winged reindeer transporting their riders up to the highest branches of the World Tree.

Behind our modern ritual of hanging socks and stringing popcorn by our modern fireplaces at Christmas time is the practice of drying the Amanita mushroom by the fireplace before consuming it. The drying process reduces the mushroom's toxicity while increasing its potency, so the shaman would guide the group in stringing the mushrooms and hanging them around the hearth-fire to dry.

Likewise, Halloween is a deeply meaningful "holy-day" beyond the fanfare. Many people know that behind of the Day of the Dead celebrations and the Christian feast of All Hallows' Eve are pagan harvest festivals and festivals honoring the dead, particularly the Celtic *Samhain*. It is said that the veil between the dead and the living is thinner on this day and that a way to lure our ancestors is through sweets. Some people believe that a way to protect themselves from being attacked by "malevolent demons" is by wearing costumes to look like the demons.

The Reluctant Metaphysician is not fixated on any one interpretation of the meaning of holidays; but instead we enjoy making meanings that are life-enhancing. The Reluctant Metaphysician not only penetrates behind the taken for granted interpretations of the mythologies our culture; but we also come up with our own imaginative versions from symbolic process traditions. For example, Halloween eve takes place on the eighth day of the eighth sign of the Zodiac (Scorpio). In numerology, a number multiplied by two means the manifestation of that quality. So, the number eight (which looks like an infinity sign) multiplied by two can signify infinity manifested by taking on an infinite number of roles. When we look at the central symbol of Halloween, the pumpkin with the candle in the center of it, the symbol speaks to us of a holiday when we find the light behind the masks (the infinite number of roles) that are worn in everyday life.

So, instead of going along with the versions of stories that give others joy on the holidays, some metaphysicians reluctantly suffer some estrangement from joining mass interpretations. We sacrifice being with the herd of commonly held viewpoints to go on a quest to find the light of alternative and iconoclastic truths.[6]

The metaphysicians' quest for the story behind the story can be applied to many spheres; it does not need to be esoteric. It can be political. For example, major corporate interests have currently taken over our airwaves with six corporations owning the major media outlets. They tell us biased stories to enhance their narrow economic interests. Medical advice we receive has been polluted by self-serving pharmacological stories told to our doctors and medical journals (Robbins, 1996; Saputo, 2009). Storylines that emphasize profits and "bottom line" thinking pave the way for environmental disasters to take place such as the Union Carbide pesticide leak at Bhopal, India and the BP Gulf Environmental Disaster.

How is it that, for the most part, whoever pays the most for advertising usually wins elections? It's because stories have a hypnotic power that can be abused by those who manipulate their tone, affect, and images for destructive gains (Hartmann, 2007). George Lakoff, a professor of linguistics at UC Berkeley, teach us that the metaphors we use and the stories we tell affect the brain itself and create conceptual schemas that filter the way we see reality (Lakoff, (1999, 2005). A saving grace for humanity is that each listener can be aware that a fabric of falsehoods is being woven in front of our eyes. Hope exists if each of us can be the Black Dogs that unravel the tapestry of deception behind the TV and radio commentators' stories, rather than being hypnotized by some of these "talking-heads" who are often worshipped as if they were Gods and Goddesses.

The opposite of the cross-cultural mythic path is the path of literalism and ethnocentrism. The importance of this perspective on healing the current darkness of our world is obvious. Fundamentalist Muslim extremists believe that their job is to engage in holy war against the West, against Jews, and against unbelievers. Similarly, the path of the some Christian fundamentalist extremists is to be captured by the belief that the only way to find god is to believe in Jesus, and if one believes and can help to create Armageddon then they alone will go up to heaven while unbelievers will burn up on Earth and go to hell. Likewise, there are factions in the Jewish settler movement that are so fixed in old biblical storylines, that to find a compromise for just settlement with their Palestinian brothers and sisters is limited. The fact that these forces are now colliding in the Middle East is a key meta-mythic battle of our times. And each of our stories, each of our practices is part of the solution to throw the "waters of each of our lives" onto the fire of literalized entrenched beliefs.

We can find our life stance in relationship to false and fabricated stories, which serve the masters of manipulation. Then we can weave the unique golden thread that we were meant to be, and contribute it to the fabric of life.

Dreams

> We are such stuff as dreams are made on,
> And our little life is rounded with a sleep.
>
> —Shakespeare, *The Tempest*, Act 4, Scene 1

It is not just mythic stories that lead us to "the mythic center of the world." It is not only awareness of political and economic storylines that can reset the compass of our lives to true North.

As ancient navigators set their ships direction by aligning themselves with the North Star, dreams reset the metaphysical compass of our lives. If we can decipher the coded language coming from our inner world, we are kept on track. Shakespeare adds to our understanding about the importance of resetting the dial of our lives with his oft quoted phrase about how our lives, which often seem on a linear track, are "rounded with a sleep" —or with a dream that shows us the way to make our lives more whole. In the Talmud it says, "A dream left uninterpreted is like a letter left unopened." Our inner dream weaver conveys messages to us through symbolic stories, but it is we who need to find the thread of meaning that connects the world of our dreams and the external realities of our lives. Dream-work is a favorite exercise of the experiential metaphysician who travels to the world behind the world to dive for pearls of meaning, just as the scuba diver dives for pearls on the ocean floor.

From where do our dreams they come…a divine source? A mechanist would say that our dreams are just created from the firing of brain cells; a metaphysician says that deeper meanings can be uncovered for those initiates versed in the language of symbol.

One of those initiates was the biblical Joseph, who interpreted the Pharaoh's dream when none of his other advisers could. The dream that disturbed the Pharaoh was of seven fat cows that became frighteningly thin. Joseph said the dream meant that there would be seven full, fat years of crops followed by seven years of thin harvest when the people would starve. Joseph advised the Pharaoh to store the grain from the years of plenty, and save it for the lean years to come. Some, like the mechanists of our age, told the Pharaoh should not listen to this mystic's view. But the Pharaoh did listen, and appointed Joseph to be in charge of the granary. Egypt thrived during those seven years and was able to feed even the people of the surrounding countries who were suffering from starvation.

And so it is that in each of us in our lives, those of us that learn how to interpret and listen to the messages from our inner worlds may help to facilitate a wise relationship to everyday life. The basic teaching of metaphysics is that those who find the thread of meaning that connects this world and the next can help to heal the world. When I ask my patients about their lives, and I want to do a "metaphysical assessment," I ask them about their dreams and repetitive dreams.

Those who work with their dreams learn that there is a "world behind the world." "The initiated" discover that this other world has much to teach us about this world. Both have a reality of their own. A metaphysician would say that the world of dreams contains "essential reality," which reveals a great inner teacher if we could learn to decipher its language. In the first holistic healing temple of the ancient world in Greece, a healing dream was the sign that healing was complete and the person was ready to leave the temple of Aesclepius.

Modern psychotherapy similarly recognizes the healing power of the story of our inner dream lives. For example, I remember a young woman with no expression on her face who walked rigidly into my office. She told me of her panic attacks and how she was afraid that her boss and boyfriend would discover she was crazy if she told him about these attacks. She told me about being disturbed by a dream where her rainbow tattoo turned grey. After quite a few months of therapy, she revealed to her boyfriend her secret fear of being rejected for being mentally ill. Then she had another dream that the color returned to her rainbow.

At the end of our therapy she reflected back on her first dream and realized that at the beginning of our therapy she hid her vulnerabilities—aptly symbolized by the dream image of the rainbow of her life that had turned grey. At the end of her therapy she found the courage to share with her boyfriend the truth of her life story—aptly represented by the dream image that showed the color of the rainbow returning. As in ancient Aesclepian dream incubation rituals, soon after having his dream my patient decided that she was ready to leave our "psychotherapy temple."

This book is about my dreams and how to get in touch with yours. It is about the stories of my life and yours, since each of our stories is all of our stories. Myths and teaching tales initiate us into seeing that we are all created from a common source (call it whatever you will: the eco-sphere, the ideity field, the morphogenetic field, or the collective unconscious), and the weaving of the stories of our lives begins there. This book is about how the forces from the wider whole of which we are a part can come during troubled times to help to lead us to our destinies. Sometimes these "messages" come from the inner world of dreams; sometimes they come from an outer event from which we derive meaning.

Joseph Campbell said that if we do not "follow our bliss," that our lives would be less meaningful. And he did not mean that we should follow the pleasure principle. He meant following your life myth.

Finding your Sacred Note

There's an old story of a Jewish husband and wife, Moishe and Sarah in old Europe. They were married for fifty years; and every day Moishe would play the same note on his cello, over and over again. One day Sarah said to him in the most caring way,

> My dear husband Moishe, I know your cello playing gives you great joy and it is quite beautiful. However, my dearest husband, I hope you know that there are other notes on the cello, and that there are other people who play those notes." Moishe looked up from his cello and said, "Yes, my dear wife Sarah, I do know that there are other notes on the cello and that there are other people who play those notes. But, those people are still looking for their notes and I've found mine.

So, this book is not just about how I found my note (or better put, "the lost chord"); I hope in reading it you will find yours. Stories, myths, poetry, dreams, spiritual practices, and the threads of ancient wisdom that come to this world from the realm of the imaginal are what can keep any of us "on track" as we navigate through the sea of life.

The Rabbi in the Woods

There is an old story about the Rabbi in the woods. In each generation his lineage holders became further and further estranged from the secret practices that healed the people:

> *Once there was a great Rabbi. When his congregation was ill and suffering, he would take the secret Book of Prayers and go out to a special place in the woods. There, he would sing a special prayer of healing while rocking back and forth in special ways. The people were healed. In the next generation, his lineage holder did not have the book because it was destroyed, but he still knew the prayers, the movements, and the sacred spot in the woods. He was able to heal the people thereby. In the following generation, the place in the woods was destroyed through fire, but the next Rabbi could still heal the people with the prayers and movements. Today, the prayers and the movements are lost, but the story of the old ways, and the "re-membering" it evokes, may still be enough to heal the people.*

And so, in the following chapters we will wonder about, wander about, and discover the primordial pathways walked by the Rabbi, and the Old Woman in the Cave. We will walk the path that has been cleared for us by sacred wisdom traditions. Songs, meditation postures, sacred movements, visualization methods, dream-work, and vision questing are some of the practices that we will explore—practices that illuminate the pathway of the Reluctant Metaphysician.

CHAPTER 2:

Our Bodies Are Storytellers: Holder of Keys to the Door of Self-Knowledge

The symbols of the Self arise from the depths of the body.

—Carl Jung

Fate: Hidden in Our Bodies

Greek mythology teaches that there is a Goddess of Fate, Moirae, who weaves our destinies on the spinning wheel. In the South American version of the tale, the old Woman in the Cave (the Great Goddess) takes the Garment of Life, and she gives a special twist to the thread that becomes each of our unique ways of Being. So, a metaphysical view of mythology might lead us to pose the question, "Could the 'twists in our bodies,' and their 'dis-eases' hold a key to our destinies?"

As somatic psychotherapists know, our bodies do indeed hold a key to our characters and our life patterns. These patterns are established early in our lives. A person with a slouched stance may have suffered from incidents that "crushed their heart," and a "puffed-out-chest person" may be arrogant. Our body postures are not just assessment tools; the twists in our bodies, as do our twists and turns off the straight and narrow pathways in life, hold keys to our destinies. As body-oriented therapists say, "The issue is in the tissue."

No less than in books, stories are written in our bodies. Just as an archeologist can discover knowledge about ancient civilization through deciphering hieroglyphics, so are hidden secrets revealed through reading the hieroglyphics of our bodies. Our interpretations lead to uncovering new worlds of meaning.

My Childhood Energy Blocks

As a six-year-old child, I remember lying in bed trying to find the best posture to go to sleep. My favorite position was to sleep on my belly with my left leg outstretched and bent, with my left arm bent at the elbow with my fingers pointing up and my right arm pointing downward next to my straight right leg. I realized that the anxiety in my stomach from so much pressure from trying to excel at school was soothed by this posture of lying on my stomach, and from my body pressing against my pillow that lay on an angle from my right ear to my heart. As I slowly breathed and directed the breath alternately up and down the left and right sides of my body, there was some strange peaceful relaxed energy that was released from my left fingers pointing upward and my right fingers pointing downward. This "energetic streaming sensation" that I experienced helped me release my tension and enter into the sought after world of sleep.

It was much later in my life that I learned that the experience of energy I felt as a six-year old is called *qi* (also spelled *chi*) in Chinese, which is the focus for a practice of cultivating the energy of life for healing in the Chinese medical system of Qigong. I also found out that the awareness of energy moving up and down is called "the raising and sinking of the Qi." The use of intention to direct qi is called *yi;* and in Qigong, it is said, "the yi leads the qi."

I also noticed, as I was lying in my favorite sleep posture, that one hip felt more blocked than the other, and that turning over and switching my position from my left leg outstretched to my right leg being outstretched helped to bring balance to my body. Bringing balance to the body by switching postures from one side of the body to the other, I later discovered, is a fundamental part of the philosophy of medical Qigong. It is called "balancing excess and deficiency." Little did I know in my early years that the sensations in my body would lead me on a quest to discover more about the energy of the body. This path led to my becoming a healing practitioner, teacher, researcher, and writer about the energy of the body and about Qigong in particular.

Though I may be getting a little ahead of the story, later in my life I was fascinated to discover the research of Dr. Felicitas Goodman, the anthropologist who coined the term "traditions of postural initiation." Her research showed how our ancestors assumed various postures for hunting and survival purposes, and how shamans of indigenous tribes used postural stances as a method to enter into a trance state for the purpose of healing, divination, and metamorphosis (Gore, 1995, p. 14).

As a young child I did not need to travel back to a pre-modern hunter-gatherer society, go to a yoga class, or practice sitting, standing, or moving meditation in order to experience traditions of postural initiation. As a young child in bed, my body was carrying a "higher-glyphic" of what I was later in life going to teach … that postures for expanding human consciousness are part of our everyday waking and sleeping lives. Every child can discover these postures naturally. What is your favorite sleep or waking posture and how is it a healing, postural ritual that brings energy and balance into your life?

When I was sick in bed during my grammar school years, I remember not being able to sleep because I was so congested. I noticed that one nostril was more filled than the other. I instinctively rolled over to my side so that the congested side was higher; and in a few moments, the congested side flowed to the opposite nostril. As I turned from side to side, in those moments of clarity when there was no congestion, I was able to fall asleep. It was much later in my life that I realized this experience was an early entryway into one of the key healing pathways of the ancient art of Tai Chi Chuan. It uses movements of filling and emptying to activate the healing powers of *yin* and *yang*.

Borne from my congestion was another part of the path of Taoist healing that I would later discover. Finding the calm place after the out-breath, a person can enter into a zone of peace beyond the opposites of yin and yang. The early Taoists called this primordial state, *Wuji* (the mother of yin and yang), the void from which they believed creation and healing energy emerges.

After many years of practicing Tai Chi, I was introduced to one of hidden purposes of Tai Chi practice. The Tai Chi set of movements repeats the cosmogenic creation myth of moving from Wuji to Tai Chi and then back to Wuji. By beginning the set in stillness, and then moving into the world of Tai Chi's balancing of opposites (of yin and yang), the practitioner enacts a parallel process of the creation of the world (Tai Chi). At the end of the set one returns to stillness. In our everyday lives we all repeat this cycle as we get caught in the world of opposites (of good and bad, right and wrong, stuck and unstuck), and we need to find the relaxed center point of equilibrium to find peace and return to stillness (Wuji).

So, whether we are congested with a cold or with the psychological issues that encumber our free flow of qi, we all are tested in life to look under the crosscurrents that pull us from side to side and find the sacred place of stillness deep within, which is beyond the forces that disturb our equilibrium.

As an adolescent and not confident in myself, I saw that other more popular boys held their chests out more proudly than I did. I experimented with expanding my chest farther and felt a bit more confident. (It was a combination of experimenting with assuming this posture as if I was more confident, and the inner work I did through the years, which helped this stance to gradually take hold.)

This was long before I discovered the ancient traditions of "shape-shifting" that would become one of my contributions to psychotherapy and Western bodymind healing methods. I did not know then that what I was learning in my own life would parallel the issues in my patients' lives and serve them.[1]

When I was in high school, I had so much tension in my neck that I was desperate to find a solution so that I could return to studying. I intuitively touched and pressed some points on my shoulders; and after a few (sometimes quite a few) breaths, the tension released. During my acupressure training many years later, I learned that one of the points I touched as a teen was called Gall Bladder 21 and that acupuncturists use this point for releasing neck tension. I further found out, during my medical Qigong training, that the principle of touching points lower than a tense point high in the body to reduce tension is a key to Taoist healing. It is called "sinking the Qi."

So, not only the famous mythologist Mircea Eliade (1952) knew that the sacred is hidden in the profane of everyday life; each of us may experience in any moment a natural depth emerge onto the surface of our lives. It may be from a posture we assume while asleep or awake, a place we touch on our bodies, or from an illness we suffer.

When I was a child I did not know that the tension I had, and the subluxated vertebrae below it, was probably related to the fact that I was a forceps baby. In the 1940s, as part of the movement to medicalize childbirth, many mothers were convinced to go against natural childbirth and were given drugs to make them sleep through childbirth and avoid pain. Then the child would be extracted with a forceps—often pulled out by its neck. Dr. Robert Bradley called this, "knock-em-out, drag-em-out obstetrics." This, I believe, created an energy block in my neck. The pictures I have of me as a young child show a major tilt to one side probably related to this "birth trauma." Later in my life, various forms of stress (including drinking coffee, or using psychedelic drugs), increased the energy that traveled through my body (and its meridian lines) and created major tension in my neck. Many a weekend I would have to lie still, and I was not even able to leave the house. So, my body carried the effects of the story that the medical system sold, that "a safe painless childbirth could be produced by using medical intervention." This perhaps sowed the seeds for my later interest in taking into account the "side effects" of medical interventions, and co-founding an integrative medical clinic that specializes in using alternatives to pharmaceuticals whenever possible.

Also, in the 1940s corporations propagandized mothers with the story that their breast milk was not as good as various companies' formulas. Years later, research showed that babies who were "bottle fed" and brought up without breast milk had increased earaches (from which I suffered). So, the hypnotic effect of stories had a direct effect on my life at an early age.

Beliefs, particularly ones that are funded by large corporations, are repeated on television; and they can alter the most natural and healthy of our instincts. For example, how many mothers changed their behavior after listening to advertising slogans such as, "Why suffer the pain of childbirth, take our drug and be pain free," or "Take our baby milk formula, it's better than your breast milk?"

There is a pathway and a solution for those of us (and our bodies) that suffer the bad and lasting effects of others' self-serving stories. I call this, "The Path of the Reluctant Metaphysician;" and the path of the "Wounded Healer" (Halifax, 1988) is one of the most important trailways of its terrain. We are those who, reluctantly, due to a life wound, another person's false story, or a symptom in our bodies are called to heal these wounds by going on a path that leads to and from the world behind the world. One part of the journey of the Reluctant Metaphysician is to be aware of collective stories that put the mind into a trance state, identify distorted beliefs that poison our perspectives, and to discover healing stories that are remedies for our souls.

Healing Practices and Healing Stores Are Borne from Our Bodily Diseases: A Metaphysical Perspective

Healing stories and practices emerge on the path of listening to our bodies. For example, when I was young I had a hernia operation, a fairly common operation for those whose testicles do not fully descend. As a child I was told that the operation was "successful." This definitive statement, congruent with the storyline of the 1950s led to the corollary belief is that no physical therapy was necessary since the operation was successful. Later in my life, as I reflected upon the metaphysical meaning of this "defect" in my body, I thought, "Perhaps this is symbolic of my sexuality not wanting to fully descend to the physical world. Maybe this was a precursor to my interest in Tantric sexuality (Douglas & Slinger, 1999)."

Whether this meaning is actually inherent in this phenomenon is not the point (Fingarette, 1963). The point is that on the metaphysical path, the person who reflects upon the phenomena of life makes meaning. (From an archetypal psychology perspective, scientific investigation is one of the children of metaphysics. It is in the same family; and it certainly would be interesting to have a test that measures how many people with hernia operations had more of a spiritual orientation to sexuality.) The path of the metaphysician, however, is one of shining a light of esoteric meaning onto the phenomena of this world; making a connection between everyday life and the world of meaning; penetrating into the world of the unseen; exploring the power of intention; wondering about the origins of our personalities; becoming aware of the elements of life (fire, earth, air and water); utilizing the sphere of energy to rebalance our lives; and revitalizing our Selves by continuously reconnecting with the divine source of healing.

The reason I call "my calling" the pathway of a Reluctant Metaphysician is that I, like most of us, do not want to have health disorders. However, when we have illnesses, we reluctantly can use these experiences to see that these issues are *divina afflictios* (divine afflictions), giving us opportunities for psycho-spiritual growth, soul making, and finding the source of healing.

Borne from our illnesses are discoveries of healing pathways. For example, I do a system of Hatha Yoga every morning that naturally developed from my need to bring balance back to my neck and pelvis.[2] Similarly, I developed a synthesized Qigong and Tai Chi system from my early bodily wounding.

However, not only recognized systems of healing such as yoga or Tai Chi are useful to a person who is on the quest for Self-healing. Natural healing discoveries can come from inner listening to our primordial Selves. Whether we vary hot and cold water in the shower in the morning or let go of tension on the out-breath, these are gifts to our human bodies. They are part of the treasure house of energetic healing methods that make us human, and that enables us to experience divine healing states. Though learning about these healing pathways should be fundamental to the curriculum of life, we are not usually trained in cultivating these ways. We are taught about the fifty United States in geography classes; but we are not trained in the hundreds of useful state-specific, energetic healing states.

I was fortunate to discover a tradition that spends as much time on educating these Self-healing energies as people do nowadays on reading, writing, arithmetic, television, and computers. It is called *Qigong*, and learning how to cultivate the energy of life is its curriculum.

From my three decades of training with Master Fong Ha, at his Integral Chuan Institute in Albany, California, I was able to find an age-old tradition of bodily energy healing that helped in the healing of my imbalances. As part of my training in Chinese healing arts I went to the Acupressure Institute of Berkeley to further my study in oriental methods of healing and received a certificate in acupressure in 1990.

Maybe the childhood energy blocks I experienced were a factor that led me to know that integrating the body was crucial for my own healing as well as to help in the healing of others. Healing the bodymind split that was so much a part of my early life figured into the development of the integrative system of bodymind healing which I was led to develop.

Along these lines, the psychological method of *Focusing* played an important role in my life and career. Focusing is a method of body-oriented psychotherapy that pays attention to the "felt sense" in the body in such a way that "felt meaning" of body blocks emerges and a "felt shift" of energy happens. This method helped to transform my way of being, as I hope it will do for you. I couldn't have known as a child that the twists in my body would be instrumental in leading me on a path to develop an integral system of psychotherapy, in which the role of the body was central.[3]

The body has played a role in all facets of my healing work as I wove together the threads of what I hope to contribute to tapestry of life.[4] Through the practices I learned over the years, I found a way to heal the blocked energy in my neck, and to find a bridge between traditions of the mind and body. Some of the traditions that influenced me, and later became fundamental parts of my approach to "energy psychology" (Mayer, 2009), included Western psychotherapy methods such as self-psychology, psychodynamic and object relations theory, cognitive-behavioral psychotherapy, symbolic process traditions, and Dr. Gendlin's Focusing method. Also, Qigong, Tai Chi Chuan (the best known system of Qigong), medical hypnosis, and acupressure self-touch became vital parts of the integrative approach I called *Bodymind Healing Psychotherapy*.

CHAPTER 3

Our Childhood Dreams:
Keys to Our Karma and Dharma

Murdered by Nazis: A Lucid Repetitive Dream

Esoteric literature says that our earliest dreams may be related to "past lives." Psychological literature says that our early childhood dreams hold keys to our deep characterological patterns.

In my early childhood I had a disturbing dream.

> *I am standing in front of an open pit in the forest, and Nazi's with machine guns are shooting at me and other Jewish men, women, and children. After we fall into the pit, the Nazi's cover over the pit with earth. I pretend I am dead, and after the Nazi's leave I dig my way out.*

I had this recurring dream when I was about four years old, and it continued through my grammar school years. There were many variations on the dream. My favorite one involved a little girl named Ann in my first grade class who could read before I could. I was in awe of her reading abilities and, as much as a six year old could be, I was infatuated with her. At nighttime, in my recurring dream she was standing with me and we fell into the Nazi's pit together. I taught her how to pretend she was dead, hold her breath, or breathe slowly and quietly. Then we dug our way out from under the dirt together.

So, long before psychology graduate school, when I heard about the ability to control dreams, I was controlling mine. I remember looking forward to sleep when I could "be with Ann."

Keeping Mystery Alive as You Interpret Your Story

Different interpretative lenses open different doors to stories' different meanings. Could this be a past life dream? A sceptic like myself would first want to rule out that I had not heard about the Nazis when I was a toddler, and that I had not translated those stories into my dream-life. When I posed the question to my parents, they said that they would have tried to keep such horror stories from me at that age. But I cannot rule out that I could have overheard a conversation. Still, it was quite amazing to me when I looked at the Jewish Encyclopedia when I was in my late twenties and saw that in the villages that were near my grandparents shtyle in Drohobych, Poland that Jews would be taken out into the forest. They were shot and put into mass graves. Occasionally a few would pretend they were dead, burrow out after the Nazis had left and would report the place of horror later to the authorities. Hmmm…is this some interesting supportive evidence for a past life hypothesis?

Along these lines, I wonder if this dream could be an example of the "cultural unconscious" manifesting in my dream life. The cultural unconscious is a variation on Dr. Jung's' concept that there are wider formative aspects to our unconscious mind than Freud's personal unconscious. The cultural unconscious is part of Jung's well-known concept of the collective unconscious. One way that the cultural unconscious manifests is in "ancestor worship," a notion that is looked down upon in our modern world of independent individualism. However, in older indigenous cultures a strong connection with one's ancestors was considered to be a fundamental part of life.

In the case of my childhood dream, esoteric metaphysicians who believe in past lives say that when Nazi's killed so many Jews that their souls sought to incarnate in the children born in subsequent years. There is another class of metaphysicians who reluctantly do not claim to know whether this is the case, but we nonetheless stay connected to our ancestors by allowing their "spirits" to "live through us." Honoring the spirits of their lives, we stand against the cruelty and racial prejudice that they would want their lives to express in a next generation. So, regardless of any absolute truth of a *dybbuck* (dislocated soul of the departed) taking over and being behind any of our lives, any person can use their connection with their ancestors to stay connected to the chain of generations in their lineage. Such a connection adds a sense of purpose to our lives, and gives us roots.

My recurring dream image can also be looked at through a psychological lens. I, and my parents, have embedded in our psyches a tendency to rescue. Jewish children are taught that *tikkun olam,* "to heal the world," is one of the major purposes of life. Here in my childhood dream was a symbolic encapsulation of what would become my lifetime path as a psychologist—helping to dig out others of the hole created by the forces of life that can make one a victim. On another psychological level, when I was 6 years old, Ann was my *anima ideal* (the Jungian term for a projected image of a man's unconscious feminine side). She was a symbolic representation of the scholar and reader of books that would become an important part of my destiny. Later in my life the theme repeated; I needed to rescue this (the symbolic Ann) from the deep earthly body blocks that an overly cerebral life creates.

On another level, the cultural dimension, the recurrent dream image represents the long history of my Jewish ancestors' oppression. My approach to being victimized in this dream image helps me to experience the liberating energy of outsmarting the persecutor—another part of the destiny to which I have been married (until perhaps "death do us part").

Following the Hermeneutic Path of Interpretation

Interpreting the stories of our lives on many levels, and not deciding on one, (I found out later in graduate school) is called "the hermeneutic path." Originally stemming from the god Hermes, this way of looking at story and not having to settle on one interpretation is part of circumambulating (circling around) a life issue and looking at it from many angles.

Some people associate metaphysics with a belief in past lives. But, as I was to learn later, there are many pathways in the terrain of the land of the Reluctant Metaphysician. One path is the Hermeneutic Path.

There is an old saying, "Beware of the man with one book." Similarly, "Be aware of the man with one interpretation of a story." Each way of looking at a story or a dream opens a door to a different reality, none of which is absolute. If more people would not get stuck in their particular stories the world would be a better place. Moslem fundamentalists would not be killing others to get their place in heaven with forty virgins.

Controlling dreams is considered *a siddhi*, a spiritual power. Perhaps when we are young children, and closer to the source of life, it is more natural to do this. I never thought of my ability to control my dreams of Ann as a child as anything special. The real special work of life is to do "the work of works," and to see how we can control the dreams of everyday outer life. One of the secret purposes of storytelling is to exercise our imaginative function. When we recognize that each of our own lives is story (a waking dream), we may become better able to step out of the roles that are seemingly imposed upon us in the play of life and become directors our own destinies.

CHAPTER 4

Two Rivers Become One: What Is Your Power Spot in Nature Trying to Tell You?

Oh, come let us give praise to the light of the world,
And become one with the Shaper of Life,
who made every person a spark divine,
and blesses each one of us in our own special way.

—The *Aleynu*, Jewish Prayer

Outward Introspection: Finding Our Deepest Selves in Nature

Each of us has a special gift, or gifts, to give to life. There are a variety of ways we may discover our dharmic life direction—from a message from our inner world, a dream, or a book we read. Sometimes a message about our life direction comes from nature itself. In the old ways of indigenous peoples, a vision quest would often be used to help guide a young Brave to discover their "medicine way" (Storm, 1972).[1]

But, not only from the inner world does such guidance come. In the old ways of following the path of *anima mundi* (the world soul), any experience in life, particularly in nature, can guide us to our destinies or at least open a new meaningful pathway through the forest of life. Contemporary cosmologists call this the "re-enchantment of the cosmos" (Lazlo, 1996; Tarnas, 2010; Kelly, 2010).

One method of tapping on, and invoking, the world soul is called "outward introspection." As we sit in nature, or are drawn to some place in nature we can metaphorize that place as an aspect of ourselves. By experiencing ourselves standing as a tree, we develop rootedness. By sitting in a cave, we experience our depth and we come out of the cave as an initiate into the deeper aspects of our lives. By sitting next to a stream, we can experience the flow of life and get in touch with how to let go and eventually merge with the Ocean of all Being.

My Life Path: Two Streams Joining

An important part of my current life path began when, as a young boy, I sat on a large rock in the woods overlooking the place where two streams joined as one. This was in a rural park in New Jersey in my secret retreat spot near a place called Hemlock Falls. While other kids were out playing baseball or drinking beer, I was more fascinated by the sound of two streams joining. This was long before the Western culture I knew had heard about meditation.

Native Americans teach that the elements of nature that draw us in our early years symbolically express a calling, leading towards our future destinies—our "medicine ways." For me this proved to be true. In workshops I teach, after telling this story I ask participants to think about an element of nature that drew them in their childhood, and to reflect upon what it says about their destiny. I invite you to do the same.

Long before I knew my destiny was to explore the Way of integrating the streams of body and mind, ancient and modern, East and West, my early years were spent huddled over books. I was only vaguely aware that my posture was affected by my hunching over them. Books were my lovers, and I carried the mark of a young man who spent much time embracing them—scholar's shoulders, they were called. As a child, my parents taught me that a book was a sacred thing; if I dropped one, I was supposed to pick it up and kiss it. Brought up by a family of intellectuals whose patriarch was a lawyer, I spent my youth in intellectual arguments trying to show how smart I was. The "Mind" was my God.

As time went on I became aware of the dark side of the worship of this "deity." My relationships suffered from endless debating, and constrictions appeared in my body from excess mental pursuits. I needed more of a relationship to the natural world and to the body to balance my overly mental nature.

Healing Traditions Based in Nature

> *Oh, what a catastrophe for man when he cut himself off*
> *from the rhythm of the year, from his unison with the sun and the earth.*
> *Oh, what a catastrophe.... This is what is the matter with us.*
> *We are bleeding at the roots, because we are cut off from the earth and sun and stars...*
> *We plucked it from its stem on the Tree of Life,*
> *and expected it to keep on blooming in our civilized vase on the table.*

> —D. H. Lawrence

Due to my healing experiences in nature as a child it is understandable that the system of healing that I later developed in my life contained the healing powers of nature as a central part of it. Later in my life, from my reading of James Hillman (1975) and the Western mystery traditions (Mathews, 1986, 1986), I learned that one of the treasures coming from the land of ancient psychology—the psychology of the "soul"—is the notion that there is a *deva* in every location in the natural world. Another name for devas are *elementals,* because they are associated with the healing powers of the elements of nature (Jung, 1974). It is said that every deva has a form, usually feminine, that communicates to those who listen.

There are devas of the waters—*nereads*, devas of the air—*sylphs*, and devas of the earth—*dryads*. These devas are specific to locale, and since they are not "major deities," they are more humble, more down to earth, and have more intimate personal messages to give us. The male counterpart to devas are *daemons*, such as Eros, god of erotic love. Devas and daemons occupy a mythic place on the ladder of creation that are not gods, and they are not human beings either—they are Beings that travel between the two realms of heaven and earth. A metaphysician who practices the re-enchantment of the cosmos gets in touch with the attributes of the elementals to experience the divine attributes of life on earth.

So, on one level, this book is a communication from "the deva where two streams become one." Before you dismiss this notion as archaic or smile thinking this idea is quaint, instead, allow yourself to wonder about the places in nature that have drawn you to them. Then, meditate upon what message is waiting to be drawn from that place in nature. We don't call our deepest ways of being "human nature" for nothing. We are inextricably connected with nature; and our own healing, our life energy, and our messages for humankind come from this connection with the wider whole of which we are a part.

The Problem with Following Your Unique Vision

Staying true to the path of our destinies is not necessarily the most practical means of living one's life. Following the path of Two Rivers Becoming One, and carrying that "medicine way" has been particularly difficult for me as an author. When my books on Qigong and psychotherapy came out I had more than one publisher say, "We want a book on just Qigong. It's an up and coming field; but we do not want a watered down book which brings in modern psychology." Similarly, with my book on relationships called *Trials of the Heart: Healing the Wounds of Intimacy,* one publisher with whom I was negotiating a publishing deal said that this was supposed to be a book on psycho-mythological stories; and when I wanted to bring in an experiential component (with my mythic journey process), one editor in chief said, "You have a choice, if you want to sing your book in the shower you can keep in that extraneous stuff, but if you want to sing your book out in the world and have our company publish it you will take that experiential stuff out."

There is a concept in the publishing industry called "the cross-over book." It is defined as two different types of books that merge as one. Publishers and bookstores do not usually like such books. They are considered a "hard sell" because publishers believe that books need to be put in a particular category in a particular section on one shelf. Likewise, a book is supposed to either be for the lay public (a trade publication) or an academic audience (and published through a university press.). But what if an author's path is to want to join those two rivers and have them become one and reach the wider public in a substantial way with references and many footnotes. When bookshelves rule the sphere of ideas you know we are in troubled times.

My books join genres. Just like the temple of Psyche in ancient Greece was a less visited temple, and more people went to the temple of Dionysus or Zeus, such has been the fate of my writing. Though my first book *The Mystery of Personal Identity* won the world astrology prize in the early 1980s, and my last books have received endorsements from many leaders in mind-body medicine, they have not received wide readership. However, I do not regret my choices. As Frank Sinatra said,

> *And now, the end is near;*
> *And so I face the final curtain.*
> *My friend, I'll say it clear,*
> *I'll state my case, of which I'm certain.*
>
> *I've lived a life that's full.*
> *I've traveled each and ev'ry highway;*
> *And more, much more than this,*
> *I did it my way.*
>
> *Regrets, I've had a few;*
> *But then again, too few to mention.*
> *I did what I had to do*
> *And saw it through without exemption.*
>
> *I planned each charted course;*
> *Each careful step along the byway,*
> *But more, much more than this,*
> *I did it my way.*
>
> *Yes, there were times, I'm sure you knew*
> *When I bit off more than I could chew.*
> *But through it all, when there was doubt,*
> *I ate it up and spit it out.*
> *I faced it all and I stood tall;*
> *And did it my way.*
>
> *I've loved, I've laughed and cried.*
> *I've had my fill; my share of losing.*
> *And now, as tears subside,*
> *I find it all so amusing.*
>
> *To think I did all that;*
> *And may I say—not in a shy way,*
> *No, oh no not me,*
> *I did it my way.*

For what is a man, what has he got?
If not himself, then he has naught.
To say the things he truly feels;
And not the words of one who kneels.
The record shows I took the blows—
And did it my way!

Staying committed to our own inner guidance, and to the spark of the divine that exists in each of us in our own unique way, is not an easy path. It does not necessarily lead to outer success. Though it would be easy to fall into the trap of envy towards others who seem to be able to adapt their books to the marketplace of life, the visions of our lives and sayings of poets can always be counted on to help us to find our unique ground in life. The great poet, Emerson, put it well in this quote,

There comes a time in every man's education
when he arrives at the conviction that envy is ignorance;
that imitation is suicide;
that he must take himself for better, for worse, as his portion.
That though the wide universe is full of good,
no kernel of nourishing corn can come to him,
but through his toil bestowed on that plot of ground
which is given him to till."

—Ralph Waldo Emerson

One of my close friends who appreciates my books and wants them to achieve greater recognition says to me, "What would you have to change in your writing to make your books sell better?" I thank him for him caring concern, and explain that my destiny is probably not to be to be a best-selling author. My way seems to be to continue to follow the place where two streams join, and to ride the river with its waterfalls, rocky places, and its unique twists and turns—to captain the ship of my life as it leads down the rapids, to its unique destiny.

CHAPTER 5:

A Lawyer Abducted by Metaphysical Forces: The Larger Forces That Can Change Our Destinies

Many who knew me, and my intellectual environment, in my early years in suburban New Jersey would not think that I would be the most likely person to have answers to metaphysical questions about the forces that influence the direction of our lives. Certainly if you heard me in my high school debating club enjoying tearing apart fallacious arguments with little regard placed on another person's feeling, it would have been hard to predict that I would be telling your now about the spiritual practices that bring healing to our lives. Being born into a family with a father who was an attorney, I was trained to analyze *everything*.

My College Years: Sprouting the Seeds of a Metaphysical Life

During my college years at Syracuse University my professors had me pegged for being a leading attorney due to what according to them was "my outstanding legal mind," and the well-thought-out decisions I made as an associate justice on Syracuse University's student court. I was flowing down the stream that was outlined for me by my pre-law curriculum. However, a cross-current pulled my life in another direction while I was in college in the late 1960s. When I minored in philosophy at Syracuse University, my moorings in the world that I had known began to loosen. I discovered another stream that led to a different world.

While I was studying philosophy as part of my pre-law curriculum I was most interested in using my learning to hone my intellect. I focused on making philosophic arguments as I avidly read the works of the early Greek metaphysical philosophers. This current of thinking moved me down a deep stream of knowledge as I read Aristotle's and Plato's metaphysics. I was fascinated to learn that there could be "a world behind the world," a world of ideal forms that comprised the essence of things.

In my junior year of college, Plato was my favorite philosopher because of his brilliant reasoning and alignment with the way of the god Apollo. I was taught that Apollo was a god of reason, and reason was also my god at the time that I was in a pre-law track ready to be an attorney. I identified with Plato and appreciated that he was connected to the lineage of Apollo, which was contrasted with the god Dionysus who I was taught represented hedonism. I did not realize at that time that I was projecting my own intellectual stance onto the symbol of Apollo, and likewise that when I looked down at those who were following the path of Dionysus I was projecting my own psychological shadow onto Dionysus. It would take some time for me to realize that Dionysus symbolized the pathway to my own repressed pleasure-seeking principle.

In these philosophy courses at Syracuse University in the late 1960s I learned that metaphysics was comprised of the root words "meta" (meaning beyond, or behind) "physic" (the physical world). Through my study of various branches of metaphysics, I exercised a deep part of my mind as I studied: ontology (the exploration of Being and what is real), epistemology (how we can know what we know), and cosmology (the study of the origins and reason for the universe's existence).

However, I remember in my senior year having the thought, "I love Plato's dialogues, but hmm…philosophy in general seems too "heady," even to me. I know I like philosophy, but my interest is more in psychology and healing people than in just a philosophy of the mind." This was long before I read about the Greek mystery tradition (Schure, 1977; Houston, 1992; Kingsley, 1999), when I discovered that Plato was part of a lineage of healers (*oulios*) who were masters of stillness and masters of altered states (*iatromantis*).

Much later in my life I discovered that Apollo was both a god of lightness (the sun) and darkness (the underworld of initiation), representing the mastery of states of awareness and of silence. Apollo was not merely a god of reason and light, as I was told in my college philosophy courses. Apollo was a god of an initiatory tradition that included "recipes for immortality" among which involved snakes, traveling on the path of the sun, making sounds like a snake, and participating in cave incubation (Kingsley, 1999).

In hindsight I can now see that this background information about my journey from my college days mirrors my own journey from "worshipping" the God of Reason to becoming an initiate into a deeper world of inner journeying. But, I am unfortunately getting ahead of the story-to-come…that twenty five years later I led two trips to the cave of Apollo,[1] and the seedlings which were planted in my college years led me to a blossoming interest in a more experiential, healing, and psychological field of metaphysics.

In addition to Plato's metaphysics opening my mind to the metaphysical side of life, in my senior year of college I was enraptured by Herman Hesse's books such as, *Journey to the East,* and his magnum opus *The Glass Bead Game.* Such books opened me to an experiential dimension of exploration of what is behind the physical world. Hesse's metaphysical Glass Bead Game, played by the fictional students of Castalia, involved an initiation into a game that made deep metaphorical and ontological connections between all arts and sciences. So, the metaphysical world that was opening to me in college was not just the intellectually interesting metaphysical concepts of ontology and epistemology; I became interested in the inner experience of initiation and transformation.

I did also have metaphysical experiences before my senior year in college. I remember when I was seven years old, I felt like my essence was that of a bird. While I was running I would try to experience what it was like to flap my wings and take flight. This was long before I trained in the animal forms of Qigong, and I practiced and taught the healing movements of the Crane. Also, this was long before I discovered that my astrological chart was that of a triple air sign. My sun, moon, and rising sign are all air signs— speaking of an affinity with birds. ☺

I also remember as a child being transfixed by the dandelions on my suburban New Jersey's lawn right before the gardener came to uproot these "pesky weeds;" I wondered whether dandelions had a purpose. This was long before I developed an interest in herbal medicines, and I found out that dandelions are a natural diuretic, help upset stomachs, lower cholesterol, reduce high blood pressure, and improve digestion. I certainly could not have fathomed that fifty years later that dandelions would be discovered to be a plant based replacement for synthetic rubber, and that Ford Motor Company would research the use of dandelions for that purpose (Bardeline, 2011). Also, it certainly was long before I grew to understand that some of the "negative emotions" that we try to expel in life have a purpose; and we should not be so quick to throw these "pesky weeds" away. As a child, I was fixated into a trance like state by an undifferentiated feeling as I sensed that there were deeper purposes behind the ordinary and rejected things of life.

I believe that the metaphysical part of all of us is he or she who is aware of the weaving of the threads of time into the fabric (space-time) of eternity. At young age, I looked at trees and wondered what I would be like and what the tree would be like in many years, and I tried to picture what people would look like when they were older.

In terms of qualities that are traditionally considered as metaphysical, my early metaphysical inklings involved the ability to control my dreams, such as my dreams of Nazis. But I did not place much importance on this because I thought everyone could do the same. Also, as I told you about earlier, as a young child I was aware of energy in my body and to intuitively know (as most of us do) how to balance imbalances. This was long before I was to train with various masters in the Taoist arts of Qigong and Tai Chi, walk the path of energy healing, and write books on these topics. However, I put these metaphysical inner stirrings of my childhood into the background because of my unconscious "worship of the God of Rationality" and my certainty that I was going to be a lawyer.

When I was in high school I was interested in people's essences. At one point I thought that when I grew up I would be a chess teacher and teach people about how to correct the imbalances in their personalities through chess. For example, some people move too aggressively, and others not assertively enough. Here was a foreshadowing of my early interest in the metaphysics of personality theory, and in Tai Chi Push Hands as a method of healing characterological imbalances.

One more item: I remember as a teenager being very serious. One of my competitive classmates said to me in a demeaning tone one day, "Why are you so serious?" Somehow, I wittily responded, "If seriousness is such a bad thing, why is the brightest star, Sirius, named after seriousness?" Not only did my retort silence this bully; but my humorful reframing of his verbal attack also foretold my later interest in life in helping my patients to banter (Mayer, 2007), and it represented an early inkling of my later interest in the healing power of "the name."

In the *Wizard of Oz,* the Straw Man thinks he is stupid and wants to go on the path with Dorothy to find a mind. But, the Straw Man shows his intelligence when he says, "Take me down from this hook at a forty-five degree angle because other wise you'll rip me apart." So, the Straw Man in each of us has talents lying latent within that can become manifest as we walk down the yellow brick road of life. Sometimes it takes real wizardry to bring it forth. So, my metaphysical inclinations were lying latent in me, hiding in the shadows of a culture that worshipped Rationality. It took being pulled off the stake of my rigid belief that "Law is for Me" (the title of the first paper I wrote in grammar school), and walking down a yellow (symbolically golden) road to bring out my latent interest in exploring the world behind the world.

Then, in my junior and senior years of college in the late 1960s, something in my basic nature joined with the eye-opening readings of Hermann Hesse and Plato. I was fuel, ready to be sparked when "the cultural revolution (Roszak, 1995)," the "consciousness movement," and "the human growth and potential movement" were born. Yes, I was primed to want to understand and experience more about what was behind the world in which I lived.

After I graduated from Syracuse University (in 1969), I was accepted to George Washington Law School, one of the best international law schools in the country. Everyone around me, and I, was sure I would follow in my father's footsteps and be an attorney. I even remember two of the top pre-law professors Doctors Sawyer and Micheljon wished me well in my work next year at George Washington Law School, and they asked me to stay in touch because they were sure I would have a valuable career as an attorney. What forces could be powerful enough to change such a well planned out course down the stream of life?

Woodstock: Social Forces and Psychedelic Experiences:

Transformation of our lives can come from the wider culture around us, and from sharing our hearts with fellow travelers on the Path—I was to learn. I had come from an isolated suburban home where I was contained in my small world. Driving on the road to Woodstock in a multi-mile traffic jam in mid-August of 1969, I was in my air-conditioned Pontiac Catalina convertible. My "brothers and sisters" of what is now called "The Woodstock Generation" were walking, as I was stuck driving in a slowing moving traffic jam. Pretty soon they were asking to ride on my car. This was the nice, polished car—the one that when someone would even lean against it, made me cringe. But the power of the moment, the power of collective giving and sharing was stronger than my attachment to having things be, "just so." Then, shortly thereafter, every inch of my car was filled with people. My car hood had three people on it, on the trunk sat three people, three people sat in the front seat, four people squeezed together in the back seat, and another two sat above the back seat. Love and camaraderie proved stronger than my fear of the scratches of life.

Woodstock was part of the forces that altered my life path from being a lawyer to embarking on the path to be a psychologist. When at the various events of this Woodstock generation, people that I knew would have bad trips and they would want to have me guide them through the rough spots. I was a lawyer to be, and yet I seemed to have an ability to stick in there with the deepest levels of people's pain and experiences of fragmentation, and to guide them through their process.

So, truth be told, psychedelics had a part in the transformation that was about to take place in my life. The quality of heart and healing stance that emerged during psychedelic journeys were the plants that I began to choose to nurture rather than my overactive mind. Time teaches us that life is a choice about which plant we water, and what we want to flower.

This was long before I knew that my destiny was aligned with helping people through underworld journeys. I had to wait many years until I cultivated this latent talent through my work as a psychologist and my studies of the Greek mystery tradition.

In the Woodstock era, I was captured by the idealism of the age, and I naively thought it was just a matter of time until psychedelic experiences would be legalized. I wanted to be among the first who could legally lead people on journeys through the heaven and hell of psychedelic experiences.

For example, I remember going to the Quebec World's Trade Faire in 1967, and I took a psychedelic to view an exhibit of what the dying process would be like in the future. There was a 360-degree theater, and an image of a dying person lying on a table in the center. The projection booth invoked a ritual whereby the dying person and the watching viewers were induced into slowly rising up above the Earth while Beethoven's Pastoral played. The ensuing journey took us above forests, seeing prancing animals below, and then up above the clouds into the stars. I thought to myself that I would like to be part of helping people (and myself when my moment came) to rise above their fears of death. Little did I know that respected researchers in the future would use psychedelics to help facilitate the dying experience (Grob, 2011).

I didn't know that the economic, political and cultural forces in the United States would undermine the potential healing, medicinal, psychotherapeutic, and environmental uses of various plant medicines.[2]

Changing Occupational Paths Mid-Stream: My Father's Disappointment

So during the summer of 1969, after being admitted to George Washington University School of Law, I made a decision to forgo a career based on argument, conflict, and the worship of Mind to pursue the study of healthier ways of speech and Being through the study of psychology. And so I enrolled in a graduate psychology program at the New School for Social Research in New York City in the fall of 1969.

My father, a prominent New Jersey attorney, was disappointed. Drawing from a place deep within, I said, "Don't worry Dad, I'll still be a lawyer, but I'll be a lawyer for the body, mind and spirit." (I didn't win that case with him.)

You know the old joke about how Jewish sons are told they can be anything they want in life—a lawyer, a doctor, or a dentist? I lived inside that story. Almost. Because a psychologist was only on the barest edge of being a doctor for my father who believed I would fare best as an attorney in my life. And certainly a metaphysician would not have fit the norms in my suburban culture of that era where material success and practical life pathways were most valued.

What are the forces that lead any of us to change our destinies? I have told you how my philosophy course and the lectures on metaphysics were part of the cross currents that changed my life direction. I also remember a close high school friend, Ellen Demel, who had dreams that were awe inspiring to me. And another high school friend, Danny Scher, an avid reader of Freudian psychology, also titillated my interest in psychology. However, I remember my lawyer subpersonality was active when I had long arguments with Danny. I told him that I felt psychology was too reductionistic regarding the forces that influence our lives and destinies.

So, though there are many outer influences that form each of our life paths, the key question with which the reluctant metaphysician wrestles is, "What is that quality within each of us (our essential nature), which is evoked by the outer forces of life and directs us downstream?"

A Lawyer Captured by Astrological Forces?

During the summer of 1969, one day I walked into a street faire with my girlfriend. We passed by an astrologer's table where a quick reading was advertised for a low price. My girlfriend said, "Let's stop and get a reading for you to find out about your upcoming life." I told her how I was the last person in the world to believe in such ridiculous things; but her insistence led me to stop at the astrologer's booth.

The astrologer calculated the celestial positions of the chart for my date and time of birth. When she began to look at it, she paused with an expression of amazement on her face. She said this is the chart of an astrologer, but "not just any astrologer, you have one of the strongest metaphysical charts I've ever seen." She went on to decipher the symbols in the chart, speaking about connection between my life and dead planetary bodies. She told me how my Sun was conjunct Uranus, which she said meant that the light force in me (the Sun) was united with the mystical forces of the world outside of the traditional Saturnian boundaries of everyday life (symbolized by the fact that the planet Uranus was outside of the last planet visible to the naked eye, Saturn). She said my life energy (Sun) was inextricably connected with unique, changeable forces (Uranus) outside of traditional norms and traditional ways of seeing things.

To be kind with her, though I did not believe in the empirical validity of anything she was saying, I said, "Well in my approach to the law I do tend to be impatient with those who argue truth based on precedent, and I am often looking for new ways of looking at the law." She replied that she felt my destiny was to be in much more innovative and spiritual spheres than the law, and that my Sun conjunct Uranus was in the Eighth House of metaphysics. So, she thought that metaphysics would be the sphere where my greatest contribution would be made.

The astrologer said that there were many other elements of my chart that put an awesome amount of substantial focus on the house of metaphysics, and therefore on an interest in the world behind the world—more than she had ever seen in a chart. Apparently, in addition to my Sun-Uranus conjunction in the Eighth House of metaphysics, I had two other placements there. She tried to explain some very esoteric concepts to me, such as the moon's north node[3] (also called the dragon's head) was in my Eighth House, and that astrologers believe that the placement of the dragon's head is the "dharma point" of the chart, i.e. the area of life that one would find their life direction. Since the north node of the moon was in Gemini (an air sign symbolizing an active mind), she said that I would find my destiny in the realm of metaphysical ideas. In addition, she told me that in my Eighth House was the planet Venus, (a symbol of that which attracts a person and an indicator of that with which one falls in love); so, since Venus was in Taurus it would be earthy dimensions of metaphysics that would attract me.

The astrologer said that the Sun-Uranus conjunction in the Eighth House was the key to my chart. Equally important was the fact that the energy of Uranus was controlled (disposited is the technical astrological term) by my moon in Aquarius, because Uranus rules Aquarius. She explained that the moon in Aquarius was at the bottom most point of the chart (the nadir) in the fourth astrological house, so I would feel this inclination towards metaphysics in the very depths of me. Adding to the strength of this inclination, was the fact that the overall structure of my chart was a funnel that pointed to the moon in Aquarius. Further, she explained to me that my moon (symbolic of the soul), was in the first degree of Aquarius. So, she continued to tell me that if I followed my soul's calling out from the very depths of me, I could be a significant contributor to those who were initiating the birth of the Aquarian revolution.[4] My role, according to this astrologer, could be to bring metaphysical, and innovative ideas to the world from the sphere of ideas (since my sun, moon, and rising sign were all in air signs).

After I politely thanked the astrologer, and we left her table, I said to my girlfriend, "See…that just goes to show you what charlatans these astrology types are. She probably doesn't even realize that she's projecting on me her world-view. She's an astrologer and has studied metaphysics, so she sees me as a follower of her path. Can you imagine anyone less likely than me to ever be an astrologer or to have a career in metaphysics? Maybe after I graduate from law school in three years, I'll get back in touch with her and let her know about the fallaciousness of her predictions."

The Actualization of Fate? An Astrological Pathway Opens

At the risk of getting too far ahead of the story of the chronology of my life story, it seems fitting to tell you that about three years later I was in a doctoral psychology program doing research on ancient, cross-cultural and metaphysical dimensions of personality description in Native America, the Kabbalah, and…in the astrological tradition. What a strange implausible twist of fate it was that in 1979 my doctoral dissertation won the world astrology prize from the Astrological Association of Great Britain for being the most valuable contribution to astrology that year.

Some of the reasons for winning the prize were: (1) The book put forth a new theoretical basis for astrology that made astrology palatable even to sceptics. Instead of proclaiming a scientific relationship between cosmos and personality, I emphasized astrological metaphor's ability to transform the meaning of our lives, to awaken wonder and to heal. (2) The book was the first to show how astrological metaphor can function as a tool in depth psychotherapy. (3) The book showed psychotherapists how to use astrological symbols to help a client explore his or her life's meaning, and shows astrologers how to use psychological methods to deepen astrological counseling. (4) It set forth an alternative language for psychologists to counter the tendency for the field of astrology to label people with pejorative language; less emphasis has been placed on offering a viable alternative. The book showed that modern psychotherapy's lost lineage was from an ancient tradition of "name givers,"and how reconnecting with this tradition could revitalize our relationship with the wider whole of which we are a part. This view contributed to the tradition of transpersonal and Jungian psychology regarding the depathologizing of personality descriptions. (5) It re-visioned astrology into an astro-poetic language so that the essence of astrology can be used without speaking a word of astrological language.

In addition, I am sure this health faire astrologer would be interested in the fact that at John F. Kennedy University in the early 1980s, I taught the first course to be offered at an accredited university on integrating astrology and psychotherapy. A key concept of this three-semester, graduate psychology course was how to use astrology in counseling without ever mentioning the word astrology. Instead, students learned in this class to use astrological metaphors to describe the energies of life—such as fire, earth, air, and water—and to reframe psychological issues, transform pathological ways of viewing one's self and relationships, and find new meaning in one's life by using this transpersonal tool.

A few years later (1983) I took my doctoral research and wrote my first book, *The Mystery of Personal Identity*. One leading astrologer of that era told me that the way that I had presented astrology as a non-deterministic healing art had influenced him to be an astrologer. These are the moments when an iconoclast appreciates having taken "the road less traveled."

Please, dear reader, don't tell me that the reason I went in this direction, was due to the influence of the astrologer at that health faire in 1969. I have learned (as I hope you will by listening to my story) that there are much greater forces—forces beyond human reason and often stronger than the voices of others—that guide our destinies. True, these forces may not control our destinies, but if we listen with our inner ear we can come into alignment with this guiding light and suffer our fates with less pain. We can set sail flowing with the currents of the guiding waters of our lives rather than getting swayed away in the cross currents of another's destiny.

The Transformative Forces of the Cosmos

> *Our psyche is set up in accord with the structure of the universe,*
> *and what happens in the macrocosm likewise happens*
> *in the infinitesimal and most subjective reaches of the psyche.*
>
> —C. G. Jung
> *Memories, Dreams, Reflections*

But, back to the chronology of my unfolding story in the late 1960s, the question arises to the metaphysically inclined, "Can forces from the world behind the world influence even an ardent rationalist?" Were seemingly fantasy-driven ideas in novels like Herman Hesse's *The Glass Bead Game* and mystical adages such as, "As above, so below," instrumental in leading me to follow the beat of a different drummer? Can forces from the world behind the world alter the paths of our lives?

I am fascinated as I look back at that time and realize that during the summer of 1969 there were significant planetary configurations that symbolized great changes in the archetypal sphere—changes that might even be instrumental in creating a resonant frequency that could get a nascent lawyer to be like myself to dance to the tune of a different drummer.

During this summer of 1969 there was a conjunction of Jupiter and Uranus, which was in exact conjunction on July 20, 1969, the day that men landed on the moon. Many years later I found that astrologers believe that Jupiter-Uranus conjunctions signify the large, culture changing forces (Jupiter), and innovative leaps (Uranus), such as the Apollo moon-landing program. The astrological configuration symbolizes well the many advances (Jupiter) in technology (Uranus) that were needed to land a man on the moon.

Jupiter is a symbol of the social order since it is the biggest planet, giving more energy than it receives. Uranus is a symbol of revolution since it revolves in a different axis than all the other planets and it was discovered at the time of the American and French Revolutions. These are examples of the metaphorical basis and bases from which the meanings of astrological symbols derive; and they symbolize well the revolutionary change of career that was happening in my life at that time. (If, at that time in my life someone gave me an astrological interpretation of my change of career, I would have smirked and said, "Come on, my change of career is just about following a path with more heart, and going with the flow of my Woodstock generation.)

The Woodstock Festival was another apt symbol of this Jupiter-Uranus conjunction—the rebellion (Uranus) of the younger generation (Jupiter) against existing social norms. This conjunction took place in the first degree of Libra (I later found out Libra was my rising sign)—an apt symbol for the turning upside down of my relationship to the study of law (Libra, the scales of justice) and the desire to learn more about more harmonious and more healing ways of relating (Libra). (If you told me any of this astrology stuff at this time in my life I would have laughed at your irrational mystical interpretations).[5] Are there primal forces playing with humanity, creating resonant fields behind the stage of our mundane world that align the iron filings of life?

Ananke: Goddess of Necessity

The Greeks call the primal forces behind life, (seemingly at times stronger than reason), by the name of a goddess, Ananke, meaning "necessity." She is one of the primordial goddesses or archetypes, and she was often depicted as holding a spindle of thread. In the Greek mystery tradition it is said that she was the most powerful dictator of fate and circumstance, and that even the gods as well as us mortals had to give her respect and pay homage to her.

Certainly a powerful force was necessary to uproot the deep roots that held me in the fertile soils of New Jersey, with my strong extended family of relatives and a "made life" awaiting me as an attorney, with financial success around the next corner. So, perhaps Necessity called out to the Reluctant Metaphysician that I was, and drew me to go on a quest forsaking material success to follow a thread that connected to another world.

CHAPTER 6

The Land Where the Sun Rises in the West and Sets in the East

This above all: to thine own self be true,
and it must follow, as the night the day,
thou canst not then be false to any man.
Farewell, my blessing season this in thee!

—William Shakespeare
Hamlet Act 1, Scene 3

The New School for Social Research

In the year 1969 after graduating from Syracuse I changed my chosen career path and enrolled in a Masters degree in psychology program at the New School for Social Research. At the New School I began the process of healing my relationship to my overly mental and argumentative tendencies.

I started to see then, and throughout the ensuing years that my worship of the old, constricted deity of Mind had taken its toll. Around the time that I enrolled at the New School I became more and more aware that my neck (the area of the body where mind and body meet) held a great deal of tension. Over the next many years my neck became subluxated to such a degree that for years I found only temporary relief after going to chiropractors, orthopedic specialists, and various other mind-body healers.

My early training in psychotherapy at the New School helped me to understand why there was such an imbalance between my mind and body. After all, in addition to being a forceps baby, I had the essence of a lawyer in my early college years. I loved debate, and was fed by intellectual arguments. I was a head disconnected from my body. One of the roots of this way of being, I learned, was that I wanted to be "smart" in my parent's eyes, and in the view of the world. But, my healing and restoration of balance did not come from this knowledge alone, I needed a tradition that did not just help me understand why I was the way I was, I needed a tradition that would help me to be in my body.

At the New School I found professors who had an influence on my development, and my future life path. I was introduced to a more holistic psychology. One professor, Bernie Weitzman, introduced me to Eugene Gendlin's Focusing method and Jungian psychology. Something in me changed as I watched Dr. Weitzman demonstrate Focusing on his real feelings in front of a class of two hundred graduate students. I became more willing to be more real with my feelings.[1]

Though I am grateful to what this master's degree in psychology gave me, during my years at the New School I felt an aching in my soul to want to learn more about body oriented psychotherapy and Jungian psychology. I just got the briefest dip into the pool of these subjects there. I wondered where I could go to plummet the depths of the sea of a more holistic psychology.

While at the New School, I sensed that there was more to healing than modern psychology was giving me. I was ripe for the growing movement that sought an integrative approach to heal the body, mind, and spirit—and to bring back into balance our relationship to the natural world. The waters of a second stream were needed to heal the imbalances of my life.

I heard that there was a newly emerging discipline within psychology called somatic psychology. I knew that a psychology of the body was going to be important to my life path when I read Wilhelm Reich's works (1970) in my master's program. But his work and those of other bio-energetic psychologists (Lowen, 1958) were barely touched upon. So, after my master's degree program, I wanted to know more about the areas of psychology that were of most interest to me.

In the summer of 1971, I was in conflict. I was wondering about the practical use of the master's degree I had obtained in two years. If I had gone to law school I could have been an attorney in just three years.

I had read in Shakespeare's' *Hamlet* about Polonius's last piece of advice to his son Laertes before Laertes went off to find his destiny and boarded a boat to Paris. But, how does one "to thine own self be true," I wondered? I didn't know what steps to take to find the boat to the land of my destiny.

Healing Anxiety with the Secret of the Golden Flower:
My First Teaching Job—Montclair State

Though I had a degree in hand, I felt lost about what the next step was in my life. I needed a job. A friend of mine told me about a friend of theirs, a teacher at Montclair State College, who had broken his leg and was looking for someone to take over his classes for a semester. I had never taught a class before. But, I took the bus from Manhattan where I lived to Montclair, New Jersey, to go for a job interview. The class was in graduate developmental psychology. When I arrived at the interview I found out that the class started the next day.

Even though I needed a job, I felt intimidated by the prospect of teaching for the first time. Somehow though, I got myself together to go to the interview; and after being offered the job I summoned my *chutzpah* to agree to teach a class the very next night. I took the bus back from New Jersey to my New York apartment.

There were formidable obstacles in the way of taking this job. First, I had always looked young for my age. At about twenty-four years old, I had just finished my master's degree, and I probably looked like the child of many of the older teachers and graduate students who were coming to Montclair State to get a degree in psychology. This added to my feeling of inadequacy. Second, I had never taught before. Third, I had never taken a course in developmental psychology. Out of all of the subject areas in psychology to which I had an aversion, developmental psychology topped them all. I believed more in the individual process of each person's uniqueness, rather than in fixed developmental categories.

When I got back to my apartment it was about 9 p.m. at night and I decided to start to write down everything I could glean from my books that related to developmental psychology. By 10:30 p.m. I had written down everything I knew. In preparation for the class I rehearsed in front of the mirror; I practiced my lecture saying out loud everything I knew about developmental psychology. It took twenty minutes…and I needed to lecture for two and a half hours in each of the fifteen developmental psychology classes I was to do that semester!

Only twenty minutes of knowledge for a class of 2.5 hours…hmmm. But amazingly, in the first class the students asked questions, and I realized there that I had within me a storehouse of knowledge upon which I could tap. These twenty minutes of notes lasted about half of the semester. I was starting to like this teaching thing.

I was reliant on my notes. They were the crutch for the intellectually based scholar I was. Then one day in the middle of the semester the unthinkable happened. On the bus ride to New Jersey I looked into my backpack to go over my notes, and I realized that I had left them at home. I had a panic attack.

To get through the panic attack, I practiced a breathing method I had just learned from a book I picked up at Samuel Weiser's bookstore in New York. The book was called the *Secret of the Golden Flower,* and the Taoist breathing method in it was called *Microcosmic Orbit Breathing.* It helped me to relax. This breathing method became a major part of my life's work many years later.[2]

I discovered on this day that when I was relaxed something came out of me, which was greater than the specific information held by my mind. I told my students that I had forgotten my notes; and I just answered questions from the students that day. It was the best class I had taught. A few students came up after the class and jokingly said that I should forget my notes everyday.

This was long before I knew about the practice of Qigong; and my knowledge of Taoism and going with the flow of life was in a nascent state, since I had just picked up my first book on it. The year was 1971. At this time I didn't realize that this was the beginning of my initiation into the realm of "the wounded healer" because the notion of "wounded healer" didn't come into the literature in the field until much later (Halifax, 1988). However during the early 1970s, my two great bodily wounds—my neck pains and my anxiety—helped to expand my understanding of a more holistic healing. My "weak points" compelled me, reluctant though I was, to learn about deeper dimensions of healing and to seek a broader and deeper psychotherapy that included the somatic realm and cross-cultural traditions of psycho-physiological healing.

After the regular teacher who had broken his leg came back to teach the class I was left adrift with no job. It was the summer of 1971. I wanted to enroll in a Ph.D. program in psychology, and I heard that there were some programs out on the West coast that were breaking new ground in the study of consciousness. They were even allowing the study of somatic psychotherapy and Eastern methods of meditation to be mixed with psychology …just along the lines of my newly emerging line of interest.

To understand my psyche at this phase of my life, a person would need to understand various "revolutions" of this transformative era. Revolutions in many spheres were taking place at this time in the early 1970s. There was a "political revolution" partly based on ending the Vietnam War, which finally came to an end in January of 1973. There was the "Healing the Earth Revolution" which began with the first Earth Day in April 22 of 1970. It was called by Senator Gaylord Nelson to raise peoples consciousness about the dangers of disrespecting the environment after the Santa Barbara oil spill off the coast of California in 1969. Mayor Lindsay of New York shut down Fifth Avenue in alignment with Earth Day values, and I joined the march right outside of where I was enrolled in my Master's degree program in psychology at the New School for Social research. About a million of us (according to Wikipedia) marched that day, joining twenty million other Americans around the country to protest environmental degradation. I remember the feeling of solidarity with my political brothers and sisters as we marched up to central park, and our youthful naiveté as we believed that with all the people in alignment with us, and the coverage by all the major media, that we could create a change in our culture's environmental policies, just as we were doing with Vietnam.

Theodore Roszack (1995) called us the "Counter-Culture." Those of us who were part of this movement felt like we were each different organs, or different cells, in a single organism. We knew that each of us had our own particular talents and purposes in the counter-cultural revolution. Some of us emphasized political activism for causes such as civil rights; others were environmentalists. Some said, "Let's go back to the farms to create our own organic food." I was part of those who believed that the answer to the multifaceted crises of Western civilization lied in consciousness. This was called the "consciousness revolution" (Laszio, 2003).

John Lennon was one leader in the consciousness revolution who encapsulated its core philosophy in the phrase, "You say you want a revolution, well you better free your mind instead." This became the ruling idea for many of us who saw the importance of the inner revolution to free the consciousness of a materialistic, racist, and hegemonistic culture. Those of us who identified with the Beatle George Harrison, followed his advice, and we moved from the up and downs of psychedelics to meditation and exploring the inner realms, "within and without you."

Revolution of Consciousness and the Psychedelic Revolution

The use of plant medicines, psilocybin, LSD and other psychologically oriented drugs to effect human consciousness pervaded our subculture in those days. This was called the "psychedelic revolution," and it was part of the wider "consciousness revolution." Some of these psychedelic plants were called "entheogens," because they opened the imbiber to altered states that were divine (*theo*).[3] In Aldous Huxley's terms, as he wrote about in his book *Doors of Perception (1977),* these psychedelics opened inner doors to non-ordinary states of consciousness. These medicinal plants opened one to experience the "God inside of us." However, as many of us learned, first a journey to hell oftentimes took place.

In this era, reading the *Tibetan Book of the Dead* (Sabhava, 1993), *The Tibetan Book of Living and Dying* (Rinpoche, 1993), *The Psychedelic Experience* (Leary, 1987), and *The Doors of Perception* (Huxley, 1977) were "required reading" for members of my subculture. We wanted to understand everything we could about the labyrinthian trails, and dangers on the path, to which the psychedelic pathway led. In these books, analogies were made between the after-death state and the psychedelic experience. Comparisons were made between the "Demons" (projections of our unworked through life issues such as fear, greed, and helplessness) in the after death realms (called *Bardo states*) and the issues that arose in the psychedelic experience.

Being a scholarly type, I was most moved by the part of the consciousness movement that advocated using plant medicines as an entryway to altered states of consciousness, and then after the door was opened to find more natural ways of going into altered states. It was like an "acid trip" without being on a drug when I practiced meditation and read about shamanistic initiations in other cultures by authors such as Carlos Castaneda (1968, 1971), Mircea Eliade (1958), Joan Halifax (1988), and Michael Harner (1990). I wondered where I had been all of my life.

Such simple yet profound truths were transmitted to members of my generation in the books of this era about how to "just be present," and about the spiritual side of life. Some of my favorite books of that era were: Alan Watts' *The Book: On the Taboo against Knowing You Are* (1966) and Ram Dass' *Be Here Now* (1971). Books about the psychology and science of consciousness such as Charles Tart's (1968) *Altered States of Consciousness*, and Richard Buck's, *Cosmic Consciousness* became "bibles of the consciousness revolution." They were as pervasive as the Old and New Testament were on fundamentalist Christian bookshelves.

Richard Wilhelm had translated the *I Ching* and the *Secret of the Golden Flower* texts into terms understandable to Westerners, and Carl Jung (1996) called him a "Gnostic intermediary." This was the path to which some of us scholarly types aspired—to be Gnostic intermediaries and translate the knowledge we were receiving to our culture.[4]

One of the books that was most moving to me was *The Origins and History of Consciousness*, by one of Carl Jung's foremost disciples, Erich Neumann (1954). Here I learned that human consciousness began in a state of *participation mystique*—a state of oneness with our surroundings. Then, according to Neumann, the aim of consciousness evolution is to go through the various stages of separation and return to the state of oneness with our differentiated self, intact. Young children, and our oldest ancestors when engaged in various altered-states in their tribal practices, have a preponderance of brain wave rhythms in the slower delta and theta rhythms. In these altered states, *participation mystique* is more available than in our normal waking state beta consciousness.

Various spiritual practices such as yoga, tai chi, music, dance can help us today to access these states without drugs. According to both Neumann's (1954) view and Ken Wilbur's concept of the "pre-trans fallacy" (Wilber, 2000), one of the aims of the evolution of consciousness is to be able to access these states without losing touch with our differentiated selves.

I was one of those who felt that the consciousness revolution without drugs was as important as the states of consciousness that psychedelic plants induced. One of the first books that "turned me on" to this path was, U. S. Anderson's *Three Magic Words* (1954), which I read in 1970 when I was in my apartment in New York getting my master's degree in psychology. My mind was expanded by the stories of "idiot savants" who could name the dates of any weather event in history, or instantly perform virtually impossible mathematical feats. The three magic words were, "I am God," and U. S. Anderson argued that within the consciousness of a human being lay a divine potential that usually remains untapped. He put forth the case that qualities like omniscience that are usually attributed to God, may lie within the human mind. This was an encapsulation of age-old mystical philosophy that was beginning to emerge in the corridors of Western science. Long before the human growth and potential movement began, U. S. Anderson was a forerunner of an era of consciousness studies that was to emerge shortly; and he excited the imagination of seekers like myself went on a metaphysical adventure to answer the questions, "What are human beings capabilities? How do we discover these deeper potentials of the world behind everyday life, and how can we use these inner resources for consciousness expansion and healing?"

As I am writing this chapter on December 19, 2010, I synchronistically turned on the TV show *60 Minutes* where Leslie Stahl was interviewing various people who had "Superior Autobiographical Memories." These people have awesome memories of almost every day of their lives, and can recall public and private memories with exactitude that would impress the most sceptical among us with how there is a world behind the world of every-day norms. By doing brain scans of these exceptional people, researchers are beginning to discover the precise parts of the human brain that are correlated with such abilities. The data thus far points to an enlarged caudate nucleus. As research continues this may have implications for many relevant aspects of our lives including Alzheimer's research, as well as expanding the function normal human memory. If anyone doubts that there is some amazing "world behind the everyday world," they just have to explore the talents of such people. Do all of us have this capacity hidden in us?

In part, due to my fascination with consciousness research, I started to consider the idea of moving to the West Coast where altered states of consciousness research was at the forefront. However, since I came from such a traditional enmeshed family, I felt that I could not actually make such a move. I had a most loving mother and caring father, and being from a relatively well-to-do middle class family my material needs were well taken care of. The bonds with my family ran deep, and the rootedness in my New Jersey life ran as deep. Everything I had known and all of my friends were on the East Coast. No ordinary force could unravel the garment of my life; yet as in the story of the Black Dog unraveling the weaving of the Old Woman in the Cave (told in the Introduction of this book) the garment of my life was about to be unraveled.

Dream of the Land Where the Sun Rises in the West

> Dreams…speak a language improvised just for us…
> The nightly evidence that we remain part of the great drama
> and dramatic pageant that the soul requires…
> Most fail to follow where their dreams would lead.
> Many trade the dream that brought them to life
> for a life someone else dreams up for them.
> Each person is a body wrapped around a soul imbued with a dream
> trying to waken from within.
> Our nightly dreaming contains a vial connection to the great mysteries of life.
> Each life, knowingly or not, participates in mystery of creation ongoing,
> each is made of "such stuff as dreams are made of."
>
> —Michael Meade (2010, p. 140)

One night, on the summer solstice of 1971, I had a dream. Or was it a dream? It was so real that it was like a place I had known more deeply than anything I had known in this life.

I dreamed that I was from "the land where the sun rises in the West and sets in the East." My spiritual mother and father were there. Their substance was not flesh, but rather was something indescribable. They were the most beautiful light bodies, yet more than light they exuded a synesthesia of color, sound, vibration that combined many senses. Love was its essence. My spiritual parents spoke and said,

> You are from the land where the sun rises in the West and sets in the East. This is a place that is located in the center of the Earth and at the same time out in the deepest recesses of outer space. Don't forget that, because you are going to leave our land and you may forget." I replied, "How could I forget; that would be impossible. Everyone knows that the sun rises in the West and sets in the East. I could never forget this place that is so filled with love and ecstasy. It is my home, so of course I will never forget it." After I said these words I could feel myself being drawn to another place, as my spiritual parents voice was still ringing in my ears, "don't forget." The next moment I was on the Earth in the midst of a dark, cloudy, thunderstorm-filled sky. I felt fear and foreboding, as I wondered, "What is this place where I am?" But in the midst of my fear, in the midst of the dark clouds above me a light came from the heavens. It came down through the top of my head, and filled me with light. My spiritual parents voice came through the clouds, as if the light itself was speaking and saying, "You are going to be going through dark and cloudy times in your life in the years to come; but if you remember from where you came (the land where the sun rises in the East and set in the West), you will be able to get through these times." This light from the heavens above filled me with as much energy as it had when I was living in my spiritual homeland.

I woke up from what seemed like much more than a dream. The experiential force that comes from such inner experiences cannot be "grokked" by another (Heinlein, 1987). Some call this a "Big Dream," or a "Lucid Dream." It was interesting and synchronistic that this dream of this great light came on the day of the summer solstice, the day of greatest light in the year.

This dream made me wonder whether we are all on a certain bandwidth of consciousness, and occasionally on days of maximum illumination another bandwidth opens and we realize that this other bandwidth is equally a part of the vibrational matrix of our lives. From this point of view, though consensual reality says that we should live in the "real world," there is another real world and another story about its nature. Plato's metaphysical story of the cave tells us that there are archetypal forms that lie behind life; and mythologies and mystics talk about the world behind the world. It is said this other world is a world as real as the world of our senses—they are inextricably interconnected. I later grew to realize that from the experiential metaphysician's viewpoint, when we lose connection with this other world our Earthly lives go out of balance with our deepest selves and purpose.

And so it was, in the next few days after having this dream, some thread started to increasingly pull me West...to the West Coast. Stronger than the force of stability from all of my life to date, this force from "the Land where my new life was to rise in the West" called me.[5]

Following the Hero's Call to Move to the West

> There is a dream in the middle of each life.
> Each of us a dream seeded in a soul around which the body is wrapped.
> The first agreement of the soul can be viewed
> as the dream that keeps calling us to a greater life.
>
> —Michael Mead
> *Fate and Destiny*

The dreams and guiding images that lie at the center of each of our lives can come in many forms: nighttime dreams, poetry, or cultural myths and archetypes that "grab us" from the world behind the world. When I was struggling with my decision about whether to move the West Coast, it was not only my nighttime big dream of the Land Where the Sun Rose in the West that helped to fuel my journey. The first poem that I had ever written helped to activate the archetypal powers that I needed to give the impetus for the quest to find a higher ground. Here it is:

THE PLATEAU

People scoff at the mountain climber,
Asking, "Why climb when it is so peaceful here in the Valley?"
How can I explain what calls me on the upward climb?
How can I justify suffering untold pain
when I could just remain at the bottom, content?
But now, lying in the grass of this mountain plateau
the long climb takes on meaning.

If you could hear the shepherd's flute here,
You would understand that there is nothing like it in the lowlands.
The music here comes not from musicians,
but from nature's all encompassing harp.

I could remain on this plateau for eternity,
yet the morning mist rises,
and the rest of the mountain above me takes on form.

This poem is one of the early inklings that encapsulated my philosophy as a Reluctant Metaphysician. The archetypes (energy potentials) of the mountain and the plateau, expressed the force in my early years that calls the complacent in each of us to reluctantly leave our comfort zone and listen to a call to something greater—the call to climb the Sacred Mountain.

Master mythologists Joseph Campbell, Mircea Eliade, and Michael Meade say that the refusal to answer the call can lead to a life without meaning. However, the hero's quest is not merely an interesting academic subject of investigation; I was to discover that Life oftentimes teaches that there also are prices to pay for heeding a dream's invocation or the hero's call. The road guided by imaginal forces is a toll road with its costs, dangers, lessons to be learned, and its shadows.

Fortunately, as a gift from the world behind the world, stories from the collective reservoir of humanity can also help us deal with the dark side of the hero's quest. For example, since I had very close relationships with my parents and friends it was difficult to tear myself away from them. Though one of the major engines that was driving my Journey to the West was personal imagery from my inner life, just like a jet plane has two engines on its wings to make it fly, so do our culture's dreams (myths) act as second engine to help us take off and remain aloft on our life journeys. Here's one…

Parcival's Quest for the Holy Grail

The myth of King Arthur's Knight, Parcival, is a story that empowers the hero in each of us to take off on Destiny's path.

> In the old times, when the kingdom was physically and spiritually dry, many Knights went on the quest to find the Grail Cup—a symbol of the holder of the Waters of Life that could restore the Kingdom. The Kingdom was in such a state of deterioration and spiritual emptiness that no one could restore it. At this time there was a young boy who lived by a castle with his mother. It was a life of contentment and satisfied needs. But then one day a White Knight rode by the mother and son, and the son saw the light of the sun bounce off of the Knight's chest-plate of armour. Something arose in the young man, some force that was beyond words, awakened a light in him. He said to his mother that he needed to follow the way of the Knight; and he had to suffer for a lifetime the guilt he had from abandoning his mother.

Such is one of the prices of the hero's quest. Recognizing that we are on a mythic path for a higher goal helps to assuage guilt; and mythogems of meaning contained in ancient tales can help the hero in each of us to deal with obstacles on our journey in life. The light shining from the breastplate of the mounted Knight in us can empower us to embark on the journey to our higher purpose in life. However, to fulfill the quest of individuation, there are demons to be confronted and the right questions must be asked and answered.

Parcival had to meet many obstacles on his path, such as doing battle with the Black Knight, and it took Parcival many years to find the Grail Castle. When he found it, a voice came from the Castle and asked, "Who does the Grail Serve?" Because Parcival couldn't answer the question, the Gates of the Castle closed to him. It took him many more years of traveling (some say twenty) to learn that the answer to the question is, "The Grail serves the Kingdom." When Parcival was able to transcend the egotistical elements of his quest, and answer the question with this answer, then the door to the Grail Castle opened. He then received the Grail Cup, and the Kingdom was restored.

Like Parcival, in order to actualize our life's purpose we must deal with the obstacles on our path such as the Black Knight of guilt or complacency. Most importantly we must know what purpose our journey serves. Each of us may get caught up in making a living, or fulfilling our ego's competitive desires. So even though it looks like we are successful, the door to the Grail Castle will not open until we can appropriately remember that the true hero's quest is to restore the Water of Life to the larger kingdom. Depending upon your own path this quest may take the form of healing work, a business venture that serves the community, becoming an environmental activist, or finding new ways of being with your loved ones or family. Being true to your quest often involves a sacrifice of your past life or way of being, suffering the regret and nostalgia of the road not taken, or bearing the guilt of that which needs to be let go of to serve the kingdom.

Dangers in Answering the Hero's Call

When we heed the call of the White Knight, various dangers arise as we meet the Dark Knight, and "the dark night,"—the shadow side of the quest to individuation. When I left my comfortable life in New Jersey, and I got into my Volkswagen bus to drive out to California, I had just graduated with my master's degree in psychology from the new School for Social Research. To tell you the truth, after reading Ronald Laing's *Politics of Experience* (1983) and other critical commentaries about mental illness and psychosis, I was undeservedly self-assured about my knowledge.

A friend of a friend, who, for confidentiality purposes I will call "Mona", accompanied me on the ride to California in my Volkswagen bus. It was the hippie era in 1972 and on the drive out West "Mona" had a psychotic breakdown. One morning after we had camped out in Kansas, Mona left her eyeglasses back at our campground, and I was about to drive back there with her to get them. She looked at some broken glass by the side of the road where a coke bottle had broken, and she said, "There are my glasses." I looked at her, perplexed and was about to say, "No, those aren't your glasses." But Mona jumped out of the car and, picking up pieces of the broken bottle, screamed, "The world is shattered, it can't be put back together again." I rushed over to calm her, but she ran as I tried to catch up to her. She was running toward a farmer's house. She got up to the farmer's door, and I called out to ask her what she was doing. She replied in the midst of incoherent gibberish, "See the hole in the door, there's the answer. There's the opening to the center of the world." She started to use the broken piece of glass to try to cut through the knothole in front wooden door to the farmer's house.

Picture the scene: This was the height of the hippie era, when tensions between Middle America and hippies were at their height. This was the era when Ken Kesey popularized the psychedelic movement with his *Electric Kool-Aid Acid Test* as he and his merry pranksters traveled across the county in their bus giving LSD to many (Wolfe, 2008). Conservative forces were on the look out for those who were trying to undermine the anti-drug American traditional values of the 1950s. And here were two longhaired hippies in tie-died tee shirts trespassing on a farmer's property.

Understandably, the farmer thought we were trying to break into his house. He did not hear my attempt at rational explanation as he opened his door with his shotgun aimed at us, and luckily he just yelled a warning as we backed up and ran back to our car. We hightailed it out of there, and on the ride to Colorado I listened to Mona's manic conversation filled with hallucinations about the demons that were in the clouds.

I was relieved when we finally got to Colorado to a friend's house. We went inside, and I started to explain to "Kenny" about what had happened while Mona was, I thought, waiting in the next room with Kenny's treasured record collection. When Kenny and I returned to his living room, Mona was in the process of breaking his records, as she screamed, "There is no wholeness, the circle of life is broken." Kenny and I decided it would be best to drive her to the hospital in my Volkswagen bus. But when I got to my car the keys were missing. I was very upset when I asked Mona where the keys were and she said, in the midst of incoherent sentences, that they were down the River of Pain. There was a river next to Kenny's house, and I did my best with Mona to try to have her help me find exactly where on "the River of Pain" were my keys? After about two hours, and discombobulated rants about how the key to the universe was lost, Mona helped me to find the keys.

We called the local hospital and emergency services came and took Mona there. Her parents flew out from the East Coast, and I was not allowed to see her again. I never found out whether this was an organically arising psychotic break or whether it was from LSD that perhaps Mona had ingested without me knowing it.

For Mona, this was meeting the dangers on her hero's path, and being swallowed by the dark forces of the psyche, as she was traveling out to her new life in California. For me, it taught me to be humble about my limitations in being able to deal with the forces of psychosis. It was another impetus for me to get further training in depth psychology. Humility is one of the lessons that can come from wrestling with the Dark Knight on the road to a new life; and respect for the powers of the unconscious comes from encountering the dark shadow-lands of the psyche.

This experience on my road to the Grail Castle was long before I learned about the forces of "symbolic reification,"—that the inner world of the psyche in the midst of psychosis can "thing-ify" the inner workings of the mind as it struggles with such issues as the loss of spiritual sight, the fragmenting of the wholeness of life, and the loss of the keys to life.

Within a few months I had completed my cross-country journey to the West to find a Ph.D. program where I could pursue my awakening interest in humanistic psychology and the psychology of consciousness. In California I began to investigate the awakening experiences I had been having—experiences that were antithetical to everything my rational mind could grasp. A new life was beginning.

CHAPTER 7:

Four Shaman: The Esalen Institute Calling

Don't just ask what the world needs.
Ask what makes you come alive
and then go and do it,
because what the world needs
are people who have come alive.

—Howard Thurman

Telegraph Avenue and the Counter-Culture: Mythology Comes Alive on the Streets

To describe the late 1960s and early 1970s to someone who was not there is to describe a foreign country. When I came to California on my Quest to the West, I noticed how almost everyone was dressed in colorful handmade clothes or commercially bought clothes with sewn designs of peace symbols, symbols of the Tao, or designs from indigenous cultures. The norm was to be a "rebel with a cause"—and the cause was a rebellion against the materialistic culture of the United States. It was called "the rainbow culture," with rainbow festivals where people camped out for the weekend, played music, and explored psychedelic inner territories.

This was the era of the reemergence of age-old meditation traditions and cross-cultural treasure houses of spiritual stories that the American materialistic culture of the mid 1900s had suppressed or ignored. The Beatles met Maharishi (and even to this day the lasting effects of the Transcendental Meditation movement remains), with many members of the TM movement practicing meditation every day. This was the era where Baba Ram Dass met his guru in India; and his travels opened up the psycho-spiritual movement of the counterculture to the wisdom of the East. In 1977, Richard Bach wrote his book, *Illusions: The Adventures of a Reluctant Messiah,* about the apparent illusions that can make a new reality. It was the era when Dan Millman wrote the book, *The Way of the Peaceful Warrior,* about meeting a master of the internal martial arts a few blocks below Telegraph Avenue on Fulton Street. (This gas station is just a few blocks from where I have now been in private practice as a psychologist for thirty years.)

The prolific astro-cosmologist Rick Tarnas (2006, p. 180) describes this time as an era when there was a sudden eruption (Uranus) and pervasive presence of the Dionysian impulse (Pluto) in music, dance film, theater, and literature. Dr. Tarnas attributes these artistic and intellectual awakenings, and chthonic evolutionary processes taking place at that time to the Uranus-Pluto conjunction of that era from 1960–1972. The amount of cross-cultural, and cross-disciplinary references he gives in his epic work, can even open non-metaphysicians' eyes to wonder. But regardless of the objective truth regarding the awesome synchronicities between cosmos and culture that he points out, and regardless of the argument about whether he is unconsciously cherry-picking data,[1] when the transiting planet Uranus (upheaval) came into conjunction with my natal Neptune (dissolving boundaries) in 6 degrees of Libra I uprooted myself from everything that was familiar to me and moved to the West Coast. I did not know until many years later that this cosmic correlation was taking place.

I was swept up and carried to the West Coast in part by this counter-cultural wave, and also by a desire to find a doctoral psychology program where I could continue my exploration of alternative methods to heal the psyche. Only "God" really knows whether divine and "celestial influences" were part of my decision making process.

I was always intellectually satisfied to say that my major life change from being on the path to an East Coast attorney to a West Coast psychotherapist was in part due to my quest for the right Ph.D. program, the social transformative climate of that era, and my dream life (the Land Where the Sun Rose in the West). However, I later discovered that at the time that the social forces of the counter-culture swept me up, it was the one time in the past century that Jupiter (social order), Uranus (rebellion), and Pluto (death of attachments and the world we know) were in a triple conjunction. According to astrological cosmologists, to be alive at the rare time of triple conjunctions of the trans-Saturnian planets is a privilege, and it is hard to describe the atmosphere to someone not alive at such a time. Synchronistically, just during this time (in 1969) Thunderclap Newman wrote the song, "Something in the Air," which encapsulated the sentiment of this era.

From my training as a psychologist, I might discount this "something," and say that it was nothing more than the hormones of youth, or the social rebellion against and the Vietnam War and the draft. However, an astrological metaphysician would retort that there may be more to this life than meets the eye, that such triple conjunctions are very rare, and that major planetary alignments mark pivotal turning points in collective history and individuals human lives. My astrological mentor, Dane Rudhyar (1969), wrote that in the period of the sixth century BC (576 BC in 15 degrees of Taurus) there was a triple conjunction of Uranus, Neptune and Pluto; and during this pivotal time in human history Gautama the Buddha, Pythagoras, and Lao Tzu were born. So, the sceptic in me must reluctantly be moved to wonder if during the time of the triple planetary conjunction of the late 1960s there was something epochally transformative taking place in "the world behind the world" that was "wanting to incarnate."

The transformative times of the birth of the counter-culture that led me to uproot and change my life are difficult to describe to those who weren't there. I am left with the bare bones of the stories of those times to try to convey the climate of the inexplicable.

When I first came to Berkeley in the early1970's and I walked down Telegraph Avenue, I was struck by the depth of eye contact. Almost everyone was looking at each other, right in the eye. I commented on this to a friend and asked why. He said, "of course, man, you never know when you might be walking past God, and it would be a misfortune if you passed God by."

Indra and the Lamed Vav

My friend proceeded to tell me the story of Indra, the King of a province in India:

> Indra was arrogant, having defeated all his enemies and he was lost in his obsessions about how to design every little detail of his castle. Even his architect Vivakarman was getting impatient with him. So Vishnu, king of the Gods, shape-shifted himself into a beggar boy; and the beggar boy told Indra a story about the ants below his feet that had conquered worlds also. The beggar boy (the disguised great God of creation, Vishnu) further diminished Indra's accomplishments by telling the great King how the circle of life was filled with beings that had conquered worlds and lost worlds. This led Indra to feel deflated, and he retreated to a cave to meditate on life. Here, Indra learned to connect to deeper spiritual forces of life and he learned humbleness. When he returned to the world from his cave he was a better, more spiritual king.

The stranger I met then told me, "See you never know who you might meet on the path, a beggar, or whoever walks by us, might be Vishnu." A Jewish friend I was with replied, "We have the same story in Judaism that a tailor might be one of the *Lamed Vav,* one of the 36 righteous men who live in the world at any time." Then, we all talked about how important it was to "Be here Now," the title of the book by Baba Ram Dass who had left his Harvard University position to travel to the East. His ideas and his journey lived in our everyday lives. Philosophic ideas and spiritual practices were lived on the streets. The books of our generation were breathed in everyday life, just like today in the third millennium people talk about the latest blog posting.

Nowadays we hear of the Water Cooler Wars, and whoever tells the best story by the water cooler in the office wins. In these days on Telegraph Avenue, similarly there were the "Waters of Life Wars." In everyday life people gathered; and whoever had the best story about the most enlightening spiritual practice that led one to the Water's of Life, or the fountain at the center of spiritual practices of the world, that person would win the Water of Life war...please forgive the militaristic analogy.

So, it was not just the books—it was also the practices that lay at the center of this Cultural Revolution. Virtually everyone I knew had read Ram Dass' book, *Be Here Now.*

The Hatha yoga practices he outlined in that book, I have still done almost every day for the last 30 years. They have evolved since that time; now I add *acu-yoga* (touching acu-points to the yoga practices) as I do various yoga practices. You can see some of these practices in my friend Michael Gach's book called *Acu-Yoga* (1981). I now wake up every morning about twenty minutes before I need to, and do these yoga practices while still in bed—good medicine for my neck and hip blockages. But, back to the early 1970's...

I left my storytelling friends and continued my walk into a juice bar on Telegraph Avenue eying the luscious carrot juice. The employee at the juice bar said, "Hey bro,' do you want some carrot juice?" I said that I did but I didn't have the money for it. He said, "Don't worry, be happy" a quote from the Indian master Meher Baba. The juice bar employee said, "Here's the carrot juice, when you have some money come back in and pay me back." He told me he was a Meher Baba follower, and loving acts were just part of his practice. Not yet converted from my East Coast sense of economic realism, I wondered what his boss would say. But this was the era where the power of the people indeed seemed to rule, jobs were plentiful, and he replied to my questioning by saying, "No worries man, doing good always comes back to you and builds Joe's (the owners) business pretty well, as you can see." It was true in my case; when I got a job teaching I paid him back and came back to this juice bar quite often.

A wide variety of Eastern practices were as commonplace here in California as was baseball on the East Coast. Here in California, where East meets West, many spiritual teachers from India came to teach. Concerts of Indian music with master sitarist Ali Akbar Khan, and his students who studied at his college of music in San Rafael, were commonplace; and *Kirtan* concerts opened our ears and the heart to divine states. In the Kirtan-tradition, Vedic Indian devotional chants are sung in a call-and-response mode with very few words. At first, I felt bored and wondered how could these masters sing for a whole hour the same words over and over again...Ram, Ram, Sita, Ram, Sita, Ram, Ram. But as I chanted along with the group I fell into an experience that brought me into what might be called a trance state. A world behind the world opened where my psychological issues, doubts, and fears were held and transformed by a bigger sea of energy. Likewise with my introduction to Tai Chi and Qigong, which I will tell you more about later, I found a practice that was to change my relationship to life.

But it was not just Eastern philosophy and practices that turned my generation topsy-turvy. Indigenous traditions from around the world also turned our worlds upside down. Carlos Castaneda's stories pervaded the conversations of our culture, as we heard about his remarkable meetings with the purported shaman Don Juan, a Yaqui shaman. Though many of his stories have been debunked (Fikes, 1993),the purpose of opening the imagination of the counter-culture to cross-cultural, shamanic knowledge was served. Michael Harner's book, *The Way of the Shaman,* and his experiences with shamanism changed our worldviews. Like many other seekers, I did a few workshops and shamanic journeying with him. As he tapped on his drum, I tapped into a world behind the world. Later, I joined a training group with a Native American shaman, Oh Shannah Fast Wolf, and I learned to respect, and have a door opened to, Native American teachings.

Esalen Institute: Center of the Human Growth and Potential Movement

In the mid 1970s in this climate of counter-culturalism, I first visited Esalen. This, for me, was like visiting the spiritual center of the world. Many of the countercultural heroes about whom I had read, taught here. One room was named after Aldous Huxley who had written, *Doors of Perception* (1977) about the plant "entheogens," like peyote and psilocybin that opened up divine doors of ecstasy (if one was willing to pay the price of traveling through hell first). One workshop space was named for Abraham Maslow, one of the founders of Humanistic psychology, who taught how to be honest, present, human, and vulnerable. Another room was named after Fritz Perls, the famous Gestalt psychologist.

To honor Fritz's contribution to emotional realness and becoming more whole as a person, this would not be the time to mention his gruff and direct manner that created breakdowns in some and transformation in others. This was the era when many teachers learned that emotional fragmentation was sometimes the byproduct of workshops on psychological evolution—such as *Erhard Seminar Training* (EST), and *The Forum*. (In time, safeguards were put into place to help to prevent such problems—for example getting a note from a therapist before a person would be allowed to be part of such experiences.)

People at Esalen and elsewhere made comparisons to the era of the 6th century BC when the Buddha, Lao Tzu, and other world religious leaders were transforming their culture; but few knew that triple trans-Saturnian planetary aspects were taking place in each of these transformative eras (Rudhyar, 1969, p. 74; Tarnas, 2007, p. 203).

At Esalen Institute, a friend of mine, who was one of the managers, offered me a free place to sleep that night in a cabin built right over a river. I walked down to the hot tubs on a full moon lit night. The fact that Esalen was located at a place where three bodies of water met was not lost on the spiritual seekers of my age. Here a river, the ocean, and sulfur hot springs joined. The metaphysically inclined people I met there, metaphorized and philosophized about the geomancy of Esalen and its magic. However, that night it was nice to retreat from all the philosophizing, and I just walked alone down to the hot tub.

It was the first time I had ever been in a hot tub, and I felt as if I melted into some sacred space under the moonlight that was on a par with any spiritual experience I had ever had. The rhythmic crashing of the ocean waves nearby added a musical accompaniment to activating an altered state. That night I had a dream that was one of the most powerful ones I ever had.

The Four Shaman Dream

*Awakening means stepping out of the daydream offered to us
and entering the greater dream that called us here to begin with.
Such a dream comes more than once in a lifetime
because it is closely woven to one's heart.
The delicate, yet permanent threads of fate are dream woven within,
and they bear a destiny waiting to be discovered...
When in touch with the thread of our life-dream
we know where we are going, even if we have never been there before.*

—Michael Meade
Fate and Destiny, 2010, p.141–2

That night I lay down to go to sleep in Esalen's geodesic dome cabin that was built right over a river. With a stream flowing under me, I journeyed into the sea of dreamland. I dreamed that:

> *I was a Native American living many centuries ago at Esalen. The eldest shaman of the tribe asked four younger shaman, including myself, to travel north and then make a circle East back to Esalen gathering the knowledge of all surrounding tribes to bring it back to Esalen. I went on that journey, and when I got around the circle three-quarters of the way I was killed by an arrow that was shot into in my neck.*

When I woke from this dream, or vision (or whatever it was), the experience felt so real I could not believe that it was a dream. Many meanings could be given to such a dream. Some of my metaphysically inclined friends interpreted this dream as a past life dream; however I am an open-minded sceptic about past lives. At that time in my life I interpreted the dream to mean that my life's journey had some part to play along with at least three others, to bring knowledge of other traditions back to Esalen.

After this powerful experience, I changed the license plate on my car to "4 Shaman" (during the first years when environmental license plates were issued in California) to honor this vision. Many times, after I published a book or wrote an article that contributed to the human growth and potential movement, I contacted Esalen to see if I could teach there—to no avail. But, as you will later see, I was to learn that it can take a lifetime of work to actualize a dream.[2]

CHAPTER 8:

What's Your and My True Name?

The first great problem in life is not to have a true calling…
A calling isn't simply an option in the plan of life;
from the view of the soul, a calling is a great necessity.
Those who respond to the call appear as vagrants
before they find the extravagant way their soul has been called.
Learning one's true way of fitting into this world
often requires becoming unfit for regular duties and common expectations.

—Michael Meade
Fate and Destiny, 2010, p. 150–151

My Doctoral Years: Saybrook Graduate School

In the early 1970s my dream of the Land Where the Sun Rose in the West led me on a "quest to the West" (to the West Coast of the United States), to find a graduate program that would enable me to study holistic ways of healing the psyche. Coincidentally, when I arrived in California from the East Coast in 1972, Dr. Eleanor Criswell, a professor at Sonoma State University in Rohnert Park, California, called the first meeting of the first program in Humanistic psychology. With my wide-eyes, and thirst for learning, I was there. The Humanistic Psychology Institute was created from these meetings. It was later called Saybrook Institute, then Saybrook Graduate School and Research Center, and it is now called Saybrook University.

Saybrook Institute was named after the town in Connecticut where founding members of the humanistic and transpersonal psychology movements met at a conference in 1964. Some of the luminaries who attended were Gordon Allport, James Bugenthal, Clark Moustakas, Abraham Maslow, Rollo May, and Carl Rogers. From that conference was birthed the desire to create a school that embodied the values of the "human growth and potential movement" and to educate practitioner-scholars in the methods and philosophies of human centered psychotherapy. These leading thinkers wanted to create a new discipline that would serve as a counterweight to the standard psychoanalytic and mechanistic psychological practices of those times. The Humanistic Psychology Institute became the educational arm of the humanistic psychology movement.

Humanistic psychology and the human growth and potential movement was inspiring to me, as was reading such humanistic authors such Maslow (1962, 1971). It felt like a gift to have some of the renowned authors of the field right at my school such as Gregory Bateson, Jim Bugenthal, Sam Keen, Stanley Krippner, and Rollo May. Coming from my narrow New Jersey background it was inspiring to be at the growing edge of the various facets of this movement, such as the "encounter movement," where the openness to feelings and real communication took place. Likewise, fascinating to me was studying the research in altered states that I was reading, which eventually became part of the field of transpersonal psychology.

In addition to traditional psychological methods, Saybrook provided me with the opportunity to study a wide variety of ancient healing traditions while obtaining my doctoral degree. Here in the early and mid 1970s, I felt blessed to be at the heart of the newly emerging the field of somatic psychology. Charlotte Selver, a master of just being present to bodily sensations, came to Saybrook Graduate School, and Tom Hanna (1988) was a co-founder of my school and a professor there. Many other leaders in the area of somatic psychotherapy came to Saybrook or gave local workshops in Berkeley, such as Moshe Feldenkrais (1991) and Stanley Keleman (1981). As I watched the healings that took place when these leaders in the field worked with workshop participants' physical and emotional issues, it helped me to feel that my moving to the "land where the sun rose in the West," did indeed have purpose.

Little did we know at the time of Saybrook's founding, that the school that we were co-creating was, forty years later, to have more American Psychological Association Division Chairs as faculty members than any other graduate psychology school in the United States.

Financial Struggles during My Doctoral Years: Teaching at Laney College

To earn some income while I was in my Ph.D. program in the early 1970s, I got a job at Laney College teaching a course in The Psychology of Consciousness. I used the book *The Origin and History of Consciousness* (Neumann, 1954) as one of the textbooks for the course; and it was a gift to me to watch how under-privileged youth in the Oakland ghetto addressed how the consciousness movement could help their lives in gangs and in difficult economic circumstances.

One of my favorite lectures in this class was on "The Essential Boat Paradox." I asked students, "If a boat went from San Francisco to China and everyday one of the pieces of the boat was changed, when it arrives in China is it the same boat?" This story helps a student to differentiate between a mechanistic, atomistic, existential philosophy versus a metaphysical essentialistic philosophy. In the former, an object or a person is the sum of their parts; in the latter there is some essential quality that defines a person that is greater than the sum of the parts. It is paradoxical that though all of our parts may change that some essential quality of ours remains.

Though I gave room for students to be on either side of the argument, I was on the metaphysical side of this equation. I was part of the philosophical renaissance of the culture that was shifting from a behavioral psychology to an existential, humanistic, transpersonal psychology. This psychological renaissance grew from the ground of the perennial philosophy (Huxley, 1944; Fadiman & Frager, 2001; Assagioli, 1965; Maslow, 1971). In alignment a humanistic psychology that addressed the dimensions of our human nature that are beyond roles, I asked students to define what were those essential qualities that made them who they were. Many poignant moments took place when students found aspects of their essential nature that were beyond race, gang affiliation, and class labels.

Was this metaphysical philosophical orientation of mine born from the zeitgeist of the cultural and spiritual revolution of the 1960s that was challenging the philosophical ground of a disenchanted cosmos (Tarnas, 1993)? Was it due to the readings to which I exposed in my doctoral program at Saybrook? Or, was my alignment with a metaphysical orientation coming from a deeper part of my essential nature? Could there be something to that astrological stuff that the health faire reading had proclaimed? Could the placement of my natal sun, the north node of the moon (the dharma point of the chart), and the planet Venus in the Eighth House of metaphysics, have contributed to a resonant field that would lead me to a metaphysical career? Since there are so many factors involved in the complexity of human choices, what does make us choose to go in one direction or another?

However, in the midst of my joy about being able to engage in exploring the metaphysical meaning of existence, through teaching these students at Laney College, like many who have pursued their dreams in life, I started to wonder whether I had made a mistake. When I looked at my financial situation, I half jokingly said to myself, "Man cannot live by metaphysical studies alone."

I was not doing so well financially. Only single courses were given to most faculty members to teach. So, like most part-time college teachers I earned barely enough to pay my rent. I was on food stamps, and I wondered whether I should have been an attorney as my father advised. The practical lawyer side of me started to argue with me, "If you had just stayed in New Jersey and gone to George Washington Law School, you could have earned a real living." I was confused about who I was and where I was going in life. In the mist of all of this, in addition to reading about traditional psychological methods I was intensively reading various texts on a wide variety of metaphysical subjects as part of my doctoral studies.

Opening the Door to the Metaphysical Inner World

Our culture mostly knows the term "metaphysics" from the early Greek philosophers like Aristotle and Plato, or from later academic philosophers such as Husserl (Fuchs, 1976), Heidegger (2000), and Merleau-Ponty (1964). I told you earlier about how in my college years I had an interest in "experiential metaphysics," as differentiated from its academic and philosophic dimensions.[1]

Each different metaphysician has his or own particular focus, and after I arrived in California my interest in particular realms of what I now call "experiential metaphysics" grew. I became particularly interested in cross-cultural approaches to the experience of, and healing attributes of, making a connection with the world behind the world.

Every culture has their metaphysicians—those who have one foot in the world behind the world. Those who follow the experiential pathways of metaphysics are called by names such as shamans, mystics, esotericists, Gnostics, and healers. Each of these terms has a slightly different connotation. So, for example, most Tai Chi and Qigong masters wouldn't label themselves as metaphysicians. However, because they use their self-cultivation practices to cultivate the energy (qi) that is behind and comes through all of life, Qigong and Tai Chi masters could be considered to be working with the metaphysical aspects of the world of energy behind the physical world.

The term metaphysics is comprised of two words, "meta" (meaning behind or beyond), and "physics" (meaning the physical world). The metaphysical arts are considered to be symbolic process traditions such as astrology and alchemy, and the Tarot, Runes, and I Ching. A less known, but equally important part of metaphysical arts are energy oriented traditions and practices that deal with the interaction between the inner mind and the external world.

For those that think that "energy" is some flaking "new age" concept, it is important to realize that one dictionary definition of "physics" is the science of matter and energy and the interactions between the two. Therefore, it is unfortunate that, for the most part, modern physical medicine has thrown out the focus on healing energy, about which early physicians such as Paracelsus (1995) spoke. So, in this vein I sometimes like to use the term "meta-physician" (spelled with a dash between the words) to refer to an integral medicine that includes the importance of the world behind the physical world and its energies.

In our modern world the term "physician" is usually associated with healing the body...most often, a body that is split off from the holistic mind-body unity known to early meta-physicians such as Aristotle, Plato, and Paracelsus. To honor this unity of mind and body I like to use the term "bodymind." The term bodymind (Dychwald, 1983; Mayer, 2004, 2007, 2009; Aposhyan, 2004) refers to the fact that the body and mind are an inseparable whole; and one branch of metaphysics involves healing the bodymind.[2]

Some of the earliest meta-physicians such as Paracelsus (who lived in the early 16th century), clearly saw that healing of the physical body involved connecting human illnesses (in the microcosm) with the macrocosm of the wider elements of nature (fire, earth, air and water) and the wider archetypal energies of the universe (symbolized by the planets). Paracelsus saw the imagination as being a key to healing, and so he is often considered one of the founders of "a psychology of the imagination" (Waite, 1894). Traditions of "inner knowing" such as Gnosticism (Pagels, 1989) are also considered to be metaphysical disciplines because they advocate for the direct mystical connection with the source of creation.

In the 1970s and 1980s my major area of focus in metaphysical terrain was on the Western Mystery Tradition's (Matthews & Matthews, 1986) symbolic process traditions, such as astrology (Rudhyar, 1970; Mayer, 1977, 1983), alchemy (Edinger, 1985), dreamwork (Jung, 1970, Hillman, 1975), and mythology. Perhaps my interest in such traditions was due to my ingrained love of storytelling. I'd gobble up courses in mythology and read many of Joseph Campbell's books such as *Hero with a Thousand Faces* (1972), Jean Houston's *The Hero and the Goddess* (1992), and Mircea Eliade's books, such as *The Myth of the Eternal Return* (1954). I read Robert Graves' *The Greek Myths* (1955), two extensive volumes, and underlined it in its entirety.[3]

The many facets of metaphysical literature became my nighttime reading at this phase in my life. I was intrigued by the encyclopedia of esoteric knowledge written by one of the foremost metaphysicians of the era, Manly Palmer Hall. His book, *The Secret Teachings of All Ages* (1962), revealed how many ancient cultures had stories and practices for plummeting the depth of the human soul. I was fascinated by the ancient mystery traditions: Rudolf Steiner's anthroposophical works (2010) confirmed to me one of my deeply held beliefs that all life-forms have their place in divine creation. One of Steiner's students, Edward Schure, and his book *The Great Initiates* (1977), gave me a wide view of various cross-cultural mystery traditions. Joseph Campbell's *The Mysteries* (1978) was an eye opener about the depth of these mystery traditions. I was particularly interested in the Greek mystery tradition (Schure, 1977; Campbell 1978; Hall, 1962; Houston, 1992).

The gift of metaphysical study in our current era is that in the past a metaphysician may have been limited by his or her culture. For example, an individual could be initiated into the Greek, Egyptian, Native American, Taoist, or Buddhist metaphysical traditions. However, during the late twentieth century, a metaphysical pluralism developed whereby students of metaphysics could study, and become immersed in, practices of a wide variety of cross-cultural approaches to the transformation of the psyche and the re-enchantment of every day life.[4]

Reading this esoteric literature, and immersing myself in a variety of cross-cultural metaphysical practices, was fascinating. It felt as if I had opened a secret door to a cave of a treasure house. It was reminiscent of the stories my father told me about how Ali Baba opened cave doors with the words "open sesame." But the place to which I had traveled was not a treasure house that my very rational father would have approved. The cave I had discovered was the Cave of the Imagination, and the secret words that opened the door to the treasure house were metaphysical the teachings of astrology, alchemy, mythology, and cross-cultural approaches to the spiritual quest.

As I read these illuminating views of the world behind the world, the part of me that doubted that I had followed the right path was filled with sense of having found my terrain and my path. Though I felt some guilt about just being a sponge, I kept absorbing and reading, knowing that this was my work now just as someone who wanted to be a cowboy was trained by riding horses. However, I wondered when would be the time that I would open others' eyes the way these authors were opening mine.

My guilt was somewhat assuaged during my doctoral years (1973–1977) when I read in Robert Graves book (1955, p. 48) about how Necessity, was the first primordial Great Goddess. This symbol resonated with me because I also felt a primordial force "necessitated me" to go in the direction of my calling. Whether this was rationalization or divine inspiration, Necessity's mythic voice helped me to deal with the angst that I felt about choosing a doctoral program that was not a mainstream school like my parents would have liked me to attend. However, then and thereafter my concerns were eased when I learned about the profound wisdom that was contained in these age-old, out of the mainstream traditions.

A story comes to mind: In old China a young boy wanted to learn to be a swordsman. His friends went to established academies of swordsmanship while Bonzi went to study with an eccentric swordsman who knew the old ways and lived alone in the woods. Bonzi was eventually initiated into the highest levels of the ancient art of swordsmanship. (We see this archetypal motif repeated in the recent movies of *The Karate Kid I* and *II*.)

Like Bonzi, while my fellow students were going to established graduate schools across the country, I had chosen a school that was "out in the woods," a school where I could study the ancient roots of psychotherapy. These old ways were not being taught in graduate schools on the East Coast, where my quest began.

When I reflect back on these years of educational choices, I wonder what compelled me to go to such an out of the mainstream graduate program. In addition to the fact that Saybrook offered training in my newly emerging areas of interest, perhaps the voice of Necessity was speaking to me in my 1971 dream of how "the light of the midnight sun rose in the West." So, perhaps an outer interest and an inner "dream weaver" combined forces to draw me to the West Coast to find these teachings. Also, before this, in my senior year of college an "inner voice" said to me that my path had to do with psychology and healing, not metaphysical philosophy. It is important to clarify for the sake of the analytical attorney sub-personality still in me that this "voice" was nothing mystical, or otherworldly, nor was it like auditory hallucination of someone "talking." This voice was more like (what I would learn in my study with Dr. Eugene Gendlin), a "felt sense." It rose from an uncomfortable body sense of something that did not feel totally resonant with my path while I was studying the intellectual dimension of metaphysical philosophers. Instead, this inner calling opened me to explore experiential metaphysics, like a young sprouting flower is compelled, and finds it necessary, to open to a light from a place above that guides its growth.

My wondering about from where our inner calling comes, led me to a land beyond the intellect where poetry, mythology, and alternative cosmologies ruled....

Pre-Modern Metaphysical Views of Our Life's Purpose: Opening to the Genii within

> *May the beauty that we love be what we do.*
> *There are hundreds of ways to kneel and kiss the ground...*
> —*Rumi*

> *Each life involves a divine errand; not simply the task of survival,*
> *but a life-mission imbedded in the soul from the beginning.*
> *Life is an experiment in which we attempt to decipher*
> *the errand the gods have sent us on.*

> —Michael Meade
> *Fate and Destiny* 2009, p. 148

There is a metaphysical notion that each of us has a *genii* inside of us. There are many names for these genii, and the gifts they bring when they come out of the bottle.

A West African tale says our genii is our "divine twin" that we meet before we come to birth and that it stays with us as a "spirit familiar" when we incarnate in our lives on earth (Meade, 2010, p. 123). It travels the path of life with us in order to remind us of our soul's purpose at pivotal moments. The Greeks call it *eudemonia,* the happiness that comes from satisfying one's inner *daemon,* the living spirit inside of us.

When my father read the tale of the *Arabian Nights* to me at bedtime, he told me about the genii in Aladdin's lamp and about the troubles and gifts that could come from rubbing the lamp of the bottled up genii. Little did I know then, that in my college years something which had been bottled up in me would come out and bring forth my deepest gifts; and as well a slew of troubles emerged as I rode away on a magic carpet away from the conservative safe land of my youth.

The genii that appears during troubled times is our inner genius. Rubbing our hands together is a primordial way of generating heat and energy; and when we are excited about having found something that excites us we rub our hands in joy. Rubbing also creates friction. Perhaps the tale of Aladdin tells us that when we rub up against that which is bottled up in us, something is released from inside which helps us to find the joy of a life that makes some of our wishes come true. Friction with ones current life can be energizing, and yet there can be a price to pay. Another basic metaphysical idea is that this genii in each of us can be contacted by listening to our "inner voice," and that listening to it leads us to the path that Life "chooses us to follow." So, in my philosophy class in college the stirring of this inner voice said that my interest was in experiential metaphysics; and in my big dream of "the land where the sun rose in the West" I was led by my inner genii to go to the West Coast to find my destiny.

Exploring the Western and Eastern Initiatory Traditions

And so it was that when I arrived in California, and through my doctoral research at Saybrook, the area of study that most energized me was psychology and its esoteric and metaphysical dimensions. I focused on reading the books about the early roots of psychotherapy in the Western initiatory traditions. Particularly eye-opening were C. A. Meier's *Ancient Incubation and Modern Psychotherapy*, and Hillman's *Revisioning Psychology* and his *Myth of Analysis* (1972). Many books of Carl Jung's Collected Works helped to give me faith that the psychological, metaphysical, and esoteric could be brought together in everyday practice in psychotherapy.

Eastern traditions fascinated me as well, since I wanted to learn more about the wider and deeper aspects of microcosmic orbit breathing, the method that had "saved me" from my anxiety and panic attack back when I lived on the East coast. In my exploration I read Alan Watts *Psychotherapy East and West* (1961), and I identified with Richard Alpert's (Ram Dass') transformation from a Harvard psychologist to a practitioner of the Eastern spiritual methods that he spoke of in his 1971 book *Be Here Now*. So, like Parcival, I rode on the horse of the human growth and potential movement looking for the metaphorical Grail Cup, or should I say, "the metaphysical Grail Cup."

My Flowering at Saybrook's Doctoral Psychology Program

Part of why I chose to enroll in Saybrook Graduate School was because they believed in a self-motivational student model of education, called a "university without walls." Many people with whom I studied had an important influence on my later work. For example, Sam Keen, my doctoral committee advisor, influenced my writing style and the further development of a circumspect view about ancient symbolic traditions. Sanford Rosenberg, a fellow student and friend who was in my same doctoral cohort, introduced me to phenomenology and the work of Fingarette (1963) that influenced my view of astrology.

Under the guidance of senior faculty there, and anyone with whom I wanted to study throughout the country, I was able to study what moved my soul. I would write it up as a course and have faculty give me feedback on its merits. I was able to go out into the world, and (with the right amount of *chutzpah*) choose the teachers with whom I wanted to work and ask them to be on my doctoral committee. I will tell you later about some of the remarkable people with whom I was able to study, such as one of the leading psychologists of the era, Dr. Eugene Gendlin; a Tai Chi Master, Fong Ha; and the leading astrologer of the era, Dane Rudhyar.

I could not know that the seeds planted in my doctoral years from my study of astrology would later lead to writing a book that would win a world prize called *The Mystery of Personal Identity* (1984), and I wrote other books (Mayer, 2004, 2007) that grew from the fertile soil that I tilled after working with these leaders of their fields.

A basic metaphysical notion is that each of us has latent in us a seed that needs to be cracked open in order for our unique souls to come to fruition. It is interesting that my journey began with Ali Baba finding the way into the treasure house by saying, "Open sesame," and that the name of a seed, a sesame seed, opened the door for him. In Hindu mythology sesame oil is used to pacify the malefic effect of Lord Shani, a symbol of the Saturnian archetype. In an Assyrian legend, when the Gods met to create the world they drank a wine made from sesame seeds.

I have always felt awe struck when I find some cross-cultural mythic parallel that opens a door to some hidden gem of meaning. Indeed, it is like discovering a mythogem when we listen to the cross-cultural wisdom that reveals that the sesame seed is connected with moments of our lives when the Saturnian forces of rigidity and cultural conformity are pacified by the sprouting seed of each of our soul's purpose. If we take the Assyrian legend to heart, there's something about the creation of a new world that is associated with sesame seeds.

It is as if each of us is a sesame seed waiting to be cracked open by the pressures of our internal growth, and by weathering the pains we meet from the outer forces everyday life. In the midst of the desert of our lives, our seed-nature is ready to bloom if we can just break through our outer casing. Little did I know that I was about to have an experience that syncrohonistically brought together many layers of cross-cultural meanings of the "open sesame" story that had been with me since the first Ali Baba tale my father told me. Like the opening of the sesame seed, a treasure house was about to open and create a new world as the seed of my soul was going to crack open.

Confusing moments and inner conflicts with the people and events around us can crack us open and lead us to the dark cave where we find our inner genii. In the dark cave, Aladdin found his magic lamp and his genii. Whether it is a journey into a cave, difficult life circumstances, or a journey into the woods at night the descent into darkness can be a pathway to find the unique vision that becomes our guiding light. Cross-cultural mythologies tell us that the dark night of the soul can activate the call for help from our guiding spirit (our daemon) to remind us of our destiny, and break open the seed of who we are.

My Forty-Night Vision Quest

*Something dreaming within us best knows how to shape a vessel
for the troubles and tribulations of our exact lives.*

—Michael Meade
The World Behind the World (2008), p.106

When I was in my first semester of my doctoral psychology program, I was at a loss regarding what should be the focus of my doctoral dissertation. The hard shell of the seed of my life was encased by a dysfunctional perfectionism and old Saturnian values regarding what would make me a respectable psychologist; yet at the same time under the surface a seed purpose was germinating from the my readings about ancient approaches to psychological transformation. How could these disparate approaches to my career be reconciled? I felt compelled and challenged to figure out the solution. My cup was overfull (interesting that in Yiddish the word "kup" means "head"). Something was needed greater than a "heady" answer.

My inner state of anxious despondency was not eased by the knowledge I had been gathering in my doctoral research. What was I to do with this interesting ancient knowledge I was gathering? I found solace in long walks in the woods, just as, I was later to learn, my supposed great, great, great grandfather, the Baal Shem Tov did.[5] One day while on a long walk, I made up my mind that I wanted to stay out in the woods for forty nights to see if I could find my Path. At the same time I wanted to see if I could cure my anxiety and phobia of being out in the woods alone in the darkness of night.

I made an appointment to speak to the director of a local park system, and I asked if I could camp out in the woods for forty nights. At first he said that would be impossible; but then I told him that I was a doctoral student who was doing a dissertation on the role of natural settings on dream life. A door opened in his eyes at that moment, and he said, "I know what you're talking about. I enjoyed reading Walden and David Thoreau's inspired writings when I was in college." He said that I could camp out in one of the group campgrounds. I replied that if I was in a group campground that could interfere with my dreams, and I wondered if I could instead camp someplace more isolated. He paused for a brief moment, and then pushed a button on his phone system. He called the general manager of the park system, and told the manager to "take this kid in a jeep through the park so he can choose a place most appropriate for his research." I chose a place I called Water Hole Mountain. It was about a mile from civilization, where there was a little water hole where various animals came at night who I could watch as I camped out under the stars.

Since I had a fear of being out in the woods at night, I brought along three lines of defense: my flute, a staff, and a knife. I never needed to use anything other than the first line of defense—my flute. One night, a wildcat came to drink at the water hole and saw me in its path. He growled; but fortunately my flute was enough to calm him down and make him realize that I was not a danger to him.

I was starting to do pretty well with my fear of being out in the woods alone at night. However, I had a continuing memory of a friend of mine who lived up in the Sierras, and who told me that one night when he was walking in the woods a deer chased him for a few hundred yards. My friend, Roger Campbell, explained to me that during rutting season a deer could be dangerous. I hoped that I would not meet one while this far away from civilization out in the forest.

It had been about three weeks of sleeping out in the woods every night. I had made a promise to myself that I would sleep out every night for forty nights in hopes of curing myself from my fear of being in the woods alone at night. Sometimes I would come out of the woods during the daytime, while other times I would stay in the woods for three days or so at a time.

But the main purpose of my venture was not forthcoming. I did not have any more clarity on what I wanted to write my dissertation. About the time I was ready to give up, and go back to my normal life, "a visitation" came from the world behind the world…

> After about three weeks of sleeping in the woods, about a mile from the nearest mark of civilization—it came. I was asleep alone on top of a ridge with a water hole nearby; and I was in a lucid, dream-like state. I was conscious of my surroundings, yet at the same time I was aware of being in a dream. I noticed that a group of seven deer were approaching me. I was particularly aware of the leader, who had very large, golden, glowing antlers. His eyes were so emblazoned that I was not sure if it was really a deer, or a Shaman wearing a mask trying to trick me. I was afraid that the deer might attack me, just as my friend Roger was attacked; but I thought that if I pretended to be asleep perhaps the deer would just pass me by. My left eye started to quiver however, and I thought that surely this was going to give me away. The deer approached, and gently kissed my eye. A warm, energized ecstasy filled me like nothing I had ever experienced before. But, a moment later, I was terrified as I realized that my eye was no longer in its socket…it was in the deer's mouth. In my panic, the first thought that came to mind was that my parents would say, "I told you so. We always told you something like this would happen when you slept out in the backyard in New Jersey, Why do you have to do things like this? Why can't you just sleep inside like everyone else? If you had only listened to us, you wouldn't have lost your eye." This thought of my parents' "I told you so," was as bad as the image of crawling back to civilization with only one eye.
>
> Even amidst these horrifying fantasies I somehow realized that, regardless of the consequences, all this had a place in my destiny—I breathed, letting go to my fate. Then, I noticed the deer in a new way. I realized that he was doing something with my eye that was not malevolent. He was rolling my eye around in his mouth, like some kind of ritual,

as if washing it. He then placed my eye back in its socket...but it was not an eye, it was some kind of jewel—a green emerald, or a piece of jade. I was awestruck!

My next recollection was waking at dawn and feeling for my eye. To my surprise it was just an eye again. I said to myself, "Oh, it was just a dream." But then I noticed a large number of fresh deer tracks around me. Had the deer actually been there? Was it a dream or a vision? For many days thereafter (and even to this day) I was filled with a sense of wonder.

When I returned to my doctoral advisor and group after the forty-day period someone suggested that I research the parallels of my experience in other cultures. I read the book *Seven Arrows,* which is about the process of vision questing among the American Plains Indians. Here amongst the legends of the native people of this land, I found a beginning place on my personal path.

I discovered from reading *Seven Arrows,* many years before the movie *Dances with Wolves* became popular, that taking a symbolic name associated with an element of nature helped to give Native Americans a sense of their life's meaning in connection with nature. I began to explore the symbology of this experience, and I felt an inner electricity awaken in my body when I thought that my purpose might lie in becoming like the deer of my vision. What a quest it would be to "kiss the eyes of others" as the deer had kissed mine, to help people to transform their fears and life issues, and to see the sacred gems hidden behind life. If I could do this gently, then I could be like a "Deer Kissing Eyes."

Shamanic Dismemberment and the Quest to Find Our Soul's Purpose

Through my doctoral research I discovered that the experience I had was like the ordeal of dismemberment that was part of many cross-cultural shamanic traditions (Eliade, 1964). In Australian and Siberian Shamanism the initiation of a shaman included being "subjected to an operation by semi-divine beings or ancestors, in which his body is dismembered and his internal organs and bones are renewed" (Eliade, 1964, p. 50). Likewise, in South American shamanism, "The Bobeno shaman introduces rock crystal into the novice's head; these eat out his brain and his eyes, then take the place of those organs and become his strength...which symbolized the shaman's helping spirits" (Eliade, 1964, p. 52). Among the Dyak of Borneo the shamanic ritual involved "cutting out his brains, washing and restoring them...inserting gold dust into his eyes to give him keenness of and strength of sight..., and piercing his heart with an arrow to make him tender hearted and full of sympathy with the sick as suffering" (Eliade, 1964, p. 52). I learned that these rituals were part of dismemberment and renewal rituals.

Specifically related to the loss of my eye, I was fascinated to read that in Norse mythology Odin gave up an eye at the at Mimir's Well of Wisdom to in order to gain wisdom. Odin was regarded as a "psychopompos" (an early name for "the psychotherapist" who was a healer of souls). Mimir's Well represents the living waters of life, which is situated at the roots of the World Tree that stands at the center of life. Odin has to sacrifice an eye that sees in the normal way to gain the great vision and insight of a deeper wisdom (Mead, 2010, p. 95).

So, as I now look back at this important experience of my life, it was indeed connected to letting go of my old way of seeing life and being initiated into what was to become my contribution to my "tribe"—to see the field of psychology through the renewed vision of a "Deer Kissing Eyes."

The Metaphysical Ailments of Our Times

> *Go confidently in the direction of your dreams.*
> *Live the life you've imagined.*
>
> —Henry David Thoreau

An important notion in metaphysics is that we each need to connect to the world behind the world to find our life's direction. I believe that we suffer from "metaphysical ailments," when we don't connect to some central life purpose. I would suggest (only half joking) that such aliments (i.e. loss of vision, disconnection from nature, estrangement from the voice of one's daemon) be put into the *Diagnostic and Statistical Manual of Psychological Disorders.*

Now, when I am writing this book in the years 2010–2011, in this American age of the deep recession of the early years of the 21st century, economic necessity oftentimes makes our young people feel compelled to do what is materially productive at the expense of what their hearts feel called to do. A connection with the soul and its genii can thereby be lost. Perhaps hidden behind the symptom of my fear of being in the darkness alone at night back in the 1970s was my metaphysical ailment of being disconnected with the daemon that was waiting to call out to me from the darkness. For a while, I did everything I could to avoid being alone in the woods at night due to my fear of going into those depths.

I, and many other Reluctant Metaphysicians, learn that the key to opening the treasure house of the soul is to be found in the darkness of our inner worlds. Before my vision quest I saw the world more in terms of economic necessities. It is fear-invoking to be abducted by the forces of the other world (whether it is a deer eating one's eye, or a spiritual life seemingly in conflict with one's material needs). Yet from this sacrifice a pathway may open to healing our metaphysical ailment.

Mythogems of Our Life's Purpose

> *Humans are living stories,*
> *each imbued with an inherent message and a meaning*
> *trying to find its way into the world.*
> *Each soul a living thread in the tale being woven as we speak,*
> *being shaped as we dream,*
> *being made anew each time we step more fully into the story*
> *trying to live through us.*
>
> —Michael Meade
> *The Two Great Stories of the World*

Some Native American tribes believe our medicine animal, (our soul's purpose) can be discerned at our birth; these tribes give a medicine animal name at birth. Other tribes give a medicine animal name from a vision quest. According to one of my Native American teachers, Oh Shinnah Fast Wolf, "Some tribes do both." Different cultures have myths and stories that speak to the importance of living a life that is in tune with the gifts that are given to us at our birth.

Michael Meade (2010) tells the old tale of a great jar with bits of wood in it that comes from the Tree of Life. Before a child is born the jar is shaken, and the first chip that falls out becomes our "lot in life." Unlike the modern psychological notion that says that we are "a chip-off-the-old block" of our parents, there is a metaphysical notion that we are a chip-off-the-old-block of Life. For example, there is a Mayan tale of a child named Poder who at his birth came to this world bearing gifts, a green cloak and a bowl of water. However, his family ignored these gifts and a midwife hid these gifts deep in the hills. The items of his birthright foretold that the child was destined to be a rainmaker. Later in his life, when he was ready, the midwife told him to journey to the holy hills alone, where the child rediscovered these gifts. Poder learned that each person comes to this life bearing gifts, and that the world has something to give us. He found his life's direction (Meade, 2010, pp. 102–109).

From a metaphysical point of view, the anecdote and antidote to the metaphysical ailment of modern life and our lack of connectedness to the world behind the world can be found in a variety of ways. For example, we can meditate on our astrological charts in the metaphorical way I have described (Mayer, 1977, 1983), undertake a vision quest, or go to places in nature with which we resonate. Listening to our big dreams can awaken us to our guiding "spirit-ally;" and myths and stories can guide us regarding how to pursue the quest. Any of these pathways can help us to open our seed-nature.

However, wise storytellers also tell us to be careful about the way stories are interpreted. My second cousin Rabbi Michael Lerner warns in his book *Jewish Renewal,* that one should not just get swept away listening to the biblical story of Abraham who is ready to sacrifice Isaac. Rabbi Lerner interprets this tale as a reminder to us to wrestle with our own interpretations—are we really hearing God's voice, or our projections of what we think God is telling us, when we hear an inner voice that says to kill our children (Lerner, 1994)?

After due wrestling with the voice of our destiny's calling, our seed-nature may pop open a door to our inner treasure house. The door may not open to the material treasures that Ali Baba found, but instead mythogems of meaning from the world behind the world may be discovered. Here we may find the treasure house of our contributions to life.

Carrying Forward the Vision: The Quest for Our "True Names"

> *It's your life—but only if you make it so.*
>
> —Eleanor Roosevelt

One of the gems that came from my vision quest and "The Medicine of the Deer" was an interest in ancient traditions of identity formation. I learned that there were traditions that believed in "a true name" that each of us has; and in the Akkadian language "to be" and "to name" are synonymous (Bergier, 1973, p. 85). In the African Fulani culture a newborn baby is a "thing" (*kinto*) until it has a name conferred on it, and then it becomes a *muntu*, a "human being" (Whitman, 1977, p. 66).

Likewise, in the Egyptian mystery tradition the process of naming was so important that it was considered a life or death matter. Ra, the Sun God hid his true name, "lest some sorcerer should acquire magic power over me thereby." Later Isis convinced Ra to tell her his true name, by telling him, "Tell me your name, father of the Gods…that the poison may go out of you; for the man whose name is spoken, he lives…(the name) becomes a potent spell against every poison" (Cassirer, 1953, p. 48). I certainly knew from my early life, when a bully mocked me for being "too serious," that naming could be a poisonous or a healing act. When I responded to him, "Since seriousness is associated with the brightest star in the sky, Sirius, it can't be such a bad thing," I was unconsciously invoking an apotropaic spell against his poisonous judgment.

My doctoral dissertation, *A Holistic Perspective on Meaning and Identity; Astrological Metaphor as a Language of Personality in Psychotherapy* (1977), contributed a perspective to the field of psychology about how ancient systems of personality description from the Native Americans, the Kabbalah, and astrology could help a person explore their identity and life's meaning. This dissertation put forth a new (phenomenological) theoretical framework for astrology, and it was the first written work to integrate astrology with depth psychotherapy.

I had traveled an unfathomably large distance…a lot further than the three thousand geographical miles from New York to San Francisco, and from the astrologer's 1969 reading at that health faire who I pooh-hood when she predicted I would be a leading astrologer and metaphysician.

Years after her astrological reading, I had begun to research a new naming system for psychological disorders which some other of my other colleagues and I felt were too pathologically oriented. However, as distinguished from a predictive theoretical stance on astrology, the orientation of my dissertation and my book, *The Mystery of Personal Identity*, was to show how to re-vision the way we look at our ways of being by using the metaphors of nature and the celestial sphere to re-sacralize our personalities.

This was not merely an academic exercise. I also was interested in my own identity. This book and my doctoral work were perhaps part of weaving of the ongoing threads that were coming from "some mystical source of creation" to guide my path and pull me to my destiny. My area of specialization had become the use of symbolic process traditions to help others and myself to find our life paths. The use of mythology, astrological metaphors, and my personal experiences from my inner world were all guiding lights.

These dreams (like the Land Where the Sun Rose in the West), and visionary experiences (of The Deer Who Kissed Eyes) seem to come from sources embedded in a nonmaterial world. These inner experiences were coming to a pretty unlikely source—this son of an attorney, who had worshipped the God of Reason, and was a promising attorney to be ("or not to be," as Shakespeare said, "That is the question!"). Yet the threads of destiny, the guidance from the world behind the world of the mythic imagination, were pulling me forward to a destiny that was in the making.

Is There Something to This Astrology Stuff, and Are the Words That Open the Door to Our Inner Genii's Cave, Astrological Symbols?

Astrologically,… [the alchemical process of integration]
corresponds to an ascent through the planets
from the dark, cold, distant Saturn to the Sun….
The ascent through the planetary spheres therefore meant something like a shedding of the
characterological qualities indicated by the horoscope,
a retrogressive liberation from the character imprinted by the archons.
The conscious or unconscious model for such an ascent
was the Gnostic redeemer, who either deceives the archons by guile
or breaks their power by force.
A similar motif is the release from the 'bill of debt to fate.'
The men of antiquity in particular felt their psychic situation
to be fatally dependent on the compulsion of the stars, Heimarmene,
a feeling which may be compared with that inspired by the modern theory

of heredity, or rather by the pessimistic use of it.
A similar demoralization sets in in many neuroses when the patient
takes the psychic factors producing the symptoms as though they were unalterable facts
which it is useless to resist.
The journey through the planetary houses, like the crossing of the great halls
in the Egyptian underworld therefore, signifies the overcoming of a psychic obstacle, or
of an autonomous complex, suitably represented by a planetary god
or demon. Anyone who has passed through all the planetary spheres is free from com-
pulsion; he has won the crown of victory and becomes like a god.
In our psychological language today we express ourselves more modestly:
the journey through the planetary houses boils down to becoming conscious of the good
and the bad qualities in our character,
and the apothesis means no more than maximum consciousness,
which amounts to maximal freedom of the will."

—C. G. Jung,
Analytical Psychology: Its Theory and Practice

Is there is a "true name" that we each have that is our original essence, our seed nature? Can we tune into this "name" by meditating on the configurations of the celestial sphere at the moment of our birth? My doctoral dissertation put forth the case that it is best to keep open the question as to whether there is an actual correspondence between the cosmos and our personality.

Here's why: The Reluctant Metaphysician keeps mystery alive by allowing the symbols to abduct him or her, and at the same time we keep our rational perspective alive. The Hermetic path values the dialogue between opposite viewpoints.

So, on one hand the symbols of astrological chart can be a meditation glyph to explore our connection to our daemon, the guiding light, which comes from the world behind the world. On the other hand, one can wonder if we are projecting our ego's needs onto the celestial sphere. Following this Hermetic pathway, we reluctantly give up our affinity with the rationalists who say that there can not be any connection between cosmos and our lives; and we reluctantly give up the comfort of aligning ourselves with those who say that definitely our astrological chart is our fate and rules our destiny. Both of these intellectual majority camps have many followers, so unfortunately the Hermetic path (one of the trail ways of the Reluctant Metaphysician) is less traveled, and therefore some estrangement from others may be a necessary consequence.

So, a new dimension was opening many years after my father told me the story of Ali Baba, and how the secret words "open sesame" opened the door to a treasure house where he found his genii. In my doctoral years and thereafter I wondered, "Is there something to this astrology stuff, and are astrological symbols some of the secret words that open the door to our inner Genii's Cave?"

It is fascinating that the astrologer, who I met at that health fair during the time that I was going to be a lawyer, had "read" my Sun and other planets in the Eighth House as pointing to a career in metaphysics. As I was doing my doctoral research I learned that the astrological system is very specific, yet it gives room for expansive, individualized interpretations of a chart's symbols. I found that indeed astrologers say that the Eighth House is the house of metaphysics, because it resonates with the sign Scorpio, which is symbolic of penetrating into the depth of things. The fact that my Gemini (intellectually curious) sun was there could be interpreted to reflect my interest in many different metaphysical systems; and in resonance with its rulership by Scorpio it symbolizes a desire to explore each metaphysical system in an in-depth way.

I also have learned, after many years of studying the system, that my interest in the in-depth exploration of metaphysics, and making a career choice in this direction, could also be seen to be correlated to the symbol of Pluto, god of depth and the underworld. Pluto is the most elevated planet in my chart, and is in Tenth house, which astrologer's call the house of one's occupation. In addition, in resonance with my Sun in Gemini in the Eighth house of metaphysics, I did seem to explore a different metaphysical system every decade or so. An astrologer would say that my breadth of intellectual explorations correlated with my Geminian curiosity.

A door to an ancient treasure house still opens, even today, wherever I look in my chart. For example, my ruling planet (the planet which rules one's rising sign) is Venus, the planet of love and receptivity. It is placed in my chart in Taurus (an earth sign) in the Eighth house, the house of metaphysics. This symbolically expresses well my love with metaphysical systems related to the earth and the body. So, regardless of the actual scientific accuracy of the astrological system, it does seem to provide at least an astro-poetic language through which a person can give meaning to their lives. And this was one of the conclusions of my doctoral research and dissertation (Mayer, 1977).

Speaking of my love of metaphysical systems which relate to the earth (Venus in Taurus in the Eighth house of metaphysics), my path led to training in somatically based metaphysical traditions that stem from the times when humans lived in tune with primordial energies and natural rhythms. The fact that I chose to study somatic practices from foreign cultures, such as the Animal Forms of Qigong and Standing Meditation Qigong (also called Standing like a Tree Qigong), an astrologer would say, resonates with Mercury in my chart in the Ninth house (which rules foreign travels and is associated with Sagittarius). The pathway of loving such traditions led to my later books about how the ancient sacred wisdom traditions, such as Qigong, can help us change our ways of seeing, and being in, our bodies (Mayer, 2004, 2007, 2009).

Throughout the next chapters you will see how the symbology of my astrology chart manifested, and how I carried forth the inspiration of my vision quest by following the pathway of "the Deer Kissing Eyes" into various shamanic and metaphysical practices. You will see how various stories and practices became keys for me to open an ancient treasure house of tools to heal the bodymind.

Some of the stories that I tell may be more or less inspiring to you depending upon your own Medicine Animal Way. I hope that in the course of listening to these stories that you will find ones that inspire you to find your unique way and your "true name." As you read them, you can wonder whether you have a "true name", and whether it has healing power for you. I can tell you that the name that came from my forty nights in the woods has taken the poison out of me (as the story of Ra and Isis tells), and has helped me at those times when I say, "I should have been a lawyer."

Many of us are like Snow White who swallowed the poison apple of our metaphorical wicked stepmother who fed us the notion that there is no world behind the world, that dreams are just neurons firing, that metaphysical subjects take you away from the objects of the "real world," and that stories are "nothing but fantasy tales for children." We each need to be kissed on the eyes, not only by Snow White's mythic Prince, but also by the wisdom of our ancestral traditions, our dreams, and our visions. By doing so, we awaken to our unique Path.

The Fulani would say that finding "our names" and our connection to the divine forces that lead our lives can change us from being a thing (*kinto*) that goes along with others' prescriptions and cultural norms; when any of us follows a path with heart we become, a *muntu*, a real human being. Or, as Isis wisely said, "For the man whose name is spoken, he lives." As you, the reader, go through the stories in the rest of this book I hope you find some story, some pathway through the forest of life that will become "dear" to you, and that it will kiss your eyes so that you can find your unique vision.

CHAPTER 9:

Living a Metaphysical Life

The Baal Shem Tov, Master of the Holy Name's Influence on My Life

After the decision I made to pursue a career in psychology rather than law, my parents were worried that I would go over the deep edge. Particularly because I began to study Eastern and mystical ways of thinking, my parents were deeply concerned about my leaving the solid career that was awaiting me as an attorney. However, after I completed my doctoral dissertation, and I was awarded a doctoral degree in psychology, my parents were somewhat relieved that I would have some ground under my feet.

At this time, in 1977, I returned for a celebration to my childhood home in New Jersey. On the plane ride back to the East Coast I could not help but think about Joseph Campbell and Mircea Eliade's notion of *The Myth of the Eternal Return*—and how for the hero to complete his or her journey a return must take place to where the quest began, where a deeper meaning of the journey can be found.

When I arrived at my childhood home in New Jersey at the celebration of the awarding of my doctoral degree, as I sat on the couch in our living room, my Aunt Hannah told me a story that she said had been kept from me. Interestingly, this next story of my life parallels the story I told you about Mayan tale of Poder, whose green cloak and bowl of water was hidden from him at birth, so that he did not know he was meant to be a rainmaker.

My aunt told me that after I finished my doctoral dissertation my parents were more reassured that I would not become a mystic, and so it was safer to tell this story to me. Then, my Aunt Hannah, the most religious orthodox member of my extended family, told me that I was a direct descendant of the Baal Shem Tov. Before getting my doctoral degree my parents were concerned that this story and my identification with the Baal Shem could have led me to becoming even more mystical than I was starting to become.

The Baal Shem Tov's given name was Israel Ben Eliezer. He was the founder of Chassidism, and he was considered to be the master storyteller of old European Jewry. One translation of his rabbinical name, The Baal Shem Tov, is Master of the Holy Name, due in part to his ability to use names, words, and stories to heal and transform the suffering of those around him.

I told my aunt, "Come on, Aunt Hannah, I'm sure many Jewish people might say they are related to him. What evidence is there to prove such an unlikely story?" She replied that there was a story in our family that one of our relatives was very in love with a girl from childhood, and the two of them wanted to marry some day. But one was Jewish and the other was not. Their parents did everything they could to dissuade these "love-birds" from getting married, and they tried to arrange a marriage with a mate more appropriate to their religious traditions.

The way the story goes, my loving ancestors continued to refuse to marry anyone else, and my ancestor was told, "Even if you weren't the direct descendant of the Baal Shem Tov, and if you were an ordinary Jew this would be considered inappropriate; but because you are a direct descendent of the Baal Shem Tov it would be particularly forbidden in our *shtyle*." Nonetheless, the two youngsters persisted in their commitment to each other such that eventually the Rabbi in the shtlye took the two on a trip to one of the most renowned Rabbis of Europe. The way the story goes, after seeing the love that these two had for each other he said, "I believe that your love is so great that if the Baal Shem himself was still alive he would recognize your marriage." And so this rabbi helped the non-Jew to go through a conversion process, after which they married.

Synchronistically, at this time my Aunt Hannah told me this story I had a quote of the Baal Shem's on the wall in my apartment back in California, even though at this time I was not very involved with Judaism, since I was more influenced by Eastern religions. But this quote from the Baal Shem really moved me and expressed my feelings about the potential of love:

> From every human being there rises a light that reaches straight to heaven,
> And when two souls that are destined to be together find each other, their streams
> of light flow together and a single brighter light goes forth from their united being.

Whether the story my Aunt Hannah told me is actually true, I will probably never know. The forces that influence any of our destinies are one part rational and at least one part mystery, (like the soup stirred up in the Cave of the Goddess of Creation, that you heard about in Chapter 1) How much is my love of regular walking in the woods genetically related to the Baal Shem Tov reputedly getting his greatest inspiration from long walks in the Carpathian Mountains? Is there a meaningful synchronicity to the fact that one of my past girlfriends, Natasha, happened to be a Polish Christian woman from Lubivicher, the same town where the Baal Shem lived, and that her father saved Jews by hiding them from the Nazis?

Deepak Chopra has coined the term "SynchroDestiny," to refer to those synchronicities that play a part in altering our life paths and destinies (Chopra, 2005). In alignment with SynchroDestiny, Natasha's son is now my godson, Alexander. His father died when he was two years old. One does not need to believe in past lives to appreciate the Synchro-Destiny in how, just as his grandfather rescued some of my ancestors from the Nazis, I now help Alexander to deal with many of the oppressive forces of everyday life.

Another most amazing occurrence from the perspective of SynchroDestiny, was the fact that the dissertation that I had just completed in psychology was on the mystery of the name in age-old traditions of personality description and how the process of "naming" figures in forming of a person's identity. So, despite my parents desire to protect me from the mystical pathway that might open if I knew I was related to this rabbinical Master of the Holy Name, I had nonetheless synchronistically followed the path of exploring the path of healing with words, names, and stories in a modern university. The question arises, was my interest and doctoral work research genetically predisposed from my very cells, psychically transmitted, mere coincidence—or a metaphysical act of SynchroDestiny?

My Name Connected to Michael Maier, the Alchemist

Likewise, my name Michael Mayer has an interesting connection with Michael Maier (1588–1622), an alchemist and court physician to Rudolf II of Austria, one of the founders of Rosicrucianism. He was one of the teachers of Carl Jung's grandfather (Jung 1961, p. 233). Also, another Michael Meier was the author of the book *Ancient Incubation and Modern Psychotherapy*, a book that deeply resonated with my interest in a psychotherapy rooted in ancient traditions.If Kabalistic theory is correct, maybe the resonance of the letters of one's name are so powerful that they can create corresponding resonant forms (Suares, 1992). Something at least this powerful, (only heaven knows what), must have been present to turn a well-directed upcoming lawyer, to embark on a path of metaphysical discovery.

Equally fascinating is that among the cabal of alchemists and metaphysicians who founded the Rosicrucian tradition were John Dee, Robert Fludd, Edward Kelly—and Michael Maier (Maier, 1989). To get a sense of the awesome parallels between my interests and Michael Maier's study of alchemical symbolism and the use of metaphors from the natural world as tools for psychological transformation, see the video by Terrance McKenna called *The Alchemical Dream: Rebirth of the Great Work* (McKenna, 2008). Synchronistically, one of my closest friends with whom I discuss metaphysics has the surname Kelly, though his first name is Sean (Kelly, 1993, 2010). Again, questions emerge about the resonance of one's name, and its having a power to open a path to our unique destinies.

Speaking of the resonance of one's name, in my doctoral dissertation, drawing on the research of Hans Jenny and his book (1974), I discussed the science behind the theory that resonance of sound can create form (Mayer, 1977, 1983). This is one hypothesis about how planetary bodies could have influence on the Earth…because certain planets such as Jupiter emit radio waves. Regarding the power of the name to create form, Hans Jenny created a tonoscope, which consisted of a disc with various granular materials on it and he vibrated the disc with various frequencies. Even the sound of human words was translated into a visual representation. When the sacred Hindu word, "Om" was uttered into the tonoscope the sand grains on it produced the pattern "O," which was then filled in with concentric squares and triangles. A *yantra* was thereby produced. (A yantra is the geometrical expression of sacred vibration found in many world religions.) One frequency used by Jenny raised particles of iron on the disc so that they stood on top of each other and then marched like an army of soldiers across the disc.

So, the question arises, does the "name of God," astrological configurations, or the sound of one's name have the capacity to create a resonant frequency that contributes to us taking a life stance and marching in a chosen direction? Regarding the parallels of others who had name Michael Mayer (Meier, Maier), and my connection with the cabal of Rosicrucians who held the names of Maier and Kelly, a metaphysician who believes in past lives might say that my friend Sean and I are reincarnations of these earlier historical figures. A different interpretation comes from the metaphysician who emphasizes the power of vibratory frequencies coming from the world behind the world to influence our lives. The Newtonian sceptic says that many people have the name Michael Mayer and are not metaphysicians; a retort comes from the Quantum theorist who says that just because a phenomena does not happen reliably, this does not preclude the validity of an anomalous phenomena. The Hermeneutic Metaphysician values the path that opens from listening to both sides of the dialogue.

The Astrological Hermeneutics of Everyday Life

Regarding the hermeneutical method of looking at astrology, in 2012 I was drawn to go a concert at a former student's house where a musician named Thoth was performing an integrative style of concert called *Tribal Baroque*. Many opposites are synthesized in his performance of tribal and classical baroque music played on a violin. The performance (with his partner Lila Angelique) combines many other opposites such sophisticated opera and deep stomping rhythms; and his voice combines deep chthonic emoting with his gentle falsetto voice. Since this was another person who was "Joining Two Streams" as I was doing in my work, after the concert I asked him for his birth date. When I got home, I looked up his chart for June 19th, 1954, at 11:56 AM in New York. It was fascinating to see that not only was he a Gemini like me (combining two worlds); but he had his Moon in Aquarius (the same sign as my Moon). I could easily discount this synchronicity by saying that many people might have the same Sun and Moon and do not have a life-focus on the eccentric joining of different worlds. But it was interesting that his Moon was in the 5th House (which is ruled by Leo and the performing arts), and he was a performing artist. Another parallel was that his Mercury was in the same sign as mine in Cancer (symbolic of the mind interested in feelings, and penetrating into the depths of feelings.) Also, his Venus (planet symbolic of aesthetics) was in Leo (symbolic of creativity).... still, not a slam-dunk for validating astrological synchronicity (but it does raise a curious eyebrow, in an open-minded sceptic). Then I noticed that Mercury (symbolic of verbal expression) ruled his chart and was in conjunction with Uranus (planet symbolic of eccentricity)—one of the trademarks of Thoth's style is a unique language he developed and sings that is "a 252 character cuneiform language to express his mythological world." The astrological synchronicity expressed in his eccentric self-created language (Mercury conjunct Uranus) can open even the sceptic to wonder. (Again to answer the sceptics retort, just because other people who have Mercury conjunct Uranus do not develop their own language does not invalidate this anomalous manifestation of this archetypal configuration. To force a scientific paradigm onto such synchronistic manifestations is to commit an "epistemological category error" (Walsh and Keepin, 2004). If you want to see Thoth and Lila Angelique perform, they do concerts all over the world.[1]

Many people have found it fascinating to look at famous people's astrological charts to attempt to validate astrology.[2] The assumption is that famous people will manifest the astrological configurations more than perhaps an average person might, because not every person manifests their talent and seed nature. When the statistician Michel Gauquelin tried to validate astrological synchronicities, he found that the place in a chart that had significance was the Twelfth and Ninth Houses. One who is interested in finding the truth regarding such claims will examine the critiques, discussions, and research about Gauquelin's claims.[3]

Reluctant Metaphysicians enjoy looking at remarkable people that we meet in everyday life and having our eyes open to wonder. Holding a meaning reorganization viewpoint (Fingarette, 1963), which does not proclaim or deny scientific validity, it is fascinating that the performing artist Thoth has Pluto in this Twelfth House, "Gauquelin position;" and his performance does seem to resonate with being chthonically plutonic.

The Metaphysics behind Our Life Choices

I remember in my freshman English class reading a poem about "a road less taken," never suspecting that it was letting me know about the path I would walk:

Two roads diverged in a yellow wood,
And sorry I could not travel both
And be one traveler, long I stood
And looked down one as far as I could
To where it bent in the undergrowth;

Then took the other, as just as fair
And having perhaps the better claim,
 Because it was grassy and wanted wear;
Though as for that, the passing there
Had worn them really about the same,

And both that morning equally lay
In leaves no step had trodden black
Oh, I kept the first for another day!
Yet knowing how way leads on to way,
I doubted if I should ever come back.

I shall be telling this with a sigh
Somewhere ages and ages hence:
Two roads diverged in a wood,
and I took the one less traveled by,
And that has made all the difference.

—Robert Frost (1920)

It is fascinating to wonder what makes one person to choose the road less traveled and another person the well-trodden road. From a psychodynamic psychological perspective often a person models their lives after a parent, or there can be a reaction formation whereby one goes in the opposite direction of one's parents. My parents were always advocates of a traditional lifestyle. So, the question arises, can my identity (or any of ours) be explained in a broader way than just being reduced to "nothing but" a reaction formation to my parents traditional values?

In my doctoral dissertation, which took a phenomenological viewpoint on identity formation I said,

> *The language through which one describes one's identity colors the way that each of us sees our self. It becomes the lens through which we view our identity and the structure through which we experience our life's meaning (Mayer 1977, 1983).*

The astrological symbol of Uranus is another lens through which to look at my interest in the road less traveled. Most astrologers associate Uranus with the archetype of Prometheus, the titan who rebelled against the gods and helped Zeus overthrown the tyrannical Cronus. Astrologers say that when a planet is in conjunction with one's natal Sun, it is the most significant aspect coloring the expression of that person's life energy—and in my astrological chart the Sun is in conjunction with Uranus.

The well-respected astrologer and cosmologist Richard Tarnas says that he has noticed in his extensive research that, "those who were born with Uranus prominently positioned (as in a major aspect to the Sun), tend to display in their lives and personalities a certain family of archetypally related characteristics: rebelliousness, impatience with conventional constraints or traditional structures, originality and inventiveness…restless seeking of one's own path in life…and a desire for unusual or exciting experiences (Tarnas, 2007 p. 126).

The question arises, can people's symbolic names become not only lenses through which to view our personalities, but also energy generators creating state-specific energy fields that allow us to open different facets of a treasure house where lay mythogems of meaning? In my case, Sun conjunct Uranus opened one door, Deer Kissing Eyes opened another, Two Streams Joining opened a third door. Throughout the years, I have seen how new symbolic names that my students and patients took did the same for them.

For example, in the late 1970s, as part of my doctoral internship I got a job as the assistant coordinator of community mental health for Contra Costa Mental Health programs at the county hospital in Martinez. The gift of this job was that I traveled to and was a consultant for various innovative programs throughout the county, such as the Phoenix Center. In this program for post-psychotic patients in recovery, I led "Medicine Name Groups" for patients who had held the name "psychotic." To such patients, diagnostic labels often felt like a semantic blackjack that beat them into feelings of inadequacy, and the humanistic approaches in the innovative era of the 1970s sought to go beyond such labels.

In the groups that I led, when such patients tried on Native American names that described their essence in a symbolic way they felt better about themselves (Storm, 1972; Mayer, 1977, 1983). For example, one patient described himself as Bleeding Bear. This big burly fellow, wounded by his parents' rejection of him, realized that the time he had spent at one of the Phoenix Programs in hibernation helped him to heal his wounds and come out into the springtime of a new life. I remember how, after giving himself this name and drawing a picture of his animal totem on a shield, Bleeding Bear walked like an empowered bear to the applause of other group members.

The "names" that give meaning to our lives do not need to be esoteric or even metaphorical. One day while I was doing my internship at Contra Costa Mental Health and bringing the metaphysical world into the county mental health system, my supervisor and boss, Dr. Ron Levinson, pulled me aside and as he looked deeply into my eyes. He said to me, "You know, the reason I hired you was not because of your psychological or spiritual background, it was because your father was an attorney, and I saw those abilities in you." Dr. Levinson was referring to how I had initiated an examination of the contract between Contra Costa Mental Health and the State Vocational Rehabilitation Department. I discovered that the funds allotted by the state to mental health patients for vocational rehabilitation was not delivered or even requested. So, I challenged this oversight, and we freed up a good amount of funding for jobs for patients in the mental health system. For me personally, this was an important step in reintegrating "my father's name," the lawyer sub-personality in me, to make my life more whole.

This was the era where leading edge psychotherapists were advocating treating mental health patients, even the most severely disturbed, as human beings…not diagnostic categories. I felt grateful that my doctoral program in humanistic psychology was at the forefront of this movement, and here in my internship at Contra Costa Mental Health I was in a position to hire those who had these values. When we freed up vocational rehabilitation funds, during the era when Governor Ronald Reagan was cutting funds from all community mental health programs, I was able to hire an artist, Anodea Judith, to go into one of the local hospital wards and teach the patients there to use airbrush equipment. We had them repaint the interior of hospital walls with beautiful rising suns, which changed the atmosphere of the hospital. These symbols became an opportunity in the groups run in the hospital ward to talk about how there are sunsets in life, and the sun can rise again. After one patient left the hospital he opened an airbrush tee-shirt business.

Why did I choose to bring an art-oriented business into the county mental health system as compared to any other? It is interesting that I have always been a lover of beauty, and the rising sign of my chart is Libra (astrological sign that is symbolic of beauty), which is ruled by Venus. Venus is my chart is in Taurus, an Earth sign in the house of metaphysics. So, this airbrush beautification of mental health settings, and talking about the symbolic meaning of the images for the purpose of healing, resonates well with these astrological configurations. (Again, no causality is implied; and the sceptic in me says that many people have a sense of beauty.)

Carrying Forth the Vision:
Teaching at JFK University—While Sleeping in the Woods

In 1978 I left my position at the County Hospital to return to teaching. The road that I had traveled, the stream that I had followed, the symbolic name whose essence I was living, led me a year after obtaining my doctoral degree to co-found the Transpersonal Psychology program at JFK University in Orinda, California. I was the first person hired to teach there when the program began in 1978. These were the days when academic schools on the West Coast were "experimental," and I had the gift of being able to design my own classes. Nowadays a fixed curriculum is pretty much set by The American Psychological Association, and it rules much of the modern approach to psychotherapists' education.

In alignment with my vision to join the streams of ancient sacred wisdom traditions and modern psychology in the early 1980s, at John F. Kennedy University I created the first curriculum in the United States for master's level counseling students to teach students how to integrate astrological metaphor into transpersonal counseling to help patients explore their life's meaning. For two semesters students learned the astrological language and the myths behind astrological symbols; the third semester they applied these symbolic processes to their psychotherapy cases. Students learned how "to speak the essence of astrology" without ever specifically mentioning a word of astrology. For example, instead they used the metaphors of fire, earth, air, and water (Mayer, 1977, 1983, 1994). The gift of teaching in a non-cookie cutter school was that there was room to supplement students' traditional education with explorations of a wider psychology rooted in ancient sacred wisdom traditions.

The courses that I taught at JFK between 1978 and 2001 often included the wider dimensions of metaphysics, and a phenomenological perspective integrating psychotherapy with various metaphysical theories.

For example, here is one story that shows a Reluctant Metaphysician's view on theories about past lives: In my classes I told the story of a woman patient who wanted to cure a long-standing, recurrent headache that had not resolved after seeing many medical professionals. So, she went to a hypnotherapist and told him that the headache most often occurred when her husband refused to do household chores. During the hypnotic regression, a powerful image arose of being the Queen of Egypt, and she ordered a disobedient slave to be killed by a stake being driven through his forehead. When she saw the slave's face, she was so upset that she broke out of her trance state. The slave in ancient Egypt looked like her husband; and the place that the stake was inserted in his head was the area of her head was where her head ached.

I asked my class about their interpretation of this story. The students agreed that this was a past life memory, and that this patient was the Queen of Egypt who was getting her karmic due for her abuse of her husband in a past life. Then, I explained to them that as upcoming therapists it was important to be aware of the theories behind their views. Their "hidden reality view" was based upon the belief that this patient's past life in Egypt was the hidden reality behind her headache. However, another metaphysical view, the "meaning reorganization view," would say that the emphasis should be placed on what meaning would be most helpful to transform the patient's current life. For example, this patient had control issues with her husband that activated the Queen-slave archetype; her difficulty in coping with him could be helped by working with this dimension of their relationship. The meaning reorganization view does not preclude that there may be a hidden reality; it uses whatever belief a patient has to help reorganize a patient's meaning (Fingarette, 1963). The emphasis is on whatever can help healing to take place in the present.

In later years, when my life mission became to join the streams of Tai Chi and Qigong with psychotherapy, JFK University gave me the opportunity to teach a three-semester course, called Tai Chi, Qigong and Psychotherapy. For two semesters, students learned Tai Chi and Qigong, and in the third semester Clinical Case Seminar they discussed the application of Tai Chi and Qigong principles to their counseling sessions. As I had done with the use of astrological metaphors in psychotherapy, my orientation was to teach students how to integrate mainstream psychotherapy with the healing wisdom contained in Tai Chi and Qigong. So, these courses taught how to integrate the essence of these traditions into counseling without ever doing a Tai Chi or Qigong Movement, and without mentioning the language of these Chinese internal martial arts. This class became the foundation of three books I later wrote (Mayer, 2004, 2007, 2009).

While I was teaching these classes I wanted to stay connected to the pathway opened by my vision quest. These were the years when spiritual seekers who took weekend transformative workshops were criticized for going back to their everyday lives the next week and cutting the thread that connected them with their spiritual experience. I decided to stay connected to the inner geography my vision quest by sleeping out in the woods as much as possible in the park near my small one room cottage in the Berkeley hills. Though it was illegal to be in this park at night, and particularly illegal to sleep in the park in the woods at night, I felt compelled to do so to reconnect with my soul. After my vision quest, my fear of sleeping out in the woods at night alone had been more than cured—staying connected with the daemon of the night now had become my favorite way to "recharge my batteries."

I often had my JFK Qigong class meet me in the woods in Tilden Park early in the morning, having slept out in the park the previous night. This eccentric way of teaching is symbolized well by my Sun conjunct Uranus in Gemini in the Eighth House (out of the ordinary ways of teaching metaphysics) as well as my Venus in Taurus (love of the Earth and the ways of nature). The night before class I would put on my backpack and walk through the park. I loved to practice Tai Chi staff forms (using the flagged pole in the middle of the putting green) under the full moon in a golf course in Tilden Park. There were no people there at night, and I remember under the full moon listening to the hoot of the great horned owls while practicing the animal forms of Qigong. It was exciting to sneak a sleep out in the woods at night there, and to wake up to the rising sun and the sounds of nature (instead of my alarm clock). Then, I would cross the stream to my students waiting for my Tai Chi, Qigong, and Psychotherapy class.

One time, I was so lost in the joy of my practice, as I was walking at night to where my class was to be the next morning, that I didn't notice that there was a police car with its lights off in the parking lot. When they pulled their guns on me, and asked why I was going to camp out in the woods, I told a story that saved me from jail. I said that I lived up the hill and was going to go backpacking in a few weeks in the Sierras, and I was getting my body in shape for that trip. My half-true story saved me from incarceration, or at least a fine. (There are advantages and disadvantages to being aligned with the energy of Gemini, related to the archetypal trickster.).

In the early 1990s I left teaching at JFK University to write my second book, *Trials of the Heart: Healing the Wounds of Intimacy* (1993). I wanted to show how ancient myths could help couples deepen their perspective regarding the lessons of intimate relationship, as Joseph Campbell showed the importance of myths for aiding an individual's individuation process in his book, *Hero with a Thousand Faces* (1972). I hoped that my book would help people to see (and to serve as a reminder to my self) that there is a metaphysical hero's journey involved in our relationship struggles. Using stories from cross-cultural mythologies, I put forth the viewpoint that intimate relationship is an initiation through the elements of fire, earth, air, and water. Coming from my life-experience with the trials of my heart, and remembering my father's stories about how Scheherazade healed the King with her stories, I described how ancient sacred wisdom stories could help to heal the wounds of intimacy.

CHAPTER 10:

Meetings with Remarkable People and Traditions

A golden thread has run through the history of the world,
Consecutive and continuous,
the work of the best men and women in successive ages.
From point to point it still runs,
And when near, you feel it as the clear and bright and searchingly irresistible light
which Truth throws forth when the great minds (and hearts) conceive (and live) it.

—Adapted from Walter Moxon,
Pilocerus Senilis, and other papers, 1887

Seeing Yourself in All Beings and All Beings in Yourself

Those on the path of life with whom we connect deeply, and those whose books we read, can form some of the essential threads of "the coat of many colors" of our lives. Virtually everyone with whom I have shared deeply could be in this chapter. So, I hope that those who I have not mentioned will not take an omission as a slight, and realize that in them too I see the light.

Hindu Mythology says that each of us is a pearl in the net of the God Indra, and each pearl contains the reflection of all the other pearls. This many thousand year-old image from the Buddhist text of the *Flower Garland Sutra* is one of the first known tales about "holography," which is the modern idea that every part is reflected in every other part of a system. Thus, Indra's tale teaches that the pearl that each of us is, contains the reflection of those whose ways of being we absorb.

Perhaps the best way this has ever been put is in this quote,

By seeing yourself in all beings and all beings in yourself, enlightenment is found.

—*The Upanishads*

Who has influenced you in your life and what does that say about the constellation of your identity? Just like the exercise of our physical bodies leads to an energizing of our physical forms, so can the metaphysical exercise of meditating on our astrological chart lead to a vitalization of our souls' purpose. Developing these "metaphysical muscles," can help us to walk our unique dharmic path, and to better appreciate the significance of those in our web of interconnections.

For example, my Sun in the Eighth House of my astrological chart, (the house of Scorpio and metaphysics), resonates with my being inspired by some of the great metaphysical thinkers of our day, such as Manly Hall and Dane Rudhyar. Even more specifically, in my Eighth House is Sun in Gemini conjunct Uranus, the eccentric planet that revolves a different way than the other planets do. This configuration is an apt symbol for my interest in the eccentric dimensions of depth psychology tradition and out-of-the-mainstream psychological thinkers such as James Hillman.

Another pearl from the net of Indra: Libra rising in my chart means that my ruling planet is Venus; and where Venus is placed, according to astrological theory, might be where I find love and attraction. My Venus is in Taurus, an earth sign that represents love of, and kinesthetic appreciation for, the earth and its fruitful creations (like the early springtime when Taurus occurs). Indeed, spiritual traditions that are "Earth-based" (and of the body) have attracted me and led me to absorb pearls of wisdom from Tai Chi Master Fong Ha and the late polarity therapist master, Kazuko Onodera.

When I mention symbols in my astrological chart such as Venus in Taurus, I do not mean to imply a deterministic view of astrology. The symbols of our charts, are expansive in nature, and can lead to many possible interpretations. An astrological placement does not predetermine who you are or who you are to meet; the deeper dimensions of the mythopoetic approach to astrological symbolism leads to meaning creation not meaning determination (Fingarette, 1963; Mayer 1977).

As one travels into the cave of metaphysical initiation and looks into "the eye of Moirae," (the Goddess of Fate), whether it is an astrological chart or our own bodies, it is easy to be captured and fascinated by the patterns of destiny that seems to resonate with a higher-order field above. For example, speaking of "the eye" of Moirae, the eye according to iridology can be "read" and various disease patterns can be discovered by looking at the spots in various sections of the eye (Jensen, 2005). The same is true regarding other parts of our bodies such as our feet; foot reflexologists say that the internal organs are represented in various parts of the foot (Kunz, 2003). Such isomorphic parallels express one of the essential axioms of metaphysics, "As above so below." This statement was first known to have come from the Hermetic mystery tradition, and was reportedly said by Thoth, the Egyptian master priest (Schure, 1977).

Thoth was one of the earliest known metaphysicians. He is also known as Hermes Trismegistus, or Hermes thrice born. Some say that he, or his essence, existed in three different traditions, in Egypt as Thoth, in Italy as Mercury, and in Greece as Hermes. In the same way that correlations have been uncovered between diseases and the spots in one's eye (iridology), and between various psychological states of mind and physical diseases (Gatchel, 1993), so there may be some mysterious correspondences between the celestial sphere and our ways of Being. It is this, I believe, that Herman Hesse was referring to in his book, *The Glass Bead Game,* one of the books that initiated my quest in my junior year of college. Remaining open minded about the correspondence between cosmos and everyday spheres of life can transform the rationalist's way of experiencing reality, as it did for me. For the open hearted, a door to a metaphysical experience of "reality," and our place in it, can thereby be opened. As the master composer Gustav Mahler puts it, while composing his symphonies he experienced himself, "…as an instrument upon which the universe plays" (Taruskin, 2005).

The way the Jungian mythic system conceptualizes it, each of our unique Selves is a combination of the archetypes of the collective unconscious and our unique ego structures. Thus Carl Jung spells, Self with a capital "S," signifying that our big Self is connected with, and a unique manifestation of, the wider forces of life as represented by people, the forces of nature, and the archetypes of life.

Maybe you will find that the remarkable people who I will tell you about next are representations of your way of being. Or, maybe their philosophies do not exactly resonate with you because you have something of your own vibratory frequency to add to the web of life, as I have done. As you hear about each of the following people, or take a fresh look at those people who have had an influence on you, I hope their contributions to the web of life will help you to better know the frequency of the unique tuning fork of your life.

Manly Hall and the Founding of JFK University's Transpersonal Psychology Program

At the time of the founding of the JFK Transpersonal Psychology program, in 1978, the dean of the program, David (Hatha) Surrenda, gave a gift to all of us new faculty. He invited us to a luncheon where the renowned Manly Hall would not only address us, but we would each have a chance to talk with him.

After all, in our early faculty meetings the faculty's expressed intention was to set up a training program that would integrate the Western and Eastern mystery traditions with modern psychology. Those of us who were scholars, researchers, and practitioners of these traditions were looking for a place to teach where this could be integrated into a psychology curriculum.

We wanted our program to be a place that could help to revive the mystical source material behind all religions, instead of what religion had become. For example, emperors like Theodosius and Constantine's Nicene Council chose the well-known Gospels of Mathew, Mark, Luke, and John to support a Christian religion whereby the priests held power. Many modern scholars, since the uncovering of the Nag Hamadi Lost Gospels (discovered in 1945), believe that the teachings of Jesus did not say that the only way to God the Father was through Jesus. According to the Christian Gnostic tradition, the revised story line had a power motive behind it, to empower the priests. According to author Elaine Pagels, several of the Gospels (such as the Gospel of Thomas) said that anyone could have a direct access to the divine. Likewise the Gospel of Mary Magdalene changed the view of the New Testament's approach to woman. The newly discovered version of the story said that woman had a special, not a subservient, place in the heart of Jesus and the politics of the early disciples. These were just some of the radical viewpoints that came out of the Gnostic Gospels (Pagels, 1989). Considered a heresy by organized Christianly, Gnosticism meant direct knowing of God and emphasized personal revelation. It fit well with the beliefs of the counter-culture of the 1960s, which attempted to bring back the mystical core of all religions and to empower women's rights.

In the age old battle of stories between the traditionalists and the mystics the mystics somewhat facetiously say that "religion" is the strong belief in the spiritual experiences of other people; "mysticism" is the direct experience of the divine force, and source of life from which all emanates. Mystical experiences are fruits on the Metaphysical Tree of Life.

This direct knowing of divine states in cross-cultural spirituality is what Manly Hall was trying to resurrect thorough his encyclopedic book, *The Secret Teaching of All Ages*. As one of the world's deepest scholars of metaphysics, he synthesized a wide variety of esoteric teachings into an encyclopedia of the ancient mystery traditions of the Greek, Egyptian, Jewish, Gnostic traditions, and so forth (Hall, 1962).

In my private meeting with Manly Hall, I told him my dream of "the land where the sun rose in the West and set in the East." I asked him what he thought about it. He replied that my dream was the dream of an initiate or priest of the Greek mystery tradition. He said that in the mystery traditions of the underworld in Greece, the imagery from my dream was prevalent. There, he said, the initiate was held in underworld caves for long periods of time until they had a vision. Often they would see the stars while deep down in the earth, and they would report seeing everything in reverse. The center of the world and a place outside in space were unified, and the sun was seen as rising in the West, not in the East. As I heard these words from such a master of the metaphysical traditions that I had been drawn to study in my doctoral years, I felt an electricity running through my body. Though my sceptical self was still with me regarding believing his interpretation, his scholarship helped me to further appreciate that my journey to the West may have had a deep meaning.

In retrospect, now many years after meeting with Manly Hall, his interpretation of my dream image is even more awesome in raising questions about the forces of SynchroDestiny involved in weaving fabric of my life, and about how the Greek mystery tradition was to play a part in it.[1] For example, a decade later after this meeting I wrote a book about the application of Greek myths and initiatory traditions to our intimate relationships (Mayer, 1993), and I co-led two trips to the ancient sites of Greece. The rationalist might say that Manly Hall influenced me to study the Greek initiatory traditions; the metaphysician might instead say that our life paths come from deeper sources and that my dream of the land where the sun rose in the West resonated with this deeper source. Again the question arises, from whence do "the callings of our life" come? The mythologist might metaphorize the source of our destinies as the Great Goddess in the Cave of Creation who gives us our unique twists and sends us messages through dreams and visions to align ourselves with our fates.

Manly Hall set the tone well for the beginning of this first Transpersonal Psychology program in the country, where the esoteric teachings of our mystically inclined ancestors were to be synthesized with modern psychology. However, our program had a wider breath, since it focused on psychotherapy. In our training curriculum we integrated traditions of the East and West, body and mind, and ancient and modern. We drew much on Jungian oriented psychology, for he was the master of interfacing the Western mystery tradition and modern psychology. Though we were not going to be a Jungian training institute, Jungian approaches to symbolic processes became an essential part of the curriculum. Our approach was nondenominational and cross-cultural; and for five years I taught courses on a wide variety of approaches to the use of symbolic processes in psychotherapy. What I liked most about teaching at JFK for twelve years from 1978–1990 was that faculty could develop our own unique approaches.

My definition of transpersonal psychology, which I presented to my students, was that, "Transpersonal psychology is an integral psychology which incorporates all other psychologies, but it adds the importance of the wider whole of which we are a part." In our Transpersonal Psychology program, our orientation was to give re-birth to the ancient sacred wisdom traditions of West and East, the indigenous traditions of the world, and the ecology of our planet. We believed that the wider dimensions of psycho-spiritual traditions and our relationship to the ecosphere also have something valuable to say about the healing of the psyche.

But then, forces in the culture emerged to attempt to diminish the role that transpersonal psychology was to play in the field. I remember Rollo May, a distinguished faculty member at the school where I had received my Ph.D. (Saybrook University), wrote a public letter in 1986 to the American Psychological Association (APA) saying that there was no need for a transpersonal psychology division in the APA. In my opinion, his view was one of the final nails in the coffin, which stopped transpersonal psychology from achieving what, I believe, is its rightful place in psychology.

At this point, in mainstream psychotherapy training, the role of transpersonal psychology has been diminished. There are some transpersonal psychology programs remaining in the country; but even its most ardent advocate Ken Wilber prefers to call his psychology "integral" rather than transpersonal. There are some good books today on transpersonal psychotherapy (Rowan, 2005; Boorstein, 1996; Scotton et. al., 1996; Fukuyama, 1999; Lefebvre, 2011); however, with the increasing "professionalization" of various career paths, the spiritual and soulful is usually removed in favor of the practical and well established. The American Psychology Association is on a march across the United States standardizing the curriculum, like a Pac-Man game eating up various psychology programs to standardize what is taught.

My two-sided Geminian nature says that there are advantages and disadvantages to standardization. One advantage is that it creates a needed base-line for psychotherapy training. One disadvantage is that it often leaves out some of what others would consider to be essential to therapists' training, such as the disciplines of somatic approaches to therapy, mythological perspectives, energetic healing, and cross-cultural metaphysical perspectives on healing the psyche.

A cross-cultural, cross-temporal metaphysical perspective would argue that psychotherapy could benefit from widening its horizons by creating a healing mandala that includes a broader array of ancient sacred wisdom traditions.[2] I took as my work as a Reluctant Metaphysician to be one of those committed to the extension of the terrain of psychology to include such fields of knowledge.[3]

Dane Rudhyar

> *What is the work of works…if not to establish in and by each one of us,*
> *an absolutely original center in which the universe reflects itself*
> *in a unique and inimitable way?*
> *And those centers are our very selves and personalities."*

> —Teilhard de Chardin
> *The Phenomenon of Man*

In the mid 1970s I was in the midst of my doctoral dissertation on ancient systems of identity formation and personality description. Due to my experience on my vision quest, I was deeply moved by the American Plains Indians system finding one's name from initiatory experiences in nature. But then I picked up a book, *The Astrology of Personality*, by Dane Rudhyar (1970). Since in my masters degree program in New York I had been most influenced by a professor, Dr. Bernie Weitzman, who was a Jungian analyst, when I came to California I was fascinated to hear that there was an astrologer who was taking a Jungian viewpoint on astrology.

One of my problems with astrology, when I had that first astrology reading by the predictive astrologer at that faire a few years back, was that I did not believe in that kind of deterministic philosophy. I thought it was disempowering to "lay predictions on a person." After reading Rudhyar's (1970) book, *The Astrology of Personality,* I found a viewpoint I could respect. I read all of his books, and started to do astrological charts in coffee houses as part of the way I paid my way through my doctoral psychology program.

One of the paths that he took in his writing was creating a book, *The Astrological Mandala* (1973), with a psychic woman who reportedly intuited the symbolic meanings of each of the degrees of the astrological chart, called Sabian Symbols. Rudhyar and other astrologers believe that the degree that most symbolizes a person's uniqueness is their rising degree. I discovered that the degree of the zodiac that was rising at the time of my birth was 25 degrees of Libra, about which Rudhyar writes, "The ability to discover in every experience a transcendent or cosmic meaning." He goes on to say, "The mind open to the multifarious wonders of natural processes, because it sees everything with fresh eyes, not only witnesses simple facts, but pierces through appearances and perceives the great rhythms of universal life…"

Though I had never read anything that I felt had captured the nature of my unique way of being more than this quote, my rational mind discounted the synchronicity of this write-up even though it corresponded so well to me. At first I said to myself that this description probably corresponded to many people. But then, gradually I saw the power of looking at astrological symbols as a tool to evoke a sense of awe about the wider whole of which we are a part. I saw that the astrological system, when used in a non-deterministic way, could help to evoke a person's unique sense of their identity, and to help one to see how it fits into the wider whole of which we are a part.[4]

I learned much from my readings of all of Rudhyar's works in my doctoral years, and I appreciated his offer to be on my doctoral committee and my meetings with him where he shared his dreams with me. We both loved studying the realm of metaphysics and symbolic processes, and I felt honored that I could expand his non-deterministic, viewpoint into the realm of psychotherapy practice.

However, Rudhyar and I had a philosophical difference regarding his synchronistic viewpoint, which is a type of "hidden reality view." I told him that I felt that astrology would be best served by applying the phenomenological viewpoint that Fingarette (1963) put forth in his book, *The Self in Transformation*. I explained to Rudhyar that Fingarette's "meaning reorganization viewpoint" does not preclude that there may be a "hidden reality" discovered by astrology; but instead it emphasizes the inner psychological process of the individual looking at his or her astrological chart, and how that reorganizes their view of their life's meaning.

The Hermeneutic Path

Gemini, my Sun Sign, symbolically resonates with Hermes, the Greek god who, like *the herm* (the three piled stones that you see on the dividing points of paths in the wilderness), marks the boundary line between things. It is interesting, therefore, to see that I have a tendency to straddle opposites. Greek mythology adds that the herm not only marks the boundary line between territories, Hermes also is the guide on the path that leads up to the heavens and down into the underworld. Thus, Hermes is "the guide of souls" (Kerenyi, 1976). Gemini, I learned, is an air sign having a propensity for thinking. Again, at first, upon hearing this I discounted this association to my love of thinking. I said to myself that many people enjoy thinking who do not have a Gemini Sun sign.

The hermeneutic path, stemming from this archetype of Hermes, attempts to synthesize conflicts between opposites of above and below, heaven and earth, and to resolve the tension between opposite choices. I learned that part of the solution to conflicts is to value the process (hermeneutics) rather than to side with one side. My desire to introduce this hermeneutical viewpoint into the realm of astrological theory created some problems for me. It eventually led to my ostracism from certain segments of the astrological community.

I made the argument in my *Mystery of Personal Identity* book (1983) that it is equally problematic to proclaim that there is a correspondence between heaven and earth (the literalistic fallacy) or to say there is not a correspondence (the sceptical fallacy). Both viewpoints stop the imagination from opening ourselves to "Wonder," as we explore the cosmos in the light of our life and unique ways of being. My hermeneutic viewpoint as applied to astrology, and thereby valuing "Mystery," was not popular with astrological believers. I was "thrown out of the temple." Nor was it very popular with sceptics who, (not understanding a hermeneutical viewpoint), felt that I was remaining open to a fraudulent system. But I sensed that my work was to reluctantly accept my fate regardless of the cost. I took the stance that a hermeneutical relationship to astrological symbols leads to awaken the sense of mystery as we wonder about the connection between our deepest essences and the wider whole of which we are a part.

Once again the theme of this book repeats. By staying true to the "story of one's own life," some suffering may come, but the unique garment of one's own life gets woven thereby. Following a hermeneutic path regarding astrology is an example of my staying connected to the metaphorical Great Goddess in the Cave of Creation who gives the thread of our lives a unique twist. Though Dane Rudhyar and I remained on good terms, respecting our differences, my ostracism from certain segments of the astrological community around him was painful and alienating for me. However, this ostracism led me on the path to write the first book on the integration of astrology and depth psychotherapy, and to re-vision astrology into a system that could be palatable even to sceptics. I was grateful that my book, *The Mystery of Personal Identity,* won the World Astrology Prize from the Astrological Association of Great Britain for its contribution to the field.[5]

So, my meeting Dane Rudhyar illustrates an answer to the question, "How does a Reluctant Metaphysician meet a remarkable person?" By staying true to the unique twist we are called to make to the fabric of their teachings, a pathway opens to our contribution to the tapestry of life.

Staying in touch with my sense of what most moved me, also led to my next life step. Since I felt that the astrology of that day lacked a bodily, grounded dimension it was synchronistic that I met the next person on my path. I knew that I had a desire to bring the body into the metaphysical healing system that I was about to develop. Regardless of whether it was because of those early body experiences that I had as a six year old, or maybe resonant with my rising, ruling planet being Venus in an Earth sign Taurus, I wanted to ground the world of symbolism in the body. The next remarkable person I met was a blessing for this next step on my journey.

Eugene Gendlin

Not all heroes are well-known heroes. In my opinion, Dr. Eugene Gendlin is not as recognized as he should be as a hero of the psychotherapeutic tradition. In the 1970s, the American Psychological Association named Dr. Gendlin, "the most distinguished professional psychologist of the year." He won this award for his research exploring the question, "What is the essence of what makes psychotherapy work, regardless of the type of psychotherapy?"

His doctoral students interviewed a large number of people, who had been in a wide variety of different therapies, and asked them to reflect upon the moments that most created change in their psychotherapy. Using a phenomenological research methodology, he then had the students write up the themes that emerged. From listening to these tapes, he extracted out his *Focusing* method, which replicated the essence of what made psychotherapy work for these people. He found that when people reported moments of unclarity about what they were feeling, they paused and tuned into a body sense where they might find a word, image, or phrase that was close, but not an exact fit with the felt sense of the problem. Then they would "resonate" those words, images, or phrases to get an exact fit with the felt sense of their problem until they experienced an "ah–ha." At this point the patient would experience a "felt shift," and new meaning would arise. From these interviews, the six steps of the Focusing process were created, (Gendlin, 1978):

1. Clearing a space
2. Finding the felt sense of the problem
3. Finding a handle-word, image, or phrase
4. Resonating
5. Asking
6. Receiving

Ancient sacred wisdom traditions and symbols can enhance the way various psychotherapy systems are viewed. For example, the astrological mandala can create a holistic view of psychotherapy systems. (Mayer, 1977, 1983, 2007); and the concept of *axis mundi* helps us to see the value of Gendlin's Focusing in a new light.

Cross-cultural mythologies speak of the importance for the initiate to create an *axis mundi* to become centered in his or her world. In the Roman mysteries of *Mithras*, and in the Tai Chi tradition, the initiate imagines his or her spine aligned with the axis of the earth so that his or her spine connects heaven and earth. Gendlin's approach can become an *axis mundi* for the psychotherapist of any tradition, because the body sense is at the root of his approach and making meaning is at the top. From the viewpoint of research in somatic psychotherapy, a major axis of healing comes from the ground of the body and felt experience, and then this felt experience is transformed by the new meanings discovered (van der Kolk, 1994, 2002).

Two key things that Dr. Gendlin's method adds to psychotherapeutic tradition are (1) an emphasis on the role of the body and felt meaning, and (2) the importance of an energy shift in the process of healing the psyche. Brain research confirms that there are changes in EEG patterns of the brain at the moment of a person's "felt shift" (Don, 1977).

I told you earlier how I was first introduced to Dr. Gendlin's method when one of my teachers, Dr. Bernie Weitzman, at the new School for Social Research in 1970 demonstrated and taught us about Focusing. It was a life transforming experience to watch this teacher drop his eyes in front of the class and inwardly access his real experience of being in front of our graduate psychology class. For example, he described his anxiety in his stomach, and how there was a felt shift when he realized that it was about his fears of his inadequacy about getting across to the class aspects of Carl Jung's teachings. I had never seen another teacher be this real with his or her felt experience in front of a class. So, it was all the more of a gift, a few years later to be introduced to Dr. Gendlin by the Jungian analyst (now a past president of the Jung Institute), Dr. John Beebe. I still remember gratefully that car ride in San Francisco where I dropped into my felt experience with Drs. Gendlin and Beebe and showed them what I understood Focusing to be, and how I felt Taoist methods of breathing and psycho-mythological processes could enhance Focusing. Shortly thereafter, Dr. Gendlin gave me the honor of being his first Bay Area Focusing training coordinator. I was one of his Focusing training coordinators for about ten years. With his approval I added the idea of using Taoist methods of relaxation to his "clearing a space" step, and I wrote a little blurb on this for the *Association of Transpersonal Psychology Newsletter* in the early 1980s. I also wrote an article that included these methods in Dr. Gendlin's *Focusing Folio* journal (Mayer, 1982).

The Taoist method of Microcosmic Orbit Breathing complements the use of Gendlin's Focusing as one of Bodymind Healing Psychotherapy's core methods, which I call *The River of Life*.[6] When lecturing to graduate students, I am still in touch with the contribution that Dr. Gendlin made to the field by this method of direct reference to the bodymind to create change in psychotherapy. I still appreciate him as a mentor that allowed me to follow my way with Focusing. As a humanistic psychologist he not only paved the way for a person to go inside to find their own unique experience, but also Dr. Gendlin's stance in his organization has always been to allow his students to add to the Focusing tradition. I believe that Dr. Gendlin's work stands at the center of the continuum of mind and body psychotherapies, and that it is an invaluable method for allowing meaning to emerge directly from the body's "felt sense."

Later, I took Focusing and added it to my mythological work to create The Mythic Journey Process (MJP), the culmination of my work on integrating the Western and Eastern Mystery traditions.[7] The MJP uses Dr. Gendlin's method of inner accessing to help a person to create and heal their life story. I owe Dr. Gendlin a debt of gratitude for helping me to find the way to ground mythological tales in the body.

Again, an answer comes regarding how a Reluctant Metaphysician meets a remarkable man—with humility, appreciation that we are standing on great shoulders, and at the same time appreciating our unique thread that we have to add to the Coat of Many Colors of Life. I am reminded of a story that is told of how to approach a master of the martial arts. Bow, but do not bow so low that your eyes break contact or the master may kick you. From the perspective of Qigong, when one looks down in a very low bow, the fulcrum point collapses where the back of the head and neck join; this results in a breaking the connection with the circuit to the energy centers located at the occiput and a person is disconnected with a dimension of his or her power. Specifically, these points are acu-point Bl-9, called the Gates of Consciousness or the Jade Pillow, and Bl-10, called the Celestial Pillar (Deadman, 2005, pp. 262–3). Each of us is an *axis mundi*, and meeting a remarkable person energizes this celestial pillar. If we bow the right amount, then that meeting can add to our stance in life.

James Hillman and the Archetypal Psychology Tradition

Books are alive. Even if you do not have a personal meeting with an author, we do have meetings with some of the deepest parts of authors when we read their books. The Jewish tradition teaches that a book is sacred, and when I was a child I was taught to kiss a book when it touched the ground. In one of the Bible's creation stories, the Gospel according to John (Genesis 1: 1) it says, "In the beginning was the word." And so, a book's words do have the ability to create new realties and new worlds.

Dr. James Hillman, a former director of the Jungian Institute of Zurich is one of those Jungian authors who added to my pathway of joining the tradition of psychology with the ancient mystery traditions. Though I never had a personal meeting with Dr. Hillman, I attended numerous of his lectures and have read many of his books. As one of the Socratic gadflies of our age, he challenged many of the basic assumptions of psychologists in his books such as *Revisioning Psychology* (1975). For example, he questioned whether the worship of "growth" and "change" by modern psychology is such a good thing. He also proclaimed that maybe our pathologies hold keys to our uniqueness and we should delve further into them to find "the soul" that is hidden there. He wondered whether our pathologies contain our "pathos," and if we could awaken something deep in us by not getting rid of our problematic ways so quickly.

One of the major contributions that Hillman made to psychology, and to "spiritual seekers," was distinguishing between "spirit" and "soul." "Spirit" is associated with the upper regions, mountain tops and traditions that advocate transcendence, whereas "soul" is associated with valleys, moist places, and transmuting traditions (Hillman, 1975).

This distinction was an important conceptual distinction for many seekers of my generation. It helped me to realize why I didn't feel totally at home with Eastern transcendence. The path I was walking needed two legs. One (of the winged sandals of Hermes) led to the realm of transcendence (rising above) of the East, and the other was firmly planted in the transmuting (working through) traditions of the West.[8]

Story of the Mullah Who Lost His Key in the Dark

There is a story of a mullah in the Middle East, who was a spiritual teacher. His key fell through a crack in the floorboard in his house into the dark basement. He went outside into the sunlight and one of his students asked, "What are you looking for?" the mullah explained that he lost his key. The student asked, Where did you lose it?" the mullah replied, I lost it in the basement of my house. The student asked, "Well then, why are you looking for it outside." The mullah replied, "Because it is light out here."

This teaching story was important for many spiritual seekers of my generation who went to Eastern transcendent traditions to find our spirituality. When we read this story in Idries Shah's *Tales of the Dervishes* in the 1970s, it opened our eyes to the importance of looking into the darkness—the underworld of emotions within—to find a different type of spirituality than one of dissociated, smiling transcendence.

During this time of my generation's embarking on the path of psychological introspection, James Hillman was one of the intellectual leaders of the movement towards "soul"—meaning the descent into the depths of the valley where deep feelings lie. The terrain that Hillman and other Jungians opened into "the world-soul" did influence many poets and storytellers of our age, such as Robert Bly, Michael Meade, and so forth. James Hillman resurrected a way of seeing from a bygone era (for example, ancient Greece). Some important concepts that Hillman brought to the soulful seekers in his book *Revisioning Psychology* (1975) were "personification," "facing the Gods," and "facing the Demons."

Hillman brought the essence of the Greek mystery tradition to modern psychology by teaching that to resacralize life, and our individual psyches, we can "personify" each of our issues as divine persons or as "demons." He advised us to capitalize letters to find the gods in our words. For example, the demon of "Doubt" might have a face pockmarked from the arrows of scorn, and a slumped chest. Perhaps, Doubt was born from the marriage of Blame and Weakness, and Doubt's sister would be Insecurity. Those who follow this pathway of seeing our inner worlds as family dynamics between the archetypes of life, can further their experience of our lives as interesting mythic dramas.[9]

Carl Gustav Jung

Actually, since Hillman is "a Jungian," major credit in this section should be given to Dr. Carl Jung. Dr. Jung was the first modern psychologist to integrate metaphysics with psychotherapy. He became estranged from mainstream psychology when he introduced his idea that there was a world of archetypes and a collective unconscious that was a fundamental aspect of our psyches. For me, he helped me to see that my metaphysical interests, (stemming from my undergraduate school readings of Plato and Aristotle) could find a home in the field of psychology. His writings also taught me how various symbolic processes could transform and heal. Dr. Jung showed how symbols generated energy—a not well enough known part of his teachings (Jung, 1960, *Volume VIII*). I built on the foundation of his contributions, (and stood on his broad shoulders) in some of the following ways:

1. I am grateful to Dr. Jung for initiating my interest in Taoism and Taoist practices due to his having written the commentary on Richard Wilhelm's *The Secret of the Golden Flower*. However, I never in Wilhelm's book or in any of Dr. Jung's works saw any experiential discussion of the Microcosmic Orbit Breathing method. My path led me to further experiential exploration of this breathing method and adapting it into a clinical healing tool (The River of Life Guided Meditation Process). Likewise, I set off on an exploration of the wider field in which the *Secret of the Golden Flower* was embedded, which led me to a many decade training in Qigong. This helped me, and the metaphysical system that I developed, to carry forth the somatic energetic component of healing further than I found in Jung's work.

2. Though Jung in his later work discussed the psychoid (meaning body oriented) nature of archetypes, his emphasis was not on the somatic. In my Bodymind Healing Psychotherapy approach I added the somatic dimension of healing.[10] For example, when appropriate, patients are instructed on how to self-touch acu-points to activate healing energy as well as to hold their heart chakras and bellies to enhance self-soothing; and I emphasize the psychoid dimension of one's life stance.

3. Jung's system of psychological types (four functions which included thinking, feeling, sensation, and intuition, and the two attitudes types of introversion and extroversion), I believe, is a layman's guide to what Jung knew about astrology. I wished that he had incorporated astrology into his theory of types. My doctoral dissertation and book *The Mystery of Personal Identity* built upon many of Jung's ideas about symbolic process, but my book went more fully into the role of astrological metaphor in helping a patient find a new relationship to their life meaning and identity.

4.   Jung developed his *Active Imagination Process* as a clinical tool for healing patients with symbolic processes. I felt that the experiential dimension of symbolic process traditions could be enhanced by the incorporation of the body. So, in my Mythic Journey Process (1982) I integrated Gendlin's Focusing, and later in my career I added naturally arising primordial Tai Chi and Qigong movements as a metaphysical tool to help people heal psychological issues by connecting to the world behind the world.[11]

The writings of Drs. Jung and Hillman led me to create The Mythic Journey Process (MJP) in the mid 1970s, which is a centerpiece of the bodymind healing tradition I have developed. Sam Keen, my doctoral committee chairman, also talked about mythic journeys, however his work was not mythic per se; his meaning of "myth" was more belief oriented (Keen, 1974, 1989). I presented my MJP process at various conferences in the 1980s and incorporated it in almost all of my books due to its central importance to the traditions that were being woven into my life's tapestry. This process is a key tool for the Reluctant Metaphysician, because when we reluctantly meet the difficulties of life, the MJP provides a way to heal and transform ourselves. It does this through connecting our bodies and mythic imagination, thereby weaving threads of meaning to and from the world behind the world.

The Mythic Journey Process consists of telling a story about your life, and transposing it into ancient times so that the inner figures that arise come from inside of you instead from a pre-conceived story. While you are doing this story telling method, you continually refer back to your body so that the myth is grounded in your felt bodily experience.[12]

I began this book by quoting Virgil's phrase, "We make our destinies by our choice of Gods." I suggested that we change this phrase to, "We make our destinies by our choices of stories." This idea that we worship our stories and archetypal ways of being as religious zealots worship their temples, mosques, or churches first came to me through James Hillman's work. Some of us worship at the temple of Hedonism, others at the temple of Asceticism. By imagining our ways of being as deities, we "Face the Gods" (put a face on the ruling archetypes of our lives), as Hillman puts it. For example, when we are in blind rage we may be captured by the archetype of Mars, when we compulsively withdraw we can be described to be following the way of the Ostrich.

I developed the Mythic Journey Process to help people become aware of the archetypes and stories that rule their lives, and to make therapeutically operational and somatically based what I absorbed from Hillman's writings. It helps me in my personal and professional life to bring the imaginal to life, so that my own, and others', endeavors and trials are seen as Mythic Journeys. This mythic pathway is synchronistically symbolized by the rising Sabian degree of my astrological chart, which reads "to see the transcendent cosmic meaning (and story) in each particular life event" (Rudhyar, 1973).

The stories we choose to live are indeed the spiritual bones of our lives. They are how we are remembered. So, the work of works is to see if we want to be remembered by our flaring temper, our withdrawing, and our sulking. Or, for the initiate into the temple of psycho-mythology (a temple of temples), at any moment we can change our temple of worship. Then, our loved ones will tell the story about our coolness in hot times, and about our speaking truth to power rather than withdrawing or sulking.[13]

Ken Wilber

When I was teaching at JFK University, Ken Wilber's works were some of the most respected in the field of Transpersonal Psychology. Though he was not a psychotherapist, his works brought forth a transpersonal psychology to the halls of traditional academia where three major psychotherapies had been "the major temples of worship:" Cognitive/behavioral, psychodynamic/neo-analytic, and humanistic/existential. Transpersonal psychology was introduced as a fourth tradition, which was an addition to, and an incorporation of, these other schools of psychology into a wider whole.

I had my differences with the psychology and philosophy of Ken Wilber and how I wanted transpersonal psychology to be brought into clinical psychology. It is not the purpose of this book to differentiate my clinical ground from his. His work stands as its own masterpiece, and others can examine my work in its own light.

Here is an amusing story about the time I met Ken at a party. After having read quite a few of his books, and being deeply impressed by his contributions to the world of transpersonal psychology, I felt grateful to be able to personally connect with him. I walked up to him and introduced myself, telling him how much I, and my students, enjoyed his work. Then I said, "By the way, my cat said that if I ever met you, she wanted me to ask you a question." He stopped and quizzically looked me in the eye and said, "What is the question?"

I said, "Well my cat was looking over my shoulder while I was reading your book, *Up from Eden*, where you were talking about how human beings were on a higher rung on the evolutionary ladder; and how the higher religions like Christianity, Buddhism and Judaism were at a higher rung on the evolutionary ladder as compared to Shamanism." I told him that my cat said, "Why is this author saying that? Only the greatest of your Olympic athletes and high wire circus performers can balance themselves on a narrow beam, but the most ordinary member the cat species can easily do that. Also, I understand that the most advanced spiritual leaders of the human race meditate about five hours a day; however almost all of the members of the cat species meditate almost all day." So, I continued, "My cat said if I ever met you she wanted me ask you to explain your reasoning, and luckily here we are. So, what should I tell her when I go home tonight?" Ken Wilbur pause for a moment and replied, "There certainly are a lot of ways of looking at things, aren't there."

I thought that was a pretty good reply, though this interchange brought up an aspect of the nascent transpersonal movement with which I was uncomfortable. The hierarchization of consciousness went against the viewpoint that I held which in part came from my readings of Rudolf Steiner (Lachman, 2007), who believed that every life form has its own unique gift. Also, the view in Wilber's *Up from Eden* (2007) was contradicted by the reverence I learned from my training with various Native American shamans, such as Oh Shinnah Fast Wolf who transmitted to us the Native American belief of the sacredness of animals and of all creation. Most importantly, because of my mystical experiences with animals, particularly deer (coming from my vision quest and the deer who had kissed my eye), I knew that the spiritual tapestry of my life, and any metaphysical worldview I was to develop, must include the value of animals and their significant place in the wondrous fabric of creation.

In this light, I feel compelled to tell you the story of Anima, the cat with whom I lived for about fifteen years. When I was writing my doctoral dissertation, I slept outside on my deck in the Berkeley Hills on many nights to "recharge my batteries" with the fresh night air and the view of the stars. One cold night, a feral cat, who had been "eyeing" me for a few nights, crawled into my sleeping bag. I named her Anima after both the Jungian idea of the importance of a man being in touch with his feminine side, and the metaphysical notion of *anima mundi*, the soul of the world. One relevant story about Anima is that at that time in my life, after coming home each night I ritually lay down for a few minutes and practiced Gendlin's Focusing method. I would focus on the issues that were brought up in my life that day, and on my body's felt sense, until there was a "felt shift." Anima joined me in this almost daily ritual. She would walk onto my body, apparently sensing just where some blocked life issue was held. Then, she kneaded on that place in my body. When her claws dug in, I took her off my body. To train her not to claw on me, I pressed her claws back inward to communicate to her that I didn't want to be clawed and I took her off my body. It did not take too long for Anima to learn to massage my body with no clawing in the place on my body that was blocked. We gave each other a massage and energy healing. At the moment when I had a "felt shift" she would walk off of my body and go on her independent way. My relationship with Anima is one of the reasons why I hold animals so dear.

Larry Dossey

Larry Dossey is a leader in the consciousness movement, an author of many books, and a regularly featured speaker at many conferences. At one conference I attended, Dr. Dossey was the keynote speaker. At this banquet, with about a hundred tables of leading-edge healing practitioners, he spoke on the theme that it is time to go beyond energy psychology and see that "intention" is the key to psychological healing (Dossey, 1992; 1994). I raised my hand and somewhat shyly came to the microphone. I thought about my twenty-five years of training in the Yi Chuan Qigong tradition, where the practice involves an integration of intention (yi in Chinese) and energy (qi). So I asked, "Is not to split energy and intention a false dichotomy?" I continued, "If the two were not intimately connected why, in the research of Dr. Bernard Grad in his experiment at McGill University (Gerber, 1996, p. 78) with various subjects holding and intending to send healing energy to barley seeds in water, did depressed people (with low energy) suppress plant growth and non-depressed people have significantly better results in facilitating plant growth?"

In a banquet room of about five hundred people, there was dead silence. Dr. Dossey paused while pondering for, what felt like, a full sixty seconds. He then did something that made me respect him even more than I had before, he said, "I don't know the answer to your question; but I'm going to think about it." At the next conference where Dr. Dossey and I were both presenting, I ran into him and jokingly reminded him who I was, "Remember me? I'm the heckler they send to harass you and ask impertinent questions at all the conferences."

He laughed and invited me to sit with him at dinner. We then discussed issues about the roots of modern bodymind healing, during which time I told him how my practice in Yi Chuan Qigong over the last twenty-five years had led me to the experience of these two streams joining.

So, here we see how the experience of a dream, image or place in nature that becomes part of a person's "Medicine Animal Name," can help to give voice to the ruling powers behind our destinies. On my path to keep true to Michael, from the Place of Two Streams Joining, my work has been to join West/East, mind/body, ancient/modern and energy/intention in the approach to healing I have co-created with that ruling force that has guided my soul's journey.

Kazuko Onodera

Kazuko Onodera, was the director of the Polarity Center of Berkeley, and one of the most adept healers I have met. She received a transmission from Randolph Stone who brought polarity therapy to the West; and Swami Sachidananda brought her into his inner circle and declared Kazuko a guru. She taught yoga, and practiced and taught polarity therapy for thirty years. But in my life, most importantly, she was my friend. From the mid 1970s through the early years of the third millennium, as two spiritual seekers we loved to exchange traditions. I taught her Tai Chi, and she transmitted the polarity tradition to me through many polarity treatments over three decades.

Anyone who thinks that they can have a spiritual approach to life without have a tradition of touch involved in it, has not been touched by the traditions that have touched my life. From Kazuko I was initiated into an energetic transmission that was beyond anything my rational mind could wrap itself around. As various places on the body were touched, an experience like that depicted in movies such as *Avatar* opened...it was like being plugged into the universal matrix of life. The ability for Kazuko to "diagnose" imbalances, and the healings that took place when my body was out of balance, were a wonder to behold.

My relationship with Kazuko influenced me to pursue training at the Acupuncture Institute of Berkeley and get a certification in Chinese Health Arts there. When I cofounded an integrative medical clinic in Lafayette, California called The Health Medicine Institute, I made sure that Kazuko was invited to join the staff with me and other health professionals. I believe that integrative medicine holds great promise for the future of health in our out-of-balance United States where, at this time, corporate greed and the profit motive rules our medical system. Once we see through the veil of the stories we have been told about our healthcare in the United States, we'll be ready for a new relationship to our healthcare (Robbins, 2006; Mayer, 2007; Saputo, 2009). A revamped healthcare system will integrate alongside of Western medicine some of the following traditions: indigenous methods of healing, naturopathy, energy-based treatments, homeopathy, chiropractic, Chinese medicine, and various forms of bodywork. But back to Kazuko and me...

One way that Kazuko and I "recharged our batteries" after long days as health professionals was to take long walks in the woods at night. We would pretend we were in ancient times and as we practiced our Yi Chuan Walking Meditation (Chuen, 1991; Mayer, 2004 p. 146–150; Mayer, 2004d). We played the game of "Yi Chuan Stalking" where we practiced Yi Chuan Qigong Walking Meditation...walking as silently as possible through the woods at night. One variation of this game was to attempt to walk up to a deer without it knowing we were approaching, and touch it. We never got more than about ten feet from a deer, but the rush of energy playing this game was what was important, not any goal. The joy was in the process. We would take breaks from the "stalking deer game" and pretend we were Samurai (Kazuko was Japanese). We played "Samurai hide-and-seek," and we surprised each other by coming out from behind a tree, and we play-attacked the other. The object of this game was whether we could keep true to our Tai Chi training and either yield to the attack while sticking to the other (this is called "no collision, no separation"). Another Tai Chi game was to discharge the other person as we became ball-like, and the other person bounced off the ball; this is called "fajing."[14]

Eventually over the years I transmitted to Kazuko the *San Shou* (combining the 108 Tai Chi movements into a two-person joined form); and so in the woods we could spontaneously "attack" the other with one of the movements in the set, and the other would counter. When we had finished playing we were reenergized, and ready to go back the next day to deal with the attacks of everyday life. Our nighttime San Shou helped us to do our healing work the next day with recharged batteries.

I am sad to say the Kazuko Onodera passed away at 68 years of age in June of 2008. However, I am grateful that I had the joy to share the Path with her as her friend.

Ram Dass

Ram Dass. Alias Richard Alpert, Ph.D., was an inspiration to the spiritual seekers of my generation. Since he was a psychologist teaching at Harvard, and left his well-established life to explore Eastern paths, he was a living symbol of the journey to the East that many of us took in those days. Like the Beatles and many others who sought a deeper wholeness through an emersion in Eastern spiritual traditions, Ram Dass' journey has been particularly meaningful to me as a psychologist who also wanted to incorporate Eastern practices in my work. His book *Be Here Now* (1971), was like a bible to my generation.

His story of meeting his guru was part of the collective turn-around of the psychedelic culture of the 1970s that helped us see there were states of consciousness beyond those evoked by psychedelics. Ram Dass tells the story of his guru, Neem Karoli Baba, who asked Ram Dass to give him all of the psychedelics he was holding; the guru took them in his hand and swallowed them all. Ram Dass was in awe, as were all of us who knew the power of psychedelics, that apparently the LSD had no effect on the guru. He explained to Ram Dass that there were many other states that were more enlightening, naturally occurring, and less damaging than was this LSD state. Ram Dass and many of us wondered what these states were.

Hatha yoga was one suggested path in his book, *Be Here Now,* and there is a section of his book that illustrates these yoga practices. I have been doing these practices almost every morning for three decades now. I do them first thing while I am in bed. I have a nice hard mattress that is the perfect blend (the middle way) between soft and hard... perfect for my yoga practice. I live a very busy life, and I don't have time for yoga, so I trick my "inner busy white rabbit" by setting my alarm clock twenty minutes earlier than I normally wake. Then, I do the yoga system that I developed, which combines Ram Dass's methods with acu-yoga. This combination honors my Medicine Way of two rivers becoming one—in this case, yoga and acupressure. Yoga means "yoking to the divine;" and I touch various points on my body while I am in these yoga postures to help me yoke myself to divine energetic states as I begin my everyday life.[15]

Ram Dass had an influence on my life in terms of his advocacy of using natural means to access altered states of consciousness through yoga and meditation. But there are many other reasons I appreciate the story of Ram Dass' life: his work with the SEVA foundation and restoring sight to many poor people in third world countries; his spiritually insightful comments on life; his modeling a modest, real, and honest spiritual being (particularly now that he has "come out" about his homosexuality); his sense of humor; and his great story telling ability.

A classic Ram Dass story is about how his guru, on his birthday, had a big kettle of soup made, and Ram Dass wondered why they went to the poorest part of India on this special occasion. When Ram Dass asked why they were not going out celebrating, his guru explained that there was nothing he enjoyed more than serving others. Serving the indigent was the guru's birthday celebration. Another one of Ram Dass' stories has served as a teaching story in many of my psychotherapy classes. Ram Dass went to see his brother in a mental institute after his brother had a psychotic breakdown. His brother was a successful attorney, and when Ram Dass came into the hospital with long hair, a multicolored hippie outfit, and all dressed in beads. His brother looked at Ram Dass and commented on his unkempt ways and countercultural lifestyle. "Why is it that I'm in a mental hospital and not you?" Ram Dass responded by asking him, "Do you believe you are God?" His brother said, "Of course." Ram Dass asked, " Do you believe I'm God? His brother said, "No." Ram Dass then explained, "That's why you're in a mental institution and I'm not; I believe we are all God."

Ram Dass embodies the qualities of an excellent teacher of an essential theme of this book—that stories and practices can change our lives. As the story of his brother in the mental institution shows, the difference between one version of a story and another can make the difference between being incarcerated or liberated. Ram Dass has been a teacher to my spiritual subculture and our larger culture through each of his life stages. When he had a stroke in his later years, and many people in a similar situation might be devastated or sulking, instead he said, "I've been stroked by God." Once again Ram Dass became a teacher of how to handle dire circumstances through his spiritual practices and reframing the story of his life as a gift from a higher source. From his experience, many have learned about how to handle disabilities. (Not just the Old Woman in the Cave can handle the Black Dog unraveling the fabric of life.)

Master Fong Ha and My Other Tai Chi/Qigong Masters

In the 1970s I watched David Carradine's *Kung Fu* series "religiously" and wondered where I could find a teacher of the internal martial arts. After searching around the Bay Area for months, and checking out many Tai Chi teachers, I found my Sifu (respected teacher), Master Fong Ha. In 1974, as I looked around at many teachers of Tai Chi to help me "get into my body," I chose Master Ha not because of his credentials, but because of the quality of his movements—embodying solidity and grace—and his personality, which was open and explorative. I felt a cross-discipline identification with him. I was seeking a psychotherapeutic style that was not rigidly attached to a single method as the answer to the quest for wholeness, and Sifu Ha was seeking the same in the area of the internal martial arts.

Master Ha's background included training with Tung Ying Chieh (first generation disciple of Yang Chengfu) and Yang Shouchung (a lineage holder of the Yang style). I was very fortunate to find Master Ha because for many years these Chinese arts were not shared with outsiders to the family, let alone Westerners. Yang Chengfu was the first Yang style Tai Chi Chuan Master who allowed the family secrets to be shared outside the family.

Master Ha was a seeker, like myself. He traveled to China ever year or so, and with his Tai Chi brothers they searched for the most adept masters of the tradition. Since many of the best Tai Chi and Qigong masters wanted to teach in the United States, Master Ha invited them to stay with him for the summer. One of the things that most impressed me about Master Ha was that he shared these grandmasters with his students. Unlike many teachers whose egos got in the way of allowing their students to see their teacher in a lesser position, Master Ha became another student in the class. He brought from China some of the most respected masters of Qigong, Standing Meditation, and the internal martial arts with whom his circle of students had the great gift to study during many decades.

The Secret of the Chinese Internal Martial and Healing Arts: Standing Meditation

On one of his trips to China, in 1974, when I had been studying with him for about six months, he met a Grandmaster of the tradition of Yi Chuan (also spelled Yi Quan) Standing Meditation Qigong, Han Xingyuan. This art involved simply standing still.

I have to admit that I was sceptical when Sifu Ha suggested that I try standing for a hundred hours over the next few months, and that by doing so, my development would be enhanced. I felt much resistance to "just standing." I associated standing with my childhood experience of being told to "stand in the corner" when I was disobedient in school. As an adult, one of the things I most detested was standing in line at various public places, being forced to stop my life and stand still when I needed to get "important things" done. To tell you the truth, I had secretly believed all my life that there was something wrong with me. At parties, I noticed that most people could spend longer times standing with one person than I could. I felt mounting tension in my body when I stood in one place for longer than I wanted. If there was anyone who would not be a good candidate for this "Standing Meditation thing," I believed it was me.

In the Tai Chi class with Sifu Ha, I had come to learn to move as I had seen him move—with grace and power. I did not want to waste my time just standing there, "doing nothing." But, reluctantly, I decided to just do this practice as I had done so many other things in life—by pushing my way through and getting it over with—then I could get onto "the real thing," the graceful movements of Tai Chi and Qigong. Little did I know...this simple method would change me at my core.

I was very curious and appreciative when Master Ha invited Master Han to come and live with him in two summers in the mid 1970s, and that I would have the opportunity to train with him. One of the things I learned from Master Han was concentration.

I remember one day going to Golden Gate Park at five in the morning to "just stand." When a car accident happened nearby and people stopped their meditation and started looking and talking, he ended the class. Though it seemed cruel to deprive us of a class after having driven so far, so early in the morning, I got a lesson in discipline and concentration. Master Han's Standing was an intense ordeal, like a trial by fire—or I should say, a trial by ice-cold San Francisco air. At first, Standing in the cold for periods of up to an hour was hard for me and the other students to bear. I remember one student who wore gloves and a hat. Master Han took them off. If this was a public school he might have been fired, sued, or accused of abuse. But by going through the rigors of his training, I learned that through this "tough love" came a soft, loving feeling that was to transform my cerebral stance in life.

I had always suffered from coldness in my hands and feet, and doing Standing Meditation in this freezing cold temperature did not help. At first, my hands and feet became colder, but this coldness that had been so much a part of the constriction of my early years began to change. By staying with the coldness and just experiencing it, the coldness gradually changed to smoothness—my skin felt like baby's skin. Red blotches appeared on my hands; and then my whole body became warm. I became initiated into a practice that is common in shamanic initiation traditions to cultivate "inner heat."[16] Now when the coldness comes, I have found a way to turn the coldness to warmth.

Master Han was a rather elderly man in his sixties, so I could not understand why he intimidated some of the best martial artists in the Bay Area. As a scholar, it was a great privilege for me to have an opportunity to study with him and some of the best martial artists of the San Francisco Bay Area. Master Han took delight in using my frail body to demonstrate the usefulness of his methods to these well-built, adept martial artists. He would put me into a certain posture and showed how with his concepts, even lightweights like me could deal with the forces that they used against me.

Researching the Roots of Standing Meditation

Master Ha has been a blessing on the path of my life. As a scholarly type, I was always asking questions about the origins of our practice and Master Ha would reply, "Just stand, and just do the practices. You will find the answers for which you are looking there." I followed his advice for quite some time, but then my inquisitive nature got the best of me. I started to do research on the tradition into which I had been trained for these years.

I discovered that Master Ha's *Sifu* (teacher), Master Han Xingyuan, had been trained by one of the grandmasters of Yi Chuan Standing Meditation Qigong, Wang Xiangzhai, who lived in Beijing in the early 1900s. He called his system the *Yi* (pronounced "ee") *Chuan,* meaning the mind, or the intentionality behind the various systems of Chuan. Wang Xiangzhai was born in 1885 and was sickly in his youth, suffering from asthma and stunted growth. When he was eight years old, his father made him study Xing Yiquan, which emphasizes static and moving postures embodying the healing powers of the five elements. He then traveled around China and studied with some of the best martial artists in the country. Not only did he heal his body, but also he became one of the best martial artists of China.

Wang Xiangzhai said that his skill came from "just standing." His method is called the Yi Chuan, the mind or intention behind the various systems of Chuan. One of Wang Xiangzhai's main influences came from Huang Muqiao, who learned a certain "health dance" that descended from the time of the Sui and Tang dynasties (581–907 C.E.). This health dance was depicted on wall pictures at the archeological site of Dunhuang. Huang reconstructed the techniques and recovered the spirit of the ancient dance. So, we may imagine that Wang Xiangzhai was initiated into some of the deepest methods that descended from the Buddhist *Chuan Fa* traditions (Tomio, 1994; Mayer, 2004). Chuan Fa means the associated arts around the study of "the Chuan." *Chuan* is usually translated as "fist."

Figure 2: Wang Xiangzhai Standing—Holding Ball of Energy

Wang Xiangzhai wrote that Bodhidharma combined the Five Animal Frolics, created in the Han Dynasty (206 B.C.–220 C.E.) by Hua Tuo, one of the first Chinese doctors, with the methods for changing the ligaments (*Ti Jin Jing*) and washing the bone marrow (*Shi Soei Chin*) to create the system of Yi Chuan (also spelled Yi Quan), mind or intention boxing.

I was most interested in the healing dimension of this art; but Master Han and Master Ha explained to me how in Chinese internal martial art tradition the self-cultivation elements of the internal martial arts and the healing attributes of the tradition were all part of the whole. In the next chapter and in the chapters that follow I'll tell you more about how to do the practice and my experience with the tradition as well. But here, I want to tell you more about how the tradition fit into my life journey of being a Reluctant Metaphysician.

I was always interested in the origins of everything. In my professional life I was interested in the origins of psychotherapy. Most of my training had been in Western forms of psychology such as cognitive behavioral, humanistic, and so forth. Sure, lip service was paid in my training to be sensitive to cross-cultural differences when we had patients from another culture. But I wanted to go deeper and I wondered, "Was psychotherapy just a Western phenomena?"[17]

Many of my Buddhist friends and colleagues had found a connection between Buddhism and psychotherapy, but I had not heard of a connection between Tai Chi, Taoism, Standing Meditation, and psychotherapy. In my practice of Standing Meditation I found one of the early roots of a type of holistic, somatic psychotherapy. This took me on a cross-cultural journey to a land that existed long before modern psychotherapy.

I learned that "psychological awareness" and mindfulness practice were a part of the static and moving traditions of postural initiation, such as Tai Chi and Qigong. In my *Secrets to Living Younger* book (2004) I discussed how, according to the research of Tomio (1994) and Goodman (1990), there is a long-lost tradition of postural initiation oriented to facilitate a transformational process.[18] In the Buddhist tradition, according to Tomio (1994), this transformative process occurs when the practitioner's *klesas* (unconscious patterns such as envy, greed, and so forth.) are worked on in the process of holding various postures and engaging in various *natas* (physical exercises which utilized sequences of attack and defense).

So, here I found the roots of an early holistic psychology that involved working on the totality of one's life stance (*sthana*), "the totality of a student's perceived and acknowledged mental stance or concurrent position in regard to their self-understanding…[it] was also a term applied to describe an individual's physical condition and health balance" (Tomio, 1994, p. 221; Diepersloot, 1997).

Tomio in his book, *Bodhisattva Warriors*, puts forth the case that the wider tradition called the Chuan Fa went through a *Diaspora*. However, in its earlier form it included healing, self-defense, spiritual unfoldment, and changing the whole of the practitioner's life stance.

The *nata* practices continued until the time of the Muslim invasions during the Pala Dynasty around 750 A.D. As a result of the invasions, the tradition dispersed and many of its teachers were slain. The subsequent slaughter of Buddhist monks caused many to flee to Southern India, China and elsewhere, and the psycho-spiritual and martial aspects of the Chuan Fa were lost as an initiatory, holistic, bodymind transformational system.

However, those who practice these traditions (such as Tai Chi and Qigong) today oftentimes do so without a conscious appreciation of how the tradition can help to change their life stance. And here is where once again my namesake, Michael, Two Streams Joining, enters center-stage. In three of my books (Mayer, 2004, 2007, 2009), I took it as my purpose to advocate for the value of joining the stream of the Western bodymind healing tradition with the various streams of the Chuan Fa.[19]

From Sifu Ha, and from each of the different masters of Tai Chi Chuan, Qigong, and Standing Meditation that he brought to the United States from China over the next two decades, I went through a gradual process of initiation into a world for which my Western education had not prepared me. Though none of the teachers overtly discussed the healing, psychological or spiritual dimensions of the practice, their teaching styles were perfect for me to get the direct kinesthetic transmission of a tradition that balanced my intellectual approach to life.

For example, after I had been practicing Yi Chuan for ten years, in 1987 Master Ha brought Master Cai Songfang to the United States to train us. Master Cai developed the school of Wuji Standing Meditation, which is related to the Standing Like a Tree style of Qigong. Master Cai was chosen in 1987 as the representative of Guangdong Province to the National Committee on Qigong Research. Many of us who had studied with Sifu Ha for over a decade had a degree of proficiency in using "the ball of our bodies' energy" to neutralize and bounce off the aggressive force of others (*fajing*) as we played "Push Hands" together. However, pushing hands with Master Cai was a humbling experience for us all. I also watched teachers and students of other martial arts traditions test his skill, and bounce off of him as if he was a ball. The amazing thing was that Master Cai was hardly doing anything; he was just standing there. From Master Cai, I learned about the power of stillness. The essence of the spirituality of the tradition was there in name, since *Wuji* means the undifferentiated, the mother of Qi, and the void prior to movement. However, he did not specifically emphasize the wider idea of healing and psycho-spiritual unfoldment, nor did most of the other Standing Meditation Masters with whom I have studied. Their kinesthetic transmission enabled me to find these healing pathways in myself. I learned that each of us has our own contribution to make the tapestry of the internal martial arts tradition. I hope to contribute my thread.

Speaking of each of us having our unique contribution to make to any tradition we practice, another major step on my path into the internal martial arts tradition came when Master Ha introduced his students and me to Master Sam Tam (a Master of Eagle Claw, Yi Chuan Qigong, and Tai Chi Chuan). The awesomeness of his internal martial art abilities was more than I ever could have hoped to find—a gift on my journey that was as great as anything that I could have expected from watching *Kung Fu* Television series starring David Carradine. Master Tam's use of empty force is a wonder to behold (see Chapter 19).

My three decades of training with Master Ha and the masters that he brought to train us have created new seedlings that have branched out in many directions. In the introduction of this book I told you the story of Icanchu and Chuna. To recreate the world after it was destroyed, Icanchu grasped a piece of charcoal, played his tune on it, from whence grew a tree. Then he threw a rock to knock down branches of the world tree from which new sprouts of life grew.

The Icanchu story parallels the creation myth of my life, and each of ours. For me, it took grasping the hard-to-understand territories of oriental worlds of knowledge, singing my tune, and throwing pieces of charcoal at the tree of standard psychotherapy to create (along with my colleagues who are inclined in this direction) a world of psychotherapy that stems from the age-old roots of ancient sacred wisdom traditions. I am thankful to say that some budding new worlds have been created from my efforts in trying to integrate Qigong and Tai Chi with my work as a psychotherapist.[20]

My tutelage with Master Ha led me in 1990 to do a 150-hour certification program in Chinese Health arts at the Acupressure Institute of Berkeley. At first I thought I might like to set up an acupressure practice, due to enjoying giving healing touch to people; instead I found it more in line with my essence to integrate the teaching of acupressure self-touch and Qigong movements with my private practice as a psychologist. I also received training in the animal forms of medical Qigong from Dr. Alex Feng; and from my friend and my brother on the path Taoist scholar Ken Cohen (1997). I integrate the teaching of the Animal Frolics of Hua Tau that I learned from them with my patients, my training groups for psychotherapists, and in my mythic journey process.

I eventually took the gifts of my training with the masters of Qigong with whom I trained for three decades and keynoted the National Qigong Association where I put forth my theory that each Tai Chi and Qigong movement had four levels of purpose: self-healing, spiritual unfoldment, self-defense and changing our life stances psychologically. I also wrote a few books showing how the teachings of these masters could be integrated with Western bodymind healing methods (Mayer, 2004, 2007, 2009). Keeping with my beginning place on the medicine wheel of life, the place where two streams become one, I have done numerous presentations about the joining of the streams of Tai Chi, Qigong, and psychotherapy at conferences, workshops, and hospitals.

Anyone who walks a metaphysical pathway in life will find countless opportunities to see how the world behind the world can add meaning to our everyday lives, regardless of our area of interest. We can each, following the myth of the Old Woman in the Cave, take the unique twist that represents the thread of each of our lives and apply it to our worlds. For example, the meaning of "Chuan" in Tai Chi Chuan, is usually translated to mean "fist" or "the supreme ultimate fist." After I meditated on the metaphysical meaning of the term, I suggested that the esoteric meaning of "Chuan" is "the ability to metaphorically hold the five elements in one's hand—fire, earth, metal, water, and wood" (Mayer, 1996).

Each mythic story and metaphysical insight adds to the way we see and practice a tradition. For example, going back to the story of Icanchu, each of us needs to grasp into our own fists the rock of ages (the hard rocks of life), and throw them at the tree of knowledge. If we throw well and hit the mark, from our knocking up against established rooted traditions and remarkable people, seedlings fall, new branches of the tree of knowledge grow, and new forms of healing may take root.

Jewish Renewal

When I was estranged from my cultural roots, due to a journey to Eastern traditions, two rabbis and a newly emerging Jewish tradition brought me back to renew my connection to my Judaism. The Jewish Renewal Tradition, originated by Rabbis Zalman Schachter-Shalomi and Schlomo Carlebach, was an inspiration for me. For example, the East Coast Judaism to which I had been exposed in my early life had taught me that Yom Kippur was "the day of atonement," the day to atone for one's sins. However, here in the Jewish renewal movement of the early 1970s, I learned that "atonement" could also be seen as a day of "at-one-ment." Dance, song, and creative rituals were used to experience at one-ment with God, in addition to examining the ways that one "missed the mark" in the past year.

To give you a sense of the birthing of the Jewish renewal tradition in the 1970s, on Yom Kippur in the midst of the holiest moments of the Jewish High Holiday ritual, Rabbi Zalman invited a Sufi sheik to do a whirling dervish dance to teach us about the mystical element of God in all traditions. In addition, in traditional Orthodox Judaism women did not hold the Torah, and yet Reb Zalman encouraged women to hold the Torah to their hearts while they spoke their truth to the Torah. Many woman shed deep tears as they expressed how they too had felt estranged from Judaism. Quite a few men and woman came back to their Jewish roots due to these two Rabbis renewing the foundation of Judaism.

Likewise, the writings of Gershon Winkler (2003), and the workshops I did with him, led me to see that Judaism was a Shamanic religion. I gained a deeper appreciation of the religion into which I was born as I camped out in the *sukkah* to help me to remember that my house is a temporary modern convenience, and that the land is my true home. As a long time fan of Spock and *Star Trek,* I was amazed to find out that the hand gesture Spock used when he said, "Be well and prosper," was the hand gesture that the high priest uses on Yom Kippur. On one Yom Kippur, when I was at the Aquarian Minion in the mid-1970s, on the Jewish high holy day of the year those who identify with the path of the high priest are invited to come up to the *binah* (the ritual platform where the Rabbi stands) and bless the congregation, sending out healing energy. The story goes that Leonard Nimoy (Spock) took this spread-fingers gesture from his own Jewish roots as he watched high priest bless the congregation. The high priest used this hand gesture with the *tallis* (the Jewish ritual prayer garment) overstretched over his hands. His thumbs touched the third eye point, and the other four fingers of each hand were spread and divided into two. The priest imagined a river of love flowing from the holy of holies out through his hands, through his parted fingers and out to the congregation. As an avid practitioner of various mudras of traditions of postural initiation, I was amazed that in the Jewish tradition such a powerful mudra existed. I particularly appreciated how in my home Jewish tradition that healing chants and songs accompanied hand gestures like this to amplify the healing intention sent to others.

Speaking of the Jewish traditions and one of the frame stories of this book about the garment of our lives, I found out something interesting about the *kittel*, a thin silken garment that many orthodox Jews wear on the Sabbath and Yom Kippur. The same garment with which one prays on high holidays is often worn when one's physical body is placed in their coffin. Thus, the ritual of at-onement in Orthodox Judaism is to fill oneself and one's garment on Yom Kippur and the Sabbath with the energy of the *Ain Sof,* the undifferentiated source of life, which existed before creation.[21] It is imagined, and prayed upon, that this experience may stay with us in "the next life, in the heavenly spheres." Some Jews prefer to be wrapped in a *tallis* in their coffin. The tallis was reportedly given by God to the Jewish people as a covenant for prayer, and the four fringes have a blue thread which connects with the four archetypal directions (East, West, North, and South) through which one can stay connected with the divine Self in what ever direction a person moves in life. It was heartening to find that in my home religious tradition there are metaphysical practices that help a practitioner to stay connected to the world behind the world.

The Jewish renewal temple that I now go to is called *Chochmat Halev*, meaning "wisdom of the heart." The musical accompaniment at the services that I go to is a sacred cross-cultural joining of musical traditions. The musical background accompanying the chanting of Jewish prayers consists of an incredible ensemble band led by piano player and singer Brian Schachter-Brooks, and many other musicians. They call their approach "avant-kabbalistic ecstatic and contemplative rituals." Different occasions bring different musicians from the community, each masters in their own right. For example, Bruce Silverman, a master drummer and leader of the group the Sons of Orpheus plays in the background at some Chochmat services in the ensemble. Bruce is also a psychotherapist, a former student of mine, and now is a friend. Another musician, Eliyahu Sills is a master flutist who mixes Jewish and Middle Eastern sacred music into riffs that cannot be described as anything less than divinely sourced. There is no hesitation in these rituals of adding music from cross-cultural sources including Muslim, Christian, and Eastern sacred traditions. Even popular American songs are incorporated when they work to lift the spirit, such as Bob Dillon's "Knocking on Heaven's door," which I learned was written to the tune of a Jewish prayer called *Avinu Malchenu*. Those who partake in the rituals of Chochmat's beloved rabbis such as Avram Davis, Sarah Shendelman, and SaraLeya are grateful to be part of such a community (which is not limited to Jewish people) that renews our spirits and souls. From our community, masters of sacred movement choreograph movements to the Jewish prayers so that they are danced and sacred meaning is embodied. The words of the prayer books have been altered to bring forth deep metaphysical meanings such as changing the word "God" to "the source of all creation." So, here I found a temple of fellow travelers who, in attunement with my path of joining streams, were merging the non-denominational streams of sound, movement, and prayerful words to tap into the world behind the world for the purpose of healing and transformation.

The songs that I learned in the Jewish renewal tradition have words and tunes for healing many psychological maladies. For example, during a troubled time when a person feels forsaken there is a chant called, "This too is for the good (*Gam zeh l'tovah*)." Such experiences re-sacralized the East Coast Judaism that I had known in my childhood and brought to my awareness a Judaism I can embrace full heartedly.[22]

One more organization that is bringing back the age-old, earth-based traditions of Judaism is Wilderness Torah (www.wildernesstorah.org). On various holidays they celebrate through camping out in nature, doing group rituals, and weaving together reading, story-telling, songs, music, nature walks, vision questing, and revelation under the stars.

Hana Matt

One remarkable spiritual leader in the Jewish Renewal Movement is Hana Matt. The story of our meeting is a fascinating tale of synchronicity.

One day after Shabbat services at Chochmat Halev I saw a woman staring at me from the distance. She walked up to me and asked if I was Michael Mayer. I asked her how she knew my name. Hana Matt then introduced herself and told me an amazing story about how she had just moved back to Berkeley after living in Jerusalem during the time of the outbreak of the Palestinian *Intifada*.

After the suicide bombings of busses and cafes, many Jewish people felt that nowhere was safe so they stayed at home. On one of Hana's ventures to quickly buy food and get home as quickly as she could, she passed a bookstore where there happened to be just one of my Bodymind Healing Qigong DVD's left. I have no idea how the DVD got there. No store in Israel has ever ordered any of my DVDs; yet perhaps some strange twist of fate destined our worlds to meet. She bought the DVD and started to practice every day the ten sets of the Bodymind Healing Qigong system that I had developed. Hana told me that the practices in the Bodymind Healing Qigong DVD helped her to "create an oasis of tranquility in the midst of the war zone." She shared these Qigong exercises with others in her apartment building; and she told me in this first time me met that the DVD helped many of them to also to find a peace in the midst of stress and worry.

It was an amazing act of SynchroDestiny that we met many years later at Chochmat Halev, and she has now become one of my spiritual sisters. Hana teaches world religious studies at the Chaplaincy Institute and The Graduate Theological Union in Berkeley, California; and she is a Jewish spiritual counselor and ritual leader. Hana told me that the River of Life practice that I developed was very similar to a practice developed by Rabbi Abulafia, a thirteenth century Jewish mystic. He introduced people to a breathing and visualization method whereby the names of God were put into an imaginary river that flowed down their bodies.[23]

Hana also showed me that some elements of the internal martial arts tradition existed in the Jewish tradition, though perhaps with a different intention. I had been practicing Chinese *Pa Kua* for many years. Pa Kua is a method of circle walking that is used in the internal martial arts to deal with a linear attack by countering with circular movements—an apt metaphor for how aggressive strength can be circumvented by a more rounded spiritual approach. One day when I went to one of Hana Matt's group healing rituals I saw her do a group exercise where a person in need of healing was put into the center of a group. Then the group held their right hand out into the center of the circle facing towards the person who needed healing. As the circle of people moved around the person, the other outer left hand of the group members scooped up imagined healing energy from outside the circle and brought it into their hearts. Then the group members focused on the sending that energy to the person in need of healing with their extended right hand. This was almost exactly like the Pa Kua circling hand movements that I had learned in my Pa Kua training. Now here in my genetically endowed Jewish tradition I saw this movement could have another deep purpose—to perform a group healing. Here in the Jewish tradition, while the group circle healing was performed, a chant took place—the words of which are, *ail na rafa na la.* This translates to mean, "God, please bring healing to this person." Being a lover of two streams joining, I was grateful that fate had connected me with Hana so that I could see how my internal martial arts practices could be conjoined with this community healing-circle practice.

It was also synchronistic on one occasion when I was with Hana that she dislocated her knee during a ritual and was in excruciating pain. She did not think she could make it to the car to get medical attention; and I happened to show up just at that moment. So, she put one hand on my shoulder and we slowly walked as we practiced the Qigong Walking Meditation method that she had learned from my DVD. We took steps very slowly and used her trauma to practice—on each step she breathed out the pain as she used the Qigong practice that was an everyday ritual in Israel. We made it to an awaiting car that brought her to the hospital. Now, we look back at this occurrence as a divine synchronicity—that I was there to do Walking Meditation with her at this traumatic time in her life.

Another synchronicity is that Hana Matt is the wife of Danny Matt, a Kabalistic scholar (Matt, 1996, 2003) who is currently working on a multi-decade project in translating The Zohar. The Zohar (meaning splendor or radiance) is one of the foundational works of Jewish mysticism published by a Moses de Leon, who ascribed his work to Shimon bar Yochai, a rabbi of the second century during the Roman persecution. He reportedly hid in a cave for thirteen years studying the Torah.

The reason I am telling you about this now is because of another teaching I learned from Hana that relates to the frame story of this book—the threaded garment. I learned from Hana that in The Zohar there is a concept of a spiritual garment that we all wear that is called the *levusha* (pronounced with the accent on the last syllable "sha").

All of our lives we weave our *levusha*. In Jewish mysticism the levusha is said to be like a hidden veil that contains the essence of who we are, similar to the Eastern concept of our auras. The Jewish mystical tradition teaches that our levusha can also function like a protective veil. It can protect us from the judgments of others.

In addition, the *levusha* can play an important part in mourning rituals. When a loved one dies, at a funeral or memorial service we can invoke five of the divine qualities that our loved one brought to life by telling stories about those essential qualities. These qualities are imagined to be threads in the spiritual garment of our lives—perhaps our loved one's patience, generosity, ability to maintain their cool at moments of stress, wisdom, or compassion.

Part of Hana's work is to go as a spiritual teacher to help those who are mourning the loss of a loved one. She draws from The Zohar's teaching of the *levusha* by inviting the mourner to tell the story of five of their lost one's essential qualities; then the mourner imagines weaving those qualities into their own spiritual garment. The recognition that we will help those divine qualities (that our loved one embodied so well), to continue living can help a mourner to bear the loss, which can feel so final, wrenching, and abrupt. What a gift of a practice for the Reluctant Metaphysician!

To add to this *levusha* practice, following my path of joining two traditional rivers of knowledge and making them become one, I like to add Qigong movements of reeling silk to this Jewish mystical practice. If it feels right to you, try to imagine that you are physically wrapping the threads from your loved ones most treasured qualities around you. With your fingers and thumb drawn together like a bird's beak you can imagine reeling threads from your image of your loved one to your heart and then twirling those essential qualities around you into a garment that will add to your "Coat of Many Colors."

Conclusion: How Should We Approach Meeting a Remarkable Person

> We are like dwarfs on the shoulders of giants,
> so that we can see more than they,
> and things at a greater distance,
> not by virtue of any sharpness of sight on our part,
> or any physical distinction,
> but because we are carried high and
> raised up by their giant size.
>
> —John of Salisbury quoting Bernard of Chartes
> *Metalogicon,* 1159 A.D.

So, in closing, when you meet with remarkable people and traditions, how should you approach such encounters? Each person who we meet, and with whom we feel a strong resonance, and particularly those who we meet through synchronistic circumstances, embodies some essential quality that can be woven into the spiritual garment of our lives. So, to hold these meetings as divine gifts is "the approach of approaches" to meetings with remarkable people and traditions.

In my Tai Chi classes at the end of each class, in front of our hearts we put our closed fist of one hand into the holding embrace of our other hand. Then, the students bow without breaking eye contact and without breaking the connection with the area beneath the occiput—as distinguished from what one would do as a supplicant. In the internal martial arts tradition we show respect without giving away our power.

As we meet others, who are aspects of our selves, it is important to be open to see what we can absorb from their ways of Being. But at the same time, we need to be aware that we each have our unique ways, our own garment in which we are weaving their essential qualities into our own quilt. This has been illustrated in each of the stories I have told; and I send you blessings to do the same in your meetings with remarkable traditions and people. How can you absorb the threads of others ways of being into the unique garment of your life, so that you will fulfill your dharma?

CHAPTER 11:

Practices to Guide Our Lives

And so God says to us, "Make for me a holy place so that I can dwell inside you. Yes, it is possible to stay connected with me at all times in all places, even as you engage in the life of the world.

—Rabbi Shefa Gold
Commentary from the *Old Testament*

Introduction

Parcival's quest for the Grail Cup is one symbol of the hero's mythic call to adventure to heal the Kingdom. But, whether it's "the Blood of Life," or "the Water of Life," finding the moist things of life to restore a dry land is one of the quintessential subjects of cross-cultural mythologies. However, the Garden of Eden where the nourishing fountain, the tree of life, our sacred ground, and the flowing waters that can restore our souls are found—these are not places outside ourselves. The hero's quest leads to an inner treasure, and entails an inner process of discovering. Oftentimes the greatest treasure, the real gold, is discovered through the practices that enrich the soul.

Some of the practices that have been central to my quest have been (1) my variation on The Secret of the Golden Flower practice that I call The River of Life, (2) Standing Meditation, (3) Tai Chi Chuan and Qigong, (4) outward introspection, and (5) as an advocate of creating a blend that is our unique spiritual system, as a good coffee connoisseur creates a family blend, I suggest developing your own your amalgamated metaphysical practice system.

The Secret of the Golden Flower

Microcosmic Orbit Breathing is one of the major practices that has been with me for many years. It is a central part of the practice of the *Secret of the Golden Flower.* I told you earlier how it "saved me" when I had a panic attack on the way to teaching my first class in the early 1970s at Montclair State College. This practice led me a broader quest to find out what this tradition was all about.

When I first picked up this book, *The Secret of the Golden Flower* in Samuel Weiser's bookstore, a few blocks from my apartment in New York City, Weiser's was one of the best-known metaphysical bookstores in the world. It was a place where spiritual seekers stuck in modern city life would go for respite. Like Knights of the Round Table in times long ago who would go on Grail quests, or other seekers would travel to the new world to discover the Fountain of Youth or journey to the East, seekers at Weiser's bookstore would peruse books hoping to find some spiritual treasure map that could lead them to find the Golden Elixir of Life.

I was one of these seekers. Richard Wilhelm's book, *The Secret of the Golden Flower*, captured my interest because in my master's in psychology program at the New School for Social Research in New York, I resonated with the philosophy and psychology of C. G. Jung, and he had written a commentary on this book. (Over three decades later I later learned from some of my friends at the Jung Institute of San Francisco that Dr. Jung was so impressed by this book that he stopped his work on his now famous, previously unknown, *Red Book* to study the Taoist Alchemy that was spoken of in this book.)

How could a spiritual practice be associated with "prolonging or creating eternal life?" This sounded pretty flakey to me when I heard about this back in the 1970s, long before it was common to see research about the correlation between stress reduction methods and longevity. Also, it was difficult for the Western mind to digest strange prescriptions in this book about how, in following "the secret wonder of the Way...something develops out of nothing" (Wilhelm, 1931). I knew Western math, and every math student knows that "0" times any number is still "0." So, I thought to myself when I read about this while in my master's program in psychology, "How could something come out of 0?" Jung in his commentary even proposed that these practices could be helpful in making a *temenos,* an enclosing circle, that could help one from having unwanted complexes from taking over their psyche. I sarcastically said to myself at this time, that, if true, this could save me spending money on my graduate psychology education.

But the book, with Dr. Jung's recommendation, titillated my interest in practicing this method and in researching the wider context in which this method was embedded. I discovered that this wider tradition was called Taoist Alchemy, and while still in New York I read two of Charles Luk's books called *Taoist Yoga: Alchemy and Immortality* (1970) and *The Secrets of Chinese Meditation* (1964), which were dedicated to the memory of C. G. Jung. I was fascinated when I read about the secret internal cultivation methods that took place in various Taoist monasteries.

So, when the TV series *Kung Fu* came on the air I was fascinated to see a depiction of training in a Taoist temple. Though I must admit having seen every episode of the *Kung Fu* series about three times, I learned through scholarly research that the practice of the Golden Flower opens to many awesome experiences that the TV versions barely touches upon. I later learned that this tradition can reveal many treasures that go beyond the fictionalized adventures of the Old West character played by David Carradine; and I discovered that the Taoist Temple into which Kwai Chang Caine (David Carradine) was initiated was modeled after an actual temple, the temple of Huashan, the legendary training ground for Taoist monks.

When I moved to California, I found out that the method of the Golden Flower was embedded in the larger Chinese tradition of Qigong, and the internal martial arts. These arts were one of the treasures I discovered on my quest to the West to restore my "kingdom."

Over time, from my own practice, and with students and patients over the years, I discovered that doing these practice can induce the experience of being a golden flower: feeling truly golden, of enormous value, radiant, loving, precious, blooming, warm, soft, and merged with all of the rest of nature.[1]

Later, from my background as a hypnotherapist I learned that the Golden Flower practice is like a hypnotic induction. But it is much more than this term usually implies. The Golden Flower is an experiential path that opens the practitioner to many other pathways. Doing the practice of the Golden Flower involves doing a breathing method; but it also involves experiencing the wider tradition of Qigong (*dao yin*) in which *The Secret...is* embedded. For example, according to the text (Wilhelm, 1931) doing the practice leads to an experience of not only the Golden Flower, but also of the Golden Elixir, the Golden Ball, or the Golden Bell.

All these names allude to different aspects of a state-specific state of consciousness. Though this state is activated through Taoist microcosmic orbit breathing and certain visualization methods, there are many other parts to the practice. For example, as the text explains, the initiate learns to "sink the plumb line." Through this practice, practitioners discover a secret place to focus their eyes, which allows the energy (qi) to sink to our bellies (*tan tien,* also spelled *dan tien*). An inner sanctum is found by looking in the direction along the nose line, where the eye's awareness goes naturally as we are focusing on how we are feeling.

I wonder if you too will actually have the imaginal experience of light circulating in the body and the felt sense of heat activating? There are now many studies in Qigong research that show that experiences like this take place. By the way, take caution in doing these practices. They are best done with an experienced teacher; and they are best to not be done obsessively or excessively.[2]

It is always interesting to see how one's life path leads to crossing the path of others who share similar interests. Coincidentally, Dr. Beverly Rubik, a biochemist with a degree from University of California Berkeley, and one of the foremost researchers of bio-photon energy, works at the medical clinic that I co-founded. Dr. Rubik has received grants from the National Institute of Health to research her interests in various aspects of the energy in the human body (Rubik, 2002). What an interesting twist of fate that I work in an integrative medical clinic where one of the foremost researchers on bio-photon energy works. Bio-photon energy is one of the modern ways of conceptualizing what occurs when a person practices the Taoist Alchemy method of the Golden Flower.

When I was first doing these practices in New York in the 1970s, "energy" was a forbidden word in traditional academic psychology, and Qigong was almost unknown in the West. We now know that the "circulation of light" and "circulation of heat," in the bodymind arise from such practices because both are aspects of the activation of energy (qi), which can be created from these practices (Rubik, 2002; Oschman, 2000; Liu, 2010).

The Quest to Bring the Qigong Perspective into the Jungian Community

Much later in my career, I wanted to bring to the Jungian community the under-standing that had come from my quest to explore the wider context of the system in which *The Secret of the Golden Flower* was embedded. However, I discovered that many in this community were more interested the intellectual and symbolic aspect of the golden flower rather than the experiential components of the breathing and the Qigong and *daoyin* practices. So unfortunately, my efforts to return the favor that I received from Jung's com-mentary on *The Golden Flower* by doing presentations in that community has thus far fallen on unfertile soil.[3]

But, back to the story at hand.... There are many other dimensions of meaning that come from the practice of bringing attention to the space after the exhalation. For ex-ample, in terms of Chinese medicine and Qigong this "turning of the light around" has connections to the central channel meridians (conception and governing vessels); and there are healing implications to activating these major meridians in Chinese medicine. In this light, I believe that this practice has implications for furthering the Jungian idea of individuation, in that it becomes a way for an individual to experience his or her "dot of consciousness" alive in the Sea of Elixir. This sea is somewhat analogous to the Jung-ian collective unconscious, the birthplace of the energy potentials that Jung calls "arche-types," and through the Golden Flower practice one can experience his or her archetypal stance as part of a wider whole. An important Jungian idea is finding the ego-Self axis, as we experience our roles within a wider sea of archetypal energy potentials in everyday life.

One of the meanings of "immortality" in the *Golden Flower* text is the Taoist Al-chemy belief and practice of keeping one's individual consciousness intact after death. I don't have first hand knowledge of the reality of this yet; but if you have a loved one who practices this method maybe you can make an agreement with them to tell you from the afterlife about whether the practice works—and please Cc me on the communication. ☺ Astrological metaphysics is related here, and it can join the streams of Chinese and Jung-ian traditions. From an integral cross-tradition perspective, the practice of microcosmic orbit breathing can open an experience of feeling one's unique astrological chart constel-lation in the midst of the Sea of Elixir. The concept of finding our unique identity in the sea of a wider cosmos is related to the "ideity field" that Dane Rudhyar talks about in his book *The Planetarization of Consciousness* (1970). The concept of the *ideity field* was his way of speaking of the astrological ego-Self axis. Rudhyar's concept of the ideity field is an interesting way to linguistically express how "I" is connected to a "deity" (God) field of cosmic proportions.

I believe Qigong can add in other ways to my Jungian colleagues' views about the text of the *Golden Flower.* For example, Dr. John Beebe (2006) speaks of the petals of the Golden Flower as being related to the eight functions of consciousness of psychological types. Each different lens creates its own reality, and since symbols are expansive in nature and can mean many different things to different people. So, the lens of Qigong opens experiential dimensions of the Golden Flower practice that the Jungian perspective does not adequately capture.

In Qigong, a practitioner experiences a centering of themselves through various practices based upon on the eight directions. These practices have implications for healing, spiritual unfoldment, self-defense, and changing one's life stance, i.e., individuating in these spheres of life. For example, when an initiate practices microcosmic orbit breath along with Tai Chi Chuan's roll back movement, and does these movements to the eight directions, the practitioner imagines drawing in various qualities from the eight directions. A centering can occur with respect to these qualities. Thus, when a Tai Chi practitioner does the movement Roll Back to the southern direction (which represents warm heartedness) at a time that he or she is feeling closed off from others, a felt shift in becoming more warmly open may occur. This is symbolic process embodied, and in my humble opinion is a next step on path on the Jungian path of the psychoid activation of archetypes.[4]

Each of us, as travelers on the path of life, can take the traditions that are meaningful to us and add our contribution. In doing so we join mythic creation goddess—the Old Woman in the Cave—and her Black Dog. We unravel the fabric of current woven traditions, and then we reweave its threads adding our unique twist. And so, over the years I took the practices in microcosmic orbit breathing and developed it into a process I call The River of Life.

The River of Life

In 1978 I became a licensed Marriage and Family therapist, and in 1986 I became a licensed psychologist. My specialty became integrating ancient sacred wisdom traditions with modern psychotherapy, and microcosmic orbit breathing method was one the practices I introduced to my students, patients, and colleagues. One challenge I had was to translate the cross-cultural esoteric practices, which had been important to me, to my patients who were often more traditional in their backgrounds. So, instead of referring to the Taoist practice of microcosmic orbit breathing to move qi up and down the central meridians of the body, over time I adapted the method into a combined visualization and breathing method for my patients.

STEP 1: USING CIRCULAR BREATHING TO FIND THE RIVER OF YOUR LIFE:

As your breath comes in, imagine it rising up your back. It rises all the way to the sky. Then as you exhale, feel the breath going down the front of your body. Notice how your exhalation gets longer and longer and deeper and deeper the longer that you are aware of your breath. Do not try to force your breath to go deeper. Then imagine that this out-breath is a river that is traveling down the front of your body. The longer and deeper your breath is, the longer and deeper your inner river becomes. Focus on the pause at the end of your exhalation, as it brings you to an inner peaceful pool, slightly below your belly. After that pause by your inner peacefulpool, the river continues to flow down to the ocean beneath your feet. Then the breath rises again for another cycle up your back.

STEP 2: USING THE BREATH TO CONSTELLATE BODYMIND BLOCKAGES:

Your life has been a journey down a river that came from the mountains, and it will eventually reach the sea. Right now on your life's journey there may be some issue that is constricting or blocking the flow of the river of your life. On the next downward cycle of your breathing, notice where the river does not flow smoothly in your body and allow an image to arise that represents a block in that place on the river of your life energy. Maybe the encumbrance feels like a boulder or an ice block.

STEP 3: TRANSMUTING BODYMIND BLOCKAGES:

As you sense any block in the river of energy, focus (Gendlin, 1978) on that body sense and allow a word, image, or phrase to emerge from it as you ask yourself, "What is this all about?" Do not try to think of an answer...allow a response to rise to the surface as if something stuck was being shaken loose from the bottom of a riverbed. Then "resonate" that word, image, or phrase back to the body sense to see if it gets the crux of what that block is about. Once you hit the bull's-eye of meaning, you will often notice a felt shift occur...perhaps a sighing breath may release as a sign that you have found the felt meaning of that blockage.

This type of breathing and imagination method became a center post of the Bodymind Healing Psychotherapy I developed. The River of Life process can help with healing a variety of psychological and physical issues such as insomnia, anxiety, chronic pain, and trauma (Mayer, 2007, 2009). The River of Life includes a transcendent dimension where a person can activate an altered state of consciousness by finding the experience of "the sea of elixir" at the end of their out-breath. As well, the River of Life has the ability to help a person work through (transmute) psychological issues through 'Focusing' on the body; and then when locating a block in the stream of one's felt experience the person adds a process of cognitive restructuring (Beck, 1979). Cognitive restructuring involves identifying a limiting belief and giving a number (Subjective Units of Distress Scale from 0 to 10) to the feeling that goes along with that belief, and then finding a more true or constructive belief and giving a S.U.D.S. number to that feeling. So, this method is a body-oriented way of transmuting a life issue so that the experience of the stream of life energy flows again.[5]

Once again, my childhood medicine name of Michael, Two Streams Joining pops up in joining these streams of Taoist practice and psychotherapy.

Experiential Dimensions of the Golden Flower Practice: How Taoist Saliva Swallowing Saved My Life in the Desert in Israel

The practices of microcosmic orbit breathing and the River of Life are not just interesting spiritual or psychological practices; and they are not just useful relaxation methods which helped to save me from my panic attack when I forgot my notes in that first teaching position at Montclair State College in New Jersey. When I read Charles Luk's (1964) interpretation of microcosmic orbit breathing in the early 1970s I could not have known that this breathing method would save my life in the year 2000.

In Charles Luk's book, *Secrets of Chinese Meditation*, he advises that the practitioner should move their tongue around their mouth many times creating a sea of saliva; then the practitioner exhales while saliva is swallowed and the eyes look downward. These actions "sink the plumb line," which involves creating a line of awareness from the eyes to the belly (*tan tien*), and "sinks the qi to the tan tien." A further dimension is to imagine that the moisture that is created circles around the microcosmic orbit during the next cycle of inhalation up the back (governing vessel) and down the front of the body (conception vessel).

When I first read about this in the early 1970s I thought that this was an interesting metaphysical practice of joining fire and water: but one day it became much more than this. In the year 2000, I had just finished teaching a workshop at Ein Gedi Kibbutz in the desert in Israel, and I was happy to be able take a day off for a nice hike up to the famous Ein Gedi waterfall. I climbed down a mountainside on a day that was well over 100 degrees in mid-morning and set out on my journey to the place where King David saw Bathsheba bathing. It was one of the more incredible experiences of my life to stand under the waterfall there after my long hike and have the water beat on my head. Not only was it a refreshing relief for my overheated body, but also it was an amazing experience after I stepped out of the waterfall. I felt like the top of my head was opened in a way that reminded me of the open channel of light that I felt coming from the Land where the Sun Rose in the West in my earlier dream. I reflected upon how it had been a long journey in my life to this point, and how here in the land of my forefathers I felt the energetic connection through this channel coming from the top of my head to my spiritual mother and father as I did in that "big dream" that I had on the summer solstice of 1971.

But coming back to reality, I looked up the mountain that I had just come down and realized, due to the terrain and lack of markings, that I couldn't go back the same way.

So, I decided to hike around the mountain back to the Kibbutz. One lone passing hiker told me that it was one hundred and fourteen degrees. Before leaving the river I had filled up my water bottle, but now it was almost empty—and there was no one around. The highway was quite a distance ahead and I was suffering the dry mouth and dizziness of heat exhaustion.

Fortunately, during that walk I remembered the Taoist saliva swallowing method, which gave water to my internal wilted Golden Flower as I practiced this method for the rest of my walk and while hiking on the highway. Initially no one picked me up (I later found out that there had been some recent Palestinian terror attacks in the area), and people were warned not to pick up hitchhikers. Luckily one of my students from Ein Gedi, who happened to be driving on the highway, recognized me and picked me up. The Taoist saliva swallowing method was partially responsible for saving my life, in addition to the car ride from this kind soul.

Standing Meditation Qigong

Many Chinese call Standing Meditation "the million dollar secret of Qigong."
Whether you are practicing Qigong for self-healing,
for building healing Qi, for massage or healing work on others,
Standing is an essential practice.
Acupuncturists feel that by practicing Standing Meditation
they can connect with the qi of the universe,
and be able to send it through their bodies
when they hold the acupuncture needle...
Standing is probably the single most important Qigong exercise.
One of the reasons that Standing is such a powerful way
to gather and accumulate fresh qi in the body
is that during the practice of Standing
the body is in the optimal posture for qi gathering and flow.

—Ken Cohen
The Way of Qigong

When I picked up the book *The Secret of the Golden Flower* in the early 1970s and went on a quest to find out the wider parameters of this tradition I discovered that this Taoist Alchemy practice was actually part of a larger tradition. This tradition is called Qigong, which is a Chinese medical, spiritual, and internal martial art tradition that is focused on cultivating the energy of life through posture, breath, intention, movements, touch, sound, and imagery. There are many systems of Qigong, including medical Qigong, animal forms of Qigong, Taoist Alchemy (of which the Secret of the Golden Flower is one example), and so forth.

But ask any Qigong master and they will tell you that the million dollar secret of Qigong is Standing Meditation.

Standing Meditation Qigong:
A Relatively Unknown Buddhist Path to Enlightenment

In the last chapter, I told you about how I learned Standing Meditation from Sifu Ha and three other masters to whom he introduced his students for our further training. I learned from these masters that Standing Meditation is a form of meditation, a system of Qigong, and a way to cultivate qi (defined as the energy of life).

It was interesting to me that almost none of my friends and colleagues in the spiritual movement of integrating East and West had heard of Standing Meditation...nor did they practice it. This is in spite of the fact that the Buddha said that there were four noble postures through which one could discover enlightenment: Lying, Sitting, Standing, and Walking. Many spiritual practitioners know about Sitting Meditation (Zazen, Vipassana, and so forth.) and Lying Down Meditation (such as practiced in yoga); but the practice of Standing is less known as a base for cultivating the human spirit and the light that mystics say is to be found within he human being.

When I had practiced Mindfulness Meditation at various Buddhist Vipassana meditation retreats, it had indeed been a great gift. It helped me to find a deeper center of awareness amidst the thoughts, feelings, sensations, and chaos of life. So, I was glad to see the adaptation of Mindfulness Meditation into various psychotherapy approaches such as Dialectical Behavioral Therapy (DBT). When I discussed the Mindfulness tradition with those who practiced these Buddhist mindfulness meditation methods, most people say that it brings them to a center of awareness in the area around their third eye chakra. This is because attention is placed on "watching" their thoughts, feelings, and sensations. On the other hand, over time I was to discover that when I practiced Standing Meditation Qigong, the awareness center that was activated was the energy of universe itself, the mother of qi (*Wuji*)...and I later learned that this energy center could be called the Golden Ball.[6]

I felt that one of my dharmic purposes as a Reluctant Metaphysician was to introduce to the public and to my colleagues the Standing Meditation Qigong practices that I had learned. Each different style of mediation has its own important psychological, healing, and metaphysical implications for which centers of awareness are activated. I wonder which energy centers of awareness you will open as you do this practice, and how they might be different than other styles of mediation that you practice?

At the beginning of my life's journey, as a child, I experienced energetic streaming sensations when I assumed various postures as I was going to sleep. However, a lifetime of intellectual pursuits (and a college and graduate school education) had cut me off from this awareness so that I had my doubts about the ability to feel and focus energy. In the early years of my doctoral psychology program (before meeting Master Ha), I thought that such energy experiences were just a "head trip." I wondered if such sensations were just blood flowing, and I wanted to see research to validate such claims.

Certain research studies helped to open my mind. For example, Dr. Basmajian, a physician and scientist, published an article in *Science Magazine* provided evidence that human beings could learn to voluntarily control a single cell. When very small electrodes that could measure electrical activity of a cell were inserted into a motor nerve cell, and auditory feedback was given to the person when that cell would fire, the person could quickly learn to fire it at will (Basmajian, 1963; Achterberg, 1985, p.199).[7]

The experience of this streaming energy once again opened when I was introduced the Wuji and Yi Chuan Standing Meditation traditions. I discovered that this "long-standing" Qigong tradition practiced the cultivation of energetic streaming (qi) by using the mind and intention (yi). I learned that through integrating breath and awareness that these energetic streaming sensations could be directed to various parts of the body for self-healing. Most importantly, I discovered that virtually anyone could cultivate this awareness through a set of practices—the most important starting point of the training was Standing Meditation Qigong.

Since I like to think of myself as an intellectually open and explorative person, I must reluctantly admit that it first took some time to "prove" the reality of qi and its healing effects to my mind, and then to my body, before I could accept the reality of these practices.

Practicing Standing Meditation and the Tree of Life

Figure 3: Wuji Standing Meditation

Standing Like a Tree

...for Man is a tree of the field.

—Deuteronomy 20:19

Keep both feet parallel, pointing straight forward, about a hip and a shoulder's width apart. The knees are unlocked, approaching being over the toes. The pelvis is slightly turned forward as if you were getting ready to sit down on a stool. The lower back is slightly pushed out so that the lumbar curve begins to disappear, allowing the lower back to approach being straight. The chest and shoulders are relaxed, causing a slight rounding of the upper back. Imagine there is a cord descending from a star attached to the top of your head so that you are like a puppet dangling from the heavens. Your chin is slightly tucked. Your arms hang loosely at your sides. The tongue is touching the top of the palate just behind the teeth. The eyes can be open in a soft gaze—half open or closed. Notice the natural flow of your breath. Pay attention to how long and deep your breath is, without trying to force it to be calm. Be aware of any sensations or thoughts that emerge during this practice, while continually returning to your breath.

As you stand, feel the way your spine makes a connection between the heavens above and the earth below. After a number of breaths, imagine yourself as a tree with deep roots. Let your exhalation slowly descend down into your roots. What are you rooted into in your life—family, friends, loved ones, and spiritual traditions?

Figure 4: The Circle That Arises from Stillness:

Let an image arise of what this root system is like. On your inhalation, imagine drawing in from those roots to strengthen your trunk. Then on your next inhalation, allow the qi to rise up to your branches, reach out for the light, and transform that light into energy as you imagine giving your fruit to others.

Figure 5: Puppet Dangling from Heaven

After standing for a while there is another part of the training in Standing Meditation that is vital to prevent stagnation of your life energy (qi). Since trees are not rigid nor are we—allow circles to emerge from your stillness by moving your weight fifty-one percent over your right heel, then over your right toes, then over your left toes, and then over your left heel. Imagine a snake or a vine spiraling up the tree, bringing the energy of the earth up and around the tree of your spine to the heavens. Stay in stillness for most of the time—practicing the Circle That Arises from Stillness occasionally and then returning to stillness.

If you practice this method of Standing Meditation and Finding the Circle that Arises from Stillness, you many find that these are quintessential practices for finding the bliss of Stillness, and for circulating the qi. I also discovered that the practice could bring up psychological and physical issues that block the qi, and that by standing in various fixed postures a pattern of alchemical transformation can be initiated that over time dissolves chronic body blockages. During this process, tingling, vibrating, shaking, and sensations of asymmetry may occur as blocks in the rivers of qi shake loose. Do not be alarmed, just breathe through these sensations, practice the Circle That Arises from Stillness, or take a break and come back to the practice when you are ready. All these qi activation signs are ways that the qi is healing old areas of blockage. Eventually this method may lead you to experience the Sea of Elixir—an experience of dissolving into that sea of cosmic bliss (altered state of consciousness).[8]

In the book, the *Secret of the Golden Flower,* it is said that the practices lead to an experience of the Golden Flower and also of the Golden Ball (Wilhelm, 1962, p. 23). It was fascinating that the same metaphor of the Golden Ball that was in this text was in the practices that I had been learning in the Yi Chuan Qigong tradition. Here are two of those postures, and the way I brought visualization practices to the tradition.[9]

Figure 6: Holding Golden Balls in the Waters of Life

While using the same stance as in the above Standing Meditation, allow your wrists to rise and then, palm down, descend down to the belly area (tan tien). Then imagine that you are standing in a slowly moving river, your palms are slightly compressing two balls down into the water with just enough pressure so that they are steadied from floating downstream. The energy in your feet sinks down into the streambed, and your knees bend just so much that you take root, which prevents the river from moving you downstream. Stand in this posture for as long as is comfortable (initially 2–4 minutes). If it starts to feel difficult, listen to your body, allow another few exhalations, and return back to Wuji Standing Meditation Posture 1 to refill your qi bank account.

Bodymind Healing Purpose: This stance comes from Yi (intention) Chuan (fist, or ability to hold the power of the five elements in your fist) Qigong. One way to use your intention while you are Holding Golden Balls is to imagine that you are sending healing energy from your palms (*Lao Gung* points) to some part of the earth that is in need of healing. Imagine that you are sending energy there on your exhalation, and replenishing yourself on the inhalation. This is a favored practice of body workers, acupuncturists (who use the posture to focus their intention on sending energy through the needles), and for healers in general. This posture is also a favored stance for developing *fongsung gong*—the Chinese term for relaxed alertness. In the West we have separate terms for "relaxation" and "alertness," but just like the Eskimos have differentiated many names for snow, the Chinese have many names for energy. This state of *fongsung gong* can be seen in cats when they appear simultaneously very relaxed, yet ready to pounce.

Figure 7: Developing the Golden Ball of the Heart and the Sphere of the Self

One of the key postures in the Yi Chuan tradition is Holding the Golden Ball of the Heart. Developing the Golden Ball of the Heart is useful in developing our heartfelt feelings while alone or with another. Scientific research supports the fact that the heart generates electrical and magnetic energy throughout the body. The magnetic field of the heart is about 5,000 times stronger than that of the brain (Church, 2007, p. 114). The heart's energy impulse travels through the body fluids faster than the nerves, and can create coherence between itself and the brain.

Start in the Standing Meditation posture, but allow the arms to rise up in front of and facing the heart, as if they are embracing a balloon. Elbows are out to the sides of the body and lower than the wrists—this helps the shoulders to relax. The wrists and forearms are slightly turned outward, embodying a posture that looks like holding a ball of liquid that is spilling out from the heart. After the posture has been maintained for a long enough time to build up qi, you imagine that the energy is spilling out and over your outstretched hands to a loved one. The breath coincides with the visualization—as you breath out you imagine giving energy to the world or a loved one, on the inhalation you replenish yourself with the energy around you. Remember to do a not forced long-breath. After a short amount of time this visualization becomes much more than that. Can you feel energy flowing out from the heart and the whole body as if you are the sun shining light on the world?

These practices are center-posts of the Bodymind Healing Qigong tradition that I developed over the last thirty years from having had the good fortune to train with some of the most respected Qigong masters of the Standing Meditation tradition. These stances stemming from ancient traditions of postural initiation have the ability to help us find our center in the midst of the impinging forces of life (Mayer, 2004). They are practices meant to cultivate the ability to roll with life in the midst of being assaulted by cross currents.[10] However, I believe that in order to really center ourselves in life, the Western psychological component is equally important. Emphasizing the importance of joining these streams was to become my life stance.

The Taoist Practice of Cultivating the Golden Ball

Perhaps it was the connection with my early power spot in nature, the place where two streams joined, that gave me the strength to present this integrative spirituality to my colleagues. Or, maybe I should give credit to the *Secret of the Golden Flower* book in Weiser's bookstore that I had brought from New York to California in my Volkswagen bus.

As I practiced Qigong in California, I thought back on how Chinese scholar Richard Wilhelm's book first introduced me to the concept of the Golden Ball. After extensive research in rare Taoist texts such as the *Book of the Yellow Castle,* he claimed to have discovered ancient practices for "cultivating golden light in the body." In Wilhelm's book it says, "The Golden Flower is the Elixir of Life *(Chin-tan)"*—in Chinese, *Chin-tan,* literally translates as "golden ball, golden pill" (Wilhelm, 1963, p. 23).

In esoteric traditions, this transmutation of the human body into a Golden Ball of light is spoken of as discovering the "luminous energy body;" and modern scientific research does confirm the our very cells are composed of photons, the light in our very cells (Rubik, 2002).

Had I stumbled upon "the grail cup" that I had been searching for these many years? Was the human body the container for the waters of life and the secret to be found in "doing nothing," just standing there?

As I practiced this method, over time I grew to realize that this experience is really not so special or esoteric. Most diligent students who practice for a while will experience this luminous energy, and will have different ways of describing the felt experience. Some will use terms like "light," while others may describe the feeling as one of being like a bubble in the sea of eternity—and when doing the practice, the bubble (that is each of our lives) dissolves into *Wuji* (the mother of qi).

The question is, how does one find the light switch, or turn on the faucet? Early in my Qigong training when I asked Master Ha how to find this light switch he said that it is found by not looking for it. So, I just stood; and eventually I began to understand what was meant in *The Secret of the Golden Flower* when it is said that something comes out of nothing" (Wilhelm, 1963).

Now that I have practiced this tradition for many decades, I can better appreciate the quotes by the grandmaster of the tradition Wang Xiangzhai, "When I stand, the universe is in my mind," and "Standing Meditation is doing nothing and finding contentment while being 'a-light'" (double entendre intended).

The Lost Golden Ball of Western Fairy Tales: Is Standing Meditation Qigong a Path to Discovering the Lost Golden Ball of Energy?

In my exploration of the cross-cultural parallels to the Chinese tradition in which I was being trained, I discovered that the symbol of the "golden ball" was not just in Chinese esoteric texts. In the 1980s and early 1990s the "men's movement" was at its height. One of the major leaders of this movement was Robert Bly, who wrote one of the best-selling books of this year, *Iron John*. He adapted the story from the famous fairy tale, *Iron Hans*, written by the Grimm's Brothers, which tells the tale of the King's son who loses his golden ball when it rolls into the cage of the wild man. In the men's movement of the 1990s, the loss of the golden ball became a symbol for Western man's loss of connection with his instincts due to a variety of factors, including: a lack of male initiation rituals, being overly civilized and overly feminized, and living in an industrialized society where the father was not present. In this tale, the King's son got back the golden ball when he gave the wild man the key to his cage. Then the King's son left the castle and was initiated by the wild man. As one part of his initiation, he dipped his hair and finger into the wild man's pond and they turned to gold. In another version of the Grimm's Brothers' tale, in the story of the "Frog Princess," the golden ball is lost in a well.

There was much discussion in the men's movement about the question, "What was this Golden Ball, referred to in mythic and esoteric traditions?" Robert Bly interprets the lost golden ball as the unity of personality that we had as children, a kind of radiance or wholeness, before we split into male and female, rich and poor, bad and good.

I believe that not only can a deeper wholeness be found by following the golden ball into the Western forests with the Western wild man; a transformative initiatory process can also be found by leaving our familiar Western ways and following the rolling ball to the East. The golden ball can be found through the cultivation methods of Eastern Standing and Moving Meditation Qigong traditions. Hopefully, by following these practices of the Reluctant Metaphysician, the King's son in you, will experience how Standing and Moving Meditation Qigong are keys that open the cage in the King's court where the Golden Ball of energy lies locked away.[11]

As many of my students have experienced, the Eastern pond that contains these practices can lead to an experience of a golden glow as the King's son did when his finger and hair turned to gold. Whether or not we want to side with the sceptic who calls this "nothing but a hypnotic induction,"[12] there is a felt experience of an inner radiance that can be evoked through this practice.[13]

Dispersing Stagnant Qi and The Golden Flower

I learned that after doing practices involving energy cultivation with Standing Meditation and the Golden Ball there is another corollary step. It is important to disperse any stagnant qi that is accumulated in the meridians, after qi is built up through the process of Standing Meditation.

One of the first practices for dispersing stagnant qi in my Bodymind Healing Qigong system involves putting your hands above your head with the palms facing the top of the head. Then the practitioner imagines that he or she is like a Golden Lotus Flower.

A Practice for Cultivating the Golden Flower

Figure 8: Dispersing Stagnant Qi Posture

So, three decades after seeing that old musty book in Samuel Weiser's bookstore, these Golden Ball practices are now a central part of the healing system I have devel-

177

oped. However, I have moved from just the stillness practices of the cultivation of the Golden Ball to ones that involve movement. Also, I have brought my love of making meaning through storytelling to those things that I touch. Perhaps the golden pond of the wild-man that the King's son touched is the ability to make anything golden through touching it with meaning. For me, this is symbolized well by the stated meaning of the Sabian symbol of my 25-degree Libra rising degree, "The ability to see the transcendent cosmic meaning in every experience" (Rudhyar. 1973).

Taoist Alchemy and Returning to the Origin of Things

I was continuing to learn more about the idea that "the Secret wonder of the Way is how something develops out of nothing" as I delved into practice of Taoist Alchemy, and the wider tradition of Qigong and Tai Chi in which it is embedded. I learned that in esoteric training traditions, before beginning the movements of Tai Chi Chuan, a person first practices Standing Meditation…and doing "no-thing."

By beginning in stillness the practitioner embodies classic Taoist cosmology. He or she experiences how energy comes from the void (called *Wuji,* or the mother of qi), and how the movement of opposites (yin and yang), is born from non-movement. In the *Secret of Golden Flower* it says, "Whoever seeks eternal life must search for the place whence human life and nature originally sprang." And in Mircea Eliade's books he also speaks of the central notion of cross-cultural healing traditions that "healing derives from returning to the origin of things" (Eliade, 1963b, pp. 14–38). These sources, and my own experience, influenced my making the importance of stillness and a return to primordial origins to be central aspects of the Bodymind Healing Psychotherapy and Bodymind Healing Qigong traditions I was to develop.

Standing Meditation, the River of Life, and Scuba Diving:
Opening of the Taoist Door to the Sea of Elixir

Whatever different spiritual paths we choose, they are apt to join together in various terrains of our lives. In December of 1986 I took a vacation to an Island next to Tahiti, called Morea. (It is interesting that Moira means fate, one of the subjects of this book.) One day, while in the process of getting a certification in scuba diving at Club Med in Morea, I was wearing just that right amount of weight on my belt that allowed me to float freely, fifty feet or so beneath the surface of the water. Like other scuba divers who find this comfortable position of "standing in the water," my arms floated freely with no tension—every joint in my body loosened as I became one with the water from whence we all came. As I breathed in, my lungs inflated like a balloon and I started to rise in the water…five, ten, fifteen feet. Since I was next to an underground mountain, it was as if I was rising up the mountain with the inhalation. As I breathed out and my lungs deflated, I sank…five, ten, fifteen feet, down the mountain.

Then I remembered the old Taoist texts that reported that the practice of Qigong leads to the experience of becoming lighter as we breathe in, as if we are rising up to the heavens. And, it is said that on our exhalation, a practitioner of Qigong becomes heavy as the qi becomes compacted, as if sinking down to the bottom of a mountain. This is amazingly similar to the experience of scuba diving—but the early Taoists didn't have scuba diving equipment!

After getting out of the water and lying in bed that night, I had a strange experience. I felt like I was floating up to the ceiling as I inhaled, and my consciousness descended down beneath my body as I exhaled. (This is much like the common experience after skiing, of driving a car down a hill and feeling as if we are still skiing.) Later, I realized that a similar experience could occur while practicing Standing Meditation, through the power of the mind to visualize being in water.

But, we do not need to scuba dive to raise the spirit and sink the qi. If we find the correct Wuji Standing position, and imagine that we are in water, on our inhalation we can feel ourselves rising up toward the heavens, and on our exhalation we can feel ourselves coming down to ground us on the earth. The air alchemically transforms into water, and we can experience a return to our primordial nature as "Beings of Light" floating freely in space. We find contentment in being "alight," just as Grandmaster Wang Xiangzhai, the grandmaster of the Yi Chuan Standing Meditation Qigong tradition says.

So, in Morea I got a taste of what the early Taoists allude to when they say that the practice of Qigong leads to *Wuji* (the mother of qi, the void, the undifferentiated wholeness of life before any opposites exist), "the sea of elixir," or "the elixir of immortality." While on this vacation a major step forward took place on my Grail Quest for the Waters of Life that had began in Samuel Weiser's bookstore. There I had read about how the practice of microcosmic orbit breathing led to the "sea of elixir." In Morea I was swimming in it.

I had read in many old texts that this state is like experiencing the bliss of returning to the fetal state, young again, floating without concerns in the amniotic fluid of our mothers' womb. In the West, this quest for "the elixir" was literalized into a search for an external substance that would make one eternally young. Many early European explorers, such as Ponce de Leon, spent their lives and resources looking in the outside world for "the fountain of youth;" what I experienced while practicing Standing Meditation while scuba diving was an internal energized state of merging with the wider whole of which we are all a part. This experience felt like the experience that I had read about in various alchemical texts, which was called by many names such as *"unus mundus"* or "oceanic consciousness." Fortunately, I was not inflated enough to think that this would literally mean that I would actually physically live forever.

In the Western esoteric tradition, it is known that this fountain of youth is an internal state…the coming together of the opposites into the experience of the *unus mundus* (one world). It is conceptualized in terms of *the philosopher's stone*, the goal of the *opus*, an experience where meaning and substance, heaviness and lightness, youthfulness and old age come together into a *mysterium coniunctionis* (Jung, 1977), a union of opposites. It was the Western alchemists' dream to find the philosopher's stone by which "they mean to refer to this one substance, i.e. the water from which everything originates and in which everything is contained." Carl Jung, in his many-year study of alchemy, "calls this stone philosophical water, not ordinary water but *aqua mercurialis*" (Edinger, 1985, p. 80; Jung, 1968, par. 336).

I wondered whether my experience was similar to what was being alluded to in the texts that I had been reading. I was to experience over many years of practice that when I practiced Standing Meditation Qigong in conjunction with the wider tradition of Qigong, that indeed it led to a state-specific state of consciousness that felt ever-youthful, glowing, vibrant, and eternally timeless—on good days. ☺

Standing Meditation: What Do You Stand for?

From experiences like the one I had while scuba diving, I realized that different types of experiential realities were accessible while doing Standing Meditation. When I asked my colleagues and students about their experience, I discovered that each of us finds different "life stances" when we practice Standing Meditation.

Who are you as you are Standing? Depending upon your life stance, you may describe the experience of Standing Mediation as *Wuji,* a nice feeling of relaxation, *unus mundus,* a trance state, or an opportunity to work on transforming your characterological and physical blockages.

A major part of what I wanted to contribute to the integrating metaphysics and modern psychology was to have a range of esoteric and grounded ways of incorporating ancient sacred wisdom into a modern person's life. For example, after an experience like I had scuba diving or when practicing Standing Meditation an alchemist might say that he or she has just experienced the *corpus glorificationis*, the glorious body, freeing the *spiritus mercurius* imprisoned in matter. A scientist would want to investigate, "What am I feeling when I am standing this way?" He or she would attempt to measure it quantitatively and qualitatively. A healer might wonder, "How can I use this state for healing myself and others?" A spiritually inclined individual may say, "I have just found my ground in Spirit, and I am standing planted in the awesome ground of my divine nature." A mystic might say, "I have found the Secret One inside where exists all of the universe, the galaxies and stars." The Buddhist, with a half smile, might say, "This is nothing special, I'm just standing here—being in the experience of the ordinary." The Hoku master practicing Standing Like a Tree in autumn might say, "The dead, dry leaves fall to the Earth, and only what is alive, fresh and strong remains." Kabir, the Sufi mystic, might call out from the other side of the grave and give us his view of the after-death state to help us discover our life stance, and say "Whatever we find now, we find then, if we merely live in an apartment now, that is what we will find when we enter the kingdom of heaven."[14]

In the workshops I now teach, perhaps in sync with my Sun conjunct Uranus in Gemini (Uranus is the planet associated with representing the openness to possibilities), I have people lift their hands into the "Golden Ball of the Heart Meditation." Then, they imagine that they are standing in the center of a universe of possibilities. In this posture I suggest that they stand with the intention of embracing all of them. I often call forth the words of Grandmaster Wang Xiangzhai, "When I stand the earth is in my hands, and the universe is in my mind."

I want to underline that I am not implying that all, or most, people who practice Standing Meditation have mystical experiences. I remember a student, who I will call Harry, who came to one of my Standing Meditation workshops. When Harry did Tai Chi movements his hands were always overextended, and when I instructed him to hold one of those postures, he first experienced impatience. I told him to stay with that feeling while he was in the posture. After a few minutes of Standing, tears came. In a session after the workshop I asked him what those tears were about. He replied that most of his life had been an exercise in being ahead of himself. Nowadays, he told me, "I don't spend enough time with my son with his homework, and when I do I'm thinking about getting back to my work projects." This insight, he told me six months later, set him on a journey to be more present with his family. Harry now practices Standing Meditation every morning and his practice is to carry a non-impatient stance in his life.

So, the Reluctant Metaphysician is not necessarily a mystic who relishes living in altered states. The Reluctant Metaphysician reluctantly is aware that entering such states often takes hard work in confronting our inner demon, which then may turn into a daemon—a guiding ally who can lead us on a new life path, for example a guiding spirit who is "present" rather than impatient.

In order to combine the psychological and the Eastern meditative traditions in my training of students I ask them to focus on the question, "What is your stance toward life today, and what do you want it to be tomorrow?" I enjoy using imagery to help my students to activate qi, since the qi follows the intention (yi). I oftentimes invite my students to imagine drawing in energy from the Earth on the inhalation, and to focus on sending out healing energy as they are breathing out?

Try it yourself, and see if you can experience how different images change the energy in your Standing Meditation postures. For example, while Standing, imagine holding the Earth in your hands, as a loving parent would hold a child. Maybe you will experience that on a given day that your Standing will lead you to feel like you are one with the universe, or like a stick in the mud. On those days when you feel like a stick in the mud, it is important to remember that through sinking your roots downward into the muck, through being in the waters of life, and learning to find your balance as the cross currents pull you, push you, try to uproot you or carry you away from the ground of yourself—all the while you are in process of growing towards blooming in the air as a lotus.

Yang Lu Chan and Yang Cheng Fu, the founders of the Yang Style Tai Chi Chuan, kept the Standing Meditation practice a carefully guarded secret—though the discerning student will realize that the Tai Chi set begins with the standing still posture and ends with it. Only on rare occasions was the secret practice of Wuji Standing Meditation shared with outsiders. One person who learned it from Yang Cheng Fu in the late 1920s in Shanghai was Mr. Ye Dami. In the 1950s Mr. Dami transmitted the knowledge to Master Cai Songfang, who was one of the teachers with whom I had the blessing to have trained during two summers. I was indeed fortunate to learn from Master Ha, and from other masters that he brought from China to teach us, that Tai Chi Chuan involves practicing each movement as a standing and walking meditation, and then practicing the 108 movements as a linked form.

Tai Chi Chuan

> *"A moving hinge gathers no rust."*
>
> —*Chinese saying*

This old saying from an old Chinese text is a key to health. Just as much as the Standing Meditation is a key to opening a treasure chest within static meditation traditions, so are movement meditation traditions entryways to state-specific states of consciousness that are enlightening and healing. The story is told that when Bodhidharma came from India to China he noticed that well-intentioned monks' bodies were atrophying. So, he spent many years meditating on this problem while he was staring at a wall. From this time meditating on the walls of life, he developed his system of *Yi Jin Jing*, a system for transforming the muscles, sinews, and bone marrow through Qigong movements.

I also believe that a holistic metaphysical system needs to include movement. Perhaps the greatest influence on the weaving of the garment of my spiritual life has been my practice of the Tai Chi Chuan and Qigong traditions.

Why Does the Reluctant Metaphysician Practice Tai Chi?

I say to my students somewhat facetiously, "For the Reluctant Metaphysician, we don't want to practice Tai Chi. We want to be in this state of open energetic connection to the world with our meridians flowing as much of the time as is possible without having to practice."

It is said that the purpose of Tai Chi is to transform the physical body into an energy body that is one with the Tao. The Tao, or the Way of Nature allows one to experience an energetic connection with the sea of life, *Wuji*. This experience is not only of floating in that sea of ecstasy, but also of moving in it playfully as a dolphin does who jumps in and out of the water or makes bubbles and dives through them. Tai Chi also allows a "shape-shifting" into the animal and divine parts of our essential nature...being light as a bird, as rooted as a tree, as well as an experientially embodying other states of consciousness.

However, as human beings, the vicissitudes of life often block our meridians and gets us stuck in the roles, blocked energy, and pains of our lives. So, the Reluctant Metaphysician practices and accepts with gratitude that Tai Chi is a gift given from the world behind the world to restore us to our God-given state of openhearted bliss.

One interesting myth of Tai Chi's origins is that is was given to humanity by extraterrestrials (Hausdorf, 1998), on whose planet the atmosphere was thicker and movement more activating of divine altered states. Hausdorf, in his book *The Chinese Roswell*, claims that these three-eyed hermaphroditic extra-terrestrial beings that landed in the Bayan Kara Ula Mountains of China 12,000 years ago were called "the Chi-Kung" (Hausdorf, 1998, pp. 28, 73). This is the earliest reference that I have seen to the use of the term Qigong (Chi-Kung).[15] Regardless of the truth of this claim, we can create a cosmically connected intention to our practice by imagining that we are tapping on gifts from otherworldly beings. And good myths can create good qi, if we take the stories in a lighthearted way.

Many people ask, "What is the difference between Tai Chi and Qigong (also spelled Chi-Kung, or Chi-Gung)?" Tai Chi Chuan is the best-known system of Qigong. Tai Chi Chuan is one method of embodying Taoist philosophy and it is a practice to cultivate qi, the vital energy of life. It is the best-known system of Qigong. Anyone who takes an introductory course in Tai Chi will learn that a central aim of the practice is to learn to move like a ball, hold postures like a ball, and change the contours of the body into being rounded like a ball, rather than being stiffly linear. These practices are meant to transform the body from a straight, rigid, or broken line into a radiating ball of energy. The wider tradition of Taoist Alchemy and Qigong, in which the Secret of the Golden Flower was embedded, has practices to cultivate the experience of the Golden Flower and Golden Ball.

Tai Chi Chuan: A Postmodern Metaphysical Point of View

In general, the viewpoint I bring to Tai Chi movements is that every one has four dimensions of purpose: self-healing, spiritual unfoldment, self-defense, and changing one's psychological life stance. I have met resistance when I have presented this viewpoint at conferences. Some say that Tai Chi is just a marital art and that those who say it is a spiritual practice are "too New Agey." Others say that it is a spiritual practice and that those who look at it as a martial art are "caught up in their unworked through aggression." Some say that my approach to looking at the psychological elements of the practice are just a modern intrusion on a self contained system that has everything needed without adding some Western psychological overlay.

Following the idea that each of us has to be true to our own unique vision and story I have presented my view, backing it up with historical and anthropological research in my *Secrets*…book (2004), and in my keynote address to the National Qigong Association Conference that year. I took the Kabbalistic idea that the interpretation of the Old Testament is incomplete without looking at it on four levels, and applied it to Tai Chi. I also believe that looking at Tai Chi and Qigong as a four-dimensional initiatory process is part of the earliest Buddhist teachings.[16]

Regardless of the historical merit of such a four-dimensional interpretation of Tai Chi movements, by practicing this way the practitioner is opened to deeper meanings and can find a multifaceted story expressed through their movements. I call this a "postmodern metaphysical point of view of Tai Chi."

Figure 9: Taoist Immortal Paints a Heavenly Rainbow

Let's take for example the second Tai Chi Chuan movement, which some call Taoist Immortal Paints the Heavenly Rainbow. The practitioner starts with their hands in the stance of having both hands palms-down, as if holding two balls in a stream; then a counter clockwise circle is made to the position seen in the figure above. One self-healing purpose of the movement can be found when the practitioner stops the movement with the hands in front of the heart (acu-point CV 17) is that the practitioner opens their heart to the direction they are facing. Secondly, a spiritual/shamanic purpose of the movement can be embodied if a practitioner imagines that, like an ancient shaman, he or she is painting a painting a rainbow across the sky. Thirdly, from the self-defense perspective, if someone is punching you, this movement makes a circle and a 45 degree angle to divert a force coming toward you; and this movement is part of learning how to yield to, not confront, and disarm an aggressive force. Fourthly, this type of movement can change your life stance toward such linear forces, particularly when you assume the correct posture of slightly pushing out your lower back (*ming men*) as you imagine catching a medicine ball in front of your heart.

From a postmodern metaphysical point of view it does not matter whether this is how any other teacher or practitioner interprets the meaning of this posture. What matters is how a posture helps the practitioner to find his or her own connection to the world behind the world. The metaphysical practitioners of Tai Chi use their own meditations as a form of postural initiation, similar to Dr. Felicitas Goodman's work (1990) with postural initiation. She has a modern person hold a posture depicted in an ancient pictograph, and the emphasis is placed on the current meanings they discover.

Following the theme of the journey to put our own unique twist onto the traditions with which we become involved is not so easy of a task in a tradition that is based upon following precise movements just the way your master teaches them to you. Traditionally, honoring the ancestors who transmitted the tradition from generation to generation is paramount, and many times for good reason. The angles and positions of postures do have their time-tested rationale for maximizing the flow of qi. However, when it comes to the purpose of movements, I believe long time practitioners also have their interpretations and views to give back to the tradition based on their soul's inclination.

Along these lines, I wanted to bring Hillman's (1975) distinction between "spirit" and "soul" into the world of Tai Chi. On a spiritual level, Tai Chi opens the practitioner to the experience of an altered state where a merging with the sea of elixir can take place; however, Tai Chi can also be a soulful tradition as the initiate becomes aware of the images, thoughts, and feelings that arise during practice. This awareness can be the beginning of a working through process. For example, as a shaking happens in Standing Meditation a practitioner can ask, "How am I shaking loose some of my old life stance?" As the practitioner practices "roll back" and a blockage is experienced in the shoulder, the practitioner can "focus" upon how to let go of an old pattern of "shouldering" too much responsibility in relationship to others.

My approach to Tai Chi has grown in part from my background in humanistic psychology, where discovery of one's own unique meaning is paramount. I oftentimes find that practitioners are looking for what a movement means and are looking for ultimate truths. Some will say the movements are just martial arts moves. Others say that Tai Chi movements come from Taoist temples where the spiritual purpose is paramount. When I go into Chinese Medical colleges to lecture on Qigong, the orientation is on medical Qigong purposes of Tai Chi movements. When I speak about the psychological purpose of the movements in most venues, practitioners take umbrage at this view as being disloyal to the tradition. Likewise, I have been criticized when I speak about how I believe that there are four purposes of each Tai Chi movement: self-healing, spiritual unfoldment, self-defense, and changing your life psychologically.

Instead of focusing on ultimate truths and contending about which of our interpretations is more "Tai Chi-ish," I believe that from a metaphysical, post-modern view it is important to see that each of these four types of intention in Tai Chi practice contains its story. Each story has its value, which opens us up to a new world of meaning. As with the example of the movement of Taoist Immortal Paints a Heavenly Rainbow, every Tai Chi movement can be seen as a letter of a long-lost, right brain hieroglyphic alphabet. These letters (postural stances) open us to discovering the consciousness of another world, just as did the discovery of Egyptian hieroglyphics.[17]

A story is being told in each dimension of Tai Chi practice. For example, Tai Chi push hands practice teaches us "not to contend and not to separate," and here the initiate learns to listen to another's story in their words and in their bodies.

One of the deep gifts of Tai Chi to those who are metaphysically inclined is that Tai Chi Push Hands practice (which I like to call Tai Chi Joining Hands Practice, or Two Person Self-development Practice) is a way to make the unmanifest world manifest. In a way that is unique in my experience as compared to other forms of spiritual practice, Tai Chi "tests" (sili) whether qualities of the unseen world can be manifested by the practitioner. In other traditions, a person surely works on developing qualities such as groundedness and yielding; but in Tai Chi Joining Hands one practices the embodiment of these qualities and having them tested in a particular way.

From a metaphysical viewpoint, the world is made of archetypal patterns (energy potentials) in the realm of "mind" which manifest as energy and then incarnate in the body. In Tai Chi Two Person practices, the initiate practices cultivating and manifesting these qualities, such as grounding and yielding. For example, in everyday life if your partner frequently criticizes you, you may attack back (collide with them) or choose to end the relationship (separate from them); in the Tai Chi Joining Hands tradition one practices not colliding and not separating from another. As a psychologist, I particularly like this way of viewing the purpose of Joining Hands practice because it becomes a way of teaching "affect regulation" skills (Schore, 2003). From this post-modern perspective, which allows for the amalgamation of traditions, this practice involves working on changing our life stories in the bodymind: moving from reactivity to equanimity; from fighting with to yielding from; and from abrupt withdrawal, due to lack of ego strength (in Tai Chi terms, keeping our ball intact), to sticking with a person and developing affect tolerance.

Further, in more advanced practice of Tai Chi and Yi Chuan Standing Meditation Qigong the initiate learns to "become a Golden Ball," so that when someone pushes on you, they bounce off of your sphere and may even spring up into the air (fajing).[18]

From a postmodern view,[19] it's about stories all the way down as far as we can go. From this perspective, the world of human beings is built upon layers of hidden stories; and as we uncover them, a primordial root system is discovered from which our lives can grow.[20]

Outward Introspection

I consider outward introspection as a quintessential metaphysical practice. How exactly the term came to me, I do not remember. I may have first heard about this practice in the early 1970s; and as soon as I heard this term it was as if a major thread of the metaphysical quilt that was part of my life's work was indelibly sewn into the center of the garment.

One of my first experiences with outward introspection was when as an adolescent I would sit by two streams joining. At that time I did not know that this type of activity reflected what was to become one of my soul's favorite playgrounds—to see how qualities of our inner landscape are reflected in the outer world.

The intellectual ground of my metaphysical interest in outward introspection started in college with the study of Plato and his ideal forms, and by Herman Hesse's *Glass Bead Game* (2002). In Hesse's book he describes taking the essence of something and transposing it into another medium. Some believe that Hesse's book was a statement about how the archetypal essences of life (similar to Plato's forms) could be transferred from an idea, to music, to art, to a planetary configuration, to a mythic story, and so forth.

In my graduate master's degree program another facet of this concept came to me when I learned about "isomorphism" (iso = same; morphic = structure), one position on the mind body problem (McDougall, 1911). An example of the isomorphic perspective can be seen when a person feels embarrassed. The mental and emotional qualities of embarrassment are transposed into the structure of the body, and the same essence is reproduced in the bodily sphere. For example, a red face may reflect embarrassment, and scrunched shoulders may portray insecurity, and so forth.

Many of the practices I have developed stem from outward introspection, whereby one takes the essence of things and transposes them into another level of reality. For example, in my approach to Standing Meditation Qigong, called Standing like a Tree, I ask my students (while in a trance state induced by microcosmic orbit breathing) to imagine their bodies as being like a tree. At the end of their exhalation, they are called to be aware of being rooted in their family, friends, loved ones, and spiritual traditions. Then, as they inhale I suggest to them that they imagine drawing up from their roots into their trunks and then branching out. The branches of the tree become isomorphically transposed into the ways they are branching out now in their lives; or further they can imagine the fruits, flowers, or fun, nutty ways of being come from their metaphorical branches. When the metaphysical practice of outward introspection is integrated with Qigong, imagination becomes embodied. For example, after a student focuses on breathing out and down into their roots, most Tai Chi students experience how it is harder to push them over.

As we look into the essence of various elements of the world, and see how we contain the essence of those things, an animistic experience of oneness with life is created. Separation between self and world dissolve for the metaphysician who sees that the essence of flowering and all other attributes of the natural world are inside of us. Outward introspection became one key element that I hope to contribute to psychotherapy so that the elements of the external world can be seen as living symbols to help us change our life stances.[21]

Developing Our Own Unique Metaphysical Practice System in Our Everyday Lives

Everyday life gives each of us an opportunity to weave together our favorite metaphysical practices with our everyday lives. For example, I earlier told you about how in Tahiti I found a way to adapt my Standing Meditation practice to scuba diving. Wherever we are, there are threads that can connect us to the world behind the world and to the cave of the Great Goddess of Creation. Like the Great Goddess in the Cave of Creation, each of us in everyday life can pick up the ingredients needed to nourish our lives, and stir them into the soup kettle. We each concoct our own special brew.

The soup in the back of the cave of the Old Woman in the Cave is connected with her work weaving the garment of life. Each of us, like her, needs to weave together the garment of our unique metaphysical practice system. This garment that we weave from our life does get unraveled at times due to our relationships with others, difficulties at work, and symptoms that arise in our bodies. We then have an opportunity to weave the threads of various healing traditions into our approach to self-healing and explore what works on our path as a wounded healer. For example, my Bodymind Healing Qigong system took me over a decade to create, because each time I would meet a new Qigong master my past system would fall apart or fray around the edges. My carefully constructed weaving would get unraveled and then rewoven. Eventually, it became the ten Bodymind Healing Qigong sets that I have now taught for thirty years; and it is still adding new threads.

Whatever metaphysical system you weave together is your way of staying connected with the world behind the world—with the cave of your creation. Or, to use a biblical metaphor, your metaphysical practice system is your "Coat of Many Colors." It is your birthright that comes from your soul's ancestral lineage, and perhaps you will pass down to the next generation. It is a symbol of your connection to the spiritual fabric of life that you carry as you walk on your path of individuation. As happened for Joseph, this gift from the lineage of our ancestors may get bloodied along the way, as jealously and other human foibles temporarily damage that weaving. However, the wisdom that comes from your wounding may make the Kings of life choose you as their advisor (as did the Pharaoh choose Joseph).

How do we each weave the metaphysical garment of our lives? Our life experiences, the people we meet, and the traditions we discover become the threads of the metaphysical garments of our lives. When we stay in touch with our own unique twist of the thread of our lives, then we find our own way of approaching metaphysical traditions. Each day I like to choose from various traditions depending upon the calling of the moment. Every-day presents different opportunities to choose ingredients from my "Chinese Menu." Not everyday can I do everything on the menu that follows:

I told you earlier how each morning when I wake up I have a ritual. Usually, when I wake, "the muses" have given me what I am supposed to write about that day. So, first I roll over in bed and scribble down those ideas. Then, I do my version of a combination of yoga and acupressure called acu-yoga, and then I get into the shower and practice *daven-ing*. Davening is a Jewish praying ritual that is done while rocking back and forth. When I go into the shower and *daven*, I usually sing the *Alenu*, a Jewish prayer about how each of us is a spark of the divine. There is a point in the prayer where daveners sing about lift-ing our hearts in prayer—at this moment in the prayer I turn on the cold water to give a jolt of energy to my heart. Here is the prayer in English (which I usually sing in Hebrew):

> *Oh come let us give praise to the source of the light of the world,*
> *and become one with the Shaper of Life,*
> *who has made every person a spark divine,*
> *and blesses each of us in our own special way.*
> *...and we know our task is to hallow all life,*
> *and lift our hearts in prayer and thanks.*
>
> — *Aleynu*, Jewish Prayer

After this practice in the shower, I have some grapefruit juice while returning a few e-mails, and I begin to write for one of my upcoming books or articles that came through from the "land of dreams" (the world behind the world). Then, I run up the hill and do a little Taoist jogging, play intensely for one minute with a neighbor's dog to get my heart pumping and activate the energy of my inner warrior, and upon returning home I practice my short set of Qigong.[22] On alternate days I lift weights or use exercise bands to stretch while listening to talk radio. Following these practices that unify mind body and spirit, I make some fresh vegetable juice and mix in some probiotics. As I sit down at my desk I return more e-mails, plan workshops, and meditate on the patients who I am about to see.

The rituals of my life and a metaphysical perspective help me to get ready to go down the hill to see patients or teach. Ah, how energizing it is to weave such activities together! But, each of us needs to weave our own garment.

In the midst of my morning rituals and throughout the day I deal with various life issues that arise: problems with technological devices, personal and business issues, and household chores. In the midst of my morning rituals, and throughout the day, various issues can unravel my garment (just like the Black Dog did in the Cave of the Goddess). When I am dealing with such life events, I try to imagine that I am creating new threads in the tapestry of my life: red threads from activating my vital energy to deal with being torn apart by the Black Dogs of life; blue threads from finding spiritual practices to deal with these issues (such as the ones that I have mentioned in this book); green threads that symbolize how a connection with nature helps me to cope; and purplish-brown threads that represent a new earthy life stance toward the vicissitudes of life.

One of the themes that I try to keep in mind during my day is what I learned in the *Secret of the Golden Flower* text, where it said that the key to life was "doing nothing." The years, and my practices, have taught me what that means. My work life, for the last three decades has been a Golden Triangle, comprised of my writing, teaching, and seeing patients. I have three offices throughout the Bay Area to make it easy for my patients to see me. So, I facetiously tell my students that my life is too busy to have time for metaphysical practices. Since I do not usually have time to go to a yoga studio, I set my clock twenty minutes before I would normally wake, and I do yoga for twenty minutes in bed. I don't have time to gather ten fellow Jews for davening , so I do it in the shower. No time and no-thing leads to the experience of "everything for which I could ask." The Golden Flower blooms by doing "no-thing." Just opening to the light around us, in time naturally helps us to bloom as we open to the heavens above.

I also facetiously tell my students that when I do not have time to practice Standing Meditation, the beautiful thing about this practice is that it can be done anywhere. I like to practice Standing Meditation on lines at the grocery store, or the bank, as I say to myself, "Oh, it's too bad there are only five people in front of me today instead of ten, so I won't have as much time to practice Standing." What a great pleasure it is to not have to take time out of my life to do "some-thing" like a spiritual practice, and instead I can do "no-thing" and "find contentment while being alight." This is the no-practice of "just Standing."

When time allows (particularly in the summertime), after a long day of seeing patients or teaching, I like to go out to one of my favorite spots in the woods, at a place that I call Bear Creek Mountain. I play Jewish renewal songs on my flute, mixed with Indian ragas, and Native American songs. Then I do a little Qigong to restore my batteries.

Late at night, when time and energy allows, I enjoy practicing my Bodymind Healing Qigong methods on the redwood deck that a Tai Chi brother of mine (Jan Diepersloot) kindly built at the back of my house. There I practice Taoist cultivation methods of "bringing down the moon," where one pretends that he or she is connected with moonlight and spreads it around, or I use my Tai Chi sword to bounce light off of the sword. I use Tai Chi sword practice to imagine cutting through body blocks that may have accumulated during the day.

Each of us has our own area of blockage—areas in "the hoses (meridian lines)"of our inner circuitry that tend to get blocked. I earlier told you about how I had a hernia operation when I was a young child, and since there was no physical therapy as post-operative care at that time in the 1950s I have had body blocks in my hip area. Along my healing pathway I have learned how my hip blockages parallel the areas of blockage in my neck (as above so below). The Reluctant Metaphysician knows that healing practices are borne from our bodily diseases; and so I choose from the particular Bodymind Healing Qigong practice that fits with the moment for me, sometimes emphasizing Tai Chi, Standing Meditation, or one of the "weapons."

The weapons in the internal arts are known to be qi extenders and they are as useful for healing as for self-defense. I use the various weapons of the Tai Chi tradition (sword, saber, and staff) to "do battle" with my internal opponent—the areas of my body that accumulate tension. Actually the term "doing battle" is a misnomer—it is more like a playful dance that is so multifaceted it is beyond description. Briefly, one plays with cutting through areas of blockage with the movements of Tai Chi sword practice. Slicing through muscular tightness with the movements of curved saber creates a circular movement of energy. The short staff is my favorite tool; with it one can swing, stretch, strengthen, energize, and so forth.

An important part of my metaphysical practice system involves Tai Chi or shamanic dance synthesized with the traditions I have just mentioned. Over the years this has become an important part of my regenerating paradigm. I teach this at various workshops at Esalen Institute and elsewhere; but most importantly I do this as my renewal practice. I have a library of sacred, cross-cultural dance music that evokes various altered states: calming, ecstatic, peaceful, or transforming. The music comes from various cross-cultural sources. For example, to move into a sacred space I listen to Middle Eastern music, when I want to work out some deep issues with movement I turn on Australian Didgeridoo music, when I want to engage in primordial ecstatic dance I like to listen to Afro-Celt music, and when I just want to create an awesome mellow space I listen to music from the spirit of the rainforest.[23] The beauty of being a modern metaphysician is that we can draw on cross-cultural, cross-temporal music as we dance. Dance and music were key healing elements that shamans of tribal societies introduced to their societies in the era before television. By the way, the way modern people are captivated by TV is a modern version (some would argue is a toxic mimic), of the age-old practice of looking into the fire at night.

Working through the energy blockages, and discovering sounds, movements, and rituals to heal has been part of shamanic rituals throughout the ages. For example, we are lucky that the Foundation for Shamanic Studies is now letting us know about some of the authentic shamanic practices from Mongolia. In their annual *Journal* (2011) are many articles on the various methods used by shamans in Mongolia. When doing their healing rituals, shamans wear costumes that have a healing purpose, as in Mongolia where one shaman wears a fringed eye curtain to obscure ordinary reality perception and turn her attention inward toward non-ordinary perception. Throughout Mongolia, while shamanic healing takes place, various musical instruments are used to create a trance state such as mouth harps, bells, and drums; and shamans make sounds to invoke healing. At times, a patient may be whipped with leather straps on the area where an energy block exists; and at least one report by an anthropologist Kevin Turner is that the shaman knew exactly where to hit (Turner, 2011). The rituals described as taking place in various tribes are very intricate and sacredly held, involving such practices as: symbolic process rituals directed by the Pau shaman where the patient searches for various sacred objects in a copper bowl to bring back their lost soul (Sifers, 2011); sound healing where a patient is encouraged to scream and make sounds; movement and dance by the patient and the shaman; various extraction methods where toxins are released, and so forth. It is heartening to see that researchers such as Sifers are not just studying these healing traditions, but also are giving back to the Pau community by forming a non-profit organization, Indigenous Lenses, which supports this culture through financial support of the remaining shamans' families. As well this organization installs toilets, solar showers, water taps, and supplies various medical needs to the community (Sifers, 2011).

From the perspective of the somatic healing practices and rituals about which I have spoken, in Mongolian shamanic rituals are examples of some of the roots of, and parallels to, various current healing traditions that involve psychodrama, dance, and community rituals such as—energetic movements to restore vital energy, catharsis to release emotions, shamanic journeys to the underworld for the purpose of "soul-retrieval," and so forth. Each tradition has its own fullness, and to get a fuller report on Mongolian shamanism please see the *Journal of the Foundation of Shamanic Studies*.[24] It would be a great life work for a researcher to investigate the efficacy and long-term effects of the healing rituals reported in this edition of this journal.

This work is related to the age-old, cross-cultural tradition of the *psychopomp* (Kerenyi, 1976; Hillman, 1979; Harner, 1990). The psychopomp was one of the earliest names for a psychological healer of the soul in pre-modern traditions, who would take a person on an "underworld journey to retrieve their soul." Creating our own rituals to retrieve our souls, based on our own unique synthesis of indigenous and modern healing traditions is the work of the modern metaphysician that seeks to tap on the world behind the eternal world to draw forth healing from our journeys through our somatic blocks and psychological issues.

Creating spontaneous dance rituals is one facet of this healing work. For those who look sceptically at dance as a vital element of any healing equation, it is interesting that in a study in the *New England Journal of Medicine,* research on leisure activities and the risk of dementia in the elderly results shows that, "Among cognitive activities, reading, playing board games, and playing musical instruments were associated with a lower risk of dementia. (But) dancing was the only physical activity associated with a lower risk of dementia" (Verghese, 2003, p. 2). Perhaps those of us, who intuitively like to have dance in our every day lives, instinctually recognize these healing effects.

Continuing with the general outline of some of my daily rituals as a Reluctant Metaphysician, before I go to sleep I like to play Jewish renewal songs on my flute and chant the song that expresses the feeling that I want to take to sleep with me. I view this late nighttime ritual as cleaning my garment or fueling my boat as I set off on the sea governed by "the dream-weaver." One of my favorite songs is one that Rabbi Schlomo Carlebach sang to his daughter, Nishama (meaning soul). It is one of my favorites because it is used to call forth the angels of the four directions to protect those that we love, or ourselves, from "the demons" of the night.

> *Ha shem, ha shem (meaning the word of God) the God of Yisreal*
> *To the left of me stands Micha-el, to the right of me stands Gabr-ael,*
> *In front of me stands Uriel, and behind me stands Raphael.*
> *And Above my head above my head stands the Shakena-el (the female side of God)*

I met Rabbi Carlebach in the early 1970s. I mentioned to him that I wanted to find out if I was related to the Baal Shem Tov, and I wondered if he could help me find out. At that time I was estranged from my Jewish roots; my path involved Eastern forms of meditation. He took me under his wing, and viewed it as part of his mission to show me what I was missing in the Chassidic and Jewish Renewal traditions. He invited me to quite a few small Shabbat gatherings where he told Jewish stories, taught me some Jewish songs, and introduced me to the Jewish experiential mystical tradition. Though he could not confirm my familial relationship to the Baal Shem Tov, he accomplished his mission with me. He showed me the fertile soil from which my Jewish roots grew.

The Hawaiian Flute Master

Talking about my staff practice and playing the flute, reminds me of a story. During the 1980s I had just finished learning Tai Chi Sword from Master Ha, and Tai Chi staff from my friend and brother on the path, Ken Cohen. I took a vacation with my girlfriend to one of the Hawaiian Islands, Kauai. So that I could continue my sword practice in Hawaii, I brought my thirty-inch sword along and had it put in the baggage compartment. It was called a Long Chuan sword and was forged at the Dragon Well, a famous place used for forging swords in ancient China where the waters were supposed to be particularly pure and just right for forging swords. Master Ha brought back this sword from China for a few of his other students and me, so I particularly treasured it.

I was walking the Kalalau trail around sunset with this sword sticking out of my backpack, and it started to rain. Jeannie and I wanted to make it up to the first river before sunset to camp, and we did pretty well on a slippery-sloped, narrow trail, as it got dark. I only slipped and fell once, almost falling down an 85-degree incline a few feet, but I got up quickly and resumed the walk to the river campsite. When I took off my backpack, I saw the unthinkable. My Long Chuan Sword was gone, and I immediately knew where the sword was...it was that one damned slip. Master's Ha's sword may be lost forever, I thought.

It was too dark and rainy to go back. But, I decided to wake before daybreak and hike back to the fateful spot. I barely slept that night, but by a miracle of inner alarm clock setting I woke just before dawn so that I could get to the spot before anyone else could find it. After the sun rose, I hiked and I reached the spot about a half hour up the trail where I had slipped. The sword was right down the hill a few feet. The sword was wet, but it was in fine shape. What a relief! I did a quick set of my sword-form right there looking over the ocean. In bliss, I put the sword back into my backpack, picked up a nice piece of bamboo and appreciated my good fortune in finding a bamboo staff on the trail, which I used as a walking stick. Then I walked back up the trail to get back to Jeannie. Occasionally, I would stop and go various staff movements to playfully work out energy blocks in my body, which had accumulated through the ordeal.

Just ahead I saw a tall, hippie looking fellow approaching me. He looked like an indigenous Hawaiian shaman dressed in colorful garb. He had a leather pack filled with flutes in his backpack. He was the first person on the trail I had seen, and as he approached me I was looking forward to talking to him. I thought to myself, "Ah, a brother on the Path." When we approached each other, I was surprised to see an angry look on his face, and I was even more surprised to hear him say, "We don't like *haole's* (a derogatory work used to describe Caucasian invaders to Hawaii) stealing our bamboo." Then I explained to him who I was, and my life path investigating the rituals of other cultures. I told him how I also saw bamboo staffs as sacred. I explained that the staff was part of my Tai Chi training and how I used it to heal my own and others' body blockages. Closeness grew between us; and then he explained how he camped out in the Kalalau valley where all his needs were met by the lush fruit and coconuts that were there. He said that occasionally he did need something from civilization, and he would sell bamboo flutes to make the extra money he needed. Then he stopped talking, looked into my eyes deeply, and said, "Let me tell you a story which I usually don't tell others." He invited me to sit down on the cliff there in the early morning hours looking over the ocean. The Flute Shaman, (my name for him) apologized for treating me in such an inhospitable and judgmental way when we first met. He said the reason he was that way was because his people in their tradition saw bamboo as a sacred plant. "The flute, and a stalk of bamboo," he explained, "is a family member to us." To bring forth his point further he told me the following story,

> When one of our parents dies, we bury them in our back yards and we plant bamboo on their graves. Then after a certain period of time when the bamboo is grown just the right amount, in a sacred ceremony we cut some of the bamboo. We make flutes out of the bamboo. Then whenever we play the flute we think of our ancestors; our hearts are connected to them through the music.

The Flute Shaman then, took one of his flutes from his backpack, and played me one of the most deeply moving, sacred tunes I had ever heard. We parted with a bow and a hug.

I thought about indigenous rituals and how beautiful it was that natives Hawaiians connected to their ancestors this way. I reflected upon American culture and how estranged we are from our ancestors, putting them in cemeteries far from our living places.

I wondered how our American culture would benefit if we stayed more connected to our ancestors in our everyday lives.

And so, that is the story of why today I play my flute almost every night before I go to sleep—to stay connected to the traditions of the primordial tunes of the ages, and to the feelings and memories of my ancestors. After meeting the Flute Shaman and I got back to California I took up the practice of North Indian Flute with Jon Meyer, a senior student of the master flutist G. S. Sachdev. Though occasionally I still play Indian ragas, in tune with my cross-cultural nature, I also play sacred tunes from Jewish and Native American traditions. Singing, or playing a musical instrument with spiritual intent directed towards our dream lives, towards our loved ones, and to the creative power that has created us can ring a tuning fork that calls for an appropriate resonant response from our inner dream-weaver.

In our "civilized life" many have lost their bearings. Many people living in cities do not know which direction is north; and still less people know how to find the North Star at nighttime. Ancestral wisdom and its traditions are a way to find our primordial Selves in the midst of chaos.[25] Each of our destinies is forged by listening to our inner calling, to our dreams, to the characters in stories we hear, or to the people who we meet on the Path of everyday life.

Practicing the Opposite of Your Favorite Metaphysical Practice

Part of the pathway of creating your unique amalgam of metaphysical practices is to consider the practice that is the opposite of your chosen practice. Sometimes the ones we need are the opposite place on the wheel of life to the ones that we have been practicing. For me, in my early life, the "temple I worshipped" was the temple of mind. I was on the path of Jnana Yoga, the yoga of mind. My life and its "turnings on the wheel" led me, as you have seen to find a path that was more body oriented. In a class I taught for three years at San Francisco State in Eastern Perspectives, I had students do a practice that was opposite to their favorite spiritual practice. A person who liked a non-physical spiritual path like Transcendental Meditation chose a bodily oriented path such as Tai Chi, and vice versa. For their final papers they wrote up their experience.

Blessings to you as you create the unique weaving of the threads of your own metaphysical practice system. Contrasting colors and textures create a better weave.

CHAPTER 12:

Dancing with Deer, Not Dancing with Wolves

Practices lead to Stories,
Stories lead to Practices.

—Insight transmitted by "The Deer who Counts Coup"
in the depths of Stanislaus Forest on one fine full-moon-lit evening

Keeping Your Life's Vision Alive by Rituals of Returning to the Source

Rituals of "returning to the Source" help each of us to keep our life's vision alive. After my vision quest I did not want to lose the thread that connected me to the world of nature, so I promised myself that I would do a vision quest at least once a year for the next decade.

One of my favorite things to do was to look at my map and see if I could find just the right spot in nature to go on retreat. My criteria were that the place needed to have four qualities: (1) Be within a one-day drive of my home in the San Francisco Bay Area; (2) have a good chance of no one being there so I could recharge my primordial self and feel what it was like to be in nature before civilization overran us with noise and modern conveniences; (3) be by a lake so I could go swimming; (4) be no more than a full day of backpacking away from my car.

I found my spot up in the Stanislaus National Forest; and I went there every year for a decade—most times alone, occasionally with another person.

Dancing with Deer

Hidden beneath your feet is a luminous stage
where you are meant to rehearse your eternal dance.

—Hafiz

Each year I would hike in to "my spot," and then I would rest for a day. On the third day of my five-day ritual I would imbibe a psychedelic. Each year I took a different entheogen: psilocybin mushrooms, LSD, or mescaline. (In keeping with my commitment in the Introduction to this book, in telling you the Mount Analogue story, not to lead you to the edge of any cliffs, I must say that this is a dangerous activity. I am not suggesting that anyone do a psychedelic alone or with another in the woods, particularly far away from civilization. In addition to it being illegal, your life could be at stake.)

On the fourth day of my once a year ritual, I would recuperate; and on the fifth day I would walk back to civilization, recharged by my connection with my primordial Self. On that third day, while "tripping," I would enter into "primordial consciousness," play my flute, meditate, practice Tai Chi and Qigong, and swim in the healing waters of the lake. At nighttime I sat in front of the fire I made and would go for walks out into the dark mystery, seeking whatever awaited me. Here is what happened on one of those trips:

> One year when I was with a women friend, she stayed by the fire as I walked out into the woods to do my practice. I found a nice clearing in the woods about one hundred yards from the fire; it was a circle of about twenty feet around. I did my Yi Chuan Standing Meditation practice in the middle of the circle and occasionally did some Qigong and Tai Chi movements under the full moon. I sensed something watching me, and a moment later saw a glitter that looked like eyes. I breathed getting ready to meet whatever was there, practicing the sinking of qi that Master Ha had transmitted to me over the years of my practice. I just noticed my fear, breathing it out…ready for whatever came. Then I started to do the very slow movements I had been trained to do from the internal martial arts tradition, playing with the place where I thought I might have seen eyes.

> All of a sudden a deer darted out of the woods directly at me. I was barely able to instinctively move into a posture called Pa Kua Fish,[1] where the Tai Chi practitioner moves with the force instead of fighting with it. As an attacker (or in this case an animal) came at me, Master Ha had taught me to gradually move my weight back with the oncoming force, not contending with it. In Pa Kua Fish this was done by having the right foot forward with my weight on it, knee bent; the left leg knee bent was about 2½ feet in back of the right leg. At the same time the front right hand, palm facing downward was outstretched as far as the front right foot; and the back left hand, also palm facing downward, was parallel with the back left leg. Both hands were in front of my heart. As the oncoming force of the deer came at me, my weight shifted back following the oncoming force of the deer. As my feet turned, my body turned and my hands came all the way around into posture that resembles a fish scales.

> I guess this old Chinese tradition that I had practiced all these years came in handy because I was able to avoid the deer hitting me with its body and its antlers. The deer entered into the woods right behind me. I stayed in stillness totally present watching the exact place and listening intently in case the deer attacked again. I summoned my greatest presence; my life was at stake yet I was completely relaxed and energized at the same time. My training was with me.

> Or, so I thought. The next minute the deer came from 120 degrees around the circle where it couldn't possibly have gone to without me hearing it. Or, so I believed.

Once again the deer came right at me, and once again I instinctively did the movement Pa Kua Fish; but this time I actually touched the deer as it was passing me. The deer went to a section of the circle that opened up a to a rocky hill. And then it did that movement we all know—the deer looked back over its shoulder at me. I took that as an invitation to follow it doing the Yi Chuan Walking Meditation that I had been practicing earlier.

As the deer walked slowly up the rocky hillside it occasionally looked back at me. I had the sense we were playing with each other. It came to mind that the deer had just been "counting coup" on me in the clearing. Just as one the highest arts of Native Americans in the old West was to not hurt an enemy but to just touch him as he was passing by, this deer was "counting coup" on me. Now I was following it up the hillside continuing our connection. I remembered the Deer Animal Frolic from one of my teachers with whom I had studied Hua Tau's Animal Frolics. So, I was able to imitate the deer's looking back over its shoulder as I did the same type of movement. The deer went into one of those stances that us humans call "being caught in the headlights" where it seemed fixated and fascinated by my movements. Or, should I say I was fixated on it, and taking my lead from it? There was a cross species connection that was awesome to experience. Under the full moon, the deer and I were moving slowly up the hillside together about forty feet apart. Finally about ten feet from the top of the hillside the deer took one of it hoofs and scratched the earth…maybe it was saying goodbye. Then it bolted over the top of the hillside. The dance was over.

Figure 10: Deer Looks Backward

Animism and the Animal Forms of Qigong

This experience still lives in my imagination, as it can in yours. Any story is all of our stories. Occasionally when the forces of life come at me from nowhere, this experience of the deer comes to mind. I breathe and see if I can live the metaphor of non-contention, and find a way to play with such forces as I did with this deer on this full-moon night. The deer is a symbol of grace, playfulness, and vitality. The Deer Animal Frolics of the internal martial arts also teach that the deer can be more powerful than most of us are aware.

The movements of Deer Rutting can emphasize the horns, which according to Chinese shamanism connects the deer's spirit to the heavens above; but also their horns can be used for defense during the rutting season. And so, in a similar way our spirituality can be grounded; the deer teaches that the same part of us which is connected to the heavens is also a formable in protecting against the competitive forces of life. The hooves of the deer are imitated with a deer hand mudra that is like the "noogie," which you may have learned as a child. As "your hooves" go forward and backward they are used not only to defend, but also to heal and energize the kidneys.

Figure 11: Deer Rutting

The Animal Forms of Qigong are a way to activate our vitality in many spheres of our lives. Every movement can be used for healing, spiritual unfoldment, self-defense, and changing our life stance. This is the power of forging a primordial connection with nature and with any of our animal brethren. Since my Medicine Animal that came from my vision quest is the deer, I most enjoy finding this connection with nature by Dancing with Deer.

Speaking of the healing secrets of our natural world, I heard a story at my temple Chochmat Halev from Estelle Frankel, one of the respected teachers there. It goes something like this....

> When God created the Torah, the book of Life, the Holy One decided to have a backup plan. Just in case the Torah ever got destroyed, God wanted the knowledge stored there not to be lost. So, God put all the knowledge of the Torah, for all who have eyes to see, in the elements and creatures of nature. Since that time, if someone forgets how to be strong they can learn from the lion; if a human forgets how to be light-hearted he or she can look at the crane; and if we lose our agility or ability to move gracefully through life the deer can inspire us.

If anyone doubts that our animal brethren have secret skills, please read *Bats Sing, Mice Giggle,* (Shanor, 2010), where you will find scientific evidence for the fact that spiders taste with their feet, decapitated cockroaches can live for two weeks, and schools of electric fish use complex electric fields to determine their location within the group. After reading Karen Shanor's book, where you find that animals have secret inner lives (even humor), you won't find it so strange that a deer might choose to play with me, counting coup.

If humanity would reactive their animistic connection with the forces of nature and realize our unity with our animal partners on this planet, the Navy might be more conscientious about using sonar in waters, and food manufacturers might be more mindful about the way they treat the animals who are sacrificed for our food. We all might be more awakened by the lessons lying hidden in every animal that we encounter, and we might listen with our inner ear to what message is coming to our life from our encounters with the animals around us. In our Bible it was said that God created the human race by combining the divine with the nature of the animals. And so if we want to reclaim our wholeness, "re-membering" our connection with animals is a step on the path to returning to our Primordial Selves and the divine in us. We can we be part of "rewilding the world" (Fraser, 2010).

I will leave it up to you as to whether to do the Deer Animal Qigong practice, or to just be inspired by my story of dancing with deer. I advocate doing the practice. But as in the Rabbi in the Woods story that I told in the introduction to this book, a good case can be made for the fact that the story contains the practice.

CHAPTER 13:

What Is the Origin of Tai Chi: A Message from Bear Creek Mountain

Meditating on the Essence of Things in Nature

Any place in nature can be a place to find access into the mysteries of life. The outer world evokes corresponding inner sanctums. This is why in the Western mystery tradition it is said that every place has its own *deva,* "an elemental," that corresponds to an element of creation. There are devas of the air (*sylphs*), devas of the water (*nereids*), and devas of the earth (*dryads*). These are metaphorical and metaphysical embodiments of the forces of nature in those places.

As one meditates in a cave, a tendency exists for different insights to emerge, as compared to the top of mountains. One of my favorite places to go near my home in California, I call Bear Creek Mountain. The "messages I have received" while in this sanctuary in nature have helped to give direction to my life. Just as an explorer brings along a compass to find their traveling direction, so do Reluctant Metaphysicians find power spots in nature to re-align ourselves with our essential nature.

Bear Creek Mountain is for me a nature temple, where I go to restore my soul. In this healing environment, I play my flute, and practice Qigong. One day I watch the still egret that has one foot in the water and one foot on land, waiting for some morsel to emerge from the depths. Another day I watch in awe the quick turns of the white Terns, as their mastery of flying and diving into the depths could inspire the most blocked writer to shift into a new direction. And the deer, as it jumps over bramble bushes, could help even the most civilized among us to remember the power of primordial movements to overcome obstacles. I have written a good percentage of my last three books at Bear Creek Mountain thanks to the convenience of wireless computers and the maintenance of pristine nature sanctuaries. What a gift to have the blessings of both worlds of technology and nature… once again, two rivers becoming one!

The "True Origin" (in the Mythic Sense) of Tai Chi

One day, as I was in this sacred power spot, the following story came to me. I had recently read Doug Wile's book, *Tai Chi Ancestors,* which is about the origin of Tai Chi (Wile, 1999). I was very impressed by the meticulousness of his scholarship.

I hope you will read his historically based version. But as I was sitting on the top of "Bear Creek Mountain," another version came to me. Joseph Campbell, in one of his workshops that I was fortunate to have taken, defined a myth as, "an untrue story that is truer than life." So, whenever I tell the following story I invoke Joseph Campbell's definition of myth, and I say that the following story is true in the mythic sense. A toolkit with mythic, metaphorical, and imaginal tools are as necessary to a metaphysician opening doors, as are hammers, screwdrivers, and keys essential implements to those who work with physical doorways.

The renowned storyteller Michael Meade bemoans how modern people now reduce myth, the primordial vehicle for awakening the imagination, with the words, "It's just a myth." When you read the following story, which has roots in the realm of mythic imagination, you may discover something important about healing your bodymind through the way of animal movements:

> Once upon a time, there were many "primitive" tribes living in old China. At the top of one of the mountains, near the place where the tigers wandered, lived a shaman. Over the years, and through studying the movements of the Tiger, he learned how to tame the wild beast with various movements. In addition, he learned how to heal parts of his body, from the strength he cultivated by dealing with and even riding the tiger (in much the same way that our modern day cowboys developed great strength while taming wild horses). The Tiger Master learned to develop, stretch, and heal his sinews, muscles, and even his lower back.
>
> Another shaman who lived by the streams studied the way of the Snake. He learned how to keep his joints flexible by imitating the energetic spiraling movements of the Snake. The Rooster Master who lived near a field was seen much of the time standing on one leg, and had superb balance. The Deer Master in the local forest developed grace by imitating the Deer, and learned how to energize his sexual vitality and prostate gland.
>
> The Crane Master, who lived by a lake, after many years of study, learned how to imitate the movement of the Crane's beak. One day, she saw a Pelican bite her own chest while taking her flesh in her beak and feeding her offspring. The Master got the idea to imitate the bird's beak to extract pain and toxic qi from her fellow tribesman. Another Master who lived on a plateau nearby was a Rain Master. It was said he could move the clouds by a secret movement called Cloud Hands. When his fellow tribesmen were emotionally distraught, they would come to him to clear their sadness, grief and other troubling emotions. Finally, The Shamanic Star Master was often seen at night practicing Gathering Starlight; his talent was bringing light to the darkness of peoples' lives. He said it was important for people to slow down and reflect. Those that copied his movement called it Grasping the Bird's Tail; they said that this movement could even slow down a bird, and could prevent it from taking off. (Some say that two of the ancestors of the Cloud Hand and Gathering Starlight Shamans married and traveled to the Middle East where they taught these movements to one of the ancestors of Sigmund Freud.)

At each solstice and equinox these Masters would meet on a hilltop to exchange gifts and knowledge. (It is said that this was the origin of our modern conferences.) At one of these Solstice gatherings, the Crane Master, known for having great vision and the important qualities of being emotional and empathetic, spoke up. He asked, "What happens if the Mongolians attack our region and all of these great arts are lost?" The Tiger Master scoffed saying, "Our skills are so great that even if these new metal balls (bullets) were shot at us, our ability to move whilst holding the great ball of life, and our strength will overcome the invaders." The Crane Master's viewpoint won the day when she said, "Why don't we, just to be safe, have each animal master take a few movements, combine them with the Masters of the other Ancient ways, and develop them into a set? Each of us can contribute a few movements."

*This imaginal story arose from a meditation
on the isolated mountain top of Bear Creek Mountain
after practicing Tai Chi there,
one fine summer day.*

—Michael, from mountains

We are lucky that the mythic Crane Master's viewpoint led to saving this sacred set of movements, for indeed the Mongolians did invade. The ancient way of the Animal Masters, and the way of the masters of the other forces of nature were lost, but elements of them were saved in an abbreviated set.

This set is now called Tai Chi Chuan. It is the supreme and ultimate method of combining yin and yang (Tai Chi), and holding the powers of the elemental forces of the universe with a sacred grasp in your hand (Chuan). Those who wish to do scholarship to prove the validity of this tale may instead choose to practice the art of Tai Chi as if this story is true, and imagine the set transporting you back to those times (beyond time). You may then find those primordial ways of moving that incorporate self-defense, healing, and spiritual unfoldment.

Tai Chi Chuan: A Postmodern Metaphysical View—Continued

Imagination is more important than knowledge.

—sign hanging in Einstein's office at Princeton

Earlier I told you about my post-modern orientation to Tai Chi, and how my own experience, Western psychology, and cross cultural initiatory traditions have influenced my views. Following along a similar post- modern vein, the origin myth I told you is looked at by most traditional Tai Chi teachers who I have met as being "just fantasy."

There often seems to be a literalistic bias in some segments of many traditional cultures, and perhaps for a good reason. They want to keep the history of their traditions in tack, and preserve their cultural knowledge. However, since my path is to penetrate into the symbolic meanings of the names of movements, I often run into problems with literalists who say for example, "your calling the second movement of Tai Chi, 'Taoist Immortal Paints the Heavenly Rainbow,' is not historically accurate. There are many names for this movement, and the lineage I represent has the oldest, and truest meaning."

I am often pained to have to call forth deeply my medicine animal name, Deer Kissing Eyes, to kindly point out that my path is to excite the imagination (symbolized by my Sun conjunct Uranus) so that my students, and my practice, can bring forth healing qi to those that follow this imaginal Path. In the deeper teachings of Tai Chi it is said that the qi (energy) follows the yi (intention). For example, when a practitioner has the intention, or imagines, that he or she is painting a heavenly rainbow, a sacralizing of the surrounding space may happen. An altered state of consciousness may be activated for the Tai Chi student, just as it is for others who practice various "traditions of postural initiation" (Goodman, 1990).

The person who coined the term "traditions of postural initiation" is Dr. Felicitas Goodman. In the tradition that she named "psychological archeology" she and her students (Gore, 1995) have experimented with imitating various postures from various indigenous sources at the Cuyamungu Institute near Santa Fe. The emphasis is on the state of consciousness that is evoked by the practitioner as various mudras and postures are held. This may or may not be the experience of the person who first held this posture.[1]

A traditional Tai Chi practitioner sticks to the exact teachings of his master, preserving a worthy lineage. A modern Tai Chi practitioner, to fit into the demands of modern life makes a shorter form, or may focus on one element of the practice such as its martial, healing, or spiritual purpose. Likewise statistical research is fundamental to a modern approach, using Occam's razor to cut away anomalies and see what is "efficacious" for a given population of people.[2]

In my view, a "postmodern Tai Chi practitioner" may value research and the classical forms and their purposes; however the anomalous nature of each person's subjective experience is also valued. For the Reluctant Metaphysician, beyond the notion of "objective truth" is the role that the imagination of the practitioner plays in evoking the interplay of both classical forms and meanings that are personal (or transpersonal) to the practitioner.

One of the first scholars to speak of "the imaginal," and who coined the phrase "imaginal realm", was the French philosopher Henry Corbin (2001). In his study of Sufi and Persian texts, he discovered that in these literatures it was believed that there existed a realm above our ordinary three-dimensional consciousness. Students of Corbin's work summarize his view of the imaginal this way:

> *While some aspects of the imagination are clearly contrived, these texts suggest that there is also a place in our imaginations where things are "real," in the sense that they are not being "imagined" by someone, but are images that have some kind of integrity or existence on their own. Thus the imagination appears to have two aspects: one intentionally fabricated; the other presents itself to us intact. Corbin used the term "mundus imaginalis" (imaginary realm) to differentiate between the "imaginary" (i.e. something equated with the unreal or with fantasy) and the "imaginal" (i.e. a world that is ontologically as real as the things we see or touch or know intellectually). In Corbin's view—and that of archetypal psychology—the images that come from the mundus imaginalis are a reality in some dimension other than the sensible and intellectual dimensions that we are most familiar with and have been taught to value and respect.* (Frenier & Hogan, 2006)

Using the Imaginal in Your Tai Chi Practice

In this light, I teach Tai Chi and Qigong movements as a practice that has four dimensions of purpose: self-healing, spiritual unfoldment, self-defense, and changing your life stance psychologically. There is some historical support for the fact that early systems of the internal martial arts were seen this way (Tomio, 1994: Diepersloot, 1997; Mayer, 2004). However, the point is not whether this is historically or objectively accurate; the issue is that when one practices this way a metaphysical experience happens that expands the sphere of the Self and connects the practitioner to deeper dimensions of meaning.

For example, I have done a few lectures for students at The American College of Traditional Chinese Medicine. I ask them what they have learned about the origins of acupuncture. They reply it derived from the times when arrows were shot and people noticed that when certain points on the body were hit with arrows that certain medical diseases would consistently occur. I then asked them to open their textbooks to the page that had a picture of Pien Chhio (Djen & Needham, 1980, p. 80).

Pien Chhio was an early acupuncturist who was reported to have brought a crown prince out of a coma with an acupuncture needle. I pointed out a picture in their textbook taken from a stone relief that depicts him as a bird-like figure treating a patient with a needle and holding his pulse. So, I then questioned the students as to whether the origins of acupuncture may lay in the earlier movements of the shamanic masters of the animal Daoyin practices. I asked, "Did these practitioners, who led and guided their qi through imitating the movements of animals, bring this experiential knowledge into the description of the meridians? I pointed out to the students that in Crane Animal frolic (of Hua Tau) practitioners lift their arms up to the side exposing the meridian of the heart which goes from under the armpit to the middle finger; and this Crane Flying practice is focused on the heart meridian (see illustration). Likewise, I showed them how Hua Tau's movement called Bear Pouncing activates the Liver meridian line, and interestingly in Hua Tau's first-century Animal Frolic set it was said that the Bear correlates with the liver.

Figure 12: Ornithoid Android Figure Treating a Kneeling Patient

Figure 13: Crane Flying

Figure 14: Bear Pouncing

Figure 15: Bear Pushes Tree

From a post-modern viewpoint, the issue is not whether these hypotheses are objectively true or historically accurate. Certainly this would be interesting for an anthropologist to uncover; but in the tradition I named psycho-spiritual anthropology (Mayer, 2004) this post-modern, metaphysical way of viewing historical snippets is to put the emphasis on the altered state invocation and healing that comes from "re-visioning" a movement's purpose.

In Tai Chi training the initiate is taught that the qi follows the yi (intention), and in modern mind-body medicine the role of belief (placebo) had been proven to effect healing. So, it would be no surprise that when a practitioner imagines that they are activating their heart meridian with a Crane practice, or their Liver meridian with a Bear practice, that healing may be facilitated (Hui, 2000). Certainly, this does not preclude an integrative medical treatment approach to address problems in these meridians and organs with health professionals. As a matter of fact, many Chinese doctors who treat diseases related to organ imbalances with acupuncture and herbs will also suggest Qigong movements to complement their treatments. Such is the case with one of my animal form teachers, Dr. Alex Feng, OMD (Feng, 2003).

I am not trying to say that Chinese Qigong masters do not use the imagination in their teachings. It is common to hear teachers of Tai Chi say, "Stand as if you are dangling like a puppet from the heavens." This is usually seen to be a way to align posture to maximize qi flow.

However, if we allow multifaceted, imaginal pathways to occupy a center place in our practice rather than emphasizing fixed cultural meanings, one can uncover many deep meanings to this stance. For example, the Chinese character for "chi (qi)" in Tai Chi (in Pin Yin it is spelled, "Taiji") is not qi (also spelled chi), meaning life energy. The *I Ching* states that the Chinese term "chi" means a ridgepole in a house. This is usually elaborated upon by saying that it is the place where yin and yang meet at the roof of a house, or the sunny and shady side of a mountain. So, in this interpretation, Tai Chi is about finding the meeting places of opposites where yin and yang meet. A shamanic meaning of "chi" is discovered if we take the idea that the ridgepole is not merely the horizontal ridgepole of a house, but in its oldest meaning it was the vertical celestial pole, according to the scholar Joseph Needham. The Pole Star remains stationary while all the constellations revolve around it (Needham, 1956, p. 464; Mayer, 2004, p. 247n).

A postmodern, metaphysical way of thinking about Tai Chi Chuan is to use classical sources, but also to allow cross-cultural traditions to fecundate the ground of the practice. In this light, an interesting cross-cultural parallel to the idea of the ridgepole is that in the Roman mysteries of Mithras the initiation ceremony involved becoming one with the central axis of the earth that led to the North Star. Even the sun was seen to be revolving around this axis. The "investiture ceremony" filled the initiate with a sense of centeredness, and created an alignment with the heavenly axis. The Mithraic mysteries add a depth of understanding when we hear that in China, the "qi" in the *I Ching* is a pole connected to the "heavenly root." By imagining that the crown of our head is connected with the North Star, and the world is circling around us, we can experience becoming the heavenly root of the Celestial Pole, connecting heaven and earth. This fits with the cross-cultural spiritual notion of the initiate becoming aligned with the *axis mundi,* the axis of the world around which the archetypal forces of the universe including yin, yang, and the five elements play out their cosmic creative dance.

Alignment with heavenly purpose and bringing this awareness into our everyday lives, our bodies, our communities, and our living spaces is a key aspect of shamanic healing. By doing so, we create a "centre of the world" where sacred space can be created. Imagination creates a reality. Try practicing Tai Chi with the intention of aligning yourself with the Axis Mundi, and see how it affects your movements and your life…. It couldn't hurt. ☺

CHAPTER 14

The Greek Mystery Cave: The (Real?) Uterus of the Great Earth Mother

Truth is a demure lady,
much too ladylike to knock you on your head
and drag you to her cave.
She is there, but people must want her, and seek her out.

—William F. Buckley, Jr.

Not only do meetings with remarkable people and traditions have the opportunity to change the garment of our lives, so do remarkable places such as the places that I have told you about—my yearly retreat spot in the Stanislaus forest and my favorite local "re-charging-my-batteries" spot at Bear Creek Mountain.

The next place I want to tell you about is "the place of places" I have discovered that most represents to me a place to rebirth the soul. In the Introduction of this book, I told you the story of the "Old Woman in the Cave of Creation." Since a major frame story of this book is this story about this Cave of Creation, and how the Old Woman or the Great Goddess helps to weave the garment of our lives there, the next story about a journey to a cave is more than apropos. However, I have some misgivings about telling you this story. Some places are too sacred to write about.

After I finished my *Trials of the Heart* book, I led two trips to Greece in the mid-1990s. When I went to the sacred sites about which I had read, I fulfilled a life dream. This was not only because of all of my readings in Greek mythology and having just finished a book on Greek mythology and relationships, but also because I suspected that I was part Greek. My grandmother's maiden family name was Mariasis, and many Greek people I have known have said this name was Greek. I still do not know whether it is true that I have some Greek heritage; but often Mystery (who must be part of the family of Moira, or fate) can be as much of a driver of our lives as genetic predispositions or family ties. All I know is that some compelling force pulled me to study Greek mythology and to travel to Greece to find out something about the origins of the psyche, and about my own origin myth.

The Cave of the Oracle of Delphi

Then the day came. Following a decade of academic research on the traditions of ancient Greece, I went to one of the most awesome places I have ever been…the cave of the Oracle of Delphi.

When tourists go on the classical tour of Greece, even the regular tourist site at Temple of Apollo at Delphi (not the cave) is one of the places in the world that is most moving to the soul. There, inscribed in stone on the temple of Apollo is the well-known aphorism, "Know thyself." These very words have led seekers such as myself to explore the metaphysical depths of the human soul. There in the museum one can view the *omphalos,* a stone that some say represents the navel of the world. Another myth say that this omphalos was Dionysus' tomb; and it has been suggested that a ritual was enacted here of bringing Dionysus' mother Semele up from the lower world, from Hades (Fontenrose, 1959, p. 377). The stone amphitheater near the museum is sacred to the Goddess Athena. All of the edifices of the old world at this famous site of classical Greece are memorable for anyone who visits. Here, tourists hear stories of ancient kings and common people who traveled to find the answers to their life questions. In the ancient Greek world it was said that the Oracle of Delphi had those answers.

However, as amazing as these places are, oftentimes those who come to well known popularized places may lose connection with deeper discoveries from still deeper places— a poignant metaphor for life. And so it was that I discovered that the real location of the Oracle was not the place to which the tourists went on their paid tours. Through my own research, and through the direction of a Greek scholar and friend, Yannis Tousoulis, I knew that there was a cave that was the earlier origin of the Oracle of Delphi.

Historically speaking, before the time of the Achaean invasion around the 1800s BC, before the Olympian gods (Zeus, Apollo, and their entourage) took over this place, it was the cave of the triple Goddess. Symbolic of this takeover, one legend says the omphalos stone (which may have been a meteorite) marked the spot where Apollo drove the serpent monster Python into the Earth (Gaia). This "serpent monster" was a symbol of the older religion of the Triple Goddess that was driven out from this cave (Graves, 1955).

There are always many different lenses through which a person can view a mythic tale. Anthropological, historical, psychological, initiatory, and mythopoetic viewpoints all add to the interpretation of these mythic tales. Just like in Tai Chi practice where all dimensions (self-healing, spiritual unfoldment, self-defense, changing our life stance) are important, so it is with the Greek mythology of caves that all dimensions of interpretation add to a holistic view. The metaphysical lens (an oft-used attachment to a Reluctant Metaphyscian's metaphorical eye-glasses) is colored by a rainbow palate of psychological, initiatory, and mythopoetic hues.

I had seen the picture of this cave of the Oracle of Delphi when I read Manly Hall's book, *The Secret Teachings of all Ages,* in the early 1970s. Later in the early 1990s, I was fascinated to hear a deep rendering of the stories about this cave when I read Joseph Fontenrose's book, *Python, A Study of the Delphic Myth and its Origins* (1959). I learned that this cave was said to be the cave where Deucalion, the Greek Noah, went when a flood destroyed the world. Noah went to a boat, whereas Deucalion went to a cave high in the Greek mountains. Adding to the mystery of this cave, Fontenrose also reports that it was a secret entryway to the underworld; and he said it led to the world of the Hyperboreans, the people of old England.

Having one foot in the mythic world of the imagination and one foot in the world of consensual reality, I wondered what I would find in this cave. The first time I went to it, in the early 1990s I was in my early forties, and yet its awesomeness turned me into being like a wide-eyed child. After a substantial hike up a Greek mountain, the opening into the dark cave in the hillside was an invitation to enter cautiously into another world. Our group and I entered into a cave that looked similar to the picture of the Oracle of Delphi that I had seen in Manly Hall's book (Hall, 1962).

Figure 16: The Oracle of Delphi

Another story about the cave is that one of the early discovers of the cave was a shepherd who found it because his sheep came back to him intoxicated. Supposedly he traced back their footprints to this cave, where fumes from the Earth were emitted. These intoxicating emanations from the Earth induced a person, or an animal into a trance state. The story goes that the female Greek priestesses would breathe these fumes, enter into a trance state, and from the messages received they would give oracular predictions. In the picture that I had seen in the Manly Hall book, a tripod was placed above a hole in the earth from where these fumes emitted.

However, now that I was here in this giant cave, there was no hole where the oracular tripod was placed in the drawing. Nonetheless, the feeling of mystery and the experience of "the esoteric" exuded from the rocks. This cave was about as big as a football field underground. My inner explorer was awakened as I was drawn to the back of the cave where in Manly Hall's picture, and in my view, the cave ended. The cave wall evoked something in me, in a way my rational self cannot explain, calling me to climb it.

I am no mountain climber, and here the back wall of the cave went up at about an 85-degree angle; and it was damp underground at the back of a dark cave so the walls were very slippery. Yet I was drawn to climb it while others clearly expressed their concern that I, and the student who was drawn to climb it with me, could slip down the wet walls, fall, and get hurt. I knew that there was no insurance policy to cover impetuous acts that endangered others and myself; yet some force circumvented my normal conscientious self, and it compelled me to make this journey up this dangerous cave wall at any cost.

Plato's Story of the Cave: The World behind the World

The student, who I will call Alex, and I in a *folie a deux*, made our way up this wall finding the handholds that a mountain climber somehow finds, and we finally reached the top. Unbeknownst to even a careful observer, I discovered that the cave wall did not end at the top-most point that the eye could see. There was an empty space at the top of the wall about four feet high where I sat with Alex. Our feet were dangling over the precipice, the upper part of the cave lip, and we looked back into the emptiness in the opposite direction from the front of the cave. As we sat there, I told him the story of Plato and the Cave about how we all live in an external world of forms, which according to Plato is the representation of another world of "archetypal realities." I was reminded of my college philosophy class where my metaphysical journey had begun; but now in this cave of mystery I had a deeper understanding of why I had wanted to learn more about experiential rather than academic metaphysics.

As we saw the shadows of our bodies reflected on the back most part of cave wall in front of us, Alex and I discussed how we all are like chained people in the cave of life looking at the shadows that pass before our eyes. We never realize that there are other forms outside the cave of life that are creating these shadows that we take as "reality." I was reminded of my first philosophy professor at Syracuse University giving the first lecture on metaphysics that I had ever heard on Plato's Cave and his theory of forms. (This was the field trip from that metaphysics lecture that I had been waiting a few decades to take!)

Unfortunately, I did not have a flashlight, so I was left with just the light of my imagination as to what was below our feet. As we were sitting at this secret opening at the top of the cave, I wondered whether in the space beneath our dangling legs that perhaps there was an entryway to some other world. Maybe, as the texts that I had researched had said, it led all the way to England to the world of the Hyperboreans, in whose land stands a treasury of golden honey, and an ancient temple of honeycomb (Fontenrose, 1980, p. 431). I had also read that it was not honey that was guarded here by dragons; but instead the substance that the Nymphs ate to get mantic inspiration was "soma," a psychedelic substance. It was either shared with the hero, or the substance was administered by force (Fontenrose, 1980, pp. 430–431).

I wondered, whether perhaps this cave was one of the entryways to the underworld, reported in Greek mythology. Could it be that at the bottom of the long drop below our feet it led to a world of honey, or the "Center of the world," as in the Jules Verne novel? I threw stones and could not hear them hit bottom. Indeed, perhaps this cave went down very, very far. I wondered whether maybe beneath my feet, many feet below, lay skeletons of those who were sacrificed in the cave and fell many feet to their death.

But, because I had not brought a flashlight, I could not see down into that darkness. I promised myself that I would come back to this cave someday with the appropriate flashlight, and go down into the darkness and explore its depths as deep down as it led me.

Second Visit to the Cave

Two years later I had an opportunity to co-lead a trip to the ancient sites of Greece with a woman scholar of Greek mythology, Demetra George. Finally, I was able to come back to the cave of my dreams with a flashlight and find the answer to my questions. What was down this big drop at the top of the cave? This second climb was not nearly as scary as the first time. When I reached the top this time, with three brave students, the moment came…While dangling our legs over the precipice, I shined my flashlight down to into this deep space to reality-check my projections. Over the lip of this precipice the space only went down six feet or so. A disappointment filled me to the deepest depths of my bone marrow. This was no entryway to the underworld; the reason my stone throws had produced no sound a few years ago was because the area six feet under our feet was sand. "Reality Bites"…as the old movie title says.

I hope most people have stopped reading this by now. We live in a culture where people want quick answers to things, and if we have paid for a book we feel entitled to know certain specifics. Sorry, I'm not going to name this cave, (that would be too much of a violation of the sacredness of this site); but true seekers will have enough information from this book to find it. I would hate to come back to this sacred place right before I die and see a McDonald's Restaurant at the front of the cave due to my having revealed its location. So, it might take you a bit more research and effort if you are meant to be here, and treat it with due respect.

After suffering my disappointment as to what was not beneath my feet, with the help of my flashlight I looked to my left. There was a long granite-like snake or dragon-like structure. From my memory now, it was about two feet wide and twelve feet long. It seemed that it would be impossible for such a structure to exist over time because the weight of it would make it collapse. It looked like a naturally growing structure growing out of this recess of the mountain. I wish I could talk to a geologist to examine this work of nature to see if it this would be possible to be a naturally growing protrusion, or if it was a human made ritual structure.

Initiation into Psycho-Archeological Realities:
The Dragon and the Earth Mother

I had read that this cave was one of the last resting places of one of the last dragons of the ancient world, Python, or some call her Delphine. One version of the myth told of Apollo, while a babe in Leto's arms, killing this dragon (or a snake in some versions) that appeared in a hollow in the rocks, with an arrow. Mythic history reports that at this time, Apollo took over the cave from the Goddess religion. What dragon slaying means changes in different versions of the story. In one version, the Great Goddess Hera ordered Python to pursue the pregnant Leto and destroy her with her unborn son; later Apollo returned to Delphi to settle accounts. Another version of the tale tells of Python being a man who was plundering the land and that the Delphians sought Apollo's aid, and Apollo fought and killed him (Fontenrose, 1980, pp. 13–22).

This area of the cave grabbed the imagination and abducted it into a journey of leaps and bounds. Could this be a stone figurine of this last dragon of the ancient world? I wondered whether perhaps this stone dragon-snake was a mason's constructed replica of some prehistoric monster that actually lived here; or perhaps, it was the very place where some dragon ritual was enacted with initiates in an ancient rite of initiation.

We all know that in many ancient caves that tribal tales were told in initiatory rituals. So, it is not too far of a stretch of the imagination to posit that this secret hidden chamber at the back of the cave was where initiates were taken to enter into rituals that would transform their souls. Perhaps esoteric secrets were transmitted here where Greek priests would lead acolytes into the deeper secrets of the Greek mystery religions.

My flashlight helped to expand my vision of this hidden antechamber; it was about fifteen square feet...a hidden room above and behind the cave. By the way, it is said that this cave is the cave of forty rooms. When I first came to this cave and I looked around, I clearly saw that there were no other rooms in this football stadium-sized cave. I said to myself that reports of all those rooms must have been "just a myth." Well, now I just had discovered one of the rooms. My flashlight scanned further. On the right of this antechamber was a hole, maybe three feet wide, going further into the mountain.

Now, it was enough for this non-mountain climber, who I am, to have risked his life climbing up the side of the back of the cave to get here. However, being cautious by nature, why would I climb into this dangerous hole...particularly because I knew the dangers of earthquakes after having lived in California for many years? How can a rational scholar like myself explain a force so strong that it could get me to let go of caution and climb into this hole? There was no caution in my fellow journeyers or in me...only "Necessity" (in Greek, Necessity is named the Goddess *Ananke* or *Themis*) ruled here. We were compelled to enter the hole, drawn by a force stronger than rationality. It is interesting that in Greek mythology it is said that this was a cave of the triple Goddess, and in Greek mythology it was said that Necessity gave birth to three daughters, known as Moirai, the three fates, a major theme of this book.

So, the three equally foolish, and equally compelled, students followed me into the hole. I asked the students to use no flashlight so we could have the experience of crawling into the earth. In the midst of my crawling, I could not help remember reading about the "reverse birth" that was part of the initiatory ceremonies of the Greek mystery traditions (Meier, 1967, pp. 110–112; Mayer, 2009, pp. 62–63). Now, here I was crawling back into the Earth Mother! This, more than anything I had ever read about, or could experience elsewhere, was a crawling into "the vagina of the earth." I felt as if I was returning to a place I had never been, yet had always been. It was as if I was in the Earth Mother's womb. Rationality was suspended as I felt as if I was visiting the origin of a primordial birthplace of humanity.

As we crawled into the narrow tunnel that appeared to be the vagina of the Earth Mother, maybe twenty feet back, I felt the need to turn on my flashlight. I saw that right ahead there was an opening where we could stand. Gratefully, the four of us had a respite from our crawl into the unknown. As we stood there in this small space, just big enough for six people to form a circle, we circled together. I scanned around the space with my flashlight and right above us, in the midst of a circle of solid rock, were two six-foot round holes in the rock about seven feet high.

An awesome imaginative realization struck me. It was as if we were standing in "the uterus of the Earth Mother," because above us were "her ovaries!" This place where we were standing looked like it came straight out of an anatomy textbook. Or, were anatomy textbooks copied from this place? I shared these thoughts with the three others, and we were all in awe.

The Initiatory Dimensions of the Journey into the Cave at Delphi

Since this was a psycho-mythologically oriented trip, we went back and forth between our inner experiences and outer rituals. Each of us went inside to experience what this place was for us. Where were we? We leaped into the realm of mythic imagination: Was the human race and the first woman's anatomy created from here? Were the same forces that created the human race and women involved in the creation of each? In the realm of psycho-geological musings, what was such a place used for in ancient initiatory rituals, and how could it be used for now for us as a birthing chamber?

In a group ritual performed in silence, we each reflected upon what wanted to give birth to in our lives. We all turned off our flashlights to prepare ourselves for the ritual to come. There was a darkness and a silence here that was deeper than anything I had ever experienced. No noise from civilization, no electrical buzz could penetrate these walls.

We each imagined in our own way being a child of the Earth Mother, "listening" to the silence to receive our call to do our dharmic work for the world. I had taught the group a Standing Meditation practice the day before, and we all now went into our Standing Meditation stance. I encouraged each member of the group to imagine what new life stance he or she would like to take when he or she was reborn from the cave, from the uterus of the Earth Mother.

I encouraged each group member in the circle to allow images to arise. Each of the four of us had our own experience. One woman journeyed through fear: She thought, "Will an earthquake come and collapse on us in this vulnerable place?" Then she realized that many fears, which were originally instilled by her mother, had limited her from taking some important risks in life. She had been in an unfulfilling job for many years to keep her health insurance. After the experience she had here in this cave, she made a commitment to herself to carry the energy shooting through her body to write a book for children. This had always been her dream.

I made a commitment to myself that I would keep this ritual cave to draw from in troubled times, and to draw inspiration and metaphors from it in my work with patients, teaching, and writing. Still to this day, in times of difficulty, I imagine myself in this cave dealing with the dragons of my life and allow messages to come to me from its different rooms (which I like to think of as sub-personalities). Now, many decades later, I enjoy leading people on ritual inner journeys in hypnotherapy sessions to their inner caves to find rebirth on a life issue.

I led the group in a chant that I had recently learned in California from the Reclaiming Collective called, "Return Again." It goes like this,

> *Return again, Return again,*
> *Return to the land of your soul.*
> *Return to what you are, Return to who you are.*
> *Return to where you were born and reborn again.*

We sang and repeated this chant many times and then just stood in silence in our Standing Meditation posture. Then, after our group ritual ended, we crawled back in a "catabasis" out through the vaginal tunnel of the Great Mother. After coming out into the antechamber the dragon figurine did not look so foreboding. It was as if the structure of the mountain itself created the perfect initiatory space. The psycho-geological metaphor spoke and said that after going into the recesses of the Earth Mother, and finding our inner power and purpose, the dragons of life seem less ominous.

It was interesting to me that my favorite mythological author, Mircea Eliade, in his book *Rites and Symbols of Initiation* (1958, p. 57–9) explored the parallels between Taoist embryonic breathing practices, cave initiation, and the Greek mystery tradition. Eliade wrote about Taoist techniques of "mystical physiology" whereby embryonic breathing plays a role in teaching human beings how to enter the womb again in order to recreate their true nature and find the fullness of their portion in life. These were the same Eastern practices that had so captivated me for all these years, and now their import was becoming actualized in this cave.

In this same section of his book (Eliade, 1958, p. 57), Eliade speaks of how alchemists such as Paracelsus say, "He who would enter into the Kingdom must first enter with his body into his mother and there die." On the very next line of the text, most amazingly to me, Eliade mentions my namesake Michael Maier's (the 15th century alchemist) amplification on this theme and how he speaks of the *Secretus Maximus* involving "the mother who of natural necessity must unite with her son." He speaks of how the mother symbolizes nature in the primordial state, which is the *prima materia* of the alchemists.

A question arose for me, "Could the very resonance of my name, from the Kabalistic perspective (Suares, 1992) have led me and Michael Maier to the same place, similar interests, and some of the same types of metaphysical experiences?" It certainly felt as if the experience that I and my group had was like a return to the Great Mother…and a new birth from her womb. Eliade speaks of how the new birth (just as our actual physical birth) is oftentimes accompanied by an initiatory ordeal that must involve the risk of death. Indeed, our group and I, who saw the stone dragon and crawled into and out of the dangerous hole in the mountain, had an initiatory experience that felt like a rebirth.

Mircea Eliade in the very next paragraph speaks of the return to the womb having to do with "whole series of initiatory rites concerning caves and mountain crevices as symbols of the womb of the Mother Earth…." He speaks of these cross-cultural mythic connections in cultures such as China; and he says that the term "*tong*," cave, also means mysterious, profound, transcendent, and that the term became equivalent to the arcana revealed in initiation. Eliade goes on to speak about how cross-cultural cave initiations figured in ceremonies of embryonic gestation and a new birth. The initiates of these ceremonies were considered "twice-born."

So, long before fundamentalist Christians spoke of being twice born here we have that same concept in ancient initiatory rituals. Also, as you can see, the weaving together of the fabric of many aspects of my life came together in this cave. It was as if I was returning to a birthplace of the fabric of my soul.

Psycho-Historical Dimensions

The Greek creation myth says that out of this cave, after the great flood that Deucalion escaped, the human species was reborn. Whether the anthropological evidence would support that the rebirth of the human species actually came from this cave at the end of the Bronze Age, I do not know. But I could certainly imagine how a rebirth could have taken place from rituals enacted in this sacred tunnel. Regarding the references in the Greek mystery traditions about initiates of the caves of the underworld going through a "catabasis" (a reverse birth)…here in this place, it seemed as though the Earth itself had carved the perfect place for such a ritual.

In some of the Greek mystery tales of the underworld it was said that the initiate would be held in the cave for weeks and months until they had a visionary experience. Trophonius was one of these initiates (Meier, 1967, p. 101). Some saw the stars in the cave and others recovered laughter. Some saw the midnight sun and they saw light emerge from darkness. This idea of the birth of the midnight sun was of particular interest to me since my dream of the Land Where the Sun Rose in the West that happened on the Summer Solstice of 1971 had ended with a dark cloudy earth and the sun shining through the top of my head, like a midnight sun. Indeed, threads of my life seemed to be coming together from the experience in this cave.

Many scholars have wondered about the historical and initiatory elements of cave rituals and of the Delphic ritual. One author, Marguerite Rigoglioso (2009) posits that the Delphic ritual in pre-patriarchal Greece was a place where female priestesses enacted a ritual of divine virgin birth. Though we may never know what exactly took place in such caves, the experiential metaphysician is interested in using the imagination to enact current rituals that further the connection with the world behind the world for healing and transformation.

Cave Creation Myths: Weaving Tales to Create New Ways of Being

Caves have long been part of creation myths. Whether we want to imagine that this cave of Deucalion was the actual cave from which the human race (or at least part of the Greek civilization) was reborn after the Great Deluge, there is something about caves and creation.

The Old Woman in the Cave

I began this book with a story told by Michael Meade (2008) in his book, *The World Behind the World*. He talks about how Cave stories have often figured in the cultivation of "soul." The South American folktale he tells of "The Old Woman who Weaves the World" is one of many cave tales that gives depth to the human experience. I like how in this tale the Old Woman has her garment undone by the Black Dog, and how she copes with this by not getting upset. She merely begins her work again.

I have told this story to many patients, (and to myself) many times to serve as a reminder of the inner work we all need to do at those times that our lives unravel. The lessons of ancient cave initiations are not only relegated to times past. Such is the power of story; when we are out of the cave the retelling reminds us of the initiatory quests that we are all called forth to undertake. Each tale opens another hidden room in the depths of each of our souls.

There are many creation myths that talk of a woman weaver in a cave and weaving. The South American story that Michael Meade tells has a parallel in a Sioux story, thousands of miles away around the Ohio River basin and the Great Lakes in the Manataka Hot Springs area. A tale was told around the fire at night about the West Mountain where there was a Woman with a dog in her cave whose dog unravels a portion of a rug, which she weaves back together. Here the story is told that there were seven hidden caves among the caves one that was used by the Animal People to perform their ceremonies. The center cave was pure crystal, and The Star people who once visited it left messages embedded in the crystal stones.[1]

The classic Cave of Creation myth from Greece tells about the Three Fates, *The Moirae*. According to Greek mythology they weave the threads of individual lives, and the fate of our lives comes from these archetypal powers. *Clotho* spins the thread of life, *Lachesis* measures the thread of life allotting to each person our time, and *Atropose* cuts the thread of our lives determining the manner of each of our deaths.

According to some tales the Moirae may have existed at Delphi, maybe even in the oracular cave there (Fontenrose, 1959). Some imagine that each of our umbilical cords are one of those threads that go from one world to the next, and "the mythic Old Woman in the Cave" gives it that unique twist that becomes our uniqueness.

A Ritual for Opening the Imaginal Caves of Our Lives

Why have caves and initiation been so co-related through time? From a metaphysical perspective we can imagine being in this cave even if we don't travel to Greece. You may experience such an initiation as you do the guided meditation that I have used with students throughout the last decades:

> Picture a cave in a side of a mountain that is about the size of a football field. Imagine traveling to this cave with an issue for which you would like help. In the middle stands a tripod with a woman oracle. We all have our issues that our mothers and fathers were carrying before our birth, as the Goddess Leto did. The issues that our parents' carry can be some of the issues that the hero confronts in his or her initiation—they can be like dragons. At times these fire breathing psycho-mythological beasts spew words of criticism to us when we are most vulnerable; they turn into dysfunctional beliefs, that burn us, tear at us, or entwine us in self-hatred. The Arrows of Apollo (the Sun God) symbolize those

pointed, on-target statements that can defeat those inner monsters that swallow us up and prevent us from seeing the light of day, the sun.

What arrow can be shot from your quiver? For example, if you have been saying to yourself that you are a failure, perhaps your mother or father gave you that message due to a need that you fit her or his idealized image. The natural child in you, a Sun God, may embed a little note on your arrow, which says, "I accept myself and the unique way that the solar light shines through me; and I don't need your judgments." Shoot the dragon. An imaginal arrow may hit the bull's-eye of a fiery attack against you. {In my last books I relate shooting verbal arrows to the art of bantering, (Mayer, 2007, pp. 220–223; Mayer 2009, p. 281–286.)}

If you have found the constructive belief that hits the bulls-eye, perhaps you will help the light to shine in your inner cave where dark forces have ruled. According to mythic research, Dionysus and Apollo were co-rulers of the cave, one in the winter months another in the summer months (Fontenrose, 1980, p. 383). Perhaps you will find a centering in your world as you place the omphalos (the symbol of the navel of the world) to mark the place where you have just journeyed. Maybe it will resurrect your inner mother (symbolized by Semele) from the underworld that has captured her; and perhaps your journey to the underworld will help her to emerge into the realm of light. (But don't get too attached to the rescuing part of your inner work, or modern psychology will label you as co-dependent. ☺)

As you follow your breath down to your own navel using the River of Life practice, you may find your inner omphalos, the place in the center of you (the tan tien) that the Taoists say leads to the Sea of Elixir. So, here inside of you both Eastern and Western mystery traditions join. Just like the Taoist alchemists say that practicing microcosmic orbit and breathing and sinking your qi to the tan tien can lead to the experience of Golden Flower or the Golden Ball (Wilhelm, 1963), here in Greek mythology the finding of the inner navel can lead you to the Dionysian God of Ecstasy. The experience that is borne from your inner journey in your inner cave may lead you to the inner golden honey of the Gods.

The Western mystery tradition honors the imaginal dimensions of life. It is said that there is another world that exists behind our world, and it is from there that we derive depth. Without a thread tied to this underworld, a connecting cord to our soul's purpose is cut off. It is for this reason that in the Greek mystery tradition the most beautiful goddess was Persephone (Queen of the underworld), a symbol of the depth born from the trials of the underworld that gives beauty.

So, the cave I have just described, the cave of the triple Goddess, exists in each of us. It is a place that we can go to when the overwhelming floods of life make us feel that we cannot survive. As Deucalion did, so can we retreat to this cave of our imagination, and do more than survive. Here we can make "soul," and create new human ways of Being.

The rock dragon that is in this secret chamber often comes to my mind. How was this carved symbol, this actual creation of the earth, used in ritual? I like to imagine that a priest or priestess took an acolyte up into this chamber to deal with the dragons (dark psychological demons) of his or her life as an initiatory story was told.

Remember the tale of Perseus who needed to free Andromeda from a cliff? Only the head of Medusa, which turned anyone who looked at her into stone, could defeat the dragon. I like to imagine that perhaps this very rock dragon was used to help the initiate to defeat the inner dragons of their lives. Maybe, just like when shamans used stories about natural occurrences to enlighten acolytes into the mythological truths of life, so was this exact rock dragon used to tell the story of the hero's defeat of the petrifying things of life (symbolized by Medusa).[2]

Musings on the Esoteric Dimension of Cave Initiations

There are many ways that this cave may have functioned in various initiatory rituals. The way it functions for us as a postmodern metaphysical ritual is only limited by our imagination. In the tradition of psychological archeology (Goodman, 1990; Gore, 1995), the stances shown in pictographs are imitated for the purposes of accessing transformative states. So, here it is being suggested that in visiting sacred sites that the experiential metaphysician allow for a psycho-archeological, imaginal journey to take place for the purpose of inner transformation and allowing Wonder to awaken.

In this spirit, here is one way that I imagine this cave's initiation ceremonies taking place: Members of the public, or acolytes, would not know that there were rooms within the cave that were unseen (perhaps forty rooms). While rituals were enacted on the "main stage," kings or members of the public may have been told stories of what to do with their lives by the Oracle. Voices and visions might appear coming out of solid rock that was coming from the hidden rooms of the cave. Through shifts in lighting, images of dragons might appear, and voices of the temple priests could lead the uninitiated into new life directions. If the cave had natural intoxicating fumes emerging from it, or if ingesting psychotropic substances was involved, this could contribute to experiences there that led to changing the worlds of kings and humans.

Ritual inductions that are performed when one is in a hypnotic altered state can be used for beneficial or non-beneficial purposes. Myths are not just fantasy tales about the old days. Are we not all living in just such a metaphorical cave today? Voices of the mass media, owned by giant corporations tell us tales that hypnotize us while many of us live in a trance state. A voice is heard from a trusted temple priest (a TV or radio announcer) and says: "The United States has the best health care in the world, and we don't need to change it." "Preventative medicine is a flaky and 'alternative medicine' and is not worthy of reimbursement by professionally run insurance companies." "Pharmacological medicine is real medicine, and don't take those untrustworthy herbal medicines."

The voices and stories told from hidden sources can be used to transform, or to deceive, to enlighten, or to subjugate. "The esoterics" are those metaphysicians initiated into the inner workings of the cave of life. We would like to live in the world of light of the Sun, yet we reluctantly enter into the darkness and take on the quest of looking behind the stories of life to explore their transforming and destructive potentials.

In the political sphere today, Thom Hartmann's (2007) book, *Cracking the Code,* unravels the myths that have hypnotized America, and he calls for each of us to take personal responsibility for changing our world.[3] Whether it is in the psychological or the political realm, the esoterics know that real change is borne from a solo journey into the depths of the cave of life. We need to face and deal with the Demons found there. From here a place of stillness, equanimity, and right action can be discovered. Creation in service of the divine and our society can emerge.

Conclusion

So, those of us who have been deeply moved by Eastern transcendent traditions would do well to visit our Western mystery tradition…a pathway that gives birth to soul not just spirit. Traveling to this outer and inner cave was for me a culmination of a meeting with Destiny. From the time when I read James Hillman's book *Revisioning Psychology* in the early 1970s, I was influenced by his distinction between "spirit" and "soul." Hillman taught us seekers on the Path that "spirit" has an affinity with high places geographically and transcendent spiritual paths; and "soul" is born from the lower places of life, the valleys, and the caves. This cave was one of the significant initiations in my life into "the path of my soul."

The cave of transformation lives in our relationships with others. At times a significant-other may ask, "Why can't you be more happy?" The voices coming from the upper regions of the cave may agree? However, deeper down in the lower rooms a voice calls out, "Initiate, come down here to turn lead into gold. Gold is not found only with the sky Gods. The deeper treasures of life are found through inner mining and inner work." It is from going down with others into their pain, spelunking and facing the "inner demons," that "the daemons" of our inner caves emerge and turn into allies. Our inner critic gets transformed into a coach, as healing words are wordsmithed by divine forces hidden in our inner caves. Then outside of the cave it may be carved in stone that we are initiates of the temple of those who are on the path of "Knowing thy Self."

So, caves are actual physical places as well as metaphysical places to which we can travel in order to survive dissolution. Not only when the floods of the world are about to destroy the human race do the prescient among us retreat to high mountain caves; but also when the emotional forces of life overwhelm us, then the wise amongst us retreat to inner caves and create our own cave meditations.

When we find our power spots in nature, it is from this stage that our life stories grow. The Western and Eastern mystery traditions agree that the stage of life provides a living mystery play where the human drama can be enacted. Power spots in nature allow our inner nature to activate the characters and characteristics of our deepest stories.

The symbol of retreating to a mountaintop when the world is being destroyed by water is one of the oldest symbols in humankind. In the earliest Mesopotamian legend, the god Enlil was going to destroy humankind by sending a flood due to the peoples' failure to appreciate the divine presence in life. Utnapishtim, (like the later Biblical Noah) who was a dreamer and retained a sense of wonder about life, was instructed in a dream to build a ship to save family, friends, and the seed of all living creatures including the wild animals. After the deluge covered the entire earth, except for the very top of Mount Nisur, that is where he went.

So, mountaintops, and mountain top caves, are some of the earliest symbols of human beings escaping from the deluges of life. When my patients and students experience external and internal criticism that seems to dissolve the very ground of their lives, when appropriate I take them on a mythic journey to this cave inside of themselves.

Those of us who have a connection to the imaginal realm can be saved from the deluges of life by making the stories of Utnapishtim and Deucalion our own. Those who have been initiated into the world behind the world, such as those who are initiates into the Caves of Life, can serve to introduce others to transformative practices that can help to rebirth us and our world during troubled times.

May you find such experiences in the journey to your inner mountaintop cave…

CHAPTER 15:

The Story-Telling Psychotherapist

God made human beings because of a love of stories.

—Rabbi Nachman of Bratzlev

Introduction

Following the path to the place where the streams of ancient sacred wisdom traditions and storytelling joined, I wanted to bring these "Waters of Life" to my psychotherapy students. I taught symbolic process courses to psychotherapy interns at John F. Kennedy University for five years from 1981 to 1986. In these courses we explored: dream work, sand tray, guided visualizations, and various imaginal methods I developed such the River of Life practice, Transpersonal Hypnosis, and the Mythic Journey Process.

During my years of teaching I have also been in private practice as a psychotherapist, from 1978 to the current time. Perhaps stemming from my appreciation of the transformative power of stories since my childhood, one of my great loves has been telling stories to my patients and using various story telling methods with them. I want to give you a feel for the breadth and depth of these story-telling methods…methods that have the capacity to change and guide each of their lives (as well as ours). For the Reluctant Metaphysician, the sufferings of life are often best dealt with and transformed by choosing from the toolkit of symbolic processes.[1]

Stories I Tell My Patients

If stories come to you, care for them.
And learn to give them away where they are needed.
Sometimes a person needs a story more than food to stay alive.

—Barry Lopez, *Crow and Weasel*

A few of my favorite stories are:

1. "The Monkey and the Banana"—To let go of attachments.
2. "Odysseus and the Sirens"—To center us in relationship to staying true to our life paths even when distractions occur.

3. "Buddha and the Sickness Demons"—To listen to the messages from our illnesses.

4. "The Jewish Farmer"—To trust in the existence of the divine mystery play of the forces of life when dire and beneficial circumstances arise.

5. "Perseus and Medusa"—For transforming blocks to our life paths and creativity.

After I tell you those stories I will show you how to develop your own story to heal elements of your own life.

1. THE MONKEY AND THE BANANA

In India the story is told that if you want to catch a monkey, put out a coconut with a hole cut in it, just the right size. Then, tie the coconut to a tree, and put a banana inside the coconut. When the right monkey comes along he will slip his hand into the coconut to get the banana; but as he holds onto the banana his fist will be too large to get out of the hole. He is captured by his attachment to having the banana, and therefore does not let go.

Children in India (in particular in Buddhist families) are sometimes taught this story to learn how to catch a monkey. However, the story behind this story addresses the importance of letting go in life, and how attachments cause suffering. One of the essential teachings of the Buddha was that attachment is at the root of suffering, and that enlightenment can be found by freeing oneself from holding on to the things of this world while following the eightfold path (of right action, right livelihood, and so forth). Hearing this story has helped innumerable numbers of my patients through the years.

2. ODYSSEUS AND THE SIRENS

The story is told in Greece of Odysseus, the hero of the Odyssey. While he was traveling in his boat the Sirens called out to his men to come and join the Sirens. The lure of the Sirens' call was so intoxicating that all of Odysseus' men jumped off the ship into the waters only to be dashed against the sharp rocks. None survived. But Odysseus, who had the strength to stay true to his mission, put wax in his ears and tied himself to the mast of his ship so that he wouldn't be tempted by the Siren's call. Only Odysseus survived.

And so it is in our lives. Everyday, the hero in us is tempted by many things that are capable of drowning us. Drugs and other addictions that entice us with a call to the short road to pleasure seduce some people.

Or, an individual or a culture may be tempted by the Siren's call of Greed. Corporations who have listened to the Siren's call have gone offshore to avoid taxes and have shipped American jobs to third world countries. Predatory capitalists in the banking and mortgage markets have lured investors into deals in murky waters and drowned members of the middle class in a sea of despair destroying lifetime investments in their houses and in the stock market. The American economy has been torn apart as it has hit against the hard sharp rocks of uncaring reality.

If we follow the teaching of Odysseus, each member of our culture is called to tie themselves to the mast of their own convictions. If we do not stay true to an alignment with higher goals, we jump into the sea of temptation and our hero's journey and our dreams (and those of our country) may end up dashed on the rocks.

Many of my patients have benefited from hearing Odysseus's story. Listening to such tales with our inner ear, can strike a chord in us that can help us to let go of relationships that are not serving our higher selves, We can move on to new jobs that better serve our life goals, and stay true to the odyssey of our lives.

3. BUDDHA AND THE SICKNESS DEMONS

The story is told of how the Buddha wanted to meet the chief demon of Illness because he had a question that he wanted answered. And so he journeyed for many days up a very steep and dangerous mountain path. Finally he reached the cave of this demon, Maha-kola-sanni-yaksaya. The demon, deep inside the cave, was one of the ugliest, pus exuding, mean looking, and smell emitting beings that anyone has ever encountered. The demon asked him what he wanted in a denigrating tone, and the Buddha bowed to the demon in deep respect and asked his question.

The Buddha asked, "Why do you bring illness and suffering to the people?" The demon replied, " If you think that with all the meditation that you and your disciples do, that it is anything compared to the power that I have to enlighten, you are mistaken." The demon continued, " I have watched the results of your disciples meditating for many hours, and I have seen that they are oftentimes still narcissistic, self-indulgent, greedy, and in general still carry on with their old unloving ways. But when I send them one of my diseases then their eyes look heavenward, they pray to the sky above and say, "Oh Great Spirit if you just make me better I will change my ways." And the demon continued, " I notice that many times, particularly when I send one of my most horrid diseases it does create major life changes in that person's life."

Hmmm…the Buddha said, "I'm glad I met you and I have seen the light in this way. So, we both have similar aims. Can't we come to some kind of agreement?" the Sickness Demon said," I'll tell you what…in the future I'll give humanity a way to heal themselves. If they can acknowledge the particular demon that is behind their particular illness, name its name, tell its origin story, wear its mask, dance its dance, or sing its song then that Illness Demon will leave (paraphrased from Larsen, 1981).

What does it mean to wear the mask of the Demon? In the temple of Aesclepius, one important part of the healing ritual was to wear a mask of the illness from which one was suffering—the origin of our modern psychodrama. If a person represses their anger due to social niceties, they first need to realize what they are really feeling and name it. Then in their healing ritual they need to tell where the repression of anger began to be buried or locked in a cage. The cross-cultural enactment through ritual of the particular Demon behind our "dis-eases" is a key to healing—through storytelling, sound, mask making, and movement.

And so it is in our lives today, that the creative healing methods from the days of old may be used to heal our lives. Movement is one of the primordial practices through which the Reluctant Metaphysician connects with the world behind the world. One who has repressed their anger might enact a psychodrama ritual whereby they retrieve it by wearing the mask of a roaring lion emerging from a cage. Or, at a moment of physical difficulty when illness or injury strikes, a person in pain may look at the moon or another celestial object, and gestures and movements may spontaneously arise as he or she brings its light down to heal the darkness of his or her life. Each person is called to develop his or her own storytelling or psychodrama ritual (as you will later see in the Mythic Journey Process).

None of us want to have illnesses; yet as the Buddha and Sickness Demon story teaches, our suffering makes our eyes turn heavenward and then we look deeply into the soul of the world. At these moments we become Reluctant Metaphysicians and are led to discover healing pathways as we journey to the underworld. There we discover stories and movement practices, which are the double keys that open doors to the deeper rooms of the cave of the Reluctant Metaphysician.[2]

4. THE JEWISH FARMER

The following story is told in various cultures; for example a similar story is told and called the "Taoist Farmer." The names and culture do not matter as much as the universal teaching contained herein:

In the olden days, when the Jews lived in Russia, a poor Jewish family had one son and one horse. But this was a great blessing for Avram and Freda. One day however their only horse ran away in a storm. A local farmer came by and said, "This is terrible, now you won't be able to do your winter plowing." But Avram, who trusted in God, said, "You never know what will happen next." Sure enough, the next day the lost horse returned with a dozen wild horses. Another man in the village passed by and exclaimed, "This is fantastic, you are now the wealthiest and most fortunate family in the shtetl." With tempered character, Freda said, "You never know what will happen next." Sure enough, the next day their son was breaking the wild horses to enable them to be worked as farm animals, and he was thrown from the horse and broke his leg." A man came by and said, "This is terrible because now you will have no son to help you through the winter." Avram and Freda in sing-song unity replied, "You never know what will happen next." Sure enough, a few days later the Czar's troops came into town and took all of the Jewish sons *away to fight in the army for the upcoming war. But Avram and Freda's son could not go because of his broken leg.*

Earthy wisdom and a faith that we are part of a wider whole, helps each one of us to realize that some greater power in the universe sends us trials and tribulations, and the ups and downs of life. Perhaps such occurrences happen so that we may learn to trust in the existence of "a divine mystery play of the forces of life" when both dire and beneficial circumstances arise. We are the actors in the play...the surfers on the great ocean of Being. The incoming and ebbing of the tides of circumstance happen with certainty no less than the rising and falling of the tides of the ocean. It is our job to ride the waves with a wonderment of, and appreciation for, what will come next...until death do us part.

5. PERSEUS AND MEDUSA

From the perspective of the Reluctant Metaphysician, a secret key to everyday life is seeing each life situation as an opportunity to find your hero's path, and to see what purpose may be found in the obstacles that life presents us. I once saw a grade B movie that presented an image that takes the "A place" in my book of capturing the idea that obstacles in life are part of a divinely inspired mythic test.

In this movie, Zeus and Hera were in the heavens above Mount Olympus wanting to have a little amusement. They saw Perseus below and said, "Why don't we take him out of his complacency and give him a difficult issue with which to deal. It will be interesting to see how he copes with it."[3]

So, in addition to just being familiar with various treasured stories from our ancestors, other keys to the inner rooms of the Cave of the Reluctant Metaphysician are forged by either creating on-the-spot stories that reframe the struggles of everyday life, or by creating our own psycho-mythological story. For the former, I will share with you the transpersonal hypnosis method I developed. For the latter, after that, I will tell you about the Mythic Journey Process that has the capacity to change our lives through a shamanic journey into the underworld.

Healing with the Elements: Transpersonal Hypnosis for a Writer's Block

The same stream of life that runs through my veins night and day
runs through the world and dances in rhythmic measures.
It is the same life that shoots in joy
through the dust of the earth in numberless blades of grass
and breaks into tumultuous waves of leaves and flowers.

—Rabindranath Tagore

From my experiences with the power of story in my life, it was natural for me to want to bring the transformative potential of stories into my psychotherapy. From my experience with the ability of astrological metaphors to create a cosmological healing story that helps a person find new meaning, I wanted to use these symbols in my psychotherapy practice. However, due to the prejudices that many people have against astrology (due to the deterministic, predictive way it has been used) I wanted to find a way to tap on the essence of the healing potentials of astrological metaphor without needing to "do astrology" with patients for whom it would not be appropriate.

To get away from the complexities and controversies of astrology, I extracted one of the important essences of astrology, the metaphors of the astrological elements (fire, earth, air, and water), and I used those in a book on couples therapy (Mayer, 1993). Honoring the idea of healing with the elements, and how important the elements of nature were to me, I developed the concept of Transpersonal Hypnosis in the 1980s. This was a step on the path to bringing the use of the metaphors of the energies of life into transpersonal psychology, and to bring my studies in esoteric psychology to mainstream approaches to psychological healing.

> A patient, who we'll call Marcy, found the metaphor of the elements of nature to be particularly transformative in treating her writer's block. A student in her early twenties, Marcy was enrolled in a program for young screenplay writers. I had a chance to work with Marcy for only two sessions because she lived out of state.
>
> When Marcy came to our first session, she told me she had not been able to write anything new on a play that she had been working on for three months, and she was considering leaving her program. Her closest friends were also writers, who seemed to be producing screenplays without any of the problems Marcy was experiencing. She felt like a failure.
>
> First, Marcy described, in detail, how hard she had tried to find a way through her writing blocks. She felt defeated and was coming to the conclusion that she just did not "have it," and that she needed to recognize she was an awful writer.
>
> Marcy was expecting me to tell her she was a good writer, as all of her acquaintances had; so she was taken aback when I told her that she was overlooking just one thing: that, of course, she was a terrible writer—everyone is. I told her that her problem was fighting this basic truth. She was startled at first, because everyone else was trying to comfort her by attempting to convince her that she was a good writer. This paradoxical intention method (Frankl, 1967), used in psychotherapeutic healing and clinical hypnosis, is also fundamental to Taoist healing—by not trying to make things happen, things happen. By being "nothing special," a very special human quality emerges.
>
> Marcy came to me as a psychotherapy patient partially because she knew that I had written a prize-winning book, The Mystery of Personal Identity, and that even though she would not have enough time to do depth psychotherapy with me, she had heard that

sometimes results could be achieved in a shorter time. Creating a bond with her as a fellow writer who was also often blocked, I told her the story of how I learned about writing blocks from writing my book. I told Marcy how I had been blocked for a period of six months about how to start my writing. I saw a sign of relief wash across her face as if she was thinking that if a prize-winning author can be blocked for six months, maybe it's not so bad that she was blocked for three months.

Drawing on the old tradition of using the transformative energy of stories to heal, I told Marcy the following story about writing my dissertation: One day, completely depressed, I gave up and walked outside for a breath of fresh air realizing that I just did not have what it took to write. As I breathed in the fresh air, all of a sudden an idea came to me; and from there my dissertation grew. I realized that the idea came "from the air," and I started to joke around with myself that this is how the expression that "the idea came out of thin air" arose. Maybe, I thought, other writers had discovered what I had— that they could not write either, and that ideas come from the air. I further wondered whether in ancient times astrologers knew this, and that is why they said that knowledge is associated with the air element. I got so invigorated by this hypothesis that the energy carried over into my writing and ideas started flowing forth for a chapter or so. I would just go out for a breath of fresh air when I got stuck and an idea would come to me.

I was becoming relatively self-assured, thinking that I could just call on the air element to write. Then one day, while working on the second chapter, it came again. I was completely blocked. I went outside and nothing happened as I tried to invoke the air element. Day after day I would go for walk and nothing came. I gave in to the belief that I was just no good at writing and I decided\to take a shower to get away from it all. While I was in the shower, I started to relax and realized how critical I was of myself. I became more aware of how I was unable to let my writing flow because my inner critic was so perfectionistic.

I realized that I had done this all of my life, and I mourned how difficult my schooling had been for me. I realized that I needed to keep my critic out of the first draft of my writing and let it in only with later drafts. As my tears merged with the water and I let go, an idea emerged for a blocked section in my writing. I realized the great healing power of water, and I appreciated that by my letting go and being with the power of the water element that it could write through me.

Then I thought, all I need to do is take showers when I get stuck, get in touch with the water element, and I will be healed. But eventually I got to the place that even a shower would not help. I went to the refrigerator and took out a piece of bread to escape the fact that I could not write at all. As the bread grounded me, I got in touch with how a grounded experiential flavor was missing in the theoretical section that I was working on in my book. I realized that the Earth element was speaking to me and helping me to be more grounded in my approach.

It was only after all of this—and many more writing blocks, even though I breathed fresh air, took showers, and ate bread—that I fully recognized my foolishness in thinking that "I" could write...I now knew that I could not write at all and that it was the elements of creation that wrote through me—in their own time and in their own way. I realized that my attachment to being able to write was similar to my attachment to having a given element heal me. Like my attempt to control the writing process itself, I had become attached to trying to control the elements of creation to write through me. I then deeply realized that it was only in letting go of trying to control the elements of writing—and being open to what comes—that the appropriate element of the universe could come to my aid.

In our two allotted sessions, Marcy and I also touched upon the roots of her blocks that came from her inner critic. Using various bodymind healing psychotherapy approaches, we worked on the psychological roots of her energy blocks regarding writing We identified one of her family of origin issues of being an overachiever to please her parents. By practicing cognitive restructuring, she learned to change her negative belief from, *I need to be a great writer to be worthwhile* to the belief that, *My destiny as a writer is waiting to be drawn out of me by the elements of the universe around me.* Marcy's subjective units of distress scale (S.U.D.S.) level significantly decreased with this new belief, showing that her bodymind was beginning to metabolize this new way of seeing her path as a writer. She also appreciated the self-soothing she experienced when she touched her heart, because she had always been self-described as "such a mental person."

Marcy also wanted to learn some Qigong movements to help her with the tension that accumulated when she was writing. I was able to show her briefly some movements, such as Opening the Shoulder Well, the wood element of Bodymind Healing Qigong (Mayer, 2004, p.104); Tai Chi Ruler, for general relaxation and balancing of energy; and Moving a Snake through the Joints, to release common body areas that accumulate tension while writing.

After our two sessions, I did not hear from Marcy for about a month. Then I received a phone call from her saying that she had broken though her writing block one night while looking into her fireplace. Marcy told me that the metaphor of "fire" had created a felt shift for her. She said that while looking there, she realized how she had always tried to be a bright light in her parent's eyes, and how comparisons with other relatives had stifled her own natural internal fire from burning. Looking into her fireplace, she had gotten in touch with the natural fire she had left behind as a child. I only heard from Marcy one last time, when she graduated from her writer's program and thanked me for the influence that our sessions and the elements of life had had on her writing.

The Mythic Journey Process: Transforming Your Demons

We have not even to risk the adventure alone, for the heroes of all time
have gone before us; the labyrinth is thoroughly known. We have only
to follow the thread of the hero path. And where we had thought to find
an abomination, we shall find a god; where we had thought to slay
another, we shall slay ourselves; where we had thought to travel outward,
we shall come to the center of our own existence; and where we
had thought to be alone, we shall be with all the world.

—Joseph Campbell

Introduction to the Mythic Journey Process

During the 1970s and 1980s, my work in integrating psychotherapy and the Western mystery traditions culminated in the development of the Mythic Journey Process. I first wrote about it in an article that appeared in *The Focusing Folio* in 1982; and then I incorporated it in three of the books that I have written since (Mayer 1993, 2007, 2009). Among the various psycho-mythological and symbolic process methods used nowadays to facilitate healing, the Mythic Journey Process is unique in how it is not as tightly structured as guided imagery, and therefore it allows one's own tale to freely emerge. However, the method also has a structure to it, which provides riverbanks through which one's unconscious stream of imagery can flow and be guided.

Mythology: The Key to the Door of Your Psyche

Ancient myths are becoming new resources for the human venture. The written works and interviews of Joseph Campbell gave respect to the study of world mythologies. James Hillman (1975), Sam Keen (1989), Robert Bly (1990), Michael Moore (2008) and a vast number of Jungian-oriented authors have shown how ancient myths and storytelling can bring soul to modern culture. It seems that we are in an age of mythological renaissance. It is a time when the mythic Sword of Excalibur can rise again—a time for reviving the gods and goddesses of imagination to give meaning to modern life.

Throughout the ages, mythic stories have been passed down describing the deep inner transformations of the psyche. We have seen how these legends can show us oceans of possibilities within us and help us begin an odyssey that will transform our souls. Today, due to awareness of many different religious and mythic traditions, we are in a unique position—we are able to set sail and find our own myths on an even larger ocean. We can create our own mythic journeys from all the past mythic literature and our imagination.

Our very lives are mythic journeys; and when we depart, most importantly it will not be our bones that will remain, it will be our stories. So, to leave a good story in our wake, in the Mythic Journey Process we create a likeness between our current life and a person or situation in ancient times. Then we make room for the power of imagination to enter through this likeness. We thereby add our story to mythic history to create "soul" in our lives, and to present mythic solutions to those that follow in our footsteps.

Identifying and Overcoming Our Inner Demons

Whether you are the most positive, rational thinker in the world or a traditional religious person who is against iconic pagan imagery, we all have our problems, obstacles, and demons lurking under the veneer of our lives. It is these archetypal aspects of the human condition that the Mythic Journey Process evokes. By facing the particular "demons" behind our psychological problems, we can deal with suffering at its root (Hillman, 1975). Picturing the form of the demon and how we will address it changes confrontation into an adventure. The demon may turn out to be the monster of our fear. The giant may be our inertia or suppressed power. By directly facing and dealing with the demon, we can rediscover our lost selves and gain access to the treasure of our inherent nature.

Throughout time, myths have recorded the numerous ways that heroes have confronted various demons. Whether it was by attacking, wrestling, or feeding them, each encounter offers us an approach to a present-day demon.

Petrifying Fear: The Story of Perseus and Medusa

Hearing a story that contains a problem like ours helps us face our demons and feel less alone in our suffering. For example, maybe our partner continually gets angry when we come home late from work. Perhaps we fear that the relationship is endangered because we need our freedom, or perhaps we feel smothered but are too petrified to discuss it because our partner reacts so strongly.

A mythic analogy to this situation can be found in the tale of Perseus and Medusa: in which each of us is Perseus, and Medusa represents our angry partner. In this myth, Medusa's face was so horrifying that it had the power to petrify into stone the people who dared to look at it. Using the example above and reading this story, we may see that maybe we are not dealing with our own personal neurosis, but with a wider, universal issue— the petrifying fear of a powerful figure. Instead of feeling alone and isolated, we can feel linked with those ancient heroes who struggled with monstrous embodiments of the same forces with which we are now coping. What once felt like neurotic suffering becomes an adventure as we explore how our problems were dealt with in the mythic past.

In order to save Perseus from being turned into stone, Athena, goddess of wisdom, gave him a shield to reflect Medusa's image. By looking into the shield instead of looking directly at her face, Perseus was able to approach Medusa and behead her. We might look to the myth of Perseus and Medusa and ask ourselves *what in my life could function like Perseus' shield?*

We can reflect on our situation aided by the distance that our own inner shields give us. In that reflection we might see that we became petrified when our mother disapproved of us. Maybe we froze the expression of our emotions due to not wanting to hurt our mothers or in order to survive. Perhaps from that early wounding we developed a pattern of constantly giving in to others' demands for fear of hurting them or being rejected by them. Metaphorically speaking, we turned to stone inside, acceding to the demand, but with a stiff upper lip, resenting the restriction. A pattern may have developed to withdraw in other ways in our relationships.

Reflecting on our partner's image in the mirrored shield, we might be able to understand his or her issues better. Perhaps our partner was feeling a loss of control in the relationship or was not feeling needed or cared about. Reflecting upon what caused the anger rather than reacting to it, we can "behead the monster," that is, diffuse our reactivity.

Reflecting in such a way in the midst of seemingly monstrous emotions requires the proper implements. Perseus was given an adamantine sickle and winged sandals by Hermes, and a helmet of invisibility by Pluto. We must learn what these implements mean and learn how to use them so that we are prepared when we meet the Medusas in our life. For example, perhaps the sword's parrying ability would be useful in its ability to point to the real issue, slice through the mire, and to find the truth of the underlying feelings.

Perseus' sickle was adamantine (made of the hardest stone). Today we know that the hardest stone is diamond, but any stone that is very hard has sustained years of pressure by the earth's forces. If it is a diamond, it has become clarified. Perhaps the myth is telling us that we must be patient regarding the hard-to-bear forces in our situation. There is a purpose behind the pressure—to create something that is clear and of great value.

The image of this sword tells us that we must combine the qualities of hardness (not being weak about the "hard truth") with the softness of a sickle's curve. On the one hand, we cannot passively cave into our partner's demands, we must be strong in our assertion that there is more here than meets the eye. But the soft lunar curve must also be present in the discussion, reflecting on both partners' underlying issues. A straight-edged-sword approach will not do. If we point our sword in a judgmental way, the mythic solution will not be found.

The imagery tells us that at a certain point in exploring our different viewpoints, Hermes' winged sandals might be useful to guide us into the underworld to see our own issues—our feelings of being smothered and our partner's difficulty with feelings of neediness. Discussing these feelings can give us winged sandals that transport us to the upper regions, as Hermes' sandals transported Greek heroes to that place of compassionate perspective. This takes place only if we are able to keep our ego under the "cap of invisibility." If we are enraged by our partner's neediness, or we withdraw in anger, the hero's goal will not be accomplished.

In one version of the myth, after Medusa was beheaded, Pegasus the winged horse emerged; and as he ascended, he kicked a mountaintop from which sprang one of the fountains of the Muses. Indeed, when two people work through issues such as these, a wellspring of creative energy is released. We may learn to use humor to dramatize our issues or be awed by the insight they bring. Love may be reborn.

Remember that Perseus' quest was for Andromeda, his beloved who was chained to a rocky cliff. Medusa's head and the weapons that Perseus accumulated in his quest were used to free her from the dragon. Often it seems that our beloved is chained to a rocky cliff and that the relationship is tottering on the edge. Ultimately it requires a quest like Perseus' to rescue the feminine in us and in our partner. The feminine symbolically represents that lunar quality of inner reflection that must be rescued from the hard rock of rigidity.

Myths record the tests and trials of the human spirit. They are keys to the psyche's secrets, which are brought to life by our imagination. Just as a rainbow is created when various elements come together (light, water, and a person at the proper angle), so do myths provide multihued illumination when we see a story from a combination of an enlightened perspective, a feeling sensibility (water), and our own particular angle. There is no single correct angle from which to interpret a story because each angle produces its unique vision that is meaningful to us at a given time.

In the The Zohar, a major text of Jewish mysticism, it says that it is important to come up with our own unique interpretation of a story, myth, or passage from the bible. This is called our *chiddush* (unique interpretation); and the interpretation I have just given about the Perseus and Medusa myth is just one interpretation. In the The Zohar, according to my friend Hana Matt, it is said that each new interpretation of a story is a new jewel in the crown of God. I like to say, "It's a mythogem."

In the Mythic Journey Process, when we feel lost, we can create our own stories and use the symbols that arise from our inner vision to help us find the way into the cave of our unconscious. There, we can meet the demon, wrestle with it, and find the jewel that we hope to put in God's crown.

Focusing and the Mythic Journey Process

The Mythic Journey Process is a way of harnessing the ancient power of myth to work through modern-day problems. It combines elements of the Focusing technique with archetypal psychology.[4]

So, once again, my medicine way of "two streams joining" was with me as I attempted to bring together the stream of storytelling with the stream of body-oriented psychotherapy. The Mythic Journey exercise consists of starting with our bodily felt sense of a chronic physical or psychological problem, and then telling a story about this problem, transposing it into ancient times as we did with the story of Medusa. While the story is being told, we continually refer to the body's felt sense, noticing how it changes along with the development of the story. We can eventually reach a point where the story begins to tell itself, and many people experience a felt shift and new meaning regarding a life issue.

The Mythic Journey Process is a contemporary embodiment of the ancient mythic journey to the underworld. Just as the mythic Greek hero Theseus used Ariadne's thread to find his way into and out of the underworld labyrinth to free the captive children from the monstrous Minotaur, so do we use our bodily felt experience as a thread into and out of our psychological underworld to liberate the energies of our inner experience. The steps of the Focusing process become guideposts along our path.

In the first step of Focusing, called *clearing a space*, we find a friendly relationship to a life issue by saying, "Everyone has their stuff to deal with and here's mine. If I had a friend, I wouldn't be hard on him for having this to deal with." Because we are often harder on ourselves than we would be on a friend with the same problem, we need to find a relationship to ourselves that is like the relationship that we would have to a friend with a similar problem.

Dr. Gendlin also found that an important factor in successful therapy was a person's ability to use his or her body's felt sense to create movement in therapy. In his book, Gendlin (1978, pp.45–50) gives an example of a traditional couple. A wife at home cleaned the table. Her husband returned home after getting a job promotion; and in his excitement, knocked the milk onto the table that his wife had just cleaned. The woman became aware of her bodily feeling of anger and began the Focusing process. She resonated the word anger against the felt bodily sense of the issue surrounding her husband's promotion. She then stopped for a moment and said, "No, that's not quite right. I'm not sure what I felt, but it's not quite anger." For some people, this can be a difficult moment because they cannot identify specifically what they are feeling. In Gendlin's Focusing process, we learn to trust an unclear felt sense and wait for something to emerge. While staying in touch with the unclear feeling of "a hole in my stomach," this woman realized, "It's not so much anger; what's getting me the most is the void I feel about being left behind in my life." At this point she sighed and there was a "felt energetic shift" in the way her body carried the problem.

In the Focusing technique, our bodily felt sense can be used as a guiding light. We can imagine that the woman might be guided to express her feelings to her husband and be comforted, or that she might look for a way to develop her life further.

Prelude to the Mythic Journey Process

The inner journey in the Mythic Journey Process parallels journeys to the under-world that have been spoken of by the earliest healers of the psyche. Shamans and temple priests of the mystery schools have spoken of it as a journey into the body of the earth or into the dark caverns of the unconscious. Myths suggest ways to prevent us from getting lost.

As modern people we can use Focusing on our experience and felt sense in combination with the Mythic Journey to follow Theseus' path. We can join these methods to serve as our thread through the psychological underworld to find and liberate the energies of the natural child within us.

So, here in the Mythic Journey Process, many aspects of the tapestry of my life's journey are woven together…the love of stories, the importance of the body in creating healing, and the role of various Taoist breathing and movement practices to make storytelling a fuller healing ritual.

In this spirit, the Mythic Journey Process starts with a grounding exercise that helps clear a space where we find our center, our inner pillar. Using a Taoist microcosmic orbit breathing technique, we can experience the tan tien center below the navel. When we do the breathing meditation properly, this center can become a pillar to return to when we encounter fear in our inner labyrinth.

The Mythic Journey Process

The Mythic Journey Process begins with a breathing meditation combined with the *clearing a space* step of Focusing and an imagery exercise:

> *Notice your exhalation…the pause…and how the inhalation comes naturally from this pause. After a few cycles, notice how your body feels different and notice the way you have settled down to be in contact with the ground under you. Are you held off the ground in any way? Feel how being with your breathing cycle can help you let go to the ground under you so that you are simply here.*
>
> *If there is any residual tension in your body, just notice it in a way that establishes a compassionate, friendly relationship to it. If a friend of yours had a similar tension, you would find room to accept him or her in spite of the issue. Find this relationship to any tension in your body, letting the natural breathing facilitate the friendly relationship. During the following process, when something arises that you want distance from, just breathe this way and return to the relaxed place—your inner pillar.*
>
> *One way to combine the breathing meditation with searching for an issue is to imagine that as you breathe out, it is like letting go of some of the tension in your body and lowering a bucket into the well of your Self, deep beneath the surface tension that you may be carrying at this moment. The bucket is tied to a secure pillar at the top. As you breathe out and lower it, you come to a place where your breath pauses before you take in the next breath. As you pause, it is as though the bucket is waiting for something deep within to fill it, some issue that stands in the way of you feeling all right. As your breath comes in, the bucket rises. It may take quite a few exhalations (lowering of the bucket) until something from deep within you comes into your bucket.*

The first step of the Mythic Journey consists of finding an issue and an associated bodily felt sense of this issue, just as in the Focusing technique. For some people, the body sense comes first; for others, the issue emerges first. If the body sense comes first, do you know what this body sense connects with in your life?

If the issue arises first, do you feel where this issue lies in your body? You might start by proclaiming *everything in my life is completely all right* and noticing what issues arise to contradict this. With each issue that emerges, you establish a compassionate, friendly relationship to it. Create enough distance so that you can acknowledge, *I recognize you're there, but I'm not going to work on you right now. Maybe I'll come back later.* Imagining yourself somewhere else in the room, feeling the way you do when you are with this issue, is one way to clear a space.

As issues pop up, give yourself time to notice how they affect the subtle barometer of your body. It is from your body's reaction that you will know which issue to choose to work with. As you approach this "friend," you can get a felt sense of the issue. For further aid in discovering the felt sense, sometimes it helps to say to yourself, *I could feel completely fine about this whole thing.* When a voice inside contradicts this statement with the idea *no I couldn't feel fine about this,* that is the felt sense. What is this sense all about? Wait for something to come up from the felt sense. See if you can distinguish between trying to think about it and just having something emerge from the sense itself. It may be a word or an image or a sound—trust whatever comes for you. To get a "handle word or image" for this felt sense of the issue, just wait as if you were a fisherman by an ice hole: You cannot rush a fish onto your hook. Just wait for what pops up from your body's sense of the issue as a whole.

What word or image seems to resonate with the sense of what this issue is all about? You will know that you have something that resonates by the response your body gives—the way its movement is facilitated when something gets to the crux of the matter.

What is the worst thing about this issue for you? At this point it helps to actually write down the issue on a piece of paper along with the bodily feeling you have noticed. Note bodily feelings in parentheses. For example:

- **Issue:**
- **Body sense** *(write this in parentheses):*
- **Handle word/image:**
- **The worst of it** *(Ask the felt sense various questions, such as what is the worst of it and what is the crux of this issue?):*

Then the mythic dimension begins.

The Mythic Dimension

The first part of the mythic dimension of the Mythic Journey Process is to take your issue and the associated bodily felt sense and to create a story about a character in ancient times who had the same problem. Begin with the words: *Once upon a time...*

There will be three parts to the mythic dimension. First, describe the problem you are facing in mythic terms: Where does this mythic character live in terms of terrain, time, surroundings, and so forth? How did this problem come about? Was it created in a relationship with a young prince or princess's mother and father, the king and queen? Use your own characters and imagery. (The second two parts of the mythic dimension will be illustrated in the following case example.)

It is important to transpose the felt sense of your own obstacle into mythic terms: What created this problem in the character's life? Was a curse or spell put on you? If so, for what reason and by whom? Give an actual face or name to the "demon," and write it in capitalized letters to "personify it," such as Fear, Blame, or Self-Doubt. Naming or "facing" the specific demon is very important and first came into the psycho-mythological field due to the insights of James Hillman.[5]

CASE ILLUSTRATION: A CRITICAL PERFECTIONIST'S MYTHIC JOURNEY PROCESS

The issue for one patient, who was a perfectionist, was an intense criticizing that led to attacking his partners. The following Mythic Journey Process was written at a key point in "John's" long-term therapy:

- **Issue:** My difficulties with relationships.

- **Body sense:** (clenched jaw).

- **Handle word/image:** Anger. He imaged his "demon" to be a Serrated Sword. Then John proceeded with part one of the mythic dimension and developed the felt sense of this demon into the following story.

- **The worst of it:** *No one is good enough; I'll never find anyone with whom to have a long-term relationship.*

Once upon a time . . .

The Serrated Sword of Criticism was given to my father's father many generations ago when he was down and out. He sat on a mountaintop praying for power and the ability to support his family when a mountain demon came to him and gave him a serrated sword with a mountain emblazoned upon it.

He said that the cuts made with it and the blood on it would proportionally increase the sword's power and would help him ascend the mountains of earthly life to be great, admired, powerful, and respected. He was told to make a family crest of it and begin practicing with his own family.

Indeed, great power and admiration came to this family of swordsmen and women through the generations. Though wounds occurred and blood was let increasingly, the sword's power was the key focus of the family. Applause was given at the family dinner table for the great swordplay of the day, whether it was against the bulls killed for dinner or the other swordsmen defeated.

Even family wounds inflicted were respected if done in a skillful way.

The second part of the mythic dimension of the Mythic Journey Process describes how impossible it seems to defeat the demon, and the problems it has caused. What methods have you tried that have not worked to defeat it? Transpose those methods into mythic terms. For example, John added to his story:

Although our royal family attained a castle on a mountaintop and much power in the world through our fine discriminating cuts, the prince's life was not a happy one. As great a swordsman as he was and as admired as he was, he was alone most of the time.

The problem was the sword, the very one that had given him such pleasure in his youth, the one for which he and his family had been admired for generations, when it was handed down to him it went out of control. Each time it was unsheathed, it would cut anything he looked at in a discriminating way. It cut all of his lovers to bits. The prince tried to break the sword, but many generations of power made it unbreakable. He tried to get rid of it at an Eastern religious temple; he denounced it and tried to bury it. But he felt impotent without it and had trouble climbing the castle steps if the sword was not in his belt (slumped chest, feeling of being defeated).

Accentuating how impossible it seemed to defeat the demon brings out the "soulful dimension" (Hillman, 1976) and can help prevent Pollyannaish solutions.

Again, check back with your body's felt sense and note it in parentheses. Concluding part two, make a statement that addresses the specific nature of the impasse and the specific obstacle or demon with which the character is dealing. Indicate how you specifically feel knowing that nothing can be done to deal with it. This is "exploring the resistance" mythically. For example, from John's story:

The Prince of the Serrated Sword felt that he could not give up the way of the sword for he was too good at it, and it was too much a part of his nature. Yet at the same time, he could not live with it. There seemed to be no end to the loneliness and the guilt that the prince felt over cutting up his lovers. The Critical Sword seemed all-powerful. (depressed, hollow feeling in my chest)

The prince used his discriminating insight to see where the power of the sword came from. He relaxed and sensed the presence of the old mountain demon above him. Above him and to the right, he noticed a demon called Smug-Faced Pride.

It added an electric glow to the sword each time the prince said, "Look at what an adept swordsman I am." Upwards and to the left, the prince was able to sense the presence of another demon, Needy-Faced Expectation. It added a desperate, angry, warlike hacking motion to the sword each time the prince said to others, "If you aren't the way I want you to be, I'll cut you up to fit into the 'right' mold."

The third part of the mythic dimension begins with writing these words:

Then one day.... Then describe what happened one-day. Let some solution to the impasse come to you. Give it time. If no solution arises in you to break the impasse, then think about who could deal with this demon: imagine some heroic figure, animal, or mythic creature and see what happens when it meets your demon. Use your creative story-writing capacity to let the story tell itself.

Continuing John's story:

Then one day, while the prince was depressed and looking into a mountain lake, he began to reflect upon whether he wanted to be a swordsman if it meant having no love. (Something lets go in my chest area: a sense of openness comes there as I sigh.) At that moment a Maiden of the Lake appeared with the golden sword Excalibur that had been thrown back into these waters many years ago.

Tears came to his eyes as the prince explained that he could not go on being a swordsman if there was no love in his life, and yet he could not give up his family's path either. He asked for her help.

With compassion, the Maiden of the Lake taught him the one movement that the mountain demon had neglected to teach his forefather many years ago. She instructed him to feel with his heart before he was about to use the golden glowing sword and caress it as if it was a beloved one from whom he was asking guidance. Then he was to look at the polished mirror that the sword's metal became, reflect as he was doing in the lake when he met her, and ask for guidance on how to use the sword in the service of love and truth.

As the prince followed her instructions, he noticed that as he held this sword in front of him, a ray of light came from his heart and bounced off the sword. His eyes could direct it, but only when they were reflecting inward with clear intent. "This light," the Maiden of the Lake said, "had the ancient power to transform anything that he wanted to heal."

The Maiden said that this was the true power of the sword that had been lost through the ages. She explained that before the sword was used for fighting, it was used for directing energy to points on the body that were in need of healing. She told the prince stories of how her teachers of the Golden Age used this sword in daytime to bring the healing power of the sun, and at night to bring the powers of the stars to earth. All this was done with the same meditation that she had just given him—using the powers of reflection and the power of the heart's glow.

With the Maiden of the Lake before him, the prince felt his heart's desire to be a healer, and he reflected upon the mountain demon above him. A light went to the demon and transformed him into a beneficent mountain spirit whose purpose was to help others to climb to their own heights (a feeling of fullness in my chest).

As he reflected on the electric light around Smug-Faced Pride, this conceited demon changed to a healing ally. The smug expression changed to a smile, like the Buddha's, as he realized that "skill" is not one's own but is borrowed from the powers of the universe, the stars, the sun, and the earth.

As the prince reflected upon Needy-Faced Expectation, he realized that much of the world's and his own suffering came from this demon's misplaced needs for power over others, for false security, ego recognition, and worldly success. With the sword's light on this demon, a new power came to the sword—a compassionate understanding of human foibles. A new form of sword dancing came from this transformed demon which gave the prince's movements a heartfelt, gentle, slicing motion, as when a person cuts a flower for a loved one and in the cutting wants the flower to suffer as little as possible.

As when the sword masters of ancient times had cut a field of wheat with deep appreciation for the forces of nature that went into producing the growth of the plant, so would the prince try to appreciate that which went into the growth of all that he was to use his sword upon. The prince vowed to make it his new practice to have tenderness when he used his sword to point out the places that became uncentered in his own and other's everyday life.

When the prince returned home, he created a new family crest with the Golden Glowing Sword of the Heart crossing over the Critical Serrated Sword. The Maiden of the Lake's sword had the power to stir the prince's compassion. In the future when the Critical Sword came out, the Maiden's sword was there to help remind the prince that its sharp power was to be put to a healing rather than a destructive use. This was not easy work, but at least now the prince knew what the work of his kingdom was. When the old sword arose, his work was to reflect on it with the heart meditation that he had learned and thereby bring love and compassionate understanding to the kingdom. (Openhearted, glowing feeling in my chest, and hope through my whole being—a feeling like I've found what my life work is.)

Your story does not have to have a happily-ever-after ending. Simply note your actual sense of the issue and transpose it into mythic terms. Oftentimes it is an important force to integrate into the story. Remember, it took Moses forty years in the desert to complete his destiny. What is the destiny, the purpose for which your character is going through his or her trials and tribulations? Sometimes this dimension of meaning and purpose can contribute to a felt shift.

After you reach a place in your story where it feels complete for the moment, notice your body's felt sense and note it in parentheses at the end of the story. Bring the adventure of this character back into your own life now. Reflecting on his or her quest, ask yourself what you can learn form the character's adventure and how your own path feels different now.

Reflection on the Mythic Journey Process

Many people experience new meaning emerging from their story and note that at a certain point in writing, they find the story writing itself. Some report that it is as if something were overtaking their writing and giving them a solution.

It is unimportant whether one calls this a muse, our higher Selves, right-brain function, the healing mind/energy of the universe, or intuition. The felt energetic shift that happens and the new meaning and perspective born on a blocked life issue helps us to heal regardless of what one calls the source of healing.

When people are stuck in a critical part of themselves, as the Prince of the Serrated Sword was, there are a variety of ways to create a shift in life stance. When combined with Gendlin's Focusing, both Tai Chi Sword Dancing practice and Western psychotherapy with its symbolic process methods go right to the crux of the psychological issue and can create a felt shift in a person's life stance. All are paths that lead to learning to wield a sword with compassion.

In this example of a Mythic Journey Process, the prince had to find a new life practice to change his "critical serrated-sword way of being" to become a compassionate coach of his own and others' limitations.

CASE ILLUSTRATION: THE PASSIVE-AGGRESSIVE OSTRICH— HEALING TRAUMA AND WITHDRAWAL

In the middle of the five-day Bodymind Healing Qigong workshops that I teach at various places, participants do a Mythic Journey Process. At the end of that process they have the option to incorporate a Tai Chi or Qigong movement that helps to anchor the felt shift, which oftentimes takes place at the end of their mythic journeys. So, I invite you to do the same. Perhaps some Qigong animal form, sword dance, or some other posture or movement of your choosing will help you to embody the shape-shifting that may take place in your Mythic Journey Process.[6] Though Tai Chi, Qigong, or other movements are not necessary for the Mythic Journey Process, they do help to bring out a somatic dimension, which has the capacity to increase the method's transformative possibilities.

The combination of these different facets of Bodymind Healing Psychotherapy can be seen in the case of a young female student who had a pattern of passive-aggressive behaviors at significant times in her life. "Roberta" was engaged in psychotherapy with another therapist to work on her passive-aggressive tendencies because they were getting in the way of her intimate relationships, particularly with her husband. She also did the Mythic Journey Process, Tai Chi, and the Animal Forms of Qigong with me as part of her Bodymind Healing Qigong certification program.

Roberta's story illustrates how the Mythic Journey Process can combine to help heal trauma and enhance a healing experience of shape-shifting from one life stance to another.

- **Issue:** My husband's aggressiveness and my withdrawal.

- **Body sense:** (anxiety in my stomach).

- **Handle word/image:** Ostrich hiding my head in the sand.

- **The worst of it:** *I feel like a weakling for not being able to stand up for myself.*

Roberta's Mythic Journey Process activated memories of her running away from a severely stressful environment in her teenage and young adult years, including a rape.

This running away produced a belief that *as soon as you sense danger, it's better to immediately leave.* In her Mythic Journey, Roberta pictured and felt the demonic forces as Attacking Giants crushing her chest, closing off her ears, making her body tense like taught metal, which resulted in her running away from these feelings, like a Fearful Ostrich. Through her Mythic Journey Process, she realized that this was an overreaction to many things that were not as dangerous as the rape of her youth. Her excessively reactive pattern resulted in her not listening to her husband when he was giving constructive critiques; instead, Roberta often withdrew with passive-aggressive behaviors, such as threats to end their marriage. In her Mythic Journey Process, her favorite movement from Hua Tao's set was Crane Opens the Door to the Heavens (Mayer, 2004, p.131). This movement is used as a non-forceful way to split the force of an aggressor. As Roberta got in touch with an image of herself doing this posture, she felt a noticeable felt shift of her stomach loosening its tight grip, and she realized that her husband was often trying to be helpful. We discussed how one of the crane's powers was to peck and differentiate the good food from the bad and spit out what was distasteful. In alchemy this is called the *seperatio* phase (Edinger, 1985). Roberta realized that as her mythic quest was to change her withdrawing behaviors, and instead express to her husband what she did not like about the way he expressed himself.

She later told me that in psychodynamic therapy, she was learning affect modulation skills to assert herself appropriately and avoid being overly reactive. Roberta reported that the crane movements were helpful in showing her how to keep her heart open yet appropriately defended when needed. Last I heard, her relationship with her husband was better and her "ostrich behavior" occurred less often. Roberta said that now she almost always caught herself when the body feeling associated with the Attacking Giants arose. She used her anchor of touching the backs of her hands together in the Crane Splitting mudra (Mayer, 2004, p. 131) to find her Crane power and to differentiate between what was harmful and what she could deal with, as she cleared the way for her heart's grounded expression.

CASE ILLUSTRATION: THE DESPERATELY GRASPING PARROT— HEALING ABANDONMENT AND NEEDINESS

The power of "naming," even without any internal martial arts practice, can be an important part of shape-shifting into another life stance. The significance and healing attributes of a mythic name can be seen with "Mary," a woman in her mid-twenties, who was in therapy for the guilt and desperation she felt from hanging out at various places as she looked for the man of her dreams. She described her disappointments going home each night without a man. She realized that the rejection she felt was similar to what she felt when her single mother would often abandon her to go out on dates when Mary was young.

- **Issue:** Finding the right man.

- **Body sense:** (hole/emptiness in my heart).

- **Handle word/image:** Needy, grasping for someone who isn't there.

- **The worst of it:** *I'll never find a life partner.*

In doing her Mythic Journey Process, Mary took her needy felt sense and imagined being a huntress in ancient times. Her demon was a Desperately Grasping Parrot, who would try to hold on to desired objects with its weak claws. The grasping claws, though, would frighten its prey away. It would chatter, parroting back clichés that it had learned in order to impress, but all the chatter only frightened away all the beautiful, wild creatures of the forest.

> *The young princess was originally given the Parrot as a present by her mother, the queen, as she abandoned the princess to go off for greater adventures than could be had with a young child (hole in my heart, emptiness). Mary's single mother actually did go out on dates quite often in Mary's formative years, and Mary traced her first memories of this sense of neediness to these times in her early life. She learned to talk incessantly whenever her mother was there, to fill up the silence. Mary would try to say all the right things, parroting what her mother might like to hear so that her mother might stay with her more.*

In her Mythic Journey Process, the curse was that the Parrot would emerge out of her needy stomach each time Mary went hunting for someone to love. The Parrot drove everyone away. The healing intervention came for her one day in her Mythic Journey Process in the form of Artemis, the Greek goddess of the hunt, who was Mary's favorite goddess in mythology.

> *One day when the princess was depressed in the forest because she had not caught anything, Artemis appeared and offered to teach the princess the secrets of hunting… how in primordial times the Master Huntress knew that love was something that came*

from our connection to the whole world (a sense of rising excitement and a sense of purpose).

As if straight out of classical metaphysical literature, Mary was describing *anima mundi*, soulful love of the world. She was expressing, in her own terms, the classical idea that at a certain point in our evolution, we as human beings transposed this *anima mundi* into *anima personalis*, a love for one human being, hopeful that this one person could contain her love for the world and universe. A large task indeed!

> *Artemis taught the princess how to hunt by enjoying all that was around her. If no deer came to her, she could still feel love for all surrounding life—the way light bounced over the meadow, the colors at sunset, and her relaxed position against the tree while she waited. Artemis told the princess that it was only in modem times, when the cult of true hunting decayed, that hunters would be devastated if they returned home without a deer. In primordial times, through the quality of waiting, the Priestesses of the Temple of Hunting always returned home with something of value. Upon hearing this, the princess (stomach opened and relaxed) and her pet Parrot were both stilled as never before (a melting sensation in my stomach).*

A few months later, Mary related how she sat watching the interesting variation of light shine on the table plants at her favorite local bar. She described a new sense of "life as practice." Though feelings of loneliness still arose, Mary said that her "hunting" now had a felt sense of adventure to it. A new context emerged, one of practicing the ancient art of "true hunting." She became more aware of her desperate, needy chatter and began to practice being a Stilled Parrot Who Enjoys the World while Waiting—her new symbolic name.

Conclusion

Many people who do the Mythic Journey Process find a new name for themselves. It is a way of metaphysical inner accessing, which is like an inner Vision Quest. As in ancient initiatory rituals, it offers a new identity, and a new life stance for the person. This new name defines a new path and a new practice in one's life. It is much like the new name Native Americans receive in their initiatory rituals in that it holds a power, linking the person to a transpersonal purpose, a path to a sacred life, and a destiny worth pursuing—as my Deer Kissing Eyes experience did for me.

The Mythic Journey Process is a *quintessential* storytelling method for the Reluctant Metaphysician. It is the culmination of my synthesis of Two Rivers becoming One, joining the Eastern and Western Mystery traditions.

The Mythic Journey Process is a way of responding to those who might ask, "Where are our heroes today? Where are those mythic adventurers who were able to deal with the archetypal demons of their age and open a path for fellow sufferers?"

Perhaps if we follow Ariadne's thread into our own underworlds, our stories—like hers—will be placed in the night sky; they will be like the crown of Ariadne (the Corona Borealis constellation) that Dionysus put there to immortalize her as a guiding light for lost souls to find their way. By opening ourselves to the realm of mythic imagination, each of our life stories can become a guiding light for humanity. For who are we, but stars in the making, hoping to shed light on the darkness of space and thereby give new life energy to ourselves, our planet, and to fellow travelers everywhere.

Not Just Stories Change Our Lives: Song, Postures, and Movements

The tapestry of storytelling methods I wove together from my journey taught me that storytelling is not just about words; their healing power can be expanded through postures, songs, and movements. In age-old indigenous cultures, in front of a fire at night a story might be told; but it was also often accompanied by song or dance. In a cave when the shaman or a priest told a story, a stance might be practiced along with song and movements.[7]

No closing story could therefore be more fitting to close this chapter than to mention how the healing tools of song and movement are now being used in Israel to help children suffering from post-traumatic stress when rockets come into their school grounds. In one project, children sing the song, "Red-Colors for Kids" to revision the trauma of the calling of "Code Red" that is sounded when there is rocket launch warning. Children in various towns such as Sderot sing a song, do dance gestures, and let go with shaking movements as they empower themselves to creatively and energetically deal with an imminent rocket attack. The results have been positive in these "Reluctant Metaphysician Children" who use the energies of sound, dance, and ritual to call on the powers of the world behind the world to deal with the very real problems of the Palestinian-Israeli conflict.[8]

CHAPTER 16:

Joining the Two Streams: Ancient Sacred Wisdom Traditions and Modern Psychotherapy

My philosophy is that psychological issues and bodily disease
are divina afflictios (divine afflictions)
giving us opportunities for psycho-spiritual growth, soul-making
and finding the source of healing.

—encapsulating my philosophy,
on my private practice brochure.

The Seeds of Creating a Bodymind Healing Psychotherapy

From my "Journey to the West," the visions of my life and the forces that had led me on this journey came together. If I was a Native American perhaps I would be walking with my shield, which would have a picture of Michael, Two Streams Joining on it. Maybe on the background of the shield would be a Deer Kissing Eyes, and at the top of the shield would be a picture of the Land Where the Sun Rose in the West and Set in the East.

I like the idea of the medicine shield, talked about in Hyemeyost Storm's book *Seven Arrows* (Storm, 1972). Indeed, having the essence of each of our life stories emblazoned on a shield is a way to ward off and shield us from those critical arrows that shoot at us, saying, "You should have lived a more practical life," or "You should have lived your life in a different way." Such is the power of each of our visionary experiences to give direction and strength to us so that we can carry forth our destinies. Particularly when we weave together the threads of our life in such a way that it connects back to the metaphorical and metaphysical Cave of our Creation, we feel aligned with our "raison d'être."

When I find symbolic keys that open metaphysical doorways of my life I am reminded of Ali Baba's cave and his treasures. However, in the inner treasure house I have discovered are mythogems that, like a crystal ball, reflect images of my life's direction. Sometimes they are astrological symbols, and at other times they are mythological tales or dream images.

The dream I had in 1971 told of a "journey to where the sun rose in the West," and indeed the West Coast of the United States and the Western mystery tradition helped to light my way. Likewise my childhood spot in nature where "two rivers become one," is a symbol that encapsulates my essential nature. Images from collective mythology also helped me to trust that each tradition that moved my soul was part of a reweaving of the garment of my life (as was the rewoven garment of the Old Woman in the Cave), into "the coat of many colors" that I wanted to pass down to the next generation. This metaphysical garment wove together body, mind, ancient sacred wisdom traditions, and modern psychology.

Many people nowadays associate metaphysics with the ideas put out in popular books such as *The Reluctant Messiah* (Bach, 1977) and *The Secret* (Byrne, 2006). The oft-quoted axiom behind many best selling books such as these is that "belief creates reality." The problem with this half-truth is that when those "believers" discover that in not all cases does their belief change reality, shame and dashed hopes can occur.

The truth is that "belief" (the placebo effect) in meta-analytic research comprises about 30–55% of healing (Rossi, 2002; Ader, 2000). This means that belief is a key tool in the metaphysician's tool chest. However, there is a big difference saying, "Belief creates reality," and saying, "Belief is a significant part of creating reality." The former can lead to a person's inflated bubble of reality bursting and a fragmentation of their world when that world view is not actualized; the latter leads to a balanced metaphysical perspective which honors human intention as a part of the wider whole of which we are a part. Transpersonal intention…as in the saying, "may thy will be done," opens our human energy gates to the divine elements of life, but this does not mean that the divine responds to our ego's wishes. This is particularly important when the physical world has its own reality—for example, when we face death or disease. Ken Wilber, a leader in the transpersonal integral psychology movement speaks poignantly in his book, *Grace and Grit*, about how he felt when members of the "belief creates reality" crowd intimated that his wife created her cancer and could cure it with belief.

From the perspective of the Reluctant Metaphysician, forces of the physical world, and the body, have their own realities that interpenetrate with the sphere of our individual beliefs. The Reluctant Metaphysician does not preclude that, when scientifically verified, laws of the physical plane may anomalously cease for a time in our quantum universe. We reluctantly accept that sexual frequency decreases with age, and physical death occurs. Though people walk through walls and fly in planes without gas in some fantasy spiritual books (Bach, 1977), the Reluctant Metaphysician accepts that Saturnian limits are an archetype of the wider metaphysical reality.

When we are struck by illness or other forces coming from the wider whole of which we are a part, we are sent on a healing journey from which we learn. We may discover that the mind at times has the power to heal the body when a spontaneous remission occurs, or we may learn that there are limits of the power of the mind to heal the body. In either case various metaphysical and psychological practices may become our initiators, guides, or healers at such times. Healing does not always mean curing.

Weaving Together Qigong, Somatic Approaches to Psychotherapy, Ancient Sacred Wisdom Traditions, and Energy Psychology

Just as symbolic process traditions are part of ancient metaphysical traditions, energetic traditions are also an important part of the healing methods of the world behind the world. The particular one that became most a part of my life is Qigong. Qigong, cultivating the energy of life, is an initiatory tradition that has a balanced view of the role combining the use of intention (yi) and energy (qi) to aid the physical body in healing. It works with activating the energy of the world behind the world (from *Wuji*, the mother of qi). Following the path of two streams becoming one, my quest became to integrate Qigong and psychotherapy into the healing toolkit of modern mind-body healthcare.[1]

The Somatic Dimensions of Psychotherapeutic Healing

One does not become enlightened by imagining figures of light,
but by making the darkness conscious.

—C. G. Jung (1945–1967)

Earlier I told you about how the imbalances in my body and the twists in it were a factor leading me on the path of being a wounded healer. So, I knew that integrating the body was crucial to my quest for my own healing as well as to help in the healing of others; and so I went looking for a tradition of bodily healing to integrate with my mental and emotional healing path.

The role of the body in psychotherapy was not appreciated in the 1970s when I was in my early training at the New School for Social Research. I had to read on my own, outside of school, Wilhelm Reich's *Character Analysis* (1980) and Lowen's *Bioenergetics* (1994). In those days these somatic psychologists were looked at as "fringe-players" at best (It is interesting that in the story of the Old Woman in the Cave and in cross-cultural mythology, "the fringes" are associated with the creative places in life.)

One of the major pathways into the realm of the body that I practiced was Eugene Gendlin's Focusing method.[2] Combining the Eastern methods of Tai Chi, Qigong, and acupressure self-touch with other Western body-oriented traditions such as Focusing helped me to find the path that I was seeking to heal the body/mind split that was so much a part of my early life. Through the practices I learned over the years, I was able to find the way to heal the blocked energy in my neck, and to find a bridge between traditions of the mind and body. Some of these traditions that have influenced me and later became fundamental parts of Bodymind Healing Psychotherapy include various approaches to Western psychotherapy, such as: self psychology, psychodynamic and object relations theory, cognitive-behavioral psychotherapy, energy psychotherapies, symbolic process traditions, and Dr. Eugene Gendlin's Focusing method.

There were many manifestations of my "medicine name" of Michael, Two Streams Joining, as I moved down the river of my life. In my teaching at various universities,[3] my trademark was joining various traditions such as Qigong and psychotherapy, astrology and psychotherapy, and East/West healing traditions. Whatever arena I entered it seems that joining streams was at the heart of my approach.[4] My overarching aim was to join ancient sacred wisdom traditions and modern bodymind healing methods.

Joining Ten Streams to Create Bodymind Healing Psychotherapy:

When it came to putting together my approach to psychotherapy, the places and visions of my past were with me. The metaphor of two streams becoming one turned into ten streams becoming one. The system of psychotherapy that I developed I first called Integrative Depth Psychotherapy, and then I changed the name to Bodymind Healing Psychotherapy. In this integral system I joined ten different streams of mind-body healing traditions such as: Taoist breathing methods, traditional forms of psychotherapy, Gendlin's Focusing method, Qigong, and symbolic process traditions.

The Ten Streams of Bodymind Healing Psychotherapy

1. Breath, microcosmic orbit, and hypnosis
2. Self-soothing
3. "Focusing" on felt meaning
4. Psychodynamics
5. Cognitive restructuring
6. Energy psychology methods, including EMDR
7. *Chi Nei Tsang*
8. Acupressure self-touch, and acu-yoga
9. Exercises from *Bodymind Healing Qigong*
10. Symbolic process approaches to healing

In my last books (Mayer, 2007, 2009) I have gone into more depth regarding what is in each of these dimensions. For example, level four (the psychodynamic dimension) includes *Ego Psychology* (Blanck, 1974, 1979), *Object Relations Theory* (Horner, 1984), and *Affect Regulation Theory* (Schore, 2003). So, in just this fourth dimension there are many facets of the BMHP integrative approach, such as: a focus on family of origin issues, developing ego strength, inner work on separation-individuation issues, developing cohesiveness of the self, learning affect modulation skills, embodying affect tolerance, and so forth. However, the main focus in this current book, and of my contribution to the field is (along with other therapists) bringing various ancient sacred wisdom traditions to the field of psychotherapy.[5]

Joining Ancient Sacred Wisdom Traditions and Modern Psychotherapy

An important part of my life myth was to join the streams of ancient sacred wisdom traditions and modern psychology. So, as I walked the path of a storyteller and a mythologist who appreciated the value of origin myths, I wanted to help to create a new origin myth for psychotherapy. The roots of this endeavor grew from the time when I was doing my doctoral research on cross-cultural mythology, and I remember reading Mircea Eliade saying that,

The origin myth of any thing determine the way it is seen, and its destiny, and creates a magical, incantational, hypnotic power.

—Mircea Eliade (1963)

Creating a New Origin Myth for Psychology

I began to wonder, "Had I and my fellow psychology students been hypnotized into a limiting story about the very nature of psychology?" Being interested in origin myths, I realized how confining it was to see psychology's origins in the narrow way that I had learned about it in my early training. In my master's program I was told that psychology began in 1879 in Wilhelm Wundt's lab in Leipzig Germany. This incantation hypnotizes students into believing that psychology's origin is in experimental psychology. In Freudian oriented courses I was told that psychology began with Freud. In cognitive therapy classes, beliefs were emphasized. Each of these origin myths creates a limiting lens; I knew my work was to create a new origin myth that included energy and cross-cultural ancient sacred wisdom traditions into psychotherapy. The nature of psychology and psychotherapy, I felt, must include nature.

The ruling kingdom of psychotherapy nowadays is Cognitive Therapy, with an almost equally powerful kingdom being the Land of Analytic (Freudian) or Neo-analytic Therapies. However, as I told you I was very influenced by James Hillman's notion that psychologists got it wrong when they mistranslated "psyche" to mean "mind." He said psychology is better translated as "the logos of soul (psyche)." From the perspective of the Western mystery tradition "the soul" is composed of four elements, fire (energy), earth (body oriented approaches), air (yes, mind is important, and so is breath), and water (feelings).

Synchronistically, in tune with my Mercury (the mind) in the astrological sign of Cancer (correlating with the belly, the mother, and the origins of life) in the ninth house (of philosophy), I have presented at numerous conferences and wrote a few books to make the case for this expansion of the origin myth about "the nature of" psychology (Mayer 1983, 2007, 2009). In other words, symbolically translated, my mind seems to resonate with exploring the philosophic foundations (ninth house), and origins (Cancer) of those subjects I study. (The sceptic in me says that many scholars have the same inclination without this aspect in their charts.)

Blank Slate versus a Hermetic Psychology

Regarding the philosophic ground of behavioral psychology…it rests on the ground of Western empiricism and the blank slate point of view. I remember when I first had to read about the empiricist philosophers in my master's degree program at the New School for Social Research in 1970. I cringed in my seat as the professor said we are born like blank slates and whatever the environment does to us is what we become. Luckily at the same time I had a class in Jungian psychology where I learned that there was another view that human beings had an *apriori* (prior to experience) disposition. I have always been inclined to agree with the "interactionist view" that apriori factors and environment together form our characters. However, when my colleagues use the term "interactionist" usually they mean that heredity and environment form us. They do not include the metaphysical dimensions of creation.

As I entered into my doctoral and postdoctoral years, my reading and experience led me to a deeper appreciation of the apriori and metaphysical factors that affect our life paths, and how our soul has a seed purpose. I grew to believe that the way we interpret our dreams and listen to our visions (as communicated from our soul's source material) helps to direct our destinies. Ever since Einstein came up with his famous equation we have known that our physical bodies and the world of matter are composed of frozen light; and just as light guides our maneuvers in the external world, so does the metaphysician believe that an inner guiding light guide can guide our destinies.

Using our astrological charts as a meditation tool can help us to tune into our soul's purpose. As discussed earlier, I take a hermetic or hermeneutic perspective on astrology and metaphysics (Mayer, 1977, 1983), whereby one does not either say, "Yes our soul's purpose is written prior to birth," or "No, it's not." The Hermeneutic Metaphysician is led on the path of Mystery and Wonder as we dive into exploration of the symbols in our astrological chart, or as we look at the apparent metaphysical phenomena of life.

In the field of psychology, Freud considered himself to be a "metapsychologist," not a metaphysician (Boothby, 2001). However, from the perspective of our definition in this book it could be argued that Freud was a metaphysician when he says that there is a personal unconscious, a world behind the world of everyday life that rules much of our behavior and beliefs. Healing in psychoanalysis is partly found by making conscious the elements of the personal unconscious. When the light of consciousness is brought to that dark hidden world of unconscious complexes, healing oftentimes occurs both physically and mentally (Gatchel, 1993).

Jung goes a step further and says there is also a collective unconscious, an even larger hidden universe of meaning behind our world. In this universe are the collective stories (the archetypes) of all human history. By drawing a connecting line between this world of the collective unconscious (the Self) and our world (of the ego), individuation and psychological healing can occur.

Though a metaphysician usually believes in the apriori seed nature of each human being, this does not mean that metaphysicians do not recognize the importance of the environment. Most metaphysicians believe that human beings have a seed nature, but also know that environmental factors affect the opening of the seed, or contribute to keeping it shut.

One important corollary of the current climate of behavioral psychology, and the view of a human being as a blank slate, is that many people adapt to the needs and conditioning of the corporate environment. I often see students doing their doctoral dissertations on subjects that are most practical and fitting with getting a job rather than what most calls from their inner world. A "psycho-mythological depression" can ensue when an essential aspect of the soul is not mined. At its best, the depression leads the students onto a journey into the underworld where the process of wrestling with alien subject material leads to a discovering of the treasure of the Self, nonetheless. However, at other times the practical student forsakes the path of the Reluctant Metaphysician, who reluctantly gives up the advantages of the road well traveled. By leaving the metaphysical road less traveled, some of these students later in their careers candidly tell me that they have regrets about not having followed a path in tune with their true interests.

This reminds me of the advice of Rabbi Zushya who said, "At the end of my life when I meet God I will not be asked, why I was not more like Moses, I will be asked why was I not more like myself." (But not to be Pollyannaish about it, I have also met students who have been happy that they have followed traditional pathways. We do indeed make our destinies by our choices of traditions.)

When psychology students wonder which psychotherapeutic school of thought they should follow, I often advise them to use the mandala of therapies (their ancestor's "coat of many colors") to find their place in the center of the whole psychological field, and then to find their own most favored place on the wheel.

The Mandala of Psychotherapies

As part of my quest to create a new origin myth for psychology, after many decades of training psychotherapists, I noticed that some of the same issues that exist in the fields of politics and religion regarding "which tradition is best" existed in the field of psychotherapy. There was often a "cold war" in the arguments between different factions within the psychotherapy community about which system was "best." Practitioners of one school could be frozen out of being hired for certain jobs, and shown less respect by members of another "temple." From my experiences with various ancient sacred wisdom traditions, I wanted to bring my metaphysical, holistic perspective into the field of psychology.

Using the Astrological Mandala as a Psychotherapeutic Meta-system

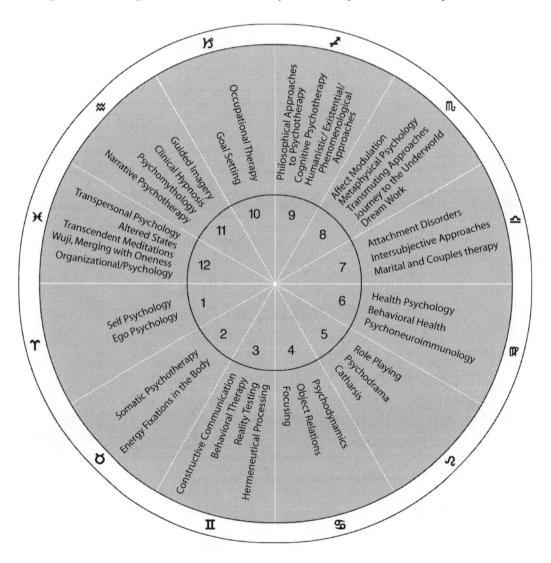

Figure 17: The Astrological Mandala as a Psychotherapeutic Meta-system

In my first book, *The Mystery of Personal Identity,* I put forth the notion of using the astrological mandala as a psychotherapeutic meta-system (Mayer, 1984). I wanted my colleagues to imagine a circle of healing traditions operating together as an integral whole. Each therapist could create his or her own healing mandala (Arguelles, 1972, 1995). For example, the psychotherapy mandala I brought to my colleagues (Mayer, 1977, 1984, 2007) had Gendlin's Focusing method at the center. In the lowest area of the circle, corresponding to underworld journey, I placed psychodynamic theories. In the upper part of the circle were cognitive-behavioral approaches. On the right side of the circle (where the astrological 7th house and the sign Libra would be) I placed relational approaches to psychotherapy. Since the astrological mandala includes elements of fire (energy), earth (somatic approaches), air (cognitive approaches), and water (feeling oriented approaches), these elements of healing all participate together as an integral whole. Just like astrologers look for the angles of relations (aspects) between planets (Rudhyar, 1970), I wanted my fellow psychotherapists to look for the interconnections between therapies instead of looking for which one is the best, thereby avoiding projecting a Western competitive worldview onto psychotherapeutic healing.[6]

When I suggested this mandala to my colleagues I told them that I did not intend to develop a fixed place for each psychotherapy tradition to fit into twelve pieces of clearly cut pie. Each system, depending upon its attributes focused upon at a given time, could be inserted into a different part of the wheel (Mayer, 1984, 2007, 2009). For example, psychoanalysis fits with the astrological fourth house symbolizing the home, since to a great extent it delves into the past home life of the individual. However, when we focus on psychoanalysis' interpretive orientation of giving meaning to experience, we might then place psychoanalysis in the ninth house of philosophy. I created a psychotherapeutic mandala so that my colleagues and I could have a well-rounded ordering principal and centering device for the therapist.

Just as the martial artist uses the ancient circle walking of the Pa Kua to center him or herself (Smith, 1992), or the Native American uses the medicine wheel to put all things in creation into a interrelated whole (Storm, 1972), I hope that increasing numbers of modern therapists use the psychotherapeutic mandala.[7] In addition to wanting to contribute this overarching viewpoint to psychotherapy, one of the major specific treasures I want to share with the field of psychology from my journey into metaphysical terrain is in the importance of "energy" to psychotherapy.

Joining the Streams of Energy and Psychology

Energy practices are not well accepted in traditional academic, medical, and psychological circles.[8] It was as if I had to do an acrobatic feat to make a presentation to the field of psychology on the importance of the role of energy in psychological healing in general, and on "energy psychology" in particular. I discovered that I could name my workshops,

Bodymind Healing Psychotherapy, and in the course description talk about energy psychology; but if I called the continuing education course "Energy Psychology" it would be rejected.[9]

I could understand the political reasons behind this rejection because of the controversy surrounding the term, "energy psychology," which has been associated with various narrow tapping technologies. In the Emotional Freedom Technique for example a patient would tap on various acu-points while saying a limiting belief (Craig, 1995). The wider field of psychology has reservations about energy psychology, and there has been much debate in the field on the efficacy of this as a treatment (Feinstein, 2008, 2009; Pignotti, 2009).

I spoke at six Energy Psychology conferences, and wrote a book, called *Energy Psychology*, to express my viewpoint that there was a need for a comprehensive energy psychology (Mayer, 2009). I argued that the tapping methods that many associate with representing the field of energy psychology, are too narrow to represent the depth and breadth of the field. I said that the field of energy psychology was in a pre-paradigmatic phase, and psychologists could add to the healing modalities of our field by being open to examine energy psychology research and its reported efficacy for certain conditions (Mayer, 2009b). I showed my colleagues through my writings and conference presentations how Qigong would add to the field of energy psychology and to psychologists' behavioral health treatments of hypertension, anxiety, and insomnia by integrating Qigong movements into behavioral healthcare and psychotherapy (Mayer 2003, 2007, 2010).

The internal process of psychological change, as Gendlin (1978) rightly pointed out, has energy activation (Qigong) as an inextricable part of it, as a patient's energetic "felt shift" emerges along with discovering new meaning. Also, symbolic process methods, such as my Mythic Journey Process (Mayer, 1994) and River of Life process (Mayer 2007, 2009), create an internal energy (Jung, Vol. VIII, p. 211-215) that helps a person find a vital, meaningful life path.[10]

By developing these psycho-energetic methods I wanted to add specific energy cultivation methods to Hillman's ideas about the importance of "soul" (Hillman, 1975) to the field of psychology. So, in addition to suggesting to my colleagues that Tai Chi and Qigong could contribute to psychotherapy as "soulful," energetic, practices,[11] I wanted to bring both the Mythic Journey and River of Life practices to psychotherapy as soulful, energetic practices.

Here, once again my attempt to bring many different streams together rang the tone from my power spot in nature where two rivers became one. But here, once again is expressed my struggle with my outlier status...in this case regarding the field of energy psychology. If she could see me now, I can imagine a smirk on that astrologer's face at that health fair back in the 1970s, and her saying, "There is that Sun conjunct Uranus again." Your life energy (Sun) is outside the Saturnian boundaries of any set system (Uranus), and you must suffer this Fate. Reluctantly, I must agree.

One of the California's leading psychologists who hired me to teach at a premier traditional teaching venue, told me, "I really like what you are doing, just try not to mention the word "energy" when you do your presentation at our school. People will think it's too 'new-agey.'" When I did the presentation, where I hoped that this psychologist would come, I told the students and licensed psychologists there about how Albert Szent Giorgi (1960), discoverer of Vitamin C and a winner of a Nobel Prize in chemistry said

> *"In every culture and in every medical tradition before ours, healing was accomplished by moving energy."*

I posed the question to the students at this workshop, "Why does psychology then have such a problem with valuing energy in psychology?"

Cross-Cultural History of Energy Healing

I explained to this class, and in many others to whom I have given continuing education classes for psychologists, that "energy" has been seen to be an important part of healing the mind and body in many cultures, and energy is called by many different names in different cultures.

Qigong, I explain to my colleagues is just the Chinese name for energy. In Japan this energy is called *ki,* and we see the powerful effects of its use in the art of Aikido. In India it is called *prana*; and in ancient Tibetan Vinayana texts of Buddhism, *kum nye* is used to cultivate it. In ancient Greece, it was called *archaeus,* the vital life force. In Judaism it is called *chai* or *ruach,* and in Kabbalah it is called *chiyyut.*

The Kung tribesmen of the Kalahari call this healing energy *num*, and say the gods gave it to them. They use this energy to heal their spouses and their community through dance and massage. Being a healer is part of normal socialization, not the function of a special class. One central event in this regard is the all-night healing dance that takes place approximately once a week and activates *num*. "*Num* resides in the belly and is activated through trance dancing and the heat of the fire. It ascends or boils up the spinal column and into the head, at which time it can be used to pull out the sickness afflicting others." The rock paintings of their ancestors show that this dance has origins that go back far into their culture's past (Halifax, 1979, p. 55; Katz, 1979).

Among Native Americans, the activation of energy is an intrinsic part of healing. A common tribal ritual used is to treat a person who falls ill by calling on *Wakantanka* (the Great Mystery) and the energies of the four directions to restore the person to harmony with the forces of nature. In sweat lodges, the medicine person who leads the ritual often sprays or throws water into the face of the person doing the sweat to produce a mild shock, thereby raising the level of emotion (Krippner, 1994, p. 8).

I tell my colleagues that according to my friend and colleague Ken Cohen, author of *The Way of Qigong*, Native Americans often use energy in healing. Writing in *Bridges*

Magazine, he tells this story, "The Seneca medicine man, Moses Shongo, would hold one hand up, fingers pointed toward the sky, and imagine that healing power was flowing directly from the Creator's 'Light of Love.' He simultaneously used the other hand to heal, sometimes with light touch, sometimes without touch…Keetoowah Christie, great grandson of the famed Cherokee warrior Ned Christie…warms the hands over a ceremonial fire and then, while praying, circling his palms on or over a diseased area. Clockwise circling is used to add energy, to fill depleted areas. Counterclockwise circling is used to remove congestion, fever, infection and inflammation…. The renowned Blackfoot Holy Man, Eagle Plume, healed his son's knee injury by pushing dried rose thorns into his son's leg…and then burned them right down to the bottom." This is similar to what the Chinese acupuncturist's do when heating the needle by burning moxa (mugwort). When Medicine Man Rolling Thunder was asked by Ken, a recognized master of the Taoist arts, about acupuncture points, Rolling Thunder responded incredulously, "You mean the Chinese know about that? That's Cherokee medicine!" (Cohen, 1994).

The Energetic Dimension in Psychotherapy and Healing

I also explained to this renowned psychologist's students that there is no reason to be phobic of the word "energy" in psychotherapy because the importance of energy is already known in the field of psychotherapy. In analytic psychology it is common to hear discussions of libido, energy cathexis, catharsis, fixation, restoring flow, and character armor. All these are energetic concepts. Likewise in Jungian writings, he has a whole chapter on "Psychic Energy" (Jung, 1960, Vol. VIII). In addition, contemporary psychologists know about the importance of the relaxation response in behavioral healthcare. Herbert Benson, the distinguished psychologist from Harvard University, first spoke it of (Benson, 1975); and currently it is commonplace to hear about the importance of sympathetic and parasympathetic nervous system arousal level in treating trauma (van der Kolk, 1987, 1996). Also, virtually all psychologists know the importance of modulating arousal levels in psychotherapy. (Schore, 2003; Aposhyan, 2004, p. 168–9). Likewise, I argued, that Dr. Gendlin, the well respected psychologist and winner of the American Psychological Association most distinguished psychologist of the year award, speaks of a "felt energetic shift" as being a key to creating change in psychotherapy (Gendlin, 1980).

I tried to get my Jungian colleagues to become interested in my notion of the importance of energy in psychotherapy by reminding them of the fact that Jung said that an archetype is an "energy potential" (Jung, 1960, Vol. VIII). In this way, I tried to make the case that a fundamental part of telling mythic stories was to change the energetic state of a person, and (following along the lines of my interest in Standing Meditation and traditions of postural initiation) to "change their life stance."

So, after enumerating all these ways that energy was already in the field of psychotherapy, I asked my colleagues, "Why would you be so dead set against incorporating an

Eastern view of bodymind healing that incorporated the idea of energy in psychotherapy? Doesn't it seem that a tradition like Tai Chi and Qigong which used methods of energy cultivation for thousands of years to heal and to survive might have something to teach us?"

I told my colleagues about the notions of *fongsung gong* (relaxed alert) in Qigong, which can create a state that has much to add to psychotherapeutic healing because it can help people to simultaneously relax and energize. This, I have told them has important implications for expanding Herbert Benson's idea of the relaxation response, and for healing hypertension, and other mind-body health problems.

However, I started to realize that many of my psychological colleagues did not have an experience of "energy" the way I had, through my experience in delving into Eastern and indigenous practices. After all, this was not part of the training in most American Psychological Association accredited universities.

As I told you, my early experience of feeling energy stream in my body as I went to sleep as a young child was one of the beginning points of my interest in soothing, relaxing, and energetic healing. Then my experiences with psychedelics and the energy blocks and openings that occurred, led me to further experience the importance of the energetic component to healing. Likewise my experiences with various Eastern practices such as *kirtan* (Indian ritual raga chanting) opened a doorway to a somatic experiential metaphysical world that helped me and others to get out of our heads and into a stream of energy that I knew could be important for healing the psyche. In addition, certification training at the Acupressure Institute was certainly a major building block of my understanding of energetic healing, as was the transmission over many decades of aspects of the Polarity therapy tradition from Kazuko Onodera. My deepest immersion into these energetic arts was through the Tai Chi and Qigong traditions.

Certainly psychotherapists appreciate the importance of "being embodied" (Keleman, 1981, 1986; Lakoff, 1999; Aposhyan, 2004), and know about the importance of the relaxation response in terms of behavioral healthcare (Benson, 1975). Energy is known to be important to psychotherapy in the sense that Reich (1980), Freud (1923, 1933), and others have discussed. However, I felt a calling to bring forth further the metaphysical, energetic, healing methods that I had discovered to my psychological colleagues.

A key idea in metaphysics is that life is composed of wavelengths of energy. Consensual reality is said to be operating on a wavelength analogous to our beta brain waves. But, there are other brain wave dimensions such as our alpha dream waves and deeper rhythms such as delta, theta, and gamma waves that are associated with various meditative states. These meditative states are associated with cellular healing (Tonya et. al., 2010).

Since I took it as my calling to bring one particular energy healing tradition, Qigong, to my psychological colleagues, I had to first address some of my colleagues' perceptions that a degree of charlatanism was associated with some Qigong claims. For example, I invited two of my medical doctor friends to a Qigong conference. There we saw a presentation where it was said that Qigong masters could make a person move or shake while the master was on another side of a wall. A demonstration was done with a few people on stage in Standing Meditation postures while the master was in another room; and indeed the people on stage begin to shake. This energetic shaking was then attributed to the master's power. However, it was not explained to the audience that shaking is often a natural epiphenomenon of assuming a Standing Meditation posture. This potential "confounding variable" was not discussed or considered, and my colleagues gave me a disbelieving look and questioned Qigong's legitimacy.

I explained to my psychological colleagues that many people in the Qigong community have been involved with trying to improve Qigong research methods (Sancier, 1996 a & b; Mayer, 1996, 2003; Wayne & Kaptchuk, 2008). I put forth the case that there was no reason to throw out the baby with the bathwater just because there are problems with some Qigong research. I gave them examples of solid research of Qigong with regard to its ability to improve sleep (Irwin, 2008), help with heart related issues (Mayer, 1999, 2003, 2010; Guo, 2008), reduce chronic pain (Wu et. al. 1999), prevent falls amongst the elderly (Province et. al. 1995), and help with many other medical and psychological issues (Sancier, 2004; Mayer, 2009; Liu, 2010). However, impressions can have emotional impact, and even for well-meaning health professionals their prior training and entrenched beliefs can be hard to change.

When I am speaking to my colleagues over a causal lunch, I try to reach them in everyday language; I tell them that the experience of qi, *Wuji*, and the Golden Sea of Elixir does not need to be looked at as something esoteric. The experience of relaxation that one gets from Taoist alchemy practice is analogous to the experience that one has after making love, when our boundaries are opened to a sea of energy. Many indigenous cultures look at the sexual act in the period of "afterglow" as a sacred opportunity for the couple to go on a journey in this sea of light. I tell my colleagues that Tai Chi and Qigong adepts have spent a few thousand years learning how to cultivate this internal sea and to play with activating the origins and movements of its currents for healing the bodymind spirit connection. Though modern advertisers seem to do well in selling products by using sex, it has not worked that well for me as I have tried to sell my colleagues on the value of Qigong. ☺

My success in trying to reach my colleagues has had mixed results. My proposals to present at the California Psychological Association conference have been rejected three times. Also, when I sent my books to various universities in hopes of getting my approach to young students—to give them the expanded vision I would have liked to have had when I was a psychology student—there have been mixed results. Some universities ignored desk copies of the book and follow up phone calls and emails; but such is the path of weaving one's unique garment and having the Black Dogs tear it apart. Following the way of the Old Woman in the Cave, the job of the Reluctant Metaphysician at such times is to watch the unraveling, and learn lessons about how to weave the garment more effectively next time.

In my process of learning to be "a reweaver," I was able to present my approach at quite a few schools and workshop venues; and many leaders in the field became advocates of the integrative weaving of traditions that I was suggesting.[12]

As one example of an open-minded leader in the field who was interested in the integration I was trying to introduce is Dr. Bessel Van der Kolk, a leader in the field of trauma research.[13] I could have included the story of meeting him in my chapter on meetings with remarkable men. I first connected Dr. van der Kolk at a conference on energy psychology where we were both presenting; he was the keynoter. He was talking about the importance of the role of the body in healing post-traumatic stress and showed brain scans and extensive research to back up the claim that somatically oriented approaches are needed for healing trauma (van der Kolk, 2002). He went on to give as an example "model mugging." After his keynote presentation we had a chance to talk and had an immediate rapport since we were both great admirers of Dr. Gendlin's work on the role of the body in psychotherapy. Then I spoke to him about the model mugging approach to re-empowering victims of certain types of trauma. I suggested an addition to the model mugging approach, whereby a past victim punches and kicks at a foam filled costume around a human being. I raised a question, saying that though model mugging may be important at some times for the purpose of catharsis, "Why have a patient resort to the same violent attacking energy that was perpetrated on them, in order to heal?" I suggested that he might consider the value of Tai Chi and Qigong and the internal martial arts in enhancing treatment during the re-empowerment stage in patient's recovery from trauma. I explained how the internal martial arts tradition helps to empower a person without reverting to violence. I was, and am, very grateful that Dr. van der Kolk then began to use my Bodymind Healing Qigong DVD in his training of trauma therapists. What a joy it is to meet remarkable, open-minded people on the Path!

However, even though there has been some incorporation of my integral approach in the field of psychotherapy, at this point it feels like I am living in the myth of Sisyphus, pushing a rock up a hill, three feet forward, and two feet backward. Though the myth of Sisyphus helps me in my moments of being in touch with the uphill battle of my life, even more helpful are the dreams, visions, and power spots of my life. At a moment when I feel a sense of loss as to whether my life mission will be completed, I remember the dark clouds around me from "the land where the Sun rises in the West." I can still visualize the light that came from the heavens above in that visionary dream in 1971. Or, I call on my medicine name from my vision quest and remember that I want to kiss the eyes of our culture (as the deer kissed mine) to help our culture become more aware of how ancient sacred wisdom traditions and practices can help to heal the modern psyche. I no longer need to visit my power spot of "two rivers becoming one." The image of it, and my life path carrying this with me, is lived in my every day life. The power of imagination in each Reluctant Metaphysician's life helps us remember our calling. From images (*yi*) come energy (qi); from energy comes imaginal direction.

I like to interpret the mythic tale of Prometheus' theft of the fire of the Gods from the heavens as an allegory about the role of the imagination and energy in healing. The stories about Prometheus tell about two of his sins: the theft of fire and the hiding of the best portion of meat from the Gods and keeping it for himself. Fire is a common symbol for imagination and energy, and meat is a common symbol for that which gives substantial nourishment in life. For Prometheus' sins, his punishment from Zeus was to have his liver eaten up by an Eagle for eternity.

One interpretation of this myth involves the importance of appreciating that the meaty and fiery stuff that gives energy to our lives comes from a source in the divine realm. Our livers can be eaten up by over-indulgence when we consume excess alcohol or food, by entitled anger when we feel that our egos deserve more, or by lingering depression when we forget our divine connection with all of life. Perhaps the story teaches us that the meaty stuff of life is not our meat, rather the divine source of life gives us meaty issues to nourish us if we can learn to pay homage to the spiritual lessons hidden there. Nor is it our fire; rather the dreams, visions, experiences in nature, and energetic healings that alter our lives are inspirational sparks from the divine realm, and we are merely tenders and guiders of its flame.

Recognizing that the elements of life are stolen from, and are gifts from, the Gods can help us to humbly weave our unique threads into the divine fabric of life as we actualize our missions. I am pleased to say that there are many others in our culture that are on a similar mission in understanding the importance of the divine gift of energy in healing, and the importance of weaving this golden thread into the fabric of our healing traditions and academic disciplines. For example, the well known "new biologist" and doctor Bruce Lipton argued in his book, *The Biology of Belief* that when the bottom of the ruling paradigm of science changes all the upper levels must change also (Lipton, 2005). He says that Einstein's insights about the interchangeability and relativity of matter and energy shifted the bottom of the pyramid of science from a Newtonian to a Quantum universe, and opened other hard and soft sciences to eventually include the fundamental importance of energy in the basis of their disciplines. Dr. Lipton believes that after the bottom of the pyramid, physics, was affected by the importance of energy, now it is beginning to come in to biology and chemistry, slowly into medicine, and then lastly into psychology (Lipton, 2006).

- Psychology
- Medicine
- Biology and chemistry
- Physics

It was very heartening to meet him at an event our Health Medicine Center sponsored event where he was the featured speaker. We exchanged books, and it was gratifying to hear his openness to the idea of integrating Qigong into psychotherapy.

Also, I am glad that I am not alone in my quest to get the wider medical system to appreciate the importance of the role of Qigong in helping the healing process. There are many who are making valuable contributions. Dr. Michael Irwin at UCLA has done interesting research showing the healing role of Tai Chi Chih (Tai Chi ruler) in helping people with insomnia (Irwin, 2008). (It is unfortunate that Michael Jackson did not hear about this study, so he could have tried Qigong instead of relying on the medication that killed him). There are many scholarly research articles on Qigong and its role in healing hypertension (Guo, 2008), chronic pain (Wu, 1999), healing trauma, preventing falls amongst the elderly, and so forth. Even well renowned doctors, such as Mehmet Oz, say, "If you want to live to be one-hundred practice Qigong, Qigong enhances longevity."

So, I am not alone in living in the myth of Sisyphus. It has been an uphill battle for many of those who appreciate the value of Qigong to get this branch of Chinese medicine used by our American medical system and our psychotherapists. This is due to a variety of factors such as the tendency of health professionals to have an understandable bias toward what they know from their training and prior experience, the need for significant research to accumulate before a given method is accepted, and so forth.

Joining the Streams of Qigong and Psychotherapy

The two streams that I have been most interested in joining are the streams of Qigong and psychotherapy. In my pioneering efforts to join these streams, I was grateful to teach a three-semester class to masters in psychology students in the 1980s at John F. Kennedy's Transpersonal Psychology program. I taught students to use the metaphors and experience of Tai Chi Chuan Push Hands practice to: ward off the verbal attacks of patients on them, and to use Tai Chi movements like "roll back" to help interns to let go of the stresses of dealing with their first patients. In addition, Tai Chi breathing methods and movements were shown to be an important behavioral health care tool; and the metaphors and practices of Tai Chi Push Hands were shown to help couples "not collide nor separate" in their communications with their partners. Then later, I brought elements of these courses to the California Institute for Integral Studies where in 1996 I taught one course to doctoral psychology students in Tai Chi, Qigong, and Psychotherapy, and another in Energy Medicine: East and West. At these schools I hoped to influence the field about the important additions that Qigong could make to psychotherapy.

In the last decades I have traveled around the country giving lectures, and workshop presentations about what Qigong gives psychotherapy and what psychotherapy gives Qigong. At psychology conferences I presented on how psychotherapy and behavioral healthcare could benefit by incorporating Qigong into its treatment protocols; and at Qigong conferences I spoke of how Western psychotherapy could add much to Qigong.

It was no easy task to advocate for this integration. It was like living out the karma of the disadvantages of the metaphysical attributes of my way of being as being an outsider. Throughout this book, I have used the example of my natal Sun being conjunct Uranus as an archetypal symbol of the outsider. Part of the metaphorical basis of this symbology is that Uranus revolves in a different direction from the other planets. Other planets rotate from east to west on a vertical axis, and Uranus rotates on its side from south to north. Thus Uranus is seen to be the planetary symbol of one who eccentrically follows the beat of a different drummer, living on the outskirts and not wanting to be limited by any one Saturnian boundary.

The symbol of Gemini is associated with the Greek God Hermes whose symbol, "the herm," marks the boundary between things. Gemini's symbolism is also represented by two pillars, related to the commonly described elements of the two-sided nature of those who have the essence of Gemini. That old astrologer at the health faire that I told you about earlier would be smiling now seeing how I am living on the boundary line between occupations.

One of the ways that this aspect of essential nature of mine manifested in my early life was when sometimes in my adolescence I was not content to just stay inside to sleep. My parents said, "Why do you have to go and camp in our backyard when things are so comfortable right in our beautiful house." Just like some force of destiny compelled me to live on the outskirts of comfortableness in my childhood, so did some larger force impel me to in my adolescence to explore in the woods where I found the place where two rivers become one. Then later in my life, my way of Being led me to go into the woods for forty nights.

There are advantages and disadvantages to each of the uniquely woven threads that comprise the garment of our lives. In mythic terms, certainly light and dark threads are twisted together as part of Clotho, Lachesis, and Atropos' creation of "the lot of our fate." My life journey of going deep out into the outskirts of civilization following the path of two streams becoming one, led me understand why it is said that, "The way you can tell a pioneer is by the arrows in his back." For example, as I attempted to join Qigong and psychotherapy some of my Qigong colleagues said, "Qigong is a holistic system in itself; why add in some Western psychological overlay. It's a defamation of the tradition." Likewise my psychological colleagues' arrows were piercing when they said, "Your psychotherapy patients are not coming to you for some ancient, outmoded Eastern tradition; your patients are coming for psychotherapy. Though it might be valuable as an adjunct (for a homework assignment like reading a book or doing physical exercise), the idea of integrating Qigong and psychotherapy goes against the standard of care. It is like alchemically mixing oil and water together; they do not mix."

Though it may seem as though it is stretching the metaphor of my vision quest too far, many times my sense of estrangement from my colleagues in both professions (Qigong and psychotherapy) felt like my way of seeing, my very eye was being torn out of its socket. Doubt emerged. But then, as in my vision quest, I realized that a sacred ritual was taking place as my eye was being eaten. When I stopped to appreciate the ritual that was taking place by the critiques of my colleagues I realized my way of seeing had value, like the emerald green stone put into my eye by the deer at Water Hole Mountain. The experience, and the image, of my vision quest of the deer kissing my eyes helped me to say to members of my profession that the ways of nature (the Tao, vision questing, and so forth), and the way of Qigong, could add something valuable if they were incorporated into being part of the origin myth of psychotherapy. My vision quest has helped me to understand that those who have their views dismembered may not appreciate every kiss. ☺

What Psychotherapy and Qigong Give Each Other

The most obvious gift that Qigong offers psychotherapy is in giving methods of relaxation to help to heal stress, one of the key reasons people go to see therapists. The interesting thing about Qigong is that it has methods that are simultaneously relaxing and energizing. This is called *fongsung gung*. I attempted to show my colleagues that Qigong could give gifts to give to the field beyond what Dr. Herbert Benson, who first coined the term "relaxation response," showed (Benson, 1983). I presented the case to my colleagues that after all, for thousands of years, sophisticated ways have been developed in Qigong and Tai Chi traditions to synchronize breath and movement to promote healing (Cohen, 1997; Mayer, 2004, 2007, 2009).

For example, these time-tested stress reduction methods have important healing implications for those who suffer from fibromyalgia, chronic fatigue, and other behavioral health issues. As well, these Eastern relaxation and internal martial art traditions are especially useful to create somatic safety zones for those who suffer from conditions of sympathetic overload; they can help traumatized patients to regain a safety zone in their bodies.[14]

I also showed in my books and articles how Qigong and Tai Chi's ability to facilitate the relaxation response could be helpful in cases of hypertension. To support my case (honoring the lawyer sub-personality still in me) I wrote three peer-reviewed articles (Mayer, 1999, 2003, 2010) on how integrating Qigong and psychotherapy could help with this disease that affects 50 million individuals in the United States (Wollam, et al., 1988; JNC-7, 2003).

Many people associate the healing attributes of Tai Chi, Qigong, and meditative traditions with their relaxing and transcendent qualities. (Transcendence involves rising above life issues by entering into an altered state of consciousness.) However, I presented the case to my colleagues that Qigong and Tai Chi not only have relaxing and transcending attributes; but they are also are body-oriented traditions that can help…to transmute stuck life issues. For example, in the case of one of my patient's recurrent panic attacks,[15] I showed how important Qigong breathing can be to induce a relaxation response; and touching acupressure point (CV-17) over the heart was important for helping this patient to self-sooth when she was anxious. However, I also showed in this case how the relaxation and self-soothing that this patient got from this breathing method and acu-point self touch was not sufficient to produce healing. Cognitive restructuring, psychodynamic work, and the transformative symbols from her dream life provided some of the necessary ingredients to transmute the psychological patterns rooted in early abandonment and fear of rejection.[16]

Many somatic psychotherapists have discussed the importance of a body-oriented approach to help a patient create a morphogenesis of their anatomy and their motoric responses as part of an embodied psychotherapy (Keleman, 1981, 1986).[17] I believe, and have written about how Tai Chi and Qigong can be similarly amalgamated with psychotherapy to transform one's life stance physically and emotionally, change reactive attachment patterns, and aid in the psycho-energetic healing of trauma (Mayer 2007).[18]

Joining Ten Streams to Make Bodymind Healing Qigong

On the other hand, I made presentations to my Tai Chi and Qigong colleagues about the value of psychological inner work and how psychotherapy can help Qigong practitioners to *deepen consciousness of psychological meanings of what arises while doing body movements*. For example, I gave my Tai Chi and Qigong colleagues and students examples of how Gendlin's Focusing method can aid a person in becoming conscious of the psychological meanings of body blocks that emerge while holding static Qigong postures. By "Focusing" on a felt sense in the body while in stillness, a "felt energetic shift," can occur, and new meaning can arise about what those body blockages are about.

My aim was to create a way of doing Tai Chi and Qigong that focused on the "soul" of the practice, not just the "spirit." For example, instead of just noticing thoughts that arise as a person does in spiritual practice, with a soulful approach a person pays attention to the memories and images that arise as indicators of inner work that may be needed regarding blocked life issues. So, if one experiences shaking in one's legs while standing instead of just noticing the shaking, a soulful approach is to ask, "How is my connection to the ground shaky in my life? What old ways of being can I shake loose." As the shaking stops, the practitioners can explore, "What new life stances can help me to come to life in a more grounded way."[19]

My medicine animal name, Michael, Two Streams Joining, was once again with me as I created the Bodymind Healing Qigong system. But it was ten (not two) streams of Qigong that I integrated and shared with numerous students over the years (Mayer, 2000, 2004).[20]

Revisioning Metaphysics

In summary, in this chapter and the previous ones you can see my re-revisioning the academic study of metaphysics from the intellectual study of ontology, epistemology, and cosmology into an experiential, healing metaphysics. Some of the keys that have helped me to open doorways to the world behind the world (that opened Ali Baba's treasure house) are: The mythogems from various symbolic process traditions such as astrology, mythology, dream-work, and vision questing. Equally important are those keys that come from various energetic healing traditions such as Tai Chi, Qigong, and acupressure.

There is an oft-mentioned notion that psychotherapists in our culture function as a priesthood, or as modern day shamans. I would add that psychotherapists can function as the experiential metaphysicians of our culture by helping our patients to heal current life issues through connecting to the world behind the world.

Two of the deepest streams spoken of in metaphysical traditions are those of *lumen* (light) and *numen* (meaning). This type of "light" that heals psychophysiological issues in the Western mystery tradition has been called *lumen naturae* (the light of nature), or *soma pneumatikon* (spirit body), which is related to the body's animating spirit (Kalsched, 1996). Dr. Jung, drawing from an old alchemical text, put it this way, "There is in the human body a certain aethereal substance…of heavenly nature, known to a very few, which needeth no medicament, being itself the incorrupt medicament" (Jung, 1955, para. 114n).

The parallels between the Western mystery tradition's notion of this healing *lumen* and the Qigong practices that have remained intact in the East are striking. So, in resonance with my name of Michael, Two Streams Joining, I have argued that joining of the traditions of *lumen*, represented by Qigong, and the traditions of *numen,* represented by Western psychotherapy are an ideal mix (Mayer, 2007, 2009). Regarding the healing tool of *numen*, after going though the descent into the felt darkness of the traumas of everyday life, a key moment in healing often comes when a person finds a new meaning such as, "This abuse led me to be a healer, or it helped me to be more sensitive to the suffering of others." A person can find their new meaningful life stance through their own natural process of Self-discovery, or from the appropriate joining of the Mythic Journey Process, Bodymind Healing Qigong, and Bodymind Healing Psychotherapy. The Reluctant Metaphysician walks the Path and turns suffering into the light of meaning.

In the next chapters you will see examples of how I put this into practice in my work with various psychotherapy patients, and how the energetic and symbolic dimensions of a healing metaphysics can be two streams that become one.

CHAPTER 17:

The Path of the Reluctant Metaphysical Healer: Tapping on the Self-healing Secrets of the Gods

At the beginning of time, the gods had just finished their divine work
of creating the first humans. One of the gods spoke up and said,
"Where should we hide the secret of their Self-healing?"
The earth goddess said, "Let's hide it the center of the biggest mountain."
"That's no good," replied another. "
One day they'll have bulldozers
and find it too easily."
"What about hiding it in the depths of the deepest sea?" replied the
god of the sea.
The wise reply came, "They'll have submarines someday and will find
it without any inner work."
A third god suggested, "What about hiding it in the Great Pyramid in
a safe up a narrow shaft?"
"Not really any better," replied another.
"Some day they'll have mechanized little vehicles that can just go up
the shaft and open the safe."
Then Thoth, the trickster god, spoke up with a wry smile,
"Why don't we just hide the secret of Self-healing
inside of their very Selves?
They'll never think of looking there."
And so it was decided.

—retold and adapted from the *Shamanic Oral Archives*

The Path of the Reluctant Metaphysical Healer

We are all reluctant metaphysicians. Each time we get sick and do not immediately use a pharmaceutical medication, and instead we go on the quest to discover our inner healing resources, we are exploring the path of the earliest Egyptian metaphysician, Thoth. According to metaphysical and mythological literature, he was the founder of the Egyptian mystery tradition (Schure, 1977). Those of us today who are on a self-healing path can look into our very selves to tap on the healing powers that our creator put there. None of us wants to have to go on this healing journey, we would rather be healthy. But when the Goddess, *Necessity*, calls we reluctantly go on a journey to discover these healing secrets. If we take the time to look within, we may be touched by the healing powers within us, or the healing powers that come from a friend or loved one.

Like Ali Baba who opened a secret door to a cave by his words (open sesame), we discover that a kind word can open a door to a healing treasure house—a felt shift may take place, spontaneous remissions may occur (Weil, 2000), and healing pathways open once we open the treasure chest of our hearts.

Thus far we have explored many metaphysical pathways to tap into the healing powers of the world behind the world: through touch, posture, movement, breath, intention, imagination, dreams, visions, and stories. I have told you about the ways that my life's work has been to tap into the world behind the world through storytelling traditions and the energetic arts of cross-cultural ancient sacred wisdom traditions for the purpose of healing. These traditions can help to heal our relationship to our personal identities and life purpose, our relationship with others, our heath, our psychological issues, our environment, and our ecosphere.

I told you about how my metaphysical journey began in my philosophy class in college where I sensed that my path was not to just use metaphysics to know more about life, but to heal. An inner knowing made me realize that I was more interested in experiential rather than academic and intellectual metaphysics. The question arises once again, from where do our inclinations in life derive?

Creating a Healing Metaphysics: Journey to the Temple of Aesclepius

The area of metaphysics that became my life's work is the healing dimension. Metaphysics teaches that many diseases incarnate from the subtle planes to the gross level. It is believed that illness oftentimes starts with imbalances on the level of mind, and manifests in the human energy field; then it incarnates in the musculature, and finally in the spine. Healing that is initiated at any of these levels can spread to other levels.

Each metaphysician might have an interest in one or more of these dimensions, or in some particular area of focus. An astrologer might say that based upon my Sun sign being Gemini in the Eighth House that I would have an interest in the intellectual aspects of metaphysics. However, it is the healing dimensions of metaphysics, and in particular the healing dimensions of symbolic processes and energy practices that are my favorites.

There are many ways to see this interest in healing reflected in my astrological chart. For example, in my first house (symbolic of our personalities and what is rising in us at the moment of my birth) is the asteroid Chiron. In Greek mythology Chiron was the teacher of Aesclepius, the God of healing in Greece and the founder of a Western holistic healing temple in Epidaurus, Greece. Chiron was represented in Greek mythology as half man/half horse. It is said by astrologers that the planetary bodies that are in a person's first house are most correlated with one's identity.

Not all metaphysicians have an inclination towards, or believe in all areas of metaphysics, and not all astrologers believe in or use asteroids to do their readings. Those astrologers who believe in the ability of an asteroid to influence a human being's life stretch any mind into incredulity, including mine. However, when entering into the area of a synchronistic, acausal worldview versus a worldview based on causal effects (Rudhyar, 1970; Tarnas, 1993, 2007), one begins to wonder. From the perspective of synchronicity, it is intriguing that Chiron represents instinctual and primordial methods of healing, and that is my area of exploration. In addition, astrologers say that the particular sign that the planetary body is in is significant, and in my case Chiron is in Scorpio, the sign of delving into deep emotions. My life path does seem to be deeply involved with working with healing emotional issues as a psychologist using somatic (horse-sense) types of approaches.

Speaking of interesting synchronicities related to my relationship to the archetype of Chiron, it is fascinating that I co-led two trips to Greece in the early 1990s with a woman author, Demetra George who wrote the book called *Asteroid Goddesses* (George, 1986). I told you earlier about the journey we co-led to the cave of the Oracle of Delphi. Another one of the places that we twice visited was the temple of Aesclepius. The tour guide pointed up the hill to where the cave of Chiron was located. As the group questioned why it was said that Chiron was half-man and half-horse, we wondered whether he practiced a form of animal movements based on the horse, similar to the Chinese animal forms of Qigong. Though the tour guide had never heard of humans doing animal movement as connected to Chiron's meaning in Greek mythology, her interest was piqued when I showed her an interesting small vase that I had bought at the museum there. It had a half-man and half-animal figurine that was doing a martial art type movement.

During the day we toured the temple grounds. As I taught the animal forms of Qigong to the students there a flock of birds "came to watch," and landed on a tree right by where we began to practice. After we finished practicing, they seemingly in perfect sync, flew away. Such synchronicities that the rational mind can just label as interesting coincidences, open the metaphysician to wondering about an enchanted cosmos and our unity with our sentient animal and aviary brethren. Poet Gary Snyder puts our human connection with other life forms into proper perspective when he facetiously suggests that in the larger scheme of things perhaps we humans are just, "a gang of sexy primate clowns… whose purpose is to entertain the rest of nature" (Snyder, 1990).

Regardless of whether an asteroid in my first house has anything to do with my affinity with the archetype of Chiron, and despite my debates with my colleague Demetra that it did not seem likely that there could be anything to this "asteroid stuff," I had to reluctantly admit that the synchronicity regarding my affinities with this archetype was interesting to say the least—a good opportunity to wonder how much such cosmological correspondences are a result of our projections, or we its.

Our group was able to stay at the hotel at the Aesclepian site, and we slept outside that night. The sacred grounds there were known as a powerful spot for dream incubation, and I thought I might try to ask for a dream about my life's direction. That night I had a dream of an Aesclepian like figure (a priest, or Aesclepius himself) walking next to my head, his lightweight robe brushed over my face while I was sleeping. The figure tapped me ever so gently on the top of my head. When I woke from the dream, it was so real that I was not sure if someone brushed by me and tapped me during the night, or if it was a dream. When I woke I asked those sleeping inside if anyone had walked outside during the night. When I heard that no one had, I was left with the felt sense of a transmission. I felt a calling to carry forth the holistic healing that this place stood for in the ancient world and, along with others, to bring this into the modern world.

Demetra pointed out that the asteroid Aesclepius was one of the most elevated planetoids in my astrological chart at 22 degrees of Cancer (near the cusp of my ninth and tenth houses), and that the most elevated planetoid was significant in terms of career and life direction. So she said that she was not surprised that I had a visit from this archetype, and that I had an affinity to healing with feelings (the astrological sign Cancer), and an interest in creating an integrated medical clinic someday. Though I could not agree that some little asteroid could have anything to do with these inclinations of mine, I had to reluctantly agree that there was an interesting synchronicity in the air.

We all have each archetype in us, such as Chiron (the teacher of healing), and Aesclepius (the holistic healer). Perhaps one of astrology's purposes as a metaphysical meditation system is to lure us into deep relationships with the archetypes so that we can incarnate those energy potentials in various facets of life.

A decade later, my life path was mostly involved with integrative approaches to healing and I co-founded an integrative medical clinic in Lafayette, California. How much is there a meaningful or anomalous coincidence between these asteroids and my path of holistic health, integrative medicine, and enjoying going into deep feelings with my patients? I am left to wonder. As I said in my doctoral dissertation, the important thing is not whether we find some hidden reality that explains "the cause" of our ways of being—the important thing is the process of opening the doorway to Mystery and wondering about our connection with the wider whole of which we are a part.

Each of us has our own particular discoveries and methods to tap on these self-healing powers that come from the world behind the world. Each of us has our archetypal deity with which we identity, a medicine animal name, or places in nature that connect us to the natural treasures that we have to give. To bring our unique treasure house of gifts to the world is not an easy task, as is illustrated by my journey of trying to channel the stream of metaphysical healing practices to the field of psychotherapy.

Joining Two Streams:
In My Private Practice as a Psychologist and in an Integrative Medical Clinic

Joining Two Streams: Qigong and Psychotherapy

Throughout my decades of teaching in psychotherapy graduate schools, I have not attempted to dissuade my students from being Freudians, behaviorists, or Jungians; nor I tell them, should they adapt my views on psychotherapy as theirs. Instead I say, "Find your own way as a therapist." As one tool I suggest to them to use the astrological man-dala (that I suggested in the last chapter) to center themselves in the midst of the tradi-tions of all psychotherapies, and I encourage them to imagine standing in the center of that wheel and find their own stance. Or, using another image I suggest that they can use my experience of threading together my garment, as simply one teaching story about how they can create their own unique "coat of many colors" to pass on to their posterity.

So that my students are realistic about the difficulties of developing non-mainstream approaches, I explain to them my difficulties in pioneering the integration of the streams of Qigong and psychotherapy. Like many other Western-trained psychologists, I had been trained to keep separate the realms of psychotherapy and various spiritual traditions.

One of these traditions that was a treasure house for me was my Tai Chi practice. This was, I believed, one "self-healing gift of the Gods" that could be tapped upon by each of us, and that I wanted to give to my patients. Here is the story of how I tried to bring together these streams of my life.

In my early years as a psychologist it was as if I was a "split personality," a psycholo-gist by day, and an avid Tai Chi and Qigong practitioner in my private life. I kept the two worlds separate. As a psychologist I was trained to believe that there were problems, detri-ments, and dangers involved in integrating Eastern modalities with Western psychology; and I internalized and adhered to those beliefs. For example, psychology as a profession has a history of being disapproving of the integration of Eastern modalities in part due to the belief that they are transcendental in nature.

Perhaps because of my connection with my power spot in nature (where two streams joined), I knew that integrating transcendent and transmuting (meaning "rising above" and "working through" respectively) approaches was a key dialectic of an integrative paradigm of healing. I am sure that in addition, it was the memory of the importance of the healing, energetic experiences of my childhood that gave me the sense of purpose that I needed to find my way to a place of more expansive vision.[1]

Situations in life call us to adapt to what is presented to us, and thereby draw from us deep qualities from our essential nature. Whether it is a story of encouragement from an elder to "be ourselves," or a storyline emerging from a dream or a place in nature, the work of the Reluctant Metaphysician is to live his or her own story, and not another's. My work with "Boris" is an example of how my medicine animal name of "Michael, Two Streams Joining" was called forth...

A Turning Point Patient: Carpal Tunnel Syndrome

All therapists have their turning point patients. For me, one of these patients was Boris, a student in medical school who was working on a research project that required a lot of writing. In our depth psychotherapy sessions, he was often distracted by his diagnosed condition of carpal tunnel syndrome. At that time in my evolution I was very careful about dual relationships and mixing different streams of my life together, having been trained in the potential dangers of mixing other disciplines with psychotherapy. So I thought, why not just refer him out to a Qigong teacher? What happens if using these health methods stops him from getting appropriate medical treatment? What happens if the complementary treatment does not work and it produces a transference issue that interferes with the therapeutic relationship?

While Boris was working mainly on issues with his father, who was a medical doctor, and the childhood physical abuse that occurred in this relationship, week after week he came into our session with his arm in a sling and a splint due to his diagnosed condition of carpal tunnel syndrome. The physical therapist with whom he was working said to keep his arm still and she worked with him each week to strengthen his wrist through various exercises. One day my compassion was stronger than my considerations about being unduly cautious. I mentioned to Boris that I had something to tell him about my life that normally I would keep to myself, but that could be relevant to him healing his wrist. He expressed appreciation for my caring, and we agreed we would continue our longstanding practice of clearing any negative feelings if they arose for him through this process. I then told him that I practiced Qigong, and that some research showed it was better to use a relaxing, energizing movement method to promote healing rather than to use splints and not move (Garlinkle et. al., 1998). I suggested that we might try to use a Qigong method, which combined stillness and movement, to explore together like scientists researching, to see if these methods helped him. He agreed.

First, I asked Boris to do the breathing method that, from our work together, had become one of his favorite ways of relaxing. This method, which I had used to help me with my anxiety in my first teaching job, was Microcosmic Orbit Breathing from the Taoist text on *The Secret of the Golden Flower.* But, Boris and I had never before discussed its roots in Qigong and Taoism. On this day we repeated this breathing method to activate a trance-like state. Then I asked him, as he inhaled, to imagine that he was in water up to his shoulders and that his hands were just floating up, wrists leading the way. From this position, on a long, unforced exhalation, I directed him to press the heels of the hands down slightly all the way to the level of the belly. He repeated this quite a few times, and by the end of the session he said that his pain had reduced from eight on the subjective units of distress scale (S.U.D.S. are measured on a ten point scale, ten being the most stress) to two S.U.D.S. This is the first Tai Chi movement called, Commencement, or Raising and Lowering the Qi.[2] Instead of practicing the movement while standing, with Boris we practiced it from a sitting position.

I explained to Boris that the underlying philosophy of Eastern methods of healing was not based on a one-time fix model. Even with Western drugs one has to continue a medication regimen; and there are usually side effects with Western medications. We discussed how his body was signaling him that he needed to get up and take more breaks. To counter potential unrealistic expectations I pointed out that Qigong is "a practice," not a one-time curative event.

So, Boris went home that week and did the Raising and Lowering the Qi movement. He came into our next session without his brace for the first time in months. In subsequent months, Boris never again needed his brace. He said that the pain would come back when he was working too long, but that he was learning to use his pain as a signal to relax and practice his Tai Chi. He was grateful I had stretched the therapeutic boundaries to introduce him to what he now described as "this cool new behavioral health method."

In addition to the healing that occurred, our process helped deepen our relationship and helped Boris begin to individuate from his father. Boris saw the limitations of his father's myopic view that Western medicine was the best answer to all health concerns. It helped to further validate his choices to take some of the new courses offered in his medical school on alternative therapies, and it gave him strength in the future to stand up to his father when their opinions differed.

Integrative Healthcare

The part cannot be well until the Whole is well.

—Plato

My work with Boris and other patients like him made me realize that resolving the split between psychology and health was a key dimension of the path of Michael, Two Streams Joining. The American culture and the psychology profession began to realize in the 1990s that the split between medicine and psychology was problematic for people's optimal health (Blount, 1998). From experiments that revealed the power of the placebo effect, belief (the placebo effect) was shown to be responsible for between 35–55 % of all healing (Rossi, 1986). This translates to mean that mind is a most important variable in the process of healing.

In the metaphysical theory of the Qigong tradition, mind/intention (yi) leads the life energy (qi), which together form equal parts of the equation of healing. So, I wanted to add to the stream of psychological thought that energy in general and Qigong in particular were an important addition to the equation of mind-body healthcare.

While I was training therapists in the integration of Qigong and psychotherapy in the 1980s, I was also learning from my experience with my patients (such as Boris), to whom I am most grateful. My specialty became self-healing methods for physical and mental-health problems. My dharmic agenda was to reach a wider audience and to impact the way our culture looks at physical and mental health. My stream joined the larger stream of fellow travelers in mind-body medicine.

In our culture's evolution, where corporate greed and multibillion-dollar pharmaceutical companies' agendas rule our approach to health, a movement began that involved stepping outside of the tide of commercialism and profit motivation. This type of approach, which is still evolving, is called integrative medicine (Gordon, 1996). Some of the attributes of this approach to medicine involve putting forth a more person-centered approach that treats the person not just the disease, and a holistic approach to healthcare that treats body, mind, and spirit. It combines conventional Western medicine with alternative or complementary treatments such as herbal medicine, acupuncture, massage, stress reduction techniques, and methods from cross-cultural healing traditions.

My interest in this path led to my co-founding and practicing as a psychologist and Qigong teacher at The Health Medicine Center (formerly the Health Medicine Institute) in Walnut Creek, California. Here a multidisciplinary team of health practitioners engages in the practice integrative medicine. Our clinic is one of many which follows an approach that honors the wonders of modern medicine and also gives due weight to the ancient reservoir of knowledge held by time-tested methods of age-old healing traditions.

Some of the illustrative cases that follow come from my experience at these clinics, and from my three decades of private practice as a psychologist. I greatly appreciate having been able to present the approach I developed at many hospitals, universities, and workshop venues.[3] But most awesome to me is to see the way that the integration of Qigong, behavioral healthcare, and psychotherapy has helped a variety of my patients to self-heal long standing issues. By following the Bodymind Healing Psychotherapy pain protocol (Mayer, 2007, 2009) using the River of Life process, and the Yin Yang Balancing method a nurse who was in a major car accident healed an ankle injury in six sessions and was able to work again (Mayer, 1996); and a therapist who had spent many years trying to heal a foot surgery was able to reduce the pain to a zero.[4] Though many people with whom I have worked report remissions of long standing problems in a single session or a few sessions, the important element of the approach that I am taking is that it emphasizes a "practice model," not a one-time fix model (Mayer, 2007). This means that the person needs to take responsibility for practicing the methods after our session, similar to the way a Qigong practitioner needs to practice in order to keep in shape.

Integrative versus Integral: Joining Streams

The Case of Boris is an example of what I call "the integrative phase" of my work, where I brought Qigong and Tai Chi movements into my work with psychotherapy patients.

The *integral* (Walsh, 2006; Wilber, 2000) phase of my work began when I strove to bring Qigong into my work with patients without ever doing a Qigong movement and without ever mentioning a word about Qigong. Because many of my patients were not interested in Qigong and could be turned off by the language of Qigong coming from their therapist, I sought to extract out the essence of what creates transformation from Qigong as a Self-cultivation practice.

For example, with no reference to Qigong, in a psychotherapy session a practitioner can introduce breathing methods (such as Qigong's microcosmic orbit breathing), and teach acu-point self-touch. However in my opinion, the greatest Qigong involves cultivating the energy of life through the practice of clearing the psychological encumbrances that block the rivers of our qi, and finding a new life stance. In this sense it does not seem to be a great stretch to say that the energy of the Qigong state can be found without movement, and in my opinion this is why Qigong and psychotherapy are a natural marriage.

An Integral Approach to Hypertension:

The next two case examples of two different hypertension patients give illustration to the distinction between integrative and integral approaches to Qigong. When I was at the Health Medicine Institute, Medical Director Dr. Len Saputo (with whom I co-founded the clinic), asked me to work in a public forum with one of his patients who was suffering from hypertension. The Health Medicine Forum (HMF) is a leading-edge group of multidisciplinary health professionals trying to combine the best of modern and age-old methods of healing. HMF is part of the movement to bring forth integrative medicine as the norm in the twenty-first century.

During the forum, in front of an audience of approximately two hundred people, each doctor or health professional on the panel described how he or she would work with this patient. I always learn so much from hearing the dialogues between Ayurvedic doctors, acupuncturists, medical doctors, psychologists, and bodyworkers. At this event, Dr. Saputo asked me to work with his patient, who was a man in his late sixties, and to take a risk and do something experiential in front of the assembled group. One of the chief medical researchers from a local hospital was there with a blood pressure monitor. He measured the systolic blood pressure rate of the patient at 168. I then did the River of Life hypnosis method with this patient in front of the group. Within about five minutes, the patient's systolic blood pressure had gone down to 128 (Mayer, 1997b). Many in the audience were impressed, as was I—because I am naturally shy, and I wondered what my blood pressure would be in front of such a large group if someone took it. ☺

However, my work with the River of Life method is not just to introduce it as a quick fix for hypertension. In keeping with my medicine spot in nature, I believe that two streams need to become one, and the stream of depth psychotherapy is equally important, as the next case illustrates. I believe that Qigong alone is not the sole key to open the doorway out of hypertension—an integral perspective is needed that includes diet, exercise, and the person's deeper psychodynamics, cognitions, and beliefs before deep, long-lasting healing can take place.

I recall a patient, who I will call Richard. He was a very wealthy married man and an executive in a local company. Richard's marriage was about to fall apart due to what his wife said was "his inconsiderateness," exemplified by his going out and buying expensive motorcycles without asking her first. An equally important factor in his upcoming divorce was that Richard's wife described him as a workaholic who slept only about four hours a night and did not pay enough attention to his young children.

Richard was suffering from severe hypertension, and he came to me after hearing about my articles and research on hypertension. Being very busy, he was interested in the quick fixes that he hoped would be part of this "Qigong/hypnosis thing." He was more than a little upset when after our first session, I suggested that a combination of marital as well as individual therapy might be important to consider. He reluctantly agreed. Later, after a few sessions of both individual and couples therapy, I asked him to do our River of Life breathing method and focus on what came up as he followed his exhalation down the river of breath through his body. As Richard focused on his body sense, he became aware of a high energy, yet disconnected quality to his energy state.

As he stayed with the felt sense of this a bit longer, he described the feeling as being like a disconnected live wire, after which a sense of anger arose in him. I asked him to stay with the sense of anger and to ask the feeling, "What is this all about?" When Richard did this, another image arose. Richard remembered a childhood scene from his dinner table when he came home with a "D" on his report card. He vividly recalled his father saying to him in a demeaning tone, "You'll never amount to anything, you dummy." All of his brothers joined in the shaming process. Laughing, mocking, and pointing at Richard, they said, "Don't worry, when you grow up, you can always work on one of Uncle Jimmy's garbage trucks and pick up the garbage from our mansions."

At that moment Richard promised himself, "I'll never rest until I make twice as much money as all of them combined." Indeed, Richard kept that promise and more than fulfilled this goal—but he had forgotten the promise he had made to himself. He did not realize how this unconscious motivation was driving him in his current life, and just how literally he was following through on his childhood promise when he had said, "I'll never rest." This insight began the process of Richard changing his behavior. He became aware of the advantages and disadvantages of this compulsion, which had made him successful but had endangered his health and family.

His wife marked this session as the beginning of Richard's change in behavior, which saved their marriage and led to the opportunity to reduce and eventually eliminate his hypertension medication.

There are many interesting points that can be learned from Richard's story. His case illustrates how the "quick fixes" of relaxation modalities may not get to the deeper underlying issues that need to be addressed.

Richard's case shows the power of using an integrative psychotherapy where two rivers become one; and because one in twenty Americans suffer from hypertension (JNC-7, 2003), and fifty percent of Americans may die from its effects (Wollam & Hall, 1988), Richard's inner work has bearing on the importance of a bodymind approach to solving a portion of this health crisis.

In speaking about the integration of meditative and psychotherapy traditions, psychologist Roger Walsh discusses how the path to an "integral tradition" evolves in stages:

> *The first is one of mutual enrichment via "pluralism" and "accommodation," moving from ... assimilation (forcing novel ideas into preformed conceptual categories) to accommodation (expanding and enriching conceptual categories). The second is an "integrative" stage in which the process of mutual enrichment, both theoretical and therapeutic, becomes increasingly systematic. The third stage is "integral" (Wilber, 2000) as the processes of mutual enrichment and integration lead to, and are conducted within, an increasingly comprehensive, coherent, and holistic conceptual framework, adequate to both meditative and psychological traditions (Walsh, 2006, p. 228).*

The Bodymind Healing Psychotherapy (BMHP) tradition that I have discussed in these last two chapters, and in these two cases of hypertension, has naturally evolved from an integration of Qigong and psychotherapy into an integral approach that weaves these traditions into an increasingly comprehensive, coherent, and holistic conceptual framework. In addition to the ten methods of BMHP that weave the two together, I extracted the essence of the two traditions (an alchemical *extractio*), amalgamating the two traditions together so that I do not need to teach Qigong movements to my patients. However, there is one more essential piece of this integral perspective that needs to be included—how Qigong movements naturally arise in psychotherapy. This confirms the teaching story at the beginning of this chapter, and demonstrates that primordial Self-healing divine gifts are indeed hidden inside of each of us. Thus the next chapter....

CHAPTER 18

Changing Your Life Stance: Trance-forming Your Life's Story

Once upon a time a young man decided to go on a quest to the Taoist sacred mountain of Hua Shan to see if his life's meaning could be restored. Although he vowed to fast from all food and wait until a vision came, after three days, nothing happened. Weak from starvation, he fainted in the middle of his prayer circle and gave up his effort. As he let go of trying, it was then that the founder of Tai Chi Chuan, Chang San Feng, appeared and offered to teach the young man how to move like the animals to restore his vital energy, and how to find his primordial Self by filling his body with the powers of the heavens and the earth.

And so this initiate learned how to move like a Snake Creeping Low. In addition to learning the physical movement, the snake taught him to descend into his darkness and find the way through his pain. Another week was devoted to watching and imitating the movements of a White Crane Spreading Its Wings. Mimicking the crane, the initiate put one foot in the water, and spread his not-so-imaginary wings. Into his awareness came a vision of how to step into his pain, and yet find a Transcendent Self that could observe his emotional process with nonattachment.

After forty nights on the mountaintop, learning from the animals, studying the ways of nature, and being visited by the spirit of various Taoist masters, he knew it was now time to leave. As he traveled down the mountain, he was very excited about all he had to teach. The first person he passed was an old lady who was washing off a glass window with a circular motion. The initiate felt a wave of disenchantment come over him as he realized that she was doing the Tai Chi movement Making a Circle between the Heavens and the Earth (also called Taoist Immortal Paints a Heavenly Rainbow), just like he had learned it from Yang Luchan, the founder of the Yang lineage of Tai Chi.

"Maybe everyone knows what I know already and will not want to learn anything from me," he thought.

After walking a little further, he saw a man drop something on the ground and bent down to pick it up. "How does this man know the secret movement called Grasping the Pearl at the Bottom of the Sea, which I learned from Yang Cheng Fu? It's supposed to be a secret way to open the lower tan tien and ground the body's energy. What I know is nothing special, everyone knows it," he said to himself dejectedly. Walking a little further, he saw a couple having an argument. The woman's arms were outstretched in the shape of a ball in front of her heart as she exclaimed to her husband, "Why can't you just listen to me?" The young initiate now reached his limit, for she was doing the special Holding the Golden Ball of the Heart Meditation posture that he learned from the founder of the Yi Chuan system, Wang Xiangzhai. Just as the initiate was ready to give up and fall back into the sea of depression he knew so well, he came to a realization that, yes, everyone he saw was doing sacred movements, but most were unconscious of their sacred character. Then he realized that his path was to teach people to appreciate the meaning and beauty of what they were already doing in their everyday lives…that our human movements, and our very Being, are divine gifts—if we could just see them as such.

—Michael Mayer
adapted and retold from shamanic oral teachings

Seeing the Sacred in the Gestures of Everyday Life

On one fine summer day while I was on top of Bear Creek Mountain, the above story "came to me" as I was practicing Tai Chi.[1] This story, which I first related to bringing new meaning to the Tai Chi/Qigong tradition, later became applied to my psychotherapy practice.

When listening to a story, a hidden physical trance induction oftentimes takes place. Whether it is with an astrological metaphor, or a story that comes to us while we are hiking on a sacred mountain, stories put us into a trance state whereby we can create a new life stance. Conversely, our bodies and the positions we hold and the movements we make can "trance-form," i.e., change the stance of our lives into a new story.

What Creates Change in Psychotherapy?

Every therapist has his or her own pet theory about what creates change in psychotherapy. Freudians, in general, look at the early family experiences and how they shape our lives; behaviorists emphasize the new behaviors that are needed to have change; and cognitive therapists emphasize new beliefs.[2] I told you about Eugene Gendlin's influence on my work and how he believed that a felt energetic shift that creates new meaning is the key to change in psychotherapy; and from listening to tapes of many different types of psychotherapy he "reverse engineered" what he considered to be the essential process that creates change in psychotherapy…thus his "Focusing" process.

From my training in the internal martial arts I began to notice that at the moment of "felt shift" in psychotherapy that various movements and postures arose, which were oftentimes the same as practiced by Tai Chi and Qigong practitioners. I found that bringing my patients' awareness to these naturally arising gestures, which were expressed at the moment of felt shift helped them to "create a new life stance." In this sense, I was taking another step forward on the path laid out by somatic psychotherapists who know that increasing somatic awareness of the movements or gestures that a person expresses at the moment of felt shift can be used as post-hypnotic anchors to ground psychotherapy insights.

I am not the first psychologist or writer to talk about the importance of one's stance in life to psychological health. Alfred Adler emphasized one's life stance as being fundamental a person's life meaning (Adler, 1982). Charles Darwin pointed out how physical movements were fundamental in the evolution of emotional expression in animal animals and man (Darwin, 1890, 2009). And many somatic psychotherapists have written and the importance of the body in psychological healing (Keleman, 1986; van der Kolk, 1987; Levine, 1997). So, though I was certainly standing on the shoulders of giants when I came to the idea of psychotherapy as changing one's life stance, none of these other authors were also standing on the somatic base of the internal martial arts, cross-cultural shamanic traditions of shape-shifting, and traditions of postural initiation.

Each of us develops our theories about psychological change from the traditions we follow, the experiences we have, and from the stories we hear. So, these cross-cultural initiatory traditions I mentioned, and as you will see even chess, helped to germinate my ideas about how change is created in the deep patterns of our lives.

Shape-shifting in the Shamanic Cave of Creation

In the Pacific Northwest, a shamanic teaching story sets the ground for a psychotherapy of shape-shifting:

A Native American fisherman paddles his kayak into an unknown bay. As he walks, exploring into this untouched new territory, he hears uproarious laughter and cautiously follows the sound until it leads him to the mouth of a cave. After carefully creeping through a great cavern, he sees, gathered around a great roaring fire, animals of all varieties, large and small, playing a game that makes them laugh from the depths of their different souls. The game is "shape-shifting" and they are embodying the postures of different forms, then changing into those forms. The fisherman is in awe as the animals turn into human form, and the human turns into animal forms (Gore, 1995, p. 14).

This story is one Native American creation myth that tells of how the human race was created. On a more personal level the tale symbolizes the cave of our everyday lives where we shape-shift from one state of consciousness to another, fueled by the fire of our intention. The power of shape-shifting from one stance to another to break fixated life stances, and to activate the healing power of "the universe of possibilities," was known in many ancient cultures.

In the folktales of China the trickster called the Monkey King shape-shifts into numerous different forms as he tries to learn the secrets of immortality. It takes the Buddha himself to rein in the Monkey, and lock him up until he learns from his egocentric mistakes (Waley, 1943). In ancient Greece, Epimenides—an initiate of this tradition—was said to have slept in a cave in Crete for years and used "rituals demanding patience, involving watching animals and following them in their movements" (Kingsley, 1999, p. 215). He was called to Athens to heal people from a plague. In Epidaurus in ancient Greece, where Western medicine originated at the world's oldest holistic healing center, shape-shifting into another identity was one of the essential elements of healing rituals. The Aesclepian priest would advise the sick to go to the Dionysian theater. Instructions were given to play a particular part in a play, or to wear a mask so that a new energy would be activated in the psyche of those in need of healing. This was perhaps the origin of modern psychodrama. The masks worn, or personae, form the etymological roots of our contemporary word, "person." So, by assuming the face and adopting the stance of another person or animal, a pathway to healing could emerge (Papadakis, 1988; Mayer, 2004).

Each of us every day has the capacity to look into the fire of creation and shape-shift into the form that is most needed for any occasion. Sometimes we need to be a lion, other times a dove. The animal movements of Qigong are one way to activate the powers to change our life stances and life stories. Animal movements and musical accompaniment form an important part of ancient story telling healing rituals in the Kivas of Native Americans, and in Greece in the temple of Aesclepius. As well, the animal movements were important in influencing the well-known popular tradition of Tai Chi Chuan.[3] In general, the ability to shape-shift is considered to be an important part of learning how to play the game of life. Chess is one game that contains, hidden behind its moves, secrets about how to play the game of life. When I was young it was one of my favorite ways of bonding with my father, who used the game to teach many life lessons. For example, he taught me that a good player (of life) always looked at the game (of life) from both sides, to see the game through the other's eyes.

As a matter of fact, when I was in my early teenage years, I thought my occupation might be to teach others how to correct personality imbalances through the game of chess. I noticed that some people were too extroverted, moving out their Queens too early; others were not assertive enough and did not capture the center of the board early in the game. Even though I had some talent for chess, and came in second place in a New Jersey chess tournament at seventeen years of age, I decided that this would not be an economically viable career. However, even though certain potential careers that we fantasize in our youth may be impractical, they may hold keys to doors that nonetheless have meaning in the larger scheme of our destinies.

Many years later I discovered that in esoteric teachings about the game of chess, there were many deep, hidden metaphysical secrets there. For example, the pawn symbolizes the ordinary person attempting to cross the board of life as he or she moves through seven grades of initiation (chakras), usually moving only one step at a time, probing straight ahead (unable to reverse course), sometimes attacking its shadow opponent positioned on an opposite color. But when the pawn has triumphed over the world's ordeals, it has moved through the seven rows (chakras), and it reaches the eighth row, it reaches—in musical terms—the higher stage of the octave. Here, paradise is regained and the pawn can transform into any piece on the board that the player wishes (Schneider, 1994, p. 291).

Anyone who has played chess knows the rush of energy that comes from having their little piece on the chessboard actualize its transformative potentials as it shape-shifts into a more flexible figurine that can reenter the game with more effective, powerful moves. Similarly, the higher octave of any of our lives is rung when we are able to change our psychological state into the form most suited to the occasion…discovering a self-assertive way of being when we are unduly inhibited, opening our ears to really listen to another when we are feeling defensive, or finding our central equilibrium when we are going to be over-reactive.

So, the metaphor of changing one's life stance on the chess board of life,[4] my immersion in the traditions of cross-cultural mythology and initiatory traditions, and my training in the internal martial arts influenced my view of the process of change in psychotherapy —and how psychotherapy involves changing one's life stance through shape-shifting.

The Case of the Repulsing Monkey

> …the path to heaven doesn't lie down in flat miles.
> It's in the imagination with which you perceive this world,
> and the gestures with which you honor it.
>
> —Mary Oliver
> Winter Hours

For example, I started to see that at key moments in my patients' evolution, at moments of major change when insights emerged about how to live their lives differently, that oftentimes gestures related to those changes would emerge. These gestures were similar or the same as that which a Tai Chi or internal martial artist would use to deal with this or her opponent.[5] For example:

> *"Emma" was a liberal arts university student who had not spoken to her father for five years. She described him as a very overpowering man whose large size alone intimidated her; in addition she said he was very narcissistic, always talking about himself and barely ever asking about her. In our therapy Emma had done much good work on her pattern of withdrawing and breaking up with people when they were self-absorbed. She had learned to stand up to significant others in her life, and to express her feelings and work thorough difficult issues in relationships. At the point when she was getting ready to go back and see her father for the first time in years I asked her, how, given all this work she had done on herself would she like to approach him. She said that she'd like to find a balanced way of approaching him; and in the course of trying to express what such a balanced stance would be a gesture spontaneously emerged. Her outstretched, right-hand palm expressed the power of boundary setting, and the left-hand palm up, expressed a welcoming gesture. Anyone who had practiced Tai Chi would have been amazed as was I, because this Tai Chi hand gesture (mudra) looked exactly like the Tai Chi movement called Repulse Monkey. Even though Emma had never practiced Tai Chi or Qigong, this spontaneously arising movement helped to anchor her at a key moment in her life. When she met with her father, she later reported that keeping this stance in mind helped her to set a boundary when he was "talking at me." She reported to me later that she actually held her hand up to the father with her hand outstretched and said "Dad, wait a second, I want to tell you about my life." Emma's Repulse Monkey gesture helped her to find a stance that was able to set boundaries and yet be welcoming to a new relationship. This helped her to reestablish a relationship with her father.*

A Dream of the Energy-Stream, Vacuum Cleaner in Reverse: Empowerment in Relationship to my Inner Foe

The idea of the importance of the role of the body and a new life stance as a key to psychotherapeutic change did not only come from my experience in nature, my readings and experiences with cross-cultural initiatory traditions, or from my patients. Many threads came together to produce this viewpoint for me. Since dreams may be "the greatest story ever told" for each of our individual lives and destinies, it is no wonder that once again a dream was instrumental in opening another door to my destiny and a contribution I hope to make to the field of psychology.

Being reared as an intellectual, not big or very muscular, I could not stand up to many of the aggressive boys in my high school. My father told me it was not worth fighting with ignorant bullies. For many years I suffered from running away from bullies, not only during daylight hours, but also at nighttime in my dreams. For years, I had a recurring dream that I was running away from bullies; sometimes I would take out a gun, but its bullets were not powerful enough to harm my attackers. After about a year of Standing Meditation Qigong practice, I had another one of my recurring dreams.

> *The same attacker that I have dreamt about before once again is coming after me. But this time instead of running away, I face him. I put my hands up in a Yi Chuan Standing Meditation posture called Opening the Golden Sphere of the Heart, and an energy comes out of my chest and arms that is like a vacuum cleaner turned in reverse. The energy is so powerful that the person is literally blown back a few feet into a wall.*

This dream felt like a major turning point in my personal therapy, in my life, and in my Standing Meditation practice.

Psychotherapy as Changing Your Life Stance

CASE ILLUSTRATION: SOCIAL PHOBIA STEMMING FROM PHYSICAL ABUSE

When people ask me from where I get my patient referrals, I oftentimes half jokingly say, "From the Cosmic Coincidence Control Center." It is indeed interesting for therapists to see how often the patients that get drawn to us are one's that have similar issues to our own.

Just as peers at times physically abused me as a child due to my size, so was Stan… even more so. As a young boy "Stan" was the smallest of all of his classmates and was a gentle and sensitive child. When other kids engaged in cruel jokes and hitting contests, Stan shied away. Because he was so small, kids enjoyed bullying him when he would not fight back. Stan's stance was, in part, constitutional—his mother remembered that he was a gentle child even in his first few years of life.

Contributing to the fixation of this stance into a characterological pattern was Stan's physically abusive brother, who told him, "I'm better than you at everything." By the time he was in his late teens, Stan felt so paralyzed that he developed a social phobia and feared contact with authority figures. He dropped out of college once and complained of multiple somatic issues including developing arthritis in his fingers. In his current occupational setting he could not assert himself to his boss to ask for the raise he felt he deserved.

Stan was first a student in my Bodymind Qigong classes, which emphasized Standing Meditation and also included some self-defense training. Then he decided to leave our student/teacher relationship to do Bodymind Healing Psychotherapy with me.[6]

A major turning point in Stan's life was when he found a stance to stand up to his brother through his internal martial arts practices. Though his martial arts practices were important in giving him sensitivity and power, the verbal dimension of actualizing his power was equally crucial and needed to be developed through psychotherapy. One of the more significant moments in our therapy occurred when Stan was at his family's home for Thanksgiving and his brother greeted him, "So, after all this time I bet you're still not better than me at anything. Let's go out play some basketball one-on-one."

His brother's demeaning messages had always made Stan cower with anxiety in his stomach. But during this Thanksgiving dinner, after much inner work in therapy and a year of Standing Meditation practice, Stan found his verbal stance to address his brother's abusive message. Stan said, "You know something, you're not better than me at every-thing." His brother paused for a moment, and said, "What do you mean; give me an example. I'm still better at basketball and at every sport, and I make more money than you." Stan found the stance he had always wanted in his childhood at this moment and continued, "You're not better than me at everything—you're not better at being a kind brother." According to Stan, when he said this to his brother, it stopped him in his tracks and left him speechless for a moment. After apologizing for the way he had treated Stan in his childhood, a new relationship developed between them.

With a combination of his study of the internal martial arts, which emphasized the power of softness, and his therapy, over time Stan transmuted his identification with being an ungrounded, wimpy male. He was able to work through his lack of self-confidence and asked for a raise at work, which he got. He learned to affect his arthritis in his hands with the power of his mind and through the use of acupressure points and the visualization methods that are a wider part of the practice done in Bodymind Healing Qigong.

This was no "total cure," but "a healing" took place. Issues still arose, but through our work together Stan had cultivated a new stance toward his issues, and he had found a way of working with them. He now had a clear vision of the path ahead of him, whereas before, his primordial ground was paved over. Stan now recognized that just like his in-ternal arts work takes practice, so does finding his psychological stance. He learned to be aware of how the abusiveness of his brother fragmented his energy. And he learned to practice "cognitive restructuring" when negative thoughts arose (Beck, 1979; Shapiro, 1995; Mayer 2007). Instead of his old thought, "I'm no good and can't stand up for my-self," his new, restructured thought and stance became, "I don't deserve to be treated badly despite any of my short-comings; and I will stand up for myself." Then, he breathes and practices returning to his grounded stance of power and self-assertiveness. It also helps that he is now able to use his Tai Chi Push Hands practice to play with his brother and demonstrate the power of his softness.

So, through these case examples you can see why I think that psychotherapy is about changing our life stances; and how I wove my training in the internal martial arts with my practice of psychotherapy. Once again the theme re-occurs: the threads that are discovered in the cave of our inner world are connected with the contributions we make to the quilt of humanity.

The case illustrations in this chapter about the interface of psychotherapy and Stand-ing Meditation Qigong, feels like the culmination of my journey to the West and show how psychotherapy can be viewed as a shape-shifting endeavor whereby a person changes their life stance.[7] I am grateful to each of those people for the depth of their inner work; and I recognize that much more transpired in the sessions with these people than brief vignettes can capture.

CHAPTER 19:

Weakling Scholar Learns the Secrets of Internal Arts' Empty Force

Look at these worlds spinning out of nothingness,
That is within your power.

—Rumi

Looking into the dark Mystery brings clarity
Knowing how to surrender is the greatest strength.
Cultivate your own light.
This is the practice of eternity.

—Lao Tzu, *Tao Te Ching*, #52

My Experience: Bullies, Qi and the No-Sword School

In the last chapter I spoke about the change that took place in a recurring dream of mine after I had practiced Standing Meditation for many years. My dream of being chased by an attacker was transformed as I, instead of running away, faced him. I put my hands up into one of the Standing Meditation postures that I had learned in my Qigong training. The energy was so powerful that the attacker was repelled. This dream has become a symbol, and a felt experience, that I call on in times of need in my waking life.

In my lineage of training for over two decades with Sifu Fong Ha, Standing Meditation practice has been integrated with the practice of Tai Chi Chuan. They are seen to be part of an integrated whole, balancing the cultivation of groundedness as well as a fluidity in yielding. In Tai Chi training, we are taught not to use any more force than is absolutely necessary. The training I have received in the internal arts has taught me to follow the example of the famous swordsman, Bonzi, of "the no-sword school." Here's the story about Bonzi:

> One day Bonzi was on a ferry and a bully was having fun unsheathing his sword and showing off his prowess by cutting nicks in people's ears. Sometimes he wouldn't be that accurate and he would cut off a piece or a whole ear. Everyone on board was cowering. When the bully did this to an old woman on board, it was too much for Bonzi to bear. He said to the bully "You shouldn't be doing this to these kind people. I don't want to get

into a fight with you, but I pray you will stop." The bully replied to Bonzi, "Unsheathe your sword you little man and I'll teach you a lesson for daring to speak up to me." Bonzi replied, "Oh I couldn't do that sir, I am Bonzi the Swordsman, practitioner of the no-sword school, and I've never lost a fight. I wouldn't want either of us to be harmed, or see our blood shed all over the deck of this beautiful boat."

The enraged bully said, "You have no choice, for if you don't unsheathe your sword, I'll kill you." Bonzi replied, "Then I have no choice but to show you my art. But I have one condition, and if that is met you can have your way of fighting me—I do not want anyone on this ferry to get harmed from one of your missing sword thrusts, or to have any of these kind people have to witness a bloody scene, so I ask you to be honorable enough to go with me on that attached rowboat to the island off the stern of this boat. "You will meet your just fate there." The Bully, steaming by now, agreed. Two passengers helped take down the small rowboat and put it into the water. Bonzi bowed to the killer, motioning to the boat said, "After you, sir." As the bully stepped into the boat, Bonzi removed the oars and with a graceful push from his foot he pushed the boat into the current of the river leaving the bully to float downstream. The ruthless cutter of ears was humiliated as everyone on board laughed. The bully yelled out his final curse calling Bonzi a coward and in a screaming, yet cracking voice, said, "I thought you were such a good swordsman." Bonzi, replied, "No sir, I am not a braggart like you. I told you I was a practitioner of the no-sword school, and I had never lost a fight. Now you know why."

In my practice of the internal martial arts, my teachers have trained me to do my best to avoid fights. This attitude is trained by practicing with other students a "game" called "Push Hands." Here the student learns not to contend with others. This is called *Wu Wei* (effortless effort). It has been an emotionally reparative experience for me, and many others like me who are of slight build and small size, to find that through the practice of yielding to another's force that we can neutralize it. With some more training, intermediate practitioners can learn to uproot, and actually make fly a few feet in the air, those who are much bigger and stronger. This practice is called *fajing*. It's nothing special. It is a matter of learning how to find our ground, sinking our qi to the earth and being sensitive to our fellow classmates. The power of this energy (*fajing*) is like an exploding ball of qi that many practitioners experience after a time of practice (Ha & Diepersloot, 1991). It is really a form of mutual play, and most students can begin to cultivate the beginning stages of this ability in about six months of practice with a teacher who has expertise in this method. The psychological effect of this practice gives self-confidence, and a new bodily identification with integral force, the ability to feel the different parts of the body as a cohesive whole—a Golden Ball, if you will.

Figures 18 and 19: Master Fong Ha Doing Tai Chi Joining Hands Practice with the Author

Figure 20: Master Fong Ha Bouncing the Author with Fajing

In the pictures above are some of the ways that I have been trained in cultivating "the Golden Ball."[1] In the pictures above, Master Ha he is teaching me how to develop the ability to yield as I push on him he demonstrates the posture "roll back." Roll Back teaches the initiate how a line of force is overcome when a master rolls with it like a ball.

In the next series of photos with Master Tam he demonstrates the dimension of the ball of life that is called "empty force," or "no force." As I strike at Master Tam, he yields; and to the attacker it feels as if the master has emptied the practitioner's ball of energy. The experience to the practitioner feels like he is falling into empty space and then is bounced back as if an exploding ball is pushing him back with an equal or greater force than the one he or she initially used to strike. This is called "Fajing," the explosive force of the ball.

Figure 21: After I strike at Master Tam, he yields maintaining his central equilibrium as I lose mine. He follows my spiraling force until I fall into the trap of emptiness.

Figure 22: Master Tam yields, not using any apparent force of his own, as I begin to recoil backwards.

Figure 23: Notice the blurriness of the picture of me, showing the speed at which I am recoiling backwards, and Master Tam's stillness.

Figure 24: I am beginning to be uprooted by Master Tam's use of my force to discharge me; and I push off his expanding sphere to maintain the cohesiveness of my sphere.

Figure 25: I am fully uprooted from the power of the "no force" method.

Figure 26: I begin to land.

Figure 27: I land with a fair degree of cohesiveness of my Qi Ball, after an experience that felt like being shot out of a cannon. It is not unusual to end up 10 to 15 feet from the point of discharge by the master of the art.

Many uninitiated people look at these practices and try to explain them from a rational perspective, or try to diminish them. Master Ha has written a good article on these practices demystifying them and explained them in the context of a kinesthetic training methodology that uses both the master's and initiate's skills (Ha & Diepersloot, 1991). One of the first steps in the training is that the acolyte learns to fill in their lower back (*Ming Men*) with qi in the process of transforming into a Golden Ball. If the Ming Men is not filled out, then when the master's force is emitted the initiate will fall over backwards, and this can be dangerous. A metaphysical perspective on this empty force, training is that it is an initiatory practice of the Golden Ball, alluded to in the Grimm's Brother's "Iron Hans" tale. From the perspective of my medicine name, Michael, Two Streams Becoming One, here we see the process of joining the streams of Western mythic understanding and Eastern internal martial arts practices.

I certainly do not consider myself to be a martial artist. Being a weakling scholarly type all of my childhood, it is a testament to the masters with whom I have trained, that such a transformation could have taken place in a body like mine.

In my two decades of practice, following the pathway of my teachers training, I have been able to avoid any major physical confrontations except on two occasions,

> *Once in Hawaii when I had practiced for about four years, I was in a bar naively doing Tai Chi dance with two women friends. This apparently angered one of the locals who looked like he was on drugs. He was about 5 feet 10 inches tall, very heavy set and muscular; his eyes were emblazoned with a scattered kind of rage as he cursed at me on the outskirts of the dance floor. He said, "Come on, do you want to fight?" I assured him in my gentlest voice that I had nothing against him and didn't want to fight. He raised his fists and kept yelling, "Come on, come on, man." I took a step away and tried to make eye contact with his friends to help me avoid a fight. His three Samoan friends, who each must have weighed over 225 pounds, looked at me without expression and said, "Take care of it yourself, man." I could feel that my Standing Practice was barely with me as my fear response shot up through my 5 foot 7 inch, 135-pound body. I barely had a chance to exhale to "sink my Qi," in an attempt to get grounded. As the man swung at me, one of the first movements of Tai Chi, called "Roll Back," instinctively came to me. It is the most basic Tai Chi movement used to take another's force and not contend with it. We adhere to the attacker's arm (as you see in the picture of Master Ha and I above), shift our weight backwards and circle the force out of the way. The angry man flew into one of his friends. He came back at me one more time, and I did a variation on the same movement again. This time, he was uprooted as I did the Tai Chi movement called "Pa Kua Fish" (as seen in my Secret's…book, 2004, p.163). The attacker flew into a table, and a few glasses fell and loudly broke on the floor. I didn't want to stay around for the next event with him and his friends; so I left with my two companions to avoid further needless confrontation.*

Though I felt the adrenaline rush of power that came from my years of Standing Meditation and Tai Chi Chuan practice, I was fully aware of my fear and limitations as a lightweight scholar who had minimal Tai Chi and Yi Chuan training under his belt. One never knows how good their art is, and there are always people more adept than we are. I believe, like Bonzi, it is better to practice the no-sword school and to use the gift of the internal martial arts for healing, rather than fighting.

It is said that training in the internal martial arts takes a lot longer than training in the external martial arts, and that those who want to be fighters should not bother with the internal arts. I certainly experienced this when confronted in the bar, and did not feel particularly self-confident, even after four years of practice, though I was grateful that the movements I had learned had saved me from at least a black eye, and maybe severe injury.

Another Bonzi story tells of his life as a young man and illustrates the longer amount of time that it takes to learn the internal martial arts....

Bonzi heard about an eccentric swordsman who lived alone way out in the woods. Bonzi went to study with this old gruff man, while many of Bonzi's friends studied sword forms with other teachers. The Old Master in the woods told Bonzi to come and live with him and just cut his vegetables every day. Bonzi kept asking when his sword lessons would begin, and the Master said, "Just learn to cut vegetables." Bonzi's friends were bragging about learning their whole second sword set, not even having to cook or prepare meals for their teachers; and Bonzi hadn't even learned one movement yet. Occasionally the Master would correct his stance as he was cutting vegetables, or lightly hit him on the buttocks with his sword and show him how to turn, but this seemed like nothing much to the young, impatient Bonzi. But from this foundation of the caring stance of cutting vegetables, learning how to turn, and after developing a loving relationship with his Master, Bonzi was able to master many forms of Sword and later became one of the greatest sword-masters of China.

Crane Splitting Hands:
Weakling Scholar Uses Empty Force to Protect Himself

My second story about being physically attacked came after practicing Standing Meditation and Tai Chi for about twenty-three years.

One day I was at a local reservoir waiting for a parking place. At this popular site, many people sit in their cars waiting in front of the diagonal spaces for a parking spot to open, because the pleasure of the nice walk in the woods is worth the wait. Sometimes the wait is considerably long, and is a test for anyone's patience. After a long wait, a car pulled out right in front of the place for which I'd been patiently (OK, I admit, not so patiently) waiting. Before I could get into the space, another car weaved around me and pulled in. The young man who had exercised this devious maneuver, turned around and mockingly smiled at me. I honked my horn, and he turned around again with a wide grin.

With tenacious intent to not give up "my space," I laid my hand down on the horn (not very non-attached, I must admit). After a few moments, it bothered the driver enough so that he angrily got out of the car. I got out of my car and "just stood" there. When I saw him get out of the car, I wondered whether my old issue with tenacity was a mistake. The young man, probably in his late 20's, was about six feet tall and solidly built, and maybe about 200 pounds. I was fifty-two years old, five feet eight inches and 145 pounds, He was huffing and walking fast towards me with rage in his face as he yelled, "You shouldn't be honking like that, man," and he began to grab towards my neck as if to choke me.

It was interesting to me that his impending assault was not frightening to me. I didn't feel any fear as I was "just standing" there. My standing practice was rooted in my body; instinctually my tailbone slightly curved under sinking my qi to the belly (tan tien) as my lower back (Ming Men) spread out. I automatically lifted my hands into a variation of the Yi Chuan "Opening the Sphere of the Heart "posture that is shown earlier in this book.

As the enraged man grabbed for my neck I instinctively changed this Standing posture to split his oncoming force along with a variation of the "Crane Opens the Heart" and "Crane Opens the Door to the Heavens" postures of the Animal Qigong set.[2] My hands opened like a Crane's wings, contacting and splitting his outstretched hands. As my hands turned around, they faced his exposed neck and chest.

Assuming these "no- force postures" leaves the aggressor feeling exposed as if the energy has been sucked out of him. The aggressor knows that he is totally, vulnerably exposed to any strike from the defender. Of course I did not take advantage of his vulnerable position, being constitutionally, and by training, a kind soul. I just stood there holding this potential; but was ready to do whatever was needed. The young man, feeling this potential, immediately changed his stance toward me and apologized, "I wasn't trying to do anything to hurt you, I…um, um, was just trying to get you to stop honking the horn." He first started to say, "You shouldn't be honking, but then he caught himself in the midst of his blaming, changed his attitude, and apologetically said, "Sorry, I know I shouldn't have tried to take your parking spot."

Though I was grateful for the skill and sense of groundedness provided by my years of training, it is a very important part of the training in internal martial arts not to be over-confident. Events of road rage and confrontation can lead to unforeseen consequences. This event did serve as another major moment in my psychological transformation. It helped to further solidify the change of attitude that I had earlier in my life that it was unthinkable that by doing "nothing" anything productive could happen. I learned that the "no-force methods of doing nothing" were more effective than using force and contending with others.

Certainly using "no-force" techniques from Standing Meditation Qigong have been important to me on a physical level, as a metaphysically oriented psychologist. However, I feel that the most important work is to carry the metaphor of these types of physical practice into our everyday psychological lives. It is the practice of practices when attacked emotionally by those at work or in our personal lives to respond appropriately and sink the Qi. The focus becomes whether we lose ourselves, our Golden Balls of divine energy, in the process.

How do we find the stance of Opening our Hearts and "split" the oncoming forces of emotional assaults in every day life? Through our body stance and our psychological awareness we look into our own heart, and through its reflection in the mirror of our own hands we breathe and begin the process of working through our issues. We "come to terms" with the feelings that we (and others) have—of fear, jealousy, and anger. In the midst of emotional difficulties the Reluctant Metaphysician practices the tempering of his or her words, modulating the expression of feelings, and embodying new life stances.

The feeling of being collapsed like a victim begins to change as words of self-empowerment arise from our depths. "Blaming others," translated into Tai Chi terms, can be seen as an improper extension of our qi over our centerlines; our excessive yang energy begins to change as we begin to take responsibility for the ways we express our anger. As it says in our bible's creation myth "in the beginning was the word, and the word was with God (the Gospel according to John)." The role of the divine creator is to shape reality by our words and our postures. Translating this into cross-cultural metaphysical terms, each of us has the opportunity in our everyday lives to recreate the world through verbal and physical stances.

I remember a story from a Buddhist journal from Spirit Rock Meditation Center in San Geronimo, California, about a young girl who was teased by a classmate who kept calling her, in a mocking, singsong phrase, "four eyes, four eyes…you're so ugly."

> *The young girl went home crying, and got some advice from her mother, who was a Mindfulness Meditation practitioner. She learned to take a new stance. The next day when the boy attempted to humiliate her again, she said, "You're right, I have four eyes, two regular ones, another one here in between my two eyes, and another one in my heart. You might want to try to develop your other two eyes."*

Finding the stance of empowerment through our meditative awareness has the capacity to change us, and others around us, at our core. Hopefully, this little girl standing up for her Self changed the little boy's cruelty to kindness. But, we cannot control another's evolution; all we can do is find our own ground.

From a metaphysical perspective, life's emotional crosscurrents give us an opportunity everyday to find new stances. This is the real practice of the internal martial arts.

CHAPTER 20:

Four Crows Joining: The Reluctant Metaphysics of My Father's Death

So it comes to pass that, when we pursue an inquiry beyond a certain depth,
we step out of the field of psychological categories
and enter the sphere of the ultimate mysteries of life.
The floorboards of the soul, to which we try to penetrate,
fan open, and reveal the starry firmament.

—Bruno Schultz

Metaphysical Rituals for Death and Dying

The years of 1997 and 1998 were difficult years for me. My father, at 88 years of age was in the hospital dying. On one of the trips when I went back to visit him in the hospital, I could see he did not have much time left. My seemingly invincible father had pneumonia and had an air tube down his throat making it impossible for him to even talk. The most difficult times are supposed to be times for those on the spiritual path to call on the powers of the heavens above. But how was I supposed to do this?

My mother and father had a supernally loving relationship. They had an agreement with each other that if they were in the hospital under dire circumstances that they would not "pull the plug." They felt that even if they were in a coma for a year, coming out and holding the other's hand and looking into the other's eyes for one minute would be worth forging through the pain. Now the hospital ethicist was telling my mother that it was time to pull the plug. My mother was adamant that every moment was sacred, and no plug or tube was to be removed. As my father went in and out of consciousness my mother's hand would hold his, and as my father opened his eyes and looked into my mother's eyes, a smile formed around the breathing tube.

For the Reluctant Metaphysician every moment is an opportunity to call on the powers of the world behind the world. One day, while I was by my father's hospital bed a ritual spontaneously came to me. I wanted to do a ritual for my dad to help him let go in a way similar to the way it is done in rituals given in the book on *The Tibetan Book on Death and Dying* (which I was using in the course I was teaching at San Francisco State at the time). However, I wanted to create a letting go ritual that would honor my father's Jewish tradition. I played my flute in the hospital room to the tune of the song, *Avinu Malchenu*—a song to honor a parent. However, new words came to me that I chanted to my father,

You've lived a good life Dad.
Now it's time to move on
Your mother and father and sister and brother will be there to greet you,
And say you've done a good job, Abe.
You've lived every moment of life,
Giving to your clients and family,
Now it's time to take your honored place,
In the arms of eternity.

Picture the difficulty of the surrounding familial situation, as I was the midst of alternately playing my flute and singing this song. My brother was visibly upset and interrupted the chanting with saying, "Don't listen to him Dad, you're not going to die." Difficult family dynamics often come up when a family faces the direst of circumstances. Not only do families often have conflicts at such times, so do different philosophies conflict.

This brings up a distinction between a spiritual path and the path of the Reluctant Metaphysician. "Letting go" is a key concept in various spiritual traditions. The Buddha said that attachment, and not letting go, causes suffering. The ritual I created for my father was a ritual for letting go. However, a metaphysical perspective (particularly coming from a Gemini like myself), honors opposite viewpoints. Each viewpoint has its own valued place on the wheel of life.

The "holding on," of my mother and brother, I realized, was as valid of an archetypal stance as my "letting go." What a beautiful love it is to hold on; as well it is a gift to let go. Both are equally valid sides of the treasured golden coin of the realm of the metaphysical world. Both are equally valid tools in the toolkit of the Reluctant Metaphysician as unwanted times are faced. I left New Jersey reflecting on this on my plane trip back to California to return to teaching my San Francisco State class on Eastern Perspectives.

Four Crows Joining

A few months later, on the day of the full moon in April of 1998, the sad news came from my mother by phone. After a few trips back to see my father during his declining health, at 89 years of age my father had passed away. He was in New Jersey and I was in California, so I booked the first flight back to New Jersey. It was a red eye flight leaving at 9 PM.

Before my plane trip I walked up the hill by my house. I passed the Cyprus tree that I had passed almost every day for twelve years.

Just at the point that I got there four crows landed on the tree, landing in a square formation. I had never seen four crows land on this tree, and I have never since seen four crows anywhere land in this type of formation.

Synchronicity and the Re-enchantment of the Cosmos

We are the agents of synchronicity,
through which the big story of life talks to itself.

—Caroline Casey, visionary activist
Bioneers conference, 2011

Synchronicity is a quintessential concept of Jungian psychology. And this synchronistic visitation of four crows was truly awesome to me. The number "four" in Jungian symbology represents completion. Just at the moment when I was wishing that my father had more years with our family, perhaps the universe was sending a message about the completeness of life.

Synchronicity is a basic tool in the metaphysician's toolkit. It is used to open doors as a locksmith uses special keys. If a rationalist examined the particular bird that appeared at this time, it would defy reason that such a perfect symbol could coincidentally appear.

In cross-cultural mythology crows are symbols of messengers from the other world, the world of the departed. In Greek mythology they are symbolic of Cronus the father figure, symbolic of the Senex. (Note the similarity in name of Crow and Cronus.) Robert Graves in his *Greek Mythology* text says that the crow "is an oracular bird, supposed to house the soul of a sacred king after his sacrifice" (Graves, 1955, p. 38).

Adding to the synchronicity of my father's death is that the ruling astrological symbol connected to Capricorn in Greek mythology is Saturn, or Cronus, whose name is related to, and perhaps derived from, the crow. How awesome that I, the sceptical unbeliever, the avid questioner of the irrational was "sent" an experience like this to behold. Even more amazing is that such a mystical event could be connected with my father's life, since as an attorney his life was a testament to valuing reason (symbolized well by the fact that he was a double Capricorn, the sign of pragmatism).

In the weeks before my father's death I was teaching a class in Eastern Perspectives at San Francisco State University. One of the major concepts in the class was on the estrangement from the wider whole of which we are a part—an alienated worldview produced by modern Western cosmology. I told my students earlier during the semester how the progress of Western civilization and its "objective world-view " had contributed to our having lost something as we moved away from an ensouled world, *anima mundi*. I referred my students to Erich Neumann's book (1954) *The Origin and History of Consciousness* that discusses this evolution of consciousness and its advantages and disadvantages.

In our classes, we discussed how one of the disadvantages of our modern non-metaphysical worldview is a "disenchantment of the world," (Weber, 1993; Schiller, 1993, Tarnas, 2007) which stems from the modern Western philosophical notion that a human being is the sole source of all meaning and purpose in the cosmos. In this class we contrasted this view with primordial, indigenous, and Eastern views that the universe is alive with meaning.

In my lecture, I spoke about how in much of Jung's career he looked at the archetypes as being in the world of the human psyche. However in his later work, and particularly with regards to synchronicities, Jung moved in the direction of postulating that the archetypes had autonomous patterns of meaning that inform both psyche and matter, and provide a bridge between the two. This is called the *psychoid* nature of archetypes. His work thereby drew on the Western and Eastern mystery tradition notion of an ensouled world, an *anima mundi* in which the human psyche shares the same ordering principle as the *unus mundus*. The synchronistic experiences in his consulting room and his life led him to these far reaching conclusions. For example, while a woman was telling him a dream about a Golden Scarab, a scarab like insect tapped on the window of his consulting room.

Synchronistic phenomena seem to underlie and underline the phenomena of everyday life, and seem to increase at times of major life events—birth, death, and times of spiritual awakening. In Jung's patient's case, this woman was dealing with a death rebirth theme that was amplified by the symbol of the scarab, symbolic of the Sun God who in the journey to the underworld changes himself into a scarab. Such synchronistic experiences led Dr. Jung to postulate a universal meaningful substrate present in the environment as well as in the inner psychological world.

Likewise, at the time of my father's death it was as if the universe was underlining the message of the class I was teaching through the visitation of the Four Crows—helping me to further get "in my bone marrow" the lesson I was teaching about death, synchronicity, and the *anima mundi*.

The Reluctant Metaphysician uses the difficult experiences of life to plummet depths of meaning—in each of our own psyches and in the soul of the world. The deeper one goes, the more a cosmology is discovered where the world is psyche and the psyche is world. As the prolific modern cosmologist Richard Tarnas (2007, p. 35) puts it,

> Is it not an extraordinary act of human hubris—literally, a hubris of cosmic proportions—to assume that the exclusive sources of all meaning and purpose in the universe is ultimately centered in the human mind, which is therefore absolutely unique and special and in this sense superior to the entire cosmos?"

When I look back at my journey as a Reluctant Metaphysician, it seems as though my life, along with others, has served as a dedication to the re-enchantment of the cosmos. Has some wider force than myself used my life as an example to show me, and others, how to re-sacralize the body, the world of dreams, human posture and movements, nature, and our relationship to the universe itself? It certainly seems as though some cosmic trickster picked the most unlikely person, ensconced in the world of rationality, to illustrate metaphysical lessons about the world behind the world. (Or, maybe not so unlikely of a choice, this Being wisely chose a person who could tell a good honest story and make a cogent argument for a good cause.) Regardless, this trickster deity abducted a person like me and filled my life with incredible, metaphysical, and synchronistic stories in order to say, "If it could happen to a sceptic like him, it could happen to you."

Richard Tarnas, a prolific metaphysician, encapsulates this view of an enchanted relationship to the cosmos through his "Two Suitors Parable." To compare the disenchanted mechanistic universe of modern cosmology to the view of the enchanted cosmos, he poses a thought experiment and asks that you imagine that you are the universe,

> Would you open most deeply to the suitor…who approached you as though you were essentially lacking in intelligence of purpose, as though you had no interior dimension to speak of, no spiritual capacity or value; who thus saw you as fundamentally inferior to himself…; who related to you as though your existence were valuable primarily to the extent that he could develop and exploit your resources to satisfy his various needs, and whose motivation for knowing you was ultimately driven by a desire for increased intellectual mastery, predictive certainty and efficient control of you for his own self-enhancement? Or would you, the cosmos, open your self most deeply to that suitor who viewed you as being at least as intelligent and noble as worthy a being as permeated with mind and soul, as imbued with moral aspiration and purpose, as endowed with spiritual depths and mystery as he? To whom would you reveal your deepest truths (Tarnas, 2007, p. 39)?

When we view the events of life with a symbolic eye, metaphysical teachings of the cosmos are transmitted, synchronicities seem to increase, and a re-animism of life takes place. If the most rational among us just acts *as if* the universe is enchanted and meaningful, that "creative Being" may kiss us on our eyes and touch our hearts—the cosmos can become our lover and soul mate.

A Metaphysical Plane Ride

On the night of my father's death I took the red eye flight to New Jersey from California. As the plane departed the moon was just starting to rise. As I flew across the country on this night flight I had a chance to slowly watch the moon rise and reflect upon my father's life and wonder where he was going now. As the moon ascended gradually through the next hours, I imagined it to be his soul ascending to the heavens. During much of the trip there was a thin cloud layer over the Earth, like a veil. The moon (representing my father's soul) penetrated through the veil. I could see the night-lights of American cities shining below the thin veil of heavens. I imagined my father looking down at the cities of civilization and reflecting on the clients he had helped in his work as an attorney and on his journey of giving in the Earth realm with his family. I thought, "Life on Earth surely is a penetration from heavenly forces outside the earth into the earthly sphere." Later on

309

this flight, thicker clouds replaced the thin veil. The full moon in all its grace and majesty was shining above and on the clouds; and for about an hour it was as if I was in heavenly clouds with my father's life.

Feeling the blessing of his life was easy in this moonlit sphere. Regardless of the objective truth of the imaginal ritual I created, I had the subjectively true experience of being in this heavenly sphere above the clouds that welcomed him back. This journey that I took is a visualization that any of us can employ when a loved a one departs (or before, and at the time of our own death).

A Mourning Ritual: Rising in a Plane with the Full Moon

Every spirit builds itself a house,
and beyond its house a world,
and beyond its world a heaven.

—Ralph Waldo Emerson

Imagine being on a plane watching your loved one's soul (the moon) rising into the heavenly sphere. First, as you are up in the sky, look back through the thin veil of clouds to the cities of the Earth, and think about what he or she accomplished while here on Earth...not just in dharmic work, but also in the realm of love. Next imagine being above the clouds, the soul of your departed one being like the moon returning to heaven. Imagine a radiating light source, representing your sense of God, welcoming back the soul of your beloved one. When the moon is at its zenith, imagine a wedding celebration where a spiritual marriage takes place as your loved one's heavenly qualities are welcomed back home. At the same time, an opening in the clouds appears—a gateway where memories travel back and forth of the qualities that came to earth in the unique way that the soul of your loved one carried them. Remember a few of their essential qualities as threads of light and imagine wrapping yourself in a garment that keeps them with you (This is perhaps Joseph's Coat of Many Colors—the metaphysical garment that is passed from one generation to another.) Every time the moon rises in the sky, is at its zenith, or anytime an opening comes in the clouds we can reflect on our ancestors, the departed ones whose essential qualities are still with us. We keep their "names" alive by weaving the threads of their lives into ours.

My father's time on this Earth was a visit from his essence, which was caring, generous, humorous, intelligent, honest, righteous, and conscientious. In the Jewish mystical tradition of the Zohar, at the time of death of a loved one, the mourner performs a *levusha ritual*. Each of the divine qualities of the departed loved one becomes a thread of a garment in which we wrap ourselves. And even long after a loved ones death, the Reluctant

Metaphysician continues to allow those who have touched our lives deeply to continue to enshroud and touch us, though we can no longer touch them.

A final synchronicity: After getting back home after my plane ride to my father's funeral, I returned to teach to my Eastern Perspectives class. The next scheduled class I was to teach was on death and dying. This cosmic coincidence was amazing. The precise week that I was preparing a class on death, my father died. The assigned book for the class was Sogyal Rinpoche's *The Tibetan Book of Living and Dying*.

In this light, it was also a cosmic synchronicity that my father passed away on the night before Passover when Jewish people commemorate the liberation from slavery in the land of Egypt to the Promised Land. So, every year when I memorialize my father's "passing over" it is exactly on "Pass-Over." Each year on Passover, I re-remember the plane flight I took in 1989 where I experienced, "where one goes after death." And for those who want to share the ritual that was given to me from my experience, I share that story with you about that mystical plane ride that you can use, or adapt, to help you find your way through the clouds of despair. Despair comes from thinking that death is the end of the line; however from the perspective of Reluctant Metaphysicians we wonder whether death may be the end of the line and the beginning of the great circle.

When I came back to my San Francisco State class, I put together various poems and sayings for my next lecture. They have given me solace during difficult times. Over the years when I have given them to patients, students, and friends these words have helped to give people comfort at their time of loss (see Appendix VI). I hope they will do the same for you.

CHAPTER 21:

War on Healers, the American Culture, and the Environment: The State of the World During the Kali Yuga

History will have to record that the greatest tragedy
of this period of social transition was not the strident clamor of the bad people,
but the appalling silence of the good people..

—Martin Luther King, 1957

The Reluctant Metaphysician's focus on the world behind the world does not need to be only "spiritual" in the narrow sense of the word. Bringing consciousness to the world behind the world of politics, our environment, and our mental and physical health is just as much part of the Reluctant Metaphysician's work. Shedding light on the stories behind the stories told about everyday reality is part of our calling.

The Dark Side of Storytelling: The Spider's Web That Can Capture Your Soul

There is a dark side to storytelling. Since the imagination has awesome transpersonal power, it can be used for the storyteller's purpose. Throughout this book I have been telling you about the uses of story to heal and transform. But stories can also be used to manipulate the listener into buying a product whether it is good or bad, to enhance the storyteller's income, and to fit the storyteller's needs—i.e., stories can be used for good or evil. At the very center of our lives, and our brains, are the meaning centers of our lives. Therefore, the forces of Greed and Egocentrism know that, like a spider, they can capture a human being in their web of meaning by spinning a self-serving tale.

So, the world of both true and false stories is a world behind the world and affects our everyday lives no less than two poles of a magnet has an effect on iron filings. The metaphysician's job is to bring awareness to false stories, and in doing so to demagnetize their effects—even if in doing so it reluctantly estranges him or her from many in the world.

Cultural Myths That Affect Healers and Healing-

The use of storytelling to capture the imagination of a culture is not a new phenomenon. For example, we can see this in the Christian takeover of the oldest holistic healing temple of the ancient Western world, the temple of Aesclepius. Its most renowned location was in Epidaurus, in Greece. I told you about how during the two trips I led to Greece this temple was a favorite of our group and mine. Between approximately the 17th century B.C and 3rd Century A.D., here were practiced surgery, *noo-therapeia* (an early version of psychotherapy), and gymnastic activities. Some of the holistic practices in this temple that were a vital part of its healing rituals included: enacting healing psychodrama in the Dionysian theater, using hands-on healing, and dream incubation.

When a dream came that signaled that the healing work was completed, the Asclepiad priest would interpret the meaning of the dream and the person was ready to leave. On the stones there were carved the stories of the healings that took place of people blind from birth who had their site restored, cripples who were able to walk, and even it was reported that some were brought back from the dead and resurrected (Papadakis, 1988). One story told of Aesclepius raising Glacous, the son of Theseus, from the dead. The Aesclepian temples spread around the Mediterranean, due to the stories about the healings that took place there.

When the advent of the Christian religion, the old Greek religion and the Aesclepian healing temples were deemed a threat, and Christian emperors such as Constantine and Theodosius II ordered the temples to be destroyed. At Ephesus, home of the great healing rituals of Demeter and Persephone, a church was built over the site. When our group visited Epidaurus, we saw the Aesclepian statues had their heads cut off. Not only did early Christianity destroy various Greek temples and archeological artifacts, they attempted to co-opt or destroy the very stories and symbols of the early Greek deities. For example, the stories of Aesclepius bringing back the dead were denigrated, and early Christianity proclaimed that only Jesus to had the power to bring back the dead.

Though our modern scientific curiosity may never be satisfied about knowing what powers to resurrect may have existed in these great healers, we do know that a war for primacy of who was the greatest healer took place. This war is not just of historic or intellectual interest. It has implications for our modern medicine today, and the vestiges of those battles have implications for the treatment that you and your loved ones receive when you go to the hospital today. The symbol of modern medicine that we see today on ambulances was co-opted from this very temple. The snake winding around a staff was the symbol of Aesclepius and his healing ways. It was a symbol that represented, in part, the primordial animal movements of energy that was key to healing. But don't try to tell that to any hospital director—the old ways are not as economically lucrative as are modern surgery and pharmaceuticals.

I do not mean to imply that we should revert back to a pre-modern practice of medicine; but I am advocating for a balanced, non-political, economically neutral view of what it the best healing method for a given situation.

The Inquisition and the Foundation of Modern Medicine

The storyline of the early Christians (who occupied mainstream Christianity) that only Jesus could resurrect is a dualistic, competitive style of thinking that carries a detrimental legacy and creates deleterious effects. The parallel story for modern medicine is oftentimes that modern medicine is the best at saving and resurrecting. This denigrates the old ways of healing. During the time of the Inquisition, from about 1250 until 1800 A.D, numerous Wiccas, midwifes, and other pagan healers were killed by the Christian leaders of the Inquisition (Ellerby, 1995, pp. 76-92). Age-old methods of healing were declared heretical and instead Christians declared that plagues and other diseases were punishments for the sin of not obeying Christian authority. Christian monks taught that bleeding a person, or prayers to Jesus were answers to treat illness (Ellerbe, 1995 p. 42). An important note here is that the Reluctant Metaphysician does not impugn the teachings of Jesus; but reluctantly we must point out how the church at many times subverted his teachings through self-serving stories (Ludemann, 1999).

The story of orthodoxies mounting power tactics against old ways of healing is well researched by John Robbins in this book, *Reclaiming our Health: Exploding the Medical Myth and Embracing the Source of True Healing* (1996). He shows how the American Medical Association in their desire for a medical monopoly joined with the pharmacological industry to denigrate and undermine old ways of healing including homeopathy, midwifery, and chiropractic. Robbins shows how their efforts were often not based on science but on economics and power considerations (Robbins, 1996).

Certainly there have been significant innumerable advances by modern medicine such as organ replacement surgery, acute care methods, and the introduction of the scientific method over superstition. However, the denigration of ancient ways of healing (including energy-based methods of healing) by modern medicine has thrown out the baby with the bathwater.[1]

In alignment with my rising sign of Libra (symbolic of a sense of justice and bringing balance to many spheres of life), the focus of my life path has been on the contributions that ancient sacred wisdom traditions can make to the emerging field of integrative medicine, rather than digging up the past for the purpose of vilification. Many cultures, not just Christianity have attempted to a lesser or greater degree to supplant the prior values and symbols of the past culture (including the United States' takeover of Native American land and culture, China's stranglehold on Tibet, and so forth.) It is not the purpose of this book to show the history of these takeovers of ancient healing traditions and their stories, rather it is to create new healing stories and paradigms.

The integrative medical clinic that I co-founded with a medical doctor, and where I have worked for a decade, is one of those places that practices the blending of modern Western medicine with ancient indigenous traditions such as Ayurveda, Chinese medicine, Native American healing rituals, and so forth. One of our approaches, called the Healing Circle, places a patient in a circle with their practitioners who all discuss with patients their approaches. The health professionals do this at no charge. Part of the payment to us is that and we all learn much from the shared information. I often do the River of Life guided visualization method with patients as part of these healing circles.

As an overarching symbol for integrative medicine, I hope that the mandala of psychotherapies that I envisioned (Mayer, 1977, 1983, 2007), will some day be applied to physical health practices, so that Western medicine with all the valuable contributions that it has to make to healing will stand in a circle whose spokes are represented by other healing traditions such as chiropractic, homeopathy, midwifery, naturopathy, energy healing, psychology, and so forth.

It is unfortunate that there has been a power struggle between Western medical doctors and psychologists for many decades. Psychologists are often kept from having privileges at many hospitals throughout this country. This is a carry over from domineering, dogmatic, and monopolistic thinking. Parity between the medical system and psychology has not been achieved despite attempts to legislate such a cooperative relationship.[2] There are many unfortunate stories of the problems and deaths that have occurred because of this lack of parity.[3] The story line has often been that psychiatrists and medical doctors know more than psychologists, rather than that they have different and overlapping specialties.

Along these lines, it is a useful practice when you listen to a story to sense the part of the body from which it is coming. Is the story coming from the power center of the body, is it coming from the heart, or from the over-intellectualized mind? The Chinese have an interesting term, *xin* (translated as "heart-mind"), which means that the heart and mind should be one when a decision is made. You can add to your story-listening ability by evaluating for yourself from what center of the body it comes, when you hear the story that psychology should be kept on the outskirts of our culture's healing institutions.

Likewise, the not so hidden forces of the pharmacological industry must be weighed in any equation that seeks to determine how economic biases influence medical treatment. With 300 billion dollars a year spent on prescription drugs per year, consumers need to be increasingly aware of the influence of drug money on research and practice (Rosenberg, 2010). A circumspect approach is needed. For example, at a time when the storyline of the positive effects of anti-depressant medication bombard us in TV advertisements, even the Journal of the American Medical Association questions the overuse of medication in an article that says, "The magnitude of benefit of antidepressant medication compared with placebo increases with severity of depression symptoms and may be minimal or nonexistent, on average, in patients with mild or moderate symptoms. For patients with very severe depression, the benefit of medications over placebo is substantial" (Fournier, et al, 2010). So, if you or a loved one are considering going on anti-depressant medication for anything other than severe problems, it is important to do your research and check into reported dangers and the efficacy for your degree of severity, your age, and so forth. (Moncrieff & Kirsch, 2005; Cipriani, et al, 2005; Kirsch, 2010; Levine, 2010, Whitaker, 2010).

It would a great victory for the forces of healing in our culture to replace the story of "pharmaceutical medication first," with the "precautionary principle." The precautionary principle states that, "If an action or policy has a suspected risk of causing harm to the public, its health, or to the environment in the absence of scientific consensus that the action or policy is harmful, the burden of proof that it is *not* harmful falls on those taking the action."[4] Particularly when research shows that the power of the mind is so powerful, why not use this as the first line of defense strategy instead of pharmaceuticals. Lest we forget, in the Greek healing tradition, *noo-therapeia* (translated as mind-healing) was essential, and one name for Aesclepius was *Aesclepius Noo-therapeia.*

It goes against scientific truth to look at psychology as just a fringe player when virtually every study in modern medicine proves the power of the mind in healing. After all, the so-called "placebo effect" is the measure against which all medical treatments are made. This translates to the realization that the mind (and belief) is a central part of creating healing. As a matter of fact in meta-analytic studies it has been shown that the placebo effect (the belief effect) is responsible for between 30–55% of all healing (Rossi, 2002, p.246; Ader, 2000). So, why are the mind and its key tool—imagination—given a back seat in much of modern medicine?

Uranus: God of the Imagination Lives in Modern Advertising

What are these constrictive forces that try to co-opt the traditions of healing and the imagination? In Greek mythology the symbol of the imagination was Uranus. His child Cronus, was envious of Uranus' power and overthrew and castrated his father. Cronus ate his children until Gaia (the Earth mother) fed him a stone, and the infant Zeus (whose name translates as "light") was able to escape. Eventually Zeus overthrew Saturn (Cronus).

We can mythologize current circumstances by saying that there are currently Saturnian forces of the established corporate order that are trying to co-opt the older traditions of healing and the imagination (Gordon, 1996; Robbins, 1996). When a person looks with an objective eye at the research of those in the field who have scientifically documented the role of belief, the mind, and the imagination in healing (Pert, 1997; Rossi, 1986, 1988, 2002; Ader, 1991: 2000; Gordon, 1996), anyone, not just someone like myself with their Sun conjunct Uranus, will become shocked by the castration that has taken place by removing psychology and other valid forms of healing from many medical settings.

Fundamentalist's Stories and the Myopia of the Cyclops

Make no mistake about it; we are in the midst of a war of the imagination, a battle of beliefs. The hero's quest nowadays is to cut the spider's web of meanings that are woven with the threads of egocentrism, literalism, and myopia. One Greek mythic symbol for myopia (narrow vision) is the Cyclops, a primordial race of giants with a single eye in each of their foreheads. As Odysseus had to battle the Cyclops, the one eyed monster that captured the sheep and him in his cave, so do we do battle the Cyclopes of self serving interests in our culture. With just six large corporations controlling most of our media "the sheeple" of our world are held in the cave of darkness.[5]

Fundamentalist of all stripes are poised for battle on the mythic battlefield of life, and sentient beings must call on the wisdom of our mythic heritage to shed light on the dark cave of the myopic Cyclops. What can free the "sheeple" from the cave of the Cyclops when the rock of literalism is so firmly placed at its entrance, blocking the light from entering?

We all are aware of how the radical fundamentalist Muslims belief in having forty virgins in their afterlife, and being indoctrinated into violent solutions for their goals has contributed to such horrific acts as the attack on the World Trade Center on 9/11//2001. But literalism and the over politicization of many other facets of life also seems to rule our current times.

Radical Fundamentalist Christians have attempted to indoctrinate students with their values. In 2010, Texas cut Thomas Jefferson out of textbooks and replaced him with the religious right icon John Calvin, who argued that riches are the sign of god's blessing, and poverty is a sign of god's curse…. And newly proposed changes in Texas schoolbooks include teaching kids the importance of gutting Social Security and Medicare and how the U.N. "is a danger to U.S. sovereignty." When the Texas school board meets, conservatives advocate chipping away at years of "liberal bias" in history classes (Mckinley, 2010).

In mythological terms, speaking of Saturn (Cronus) trying to swallow up his children, Texas has a very big mouth. This state serves 4.7 million students and accounts for a large percentage of the textbook market, and they influence what is taught in the entire United States. Textbooks for children are becoming a Tea Party Manifesto.[6] To use another mythic image, there are forces in America who, as Odysseus did, are trying to lead the sheep out of the cave of the Cyclops. California State Sen. Leland Yee (D) introduced a bill to stop Texas textbooks from getting into California classrooms.[7]

This corporate sponsored educational movement that began in Texas is spreading. The American Coal Foundation through its funded organization, Scholastic, is spreading into grammar school classroom across the country promoting its "teachable materials" such as *The United States of Energy*.[8] In these "educational booklets," young impressionable fourth grade students are told about the virtues of coal as an energy source without mentioning its environmental and health effects.

Trying to overthrow the Jefferson ideal of education preparing the individual for citizenship through developing critical thinking, nowadays, rich conservatives want a lot more than their names on university buildings in exchange for big donations. The Koch brothers, who help fund the Tea Party and dirty energy lobbying, recently endowed two economics professorships at Florida State University in exchange for a say over faculty hires. Banker John Allison, long-time head of Branch, Banking & Trust, has donated to sixty universities in exchange for their agreeing to teach Ayn Rand's *Atlas Shrugged*—some agreements even include the stipulation that the professor teaching the course "have a positive interest in and be well versed in *Objectivism*" (Denvir, 2012).

These are just a few of the examples of corporate subversion of the very essence of objective education that is insidiously narrowing and capturing the minds of our youth.

The Fair and Balanced Storyteller versus Taking a Stance

> *A time comes when silence is betrayal...*
> *The hottest place in Hell is reserved for those who remain neutral*
> *in times of great moral conflict.*
>
> —Martin Luther King
> Riverside Church, New York, April 4, 1967

Many, like myself (even without Libra Rising in their astrological chart), struggle with the idea of being fair and balanced versus taking a stance. Symbolic images are helpful in resolving such conflicts. For example, we can take the image of the scales itself and turn it into an image for weighing the concept of a fair and balanced approach. If we take the image of the scales of justice, on one side we can imagine being light as a feather and fair and balanced; on the other side we can place the archetype of taking a stance and "getting heavy"—entering into the mythic play of life as a character that we feel would add most to a given situation.

As Virgil said, "We make our destiny by our choice of Gods;" and we often worship our stories as if they were Gods. Our storylines often become the boundaries demarking the walls of our temples. The storyline of "the political far-right" is that "we have to save our country from "liberal bias," and the perspective of "the left" is that "our children in science classes need to be educated with science not religious, corporate, and political indoctrination." The metaphysician does not always choose the story line of the temple of "Relativism," which says that everything is relative and political and that all positions are merely views. The storyteller, the trickster, and the metaphysician are not afraid to take a stance on the story that best serves humanity in his or her view. We make our lives by the stories we tell and the stances we take.

Balancing opposites by telling stories on each side of the issue is the stance of one dimension of the archetype of Hermes. One of his symbols, *the herm,* marks the boundaries between one territory and another on the earth. But not only does the herm mark horizontal balance, it is also a marker of the place to gain access to the underworld, into depth and taking an emotional stance (Pedraza, 1977). Another of Hermes' accoutrements are his winged sandals, which symbolize rising up to a higher perspective. So, Hermes is the guide on the path of life. Sometimes that path requires balance and rising above the fray; at other times a forceful chthonic stance is needed that draws from the depths of one's emotions and core beliefs. Every path has its problems. The former path has the advantage of being circumspect and the danger of being unassertively wishy-washy; the later path has the advantage of being a person who stands for something, yet it can be fraught with the dangers of emotional bias and alienating others. The task of the Reluctant Metaphysician is to choose when to be balanced and see both sides, versus when to take a stance.

The Texas Book Controversy and Modern Psychological Education

It has been disturbing to me to see that any kind of analogy can be made between the Texas book conspiracy and my chosen field of psychology. However, with the increasing attempt of psychology to become "medicalized," currently there is a narrowing of the training curriculum toward "evidence-based" approaches. The call for evidence-based treatment has merits and detriments. Since much research has been done on cognitive behavioral psychotherapy, it has been anointed as one of the rulers of the Kingdom of Psychology; but just as in medicine, just because the established powers have done research in those areas does not necessarily mean that those treatments are the most efficacious.

Psychology is still struggling with the fact that the transformation of the troubles ailing the human soul is not only a clinical endeavor, but also a mythological and metaphysical one. The core curriculum of most psychology programs today rarely includes as a significant part in the training of therapists: Jungian psychotherapy, symbolic processes, mind-body medicine, ancient sacred wisdom traditions, and metaphysical approaches to psychology. The creation of a new origin myth for psychology that includes these traditions is an important part of the work of the Reluctant Metaphysician, as is a mandalic view for psychotherapy that integrates all systems of current and age-old methods of healing the bodymind.

The Wider Frame Stories—Cultural, Economic, Political, Environmental

When our days become dreary with low-hovering clouds of despair,
and when our nights become darker than a thousand midnights,
let us remember that there is a creative force in this universe,
working to pull down the gigantic mountains of evil,
a power that is able to make a way out of no way
and transform dark yesterdays into bright tomorrows.
Let us realize the arc of the moral universe is long, but it bends toward justice.

—Martin Luther King
Where do we go from here? August 16, 1967
Address to the Southern Christian Leadership Conference

In this chapter I mostly wanted to focus on the war on healers; yet current healers exist in a wider cultural context. The part cannot be disconnected from the whole. Just as the healers in the time of the inquisition could not be separated from the larger frame story of that era that Jesus was the only way to God and to healing, so are healers today living in a web of cultural, political and economic forces. Shining some light on the spider's web, and the threads of the story that weave it, can protect us from getting caught.

CULTURE WARS:

We are living in a time of a "culture war" when forces on different sides are fighting battles in the arena of religious values, sexual orientation, art, women's bodies, education, the environment, global ecology, politics, economics, and the law (Hunter, 1992; Mooney, 2006). Even science itself is under attack in the culture wars, as Chris Mooney shows when he discussed the tricks that special interests use when scientific consensus becomes politically inconvenient. One right wing strategy has been to banish science from centers of power—for example, when the GOP-led Congress dismantled its own, nonpartisan advisory tool, the Office of Technology Assessment, because its counsel kept conflicting with ideological views. Another is for political aides to edit the reports of scientific panels, so that final versions offer conclusions quite different than panel members intended. Threats to job security can squelch whistleblowers. Another method has been to pack advisory groups with "experts" who were selected on a basis of ideology, or industry affiliation, or promises to reach a predetermined outcome (Mooney, 2006, 2009). There is accumulating scientific evidence, by the way, that in general, there are differences in the thinking processes and personality traits of Republicans and Democrats. Mooney explores brain scans, polls, and psychology experiments to explain why conservatives today believe more factually wrong things; appear more likely than Democrats to oppose new ideas; are less likely to change their beliefs in the face of new facts; and sometimes respond to compelling evidence by doubling down on their current beliefs. Mooney traces the roots of the culture wars in personality styles of authoritarian versus explorative, and emotion based versus fact based (Mooney, 2012b). On the other side of the mythic battle for the "psyche-logical," high ground of our era are radio talk show hosts such as Michael Savage who argue that liberalism is a mental disorder (Savage, 2005). The Reluctant Metaphysician who enjoys the process of looking behind the world of ideas to examine their roots will watch with interest the unbiased examination of Mooney's conclusions as they meet various conservative viewpoints, and a hermeneutic circumambulation hopefully takes place to shed light on the psychology and facts behind the culture wars.

Me-Society versus We-Society

Another part of the cultural wars is epitomized by the difference in values between those who advocate a "me-society" versus a "we-society." The advocates of the "me-society" say that whoever can rise to the top should do so, and whoever leaves life with the most possessions wins the game. On corporate boards oftentimes there are not even representatives from the working people of those organizations. The story line goes that the workers will not understand how things work as well as the higher ups who have a better perspective. And yet during the recessionary years of the 21st century when the U.S. economy was declining, the German economy was doing better. Germany is run by a different story.

All German corporations are required to have a board of directors comprised of 50% of workers (Geoghegan, 2010: Hartmann, 2010). So, while the U.S. economy was declining in the recession of 2010, the official figures showed that the German economy leaped forward by 2.2% in the three months to the end of June 2010, its fastest quarterly growth in more than 20 years. One big factor in the continuing growth of the German economy is that during the Great Recession, German workers never saw layoffs or significant reductions in pay. During the financial crisis the German government filled in the pay gaps of workers who worked fewer hours. Then, other workers could fill in those hours in a "work-sharing" model that reduced overall unemployment.[9]

In the United States we have been sold on the story of "American exceptionalism," which says that we are the most productive, greatest country in the world with the best healthcare and standard of living. The moral problems inherent in such an inflated view of America's place in history are clearly outlined in progressive textbooks (Zinn, 1980). In psychotherapy, when a patient has an inflated self-image, psychotherapists try to help such narcissistically inclined individuals to look at the consequences of such grandiosity in their lives, interpersonal relationships, and the world they create thereby. Many of these "exceptional individuals" put down others, and suffer from the way that their exercise of power damages their own lives and those of others. Undue inflation leads to problems being receptive to lessons from life, and in being vulnerable to learn from others.

Blaming and denigrating others is a narcissistic defense that wards off the pains of self-examination and human vulnerability. Similarly, some of those advocates of American exceptionalism distort the gains of the democratic socialist countries of Europe by calling them "communists." In the book by Thomas Geoghegan (2010) called, *Were You Born on the Wrong Continent?*, he discusses how the European Union is surpassing the United States in many categories including productivity, healthcare, and so forth. In Germany there are six weeks of federally mandated vacation and free university tuition.

Healthcare in the twenty-seven countries of the European Union is considered to be a right, unlike in the U.S. They have better health results than we do in the U.S., at half the price. Maybe this is partly because they don't have corporate executives taking massive executive salaries like Bill McGuire, CEO of United Health Care who took away1.5 billion dollars in five years. He received an approximate farewell package of 1.1 billion dollars.[10] When I told one of my colleagues this, he sarcastically quipped, "McGuire and other CEO's deserve that amount for being able to figure out how to rip off every health professional in the country of 40% of their income." In the United States, for reasons such as this, we are #37 in the world in healthcare. There are lessons to be learned from other countries, if we could let go of our fixed belief in American exceptionalism.

WAR ON OUR ECONOMY

I, and those of my generation, were brought up with a cultural myth—if you worked hard, went to school and got a good education, you would have enough resources to bring up a family, send your kids to college, and after having contributed to the social insurance programs of Medicare and Social Security you would be taken care of in your old age. This social contract was put firmly into place during the time of President Franklin Roosevelt's New Deal, and President Theodore Roosevelt's Square Deal. Theodore. One central component of the American Dream is that children will do better than their parents; however now there is increasing "downward mobility" (DeGraw, 2011; Reich, 2012). Now, according to a Pew Research Poll, "nearly a third of Americans who were part of the middle class as teenagers in the 1970s have fallen out of it as adults" (Eichler, 2011). It seems that more and more of my friends and colleagues who were brought up on the myth of the American Dream are waking up to the nightmare of a new reality. More and more of people who were in the middle class are turning into the working poor (*Huffington Post,* 2011; Cook, 2012).

According to a survey by the Employee Benefit Research Institute, workers are cashing in their retirement plans just to stay afloat. Their grim statistics show the percentage of American workers who have less than $10,000 in savings grew to forty-three percent in 2010. Almost twenty-five percent of all workers have postponed their planned retirement in 2010. A CareerBuilder.com survey, in 2010, reports that sixty-one percent of workers are living paycheck to paycheck, as compared to forty-three percent in 2007.[11]

Speaking of retirement plans, one of the most sacrosanct aspects of the American social contract has been a pension plan. Corporate workers have been told the story that their pensions were tucked away in the safe hands of their companies. Yet for those who examine the world behind the world of cherished beliefs, the truth is that many corporations have figured out clever ways to plunder the nest eggs of American workers (Schultz, 2011). After working hard for many years many workers reluctantly are faced with the truth of cut benefits and stolen assets.

So, the Reluctant Metaphysician's job is not only a "spiritual" one, it is to point to the political and economic truths of the world behind the world of everyday beliefs—to bring awareness to the magnets (and magnates) behind everyday life who are controlling the forces of our lives.

As I was reflecting on the hard-work-myth of my childhood and I and others watch the economic collapse, and unraveling of culture in this 21st century, I turned on the radio and on the *Thom Hartmann* show a caller said, "The New Deal has turned into 'The Raw Deal.'"

An attempt is being made to rewrite the social contract. Opposing worldviews are colliding in the mythic battle of our times. The story line of supply side economics is that if we give tax breaks and rewards to the wealthiest among us it will "trickle down" to the middle class. However, even David Stockman, the Reagan's budget director and promoter of supply side economics, in an op-ed in the *NY Times* has recanted and admitted that philosophy of supply side economics was incorrect.[12]

I wonder if advocators of trickle down economists are looking at the fact that after years of their philosophy in place that in 2010 the 500 biggest non-financial corporations now have 1.8 trillion dollars in cash, more than at any time in the past fifty years. Companies like GM received $50 billion dollars in bailout money; but even though they made 2.2 billion in profit in the second quarter of 2010, according to the *Wall Street Journal* they only added 2,000 jobs in all of North America.[13]

Everyday we see the results of the outsourcing of jobs to other countries when we need product assistance. We wait in "phone-jail hell" and speak to a foreign worker who is often ill informed about our local needs. This all began when Jack Welch, CEO of General Electric, had the brilliant idea (brilliant for corporate profits) of outsourcing jobs when he reportedly went on a vacation to India and he realized that there were English speaking people there that would work for pennies on the dollar. During the George W. Bush administration thirty-nine percent of manufacturing jobs were lost, many of them shipped off shore.[14]

The Republican Party is promoting an agenda that is creating detrimental effects for the citizens of the United States in economic, environmental, and health spheres. So, what is the stance of a Reluctant Metaphysician during such times, and how does he or she use a relationship to the world behind the world to create healing and right action?

A Reluctant Metaphysician, (who prefers to take a balanced, apolitical perspective on life and to advocate for opposite forces reconciling), cannot help but notice that part of the symbol of the Republican Party was turned upside down during the George W. Bush presidency in the year 2000 (Mother Jones, 2008). Before this, the top of five-pointed star (the pentagram) was pointed upward, an age-old metaphysical symbol of the head of the human being place above the four limbs. It is interesting that the new symbol of the Republican Party changed during the time of the Bush administration. When it was put up on the logo of the Republican Party website it had the fifth point of the head of the star below the four limbs. This inverted star is an age-old symbol of the goat (two horns, two ears, and a chin), and the devil. How symbolically appropriate in this topsy-turvy world that the party that professes the high ground on moral issues uses as their symbol the logo used by Satanists. Since we are living in a world of "metaphysical dissociation" where esoteric symbols are not studied or taken seriously, we suffer the consequences of the manifestation of this symbol grabbing us in reality. The job of the Reluctant Metaphysician is to bring the meaning of such symbols to light.

However, it is not only Republicans and Republican presidents that are to blame for the disintegrating state of our nation. During President Bill Clinton's rein, "free trade" bills like the North American Free Trade Association (NAFTA) were passed that shipped off American jobs to other countries. Ross Perot proved to be correct with his 1992 presidential campaign statement that if we pursued trade policies such as NAFTA that there would be a "giant sucking sound" as American jobs went to other countries. Our Congress has colluded with these detrimental trade policies by giving tax breaks to these corporations, and still has not imposed tariffs on imports to protect our industries and jobs (Hartmann, 2010).

There is no shortage of Republican and Democratic politicians who are turning the star of the heavens upside down. And if you think that our very courts are not involved in the era of the upside down star, just look at how the Supreme Court Justice Clarence Thomas violates conflict of interest laws (Lichtblau, 2011), and in the *Citizens United* case the highest court in our land has undermined the democratic underpinnings of campaign financing laws and gives corporations "free speech"—in this case a euphemism for buying our government (Peters, 2011; Linkins, 2011).

Lest we think that only two branches of government are involved and would not enter into democratic President Obama, we only have to look at President Obama's signing of the National Defense Appropriations Act's Amendment 1031 which allows for the military detention of American citizens and ends core principles of our democratic system of government—*habeas corpus,* and *posse comitatus* (Wolf, 2012). If anyone submitted a fiction article to any publication ten years ago that said a constitutional lawyer who was the editor of the best law journal in the United States would become president and sign such an act, it would have been laughed at as too unbelievable—unless it was submitted to the DC Comic Book series where in that "bizarro world" everything is in reverse. Many forces in our culture joined in protest about President Obama's position on indefinite detention of American citizens, and these protesting voices may have led him to back off on his position in some respects. It has become a controversial matter of speculation as to how the changes in NDAA Amendment will be interpreted.[15]

Each of us needs to weigh in our own informed way what it would mean to have a correctly aligned star (the top of it pointing to the heavens), ruling our economy, environment, justice system, presidency, and health. If we allow ourselves to look at the harsh realities of what is happening in the economic sphere, it seems that our country increasingly resembles the feudal era when serfs begged bosses for another crumb. Senator Bernie Sanders, an Independent, has lamented this state of affairs, as he cites research that this economic climate has created a society where now one percent of America's population earns more than the combined bottom fifty percent; and one percent of our population owns more wealth than the combined bottom ninety percent.[16] Underlining how the United States has turned from a democracy into an oligarchy is the fact that the top 400 people in the United States own more wealth than the bottom fifty percent of our population (De Graw, 2010). It is hard to not be induced into "statistically dissociation" when we hear such numbers,[17] and not to realize that we are living in a "Predator Nation" (Ferguson, 2012).

In capitalist countries such as ours, corporate executives have always earned much higher salaries than the workers they manage. In 1978 the compensation of CEOs was thirty-five times higher than compensation of average workers. A metaphysician does not inherently have a problem with any given financial model, per se; but rather we look at the principles from the world behind the world that underlie the model. In a capitalistic model the hero myth is behind it, and it has the advantage of incentivizing people to rise to activate the hero in himself or herself. However, in the year 2000 the CEO-to worker pay ratio skyrocketed to 299–1, and even during the recession in 2010 the ratio is 243–1 (Michel, 2006; Bivens, 2011). The metaphysician asks, "When does the CEO-worker ratio change from a model that incentivizes, to a wage theft model that exploits?"

Ed Luce with the *Financial Times* has also documented the "crisis of middle-class America," with important facts. He notes the "median wage stagnation" that has hit most American families." He says, "the annual incomes of the bottom ninety percent of U.S. families have been essentially flat since 1973…. That means most Americans have been treading water for more than a generation." At the same time, the *Financial Times* notes, America's CEOs have seen their compensation go up over a hundredfold. The result is a level of inequality not seen in this country since 1929, and the conversion of the middle class of 1940 to 1980 into the terrified working poor of the post Reaganomics era. The vast majority of Americans in the year 2010 live paycheck to paycheck, with no significant savings, and only a job loss and a few weeks from being homeless and on the streets. One out of every six Americans is (in 2009–10) being served by at least one government anti-poverty program.[18]

How does each of us respond to such a state of affairs? Earlier we spoke of the myth of the Old Woman in the Cave, and that when the Black Dog unraveled her woven garment she was able to keep her equanimity and stay true to her purpose. Now we are living in a time of the unraveling of culture—the Black Dogs of predatory capitalism are pulling the strings.

According to Paul Wooley who runs a think tank in London called the Centre for the Study of Capital Market Dysfunctionality, the presumption that financial innovation is socially valuable is not backed by physical evidence. He says that those that who in the "financial services" sector, that are among the top one percent of our American elite, create "value" by tapping on keyboards and punching in algorithms; trashing mortgages; and making money by playing with money, manipulating abstractions with credit default swaps, future exchanges, hedge funds, and derivative pools. These financial instruments have only exchange value as opposed to real value. These traders chase after financial bubbles and then prick them. According to Wooley, "They are only services in the sense of the vampire at a vein" (Ketcham, 2011, p. 3). Yet these financial vampires who are sucking the blood out of the American dream and the American culture are well rewarded in spite of the fact that they go against the social contract that says that productive, hard work for society creates well deserved personal gains.

It is a time when each of us needs to find our own way to deal with the unraveling of the social contract. For the Reluctant Metaphysician, the practices outlined in this book are ways to keep our equanimity during troubled times. In addition, since Reluctant Metaphysicians' purpose is to keep our unique dharmic purpose and astrological chart in our hearts and mind, we know that we each need to find the unique contribution that our twisted thread can make. Some people will become engaged in the political process, such as signing petitions as a step in the right direction to attempt to counter the corporate forces that support corruption.[19] Other people may choose to encourage our politicians to have appropriate regulations to counter the prevailing power structure who believe, "Greed is good." Those with a focus on the power of stories may find their own ways to unmask the story of "deregulation," which oftentimes is a cover story that allows corporate greed to flourish.

It is not so easy for any of us to take our overspent time to knit back together the torn social fabric of our civilization; yet we reluctantly must move out of our complacency if we are to reweave the garment of culture. Reluctant Metaphysicians, calling on the archetypes behind the drama of life, can use a wide array of tools that fit with our own nature. Primordial metaphors, such as the use of the image of the vulture (Palast, 2011), speak to our souls and wake us from cultural dreams. Effective political actions that arise from grass roots politics are exemplified by Vinny Demarco in Maryland where he has organized successful efforts to pass gun control laws, and hiked cigarette taxes to prevent youth smoking thereby extending health care to hundreds of thousands of low-income workers. His strategic template includes skillful access to the media for engaging public support, coalitions of broadly based groups, and a hard press on candidates to support legislation before they are elected (Pertschuk, 2010).

Each of us can express ourselves in our unique ways, in mediums such as music, poetry, activating the trickster archetype are ways to draw from the creative gifts of the world behind the world. Speaking of activating the trickster archetype, the group YesMen.org is a sterling example. The Yes Men are a network of activists created by Andy Bichelbaum and Mike Bananno [these names are aliases]. Through actions of tactical media, the Yes Men primarily aim to raise awareness about what they consider problematic social issues. Among their innovative tactics they pose as a powerful entity (typically a corporate or government representative or executive) and make ridiculous and shocking comments that caricature the ideological position of the organization or person. The Yes Men have posed as spokespeople for the World Trade Organization, McDonalds, the United States Department of Housing and Urban Development, and Dow Chemical. The result often leads to false news reports, which the Yes Men use to get publicity for problems concerning these organizations. For example, one of the Yes Men went on the news to claim that Dow planned to liquidate Union Carbide and use the resulting $12 billion to pay for medical care, clean up the Bhopal disaster site, and fund research into the hazards of other Dow products. After two hours of wide coverage, Dow issued a press release denying the statement, ensuring even greater coverage of the phony news of a cleanup. By the time the original story was discredited, Dow's stock had declined in value by $2 billion.

One of the effects of the Yes Men's trickster tactics is that organizations that are not serving the public interest are then later forced to re-acknowledge an event in question, suffer the consequences of bad publicity, and sometime the organizations take remediating actions. After the Yes Men prank, the Department of Housing and Urban Development in Louisiana decided not to tear down suitable housing units of Katrina disaster victims.[20]

We have all become so accustomed to the internet that we can take it for granted; yet it is one of the greatest tools in history for a Reluctant Metaphysician to reach the masses through creative harnessing of the terrain of the world behind the world. One facet of this world in the modern era is the "technological world above the clouds."

Chevron can spend millions of dollars in advertising to promote its Green image, but an ordinary person can put together a website such as www.ChevronThinksWereStupid. org or www.funnyordie.com and like the court jester in the King's court of yesteryear, that individual can bring an alternative view to the masses through satire. Many people learned about Texaco/Chevron's pollution of Ecuador through the creative efforts of people such as these. Likewise, blog postings let the world know about countries that are empowering themselves regarding multinational corporations like Chevron and Transocean polluting the environment. For example, in Thom Hartmann's blog he reports that Brazil arrested seventeen Chevron executives for environmental crimes after an oil spill off the coast poured about three thousand barrels of oil into Brazilian waters in November of 2011. If found guilty these executives could face up to thirty-one years in prison.[21] Contrast this with the lack of prosecution of those executives who were responsible for our various oil spills such as the Gulf disaster.

Other ways that a Reluctant Metaphysician can find a sense of empowerment, in a seemly all powerful corporate world, are by writing a review on user-review websites such as Yelp, signing petitions, recycling, joining protests, and boycotting products that support values that go against ours. After seeing the movie, *Walt-Mart: The High Cost of Low Prices,* many people stopped buying products at Wal-Mart. Various consumer protests are proving influential in changing company policies, for example: targeting Target Stores' contributions to extreme right wing causes; bringing awareness to Nike sneakers' labor policies; and bringing attention to Apple Computer's technological waste, outsourcing, and labor policies (Duhigg, 2012; Gupta, 2012). There are economic realities involved in, and problems with, corporate choices.[22] Reluctantly, some metaphysically inclined individuals hold in each hand one of the sides of this issue—recognizing that lower prices and viable business models can result from outsourcing to foreign countries; and on the other hand, dire economic, health, and environmental consequences can result from such choices. So, we mindfully search for sustainable solutions as we focus on our hearts and our spines, which stand between the two sides as we find our stance in our sphere of influence.

In the past when my generation fought against the Vietnam War, hippies used street theater and media events to raise consciousness. These are all ways that ordinary citizens can become effective activists. Though this is more difficult nowadays with corporate control extending into many media outlets, there are alternative media sources that are growing, such as the internet.

A major tool of Reluctant Metaphysicians is the use of words, images, symbols, and stories to stimulate the creation of appropriate actions. Many progressive radio talk show hosts now speak of our country having been changed from a democracy to a "kleptocracy," a government ruled by thieves that exists to increase the personal wealth of its officials and the ruling elite at the expense of the wider population. Thom Hartmann, a Progressive radio talk show commentator suggests that members of Congress (and the Supreme Court) should be required to wear a patch designating their financial funding sources, as NASCAR drivers do. This facetious suggestion points out well how our Congress has literally become "the best government money can buy," with undue corporate influence of the legislative process and a revolving door between corporations and government institutions (Adams, 2007). Thom Hartman also uses language well when he says, "Trickle Down Economics has created a society of peons." This well chosen terminology, using the word "peon" with its double entendre, is story-telling at its best because it helps us realize that we are being "peed-on" by the supposed trickles that will "generously be given to the working people."

This false story, and its creation of conditions for economic downfall, is not limited to the United States. Toxic philosophies can spread, no less than toxic substances put into our waterways. If we have any doubts about the detrimental effects of self-serving and false stories, we can look to the Wall Street banking community and how its philosophies have spread overseas. One spider's web that was spun by this community was the deceptive tale about need for "deregulation." These "banksters" sold the public and President Bill Clinton on the need to repeal the *Glass–Steagall Act* (Reich, 2009), and on the need to pass the *Gramm–Leach–Bliley Act* (GLB), also known as the *Financial Services Modernization Act* of 1999. It allowed commercial banks, investment banks, securities firms, and insurance companies to consolidate. One result of the lessening of regulations and mergers of banks and investment goals was selling faulty mortgage backed securities and derivatives, which created a world wide financial crises that crashed the economies of Iceland, Greece, and Ireland (Taibbi, 2011; Lyall, 2008; Lewis, 2011), not to mention the United States housing market and economy.

Because of "regulatory capture" of the mortgage rating agencies by corporate interests, rating agencies like Moody's did not do their jobs of protecting the public (Faux, 2011). Many well meaning citizens who listened to the tale spun by corporate financial interests did not realize that the fine sounding word, "deregulation" hid the puppet-masters who were "wanting to play football on an unregulated field"—it caused the game to fall apart.

It is heartening to see the Occupy Wall Street begin in the fall of 2011. So, not only in Arab countries, with their "Arab Spring," do people have the gumption to stand up against forces of oppression. Is "the Fall" of American corporatocracy beginning?

WAR ON HEALERS: WAR ON PSYCHOTHERAPISTS

This wider dimension of national economics has impacted the psychotherapy community. I first saw this in the dismantling of the mental health system of California when Ronald Reagan was governor. When I was doing my internship for Contra Costa Mental Health in the mid 1970s, Reagan dismantled many of the state mental hospitals and said that he would shift money to the community mental health centers. That promised money never came into the community mental health system. As a result, a homeless street population of mentally ill people grew who did not get the services they needed.

Many of these policies have continued to this day throughout the United States. For example, currently in the years of economic recession and budget cutting there are many cutbacks in mental health funding and services. Without implying causality, one cannot help but be struck by the symbolism of Arizona slashing its mental health services budget in 2011 by thirty-seven percent (Vestal, 2010), just at the time that a mentally ill person shot congresswoman Gabrielle Giffords. How many mental health professionals will lose their jobs, and how many people in need of mental health services will not treated, while corporate profits are soaring in our culture (Goodman, 2010)?

Just as there has been a movement towards corporate rule in the wider culture, so has it been in our training of healers. "As above, so below," is the old Hermetic axiom. In virtually every area that mental health professionals go in their careers the effects of the corporate economy has its effects. In the teaching of healers, in many schools, the teachers are most often hired to teach individual courses and the administrators are more often given pensions and health benefits than are the teachers…"the trickle," most of the time does not come down. I have never seen a study on how this affects the quality of the training of psychotherapists. But, I know from my experience after eighteen years of university teaching that, as with many teachers throughout this country, many of the best teachers of psychotherapy left college teaching due to not being able to make a living.

Recently, one of my younger psychotherapy colleagues told me the story of how he had prepared (non-payed) all summer to teach a psychotherapy course. Then, at the first class of the semester there were seventeen students. He was told that it needed eighteen students for the class to go. He was told that if he came back the following week that additional students might register. The next week there were still only seventeen students. The head of the department said that even though only one more student was needed to meet their standard, the class needed to be cancelled. All of this psychotherapist's preparation for the class was not a factor, nor was it compensated. So, here we can see how wider macro-economic variables have crippled working people and teachers.

Make no mistake about it; we are in the midst of a war on higher education that is substituting economic efficiency and corporate values for quality education (Deressiewicz, 2011; Denvir, 2011). This has created the very real national phenomena called "the disposable professor," which is compromising our children's education (Smith, 2012). The example of my young psychotherapy colleague's experience is one small example of the effect of the destruction of unions by forces that want to have Labor union's power lessoned. I have spoken to other faculty members of psychology and faculty of other departments who have had similar experiences in this age of the battle against healers and educators.

Teacher unions are one factor that could be part of the solution. However, unions in the private sector nowadays are only about 7.2% of the work force, whereas in 1955 non-agricultural union members numbered over 33% of the work force.[23] Certainly there have been problems with union boss's excesses, and other detrimental aspects of unions; but it should be realized that there is probably a deeper rationale behind the anti-union story told in much of the mass media.

Most people recognize that one of the reasons for the anti-labor policies of corporations is that corporate executives want to maximize profits and lower their labor costs;

but there is another reason why labor unions have been delegitimized. Labor unions support democratic candidates for the most part. According to astute political observers, that is another major reason why beginning with Ronald Reagan there was an attack on labor unions (Hartmann, 2010). In the sphere of teachers of psychotherapy, I hope I have shown you how has been detrimental.

Battling the Bureaucratic Hydra That Has Defeated Many a Health Practitioner

The culture of Rulership by Corporate Greed has taken over most of the land of the soul—the terrain of psychotherapy. Psychologists are increasingly dissatisfied with the reduction of fees, and the paperwork and "phone jail" time that is needed to be providers for managed care companies. One of my colleagues quipped, "I'm tempted to give the analogy to my patients—If you were going to go to a mechanic to get your car fixed, would you ask if he accepted your insurance card, which would require about an extra twenty minutes of work documenting the reasons for their repair? Then, by the way, there may be another phone call or two required which will take another twenty minutes or so to make sure your paperwork is in order and to make sure that this is a valid claim. And, Mr. Mechanic, would it be OK to have your payment delayed for two to three months with possible phone calls and 'phone jail' while you are waiting to hear why the records were lost? One last item, Mr. Mechanic, my insurance company requires you to take a forty percent cut in pay…. So, when can you begin the work?"

Regarding the field of psychotherapy, when corporations have subsumed the power to rule on decisions about the human psyche (our very souls), with the profit motive as the top criterion, you know we are in troubled times.

Regarding the bigger picture of corporate health care, though there are some distinctions between various managed care companies, as I was writing this section of the book I took a break, went out to lunch, and synchronicity was once again apparently in the air. As I read the *S.F. Chronicle* (Tuesday, November 30, 2010), I saw a story about how California State regulators fined seven insurers nearly $5 million for systematically failing to pay doctors and hospitals fairly and on time. For example, Anthem Blue Cross was fined $900,000, and Blue Shield of California was fined $900,000 (Colliver, 2010). With so many people talking about the side effects of medication, the question is, "What are the side-effects of such long-standing practices by insurance companies on patients not being able to get the services they need?"

One result is that many doctors and psychologists will no longer take patients from insurance companies, or they put insurance company patients on a lower rung regarding accepting such patients. Another side-effect of the current system is that many of the most qualified medical and mental health professionals go into early retirement or switch to an area of their practice that does not involve patient care after such frustrating experiences. I have heard many of my medical doctor friends and mental health professional colleagues say, "I've always loved my work with patients, and I still do; but now since managed care has come on the scene I hate my job." For a more extensive discussion, from an insurance company insider, on how corporate policies are killing health care and deceiving Americans see Wendell Potter's book, *Deadly Spin* (2010).

Since most consumers place cost reduction at such a high priority level, they do not often think about what this type of bureaucratic macro-environment is doing to their allied health practitioners. Corporations as well as consumers may eventually become more aware of the connection between health practitioners' dissatisfaction and consumers' deteriorating care. Perhaps an enlightened pubic will eventually change corporations control and influence, despite their vast reservoirs of money that is often able to defeat single-payer plans.

In single-payer plans, the financing of the costs of delivering universal health care for an entire population are made through a single insurance pool out of which costs are met. There may be many contributors to the single pool (insured persons, employers, government, and so forth.) Australia's Medicare, Canada's Medicare, the United Kingdom's National Health Service, and Taiwan's National Health Insurance are examples of single-payer universal health care systems. Medicare in the United States is an example of a single-payer system for a specified, limited group of persons within our country.[24]

Health practitioners, for the most part, much prefer single-payer plans such as government run options, as compared to corporate-managed care with its reduced reimbursement rates, unwieldy paperwork, and excessive profits which go into corporate coffers. One organization that is at the forefront of physicians' single-payer efforts is Physicians for a National Health Program.[25] In 2010, twenty-one percent of healthcare costs were spent on paperwork for insurance administration and an additional thirteen percent is used to cover other administrative tasks, such as maintaining medical records. Now we know where some of those dollars are going, which come out of practitioners' salaries and add to consumer's costs.

By the way, the CEO of United Healthcare, Bill McGuire, reportedly held stock options worth $663 million according to *Managed Care Matters* (2011). He was found by the SEC to have fraudulently backdated his stock options (Cook, 2009). This is at the same time that reimbursement fees to physicians were being cut back.[26] Time will tell how much the new health care plan (with its advantages and disadvantages) signed by President Obama in 2010 will help to rectify the problems with "the war on health care professionals."[27]

Many in the United States have been willing to put up with this state of affairs in the medical arena because we have been living with an idealized image that the U.S. has the best medicine in the world. The truth is that even though we spend more per capita than any other country, our healthcare is not among the world's best in spite of the propaganda we hear. For example, our infant mortality rate is higher than many countries where far less is spent on healthcare. In Shanghai, China the infant mortality rate is 9.9 out of 1,000, whereas in New York City it is 10.8 per 1,000 (Reinhardt, 1996; Starfield, 2000).

To see a balanced overview about the realities of the healthcare that other Western European countries have as compared with the United States see T. R. Reid's *The Healing of America: A Global Quest for Better Cheaper and Fairer Health Care* (2009). For example, many of us have been told the story that European Healthcare is "socialized medicine." He says that, "of course, every health care system has its troubles: Reid finds poorly paid doctors in Japan, endless lines in Canada, mistreated patients in Britain, spartan facilities in France. Yet all of them cover everybody, produce better health results, and spend far less than the United States. And none leaves its citizens one diagnosis away from financial ruin!"

Here's one more relevant tidbit: Did you know that an MRI in Japan costs $160, and in the U.S.it costs approximately $1,700?[28]

WAR ON PLANT MEDICINES

I told you earlier about how in the late 1960s I naively thought that various psychedelic medicines would be legalized and how the larger economic, political and cultural forces shut down the potentially beneficial uses of those substances. Though my path led me to want to find ways to open the doors to altered states of consciousness without the use of entheogens and various psycho-active plants, these plant medicines played an important part in opening "the doors of my perception (Huxley, 1977)," and those of others of my generation. [29] For example, Apple Computer founder Steve Jobs told a *New York Times* reporter that his LSD experience, "one of the two or three most important things I have done in my life" (Markoff, 2005). Another example is Francis Crick, one of the discoverers of DNA, told friends that he first saw the double-helix structure while tripping on LSD (Grim, 2011).

I am happy to say that in the year 2010, after years of reactivity against psychedelic use, renewed research is taking place on the role of psychedelics in healing. For example, one study in the *Journal of Psychopharmacology* (Mithoefer, 2010) reported that eight percent of sufferers of post traumatic stress lost symptoms after taking the drug Ecstasy (3-4-Methylenedioxymethamphetamine, or MDMA). Also, in a mind-bending flashback, a new analysis of six randomized controlled trials from the 1960s and 70s researchers from a Norwegian University and from Harvard found that a single dose of LSD had a significant beneficial effect on alcohol misuse for up to 12 months (Krebs & Johansen, 2012). In alignment with the metaphysical postulate that (with proper intention, procedures, and safeguards), connecting with the world behind the world can improve the world of everyday life, the researchers hypothesize that, "LSD can help prevent a relapse of alcohol abuse...by eliciting insights into behavioral problems and generating motivation to build a meaningful and sober lifestyle" (Cool, 2012; Krebs & Johansen, 2012).

Certainly, due caution needs to be exercised in the use of such "plant medicines" and quality research needs to continue to be undertaken. So, it was unfortunate that counter-veiling forces, which opposed the consciousness movement during the 1960s and 1970s, shut down much of the research of various medicinal plants for years. This deprived our culture of a circumspect exploration of the uses of such plants.

Another example to underline this issue is a 2010 study in the *Canadian Medical Association Journal* (Walt et al., 2010), which showed that a single dose of cannabis smoked three times daily for five days reduced the intensity of pain, improved sleep and was well tolerated. And, there have been numerous other research papers on the role on cannabinoids to alleviate various disease symptoms such as the nausea associated with cancer and chemotherapy (Doblin, 1990) and to ameliorate the effects of various diseases (Pacher, 2006; Norml, 2010).

More broadly speaking, due to the association of the hemp plant with hippies' marijuana use, economic and political forces joined to deprive our culture of the benefits of hemp for fuel and other utilitarian uses (McCabe, 2010). Up through current times, there have been lobbying forces representing the economic interests of prisons, police, beer, and the alcohol industry that have joined to suppress and punish the use of marijuana without regard for its social, societal, and medicinal benefits when used appropriately (Fang, 2012).

There is a whole field of healing plant medicines that can be of benefit to humanity (gifts from the plant world), that are awaiting our sacred relationship to them. There are various types of psychoactive plants such as: *entheogens* such as psilocybin and mescaline (*theo* in Greek refers to the activation of the God within us); *empathogens* such as in MDMA, also called Ecstasy (which activate empathy, emotional states, and social effects); *hallucinogens* such as Ayahuasca (which activate imagery); and *psychedelics* such as LSD (which activate the psyche, mind, and perceptual changes). Some of these are overlapping categories.[30]

WAR ON THE ENVIRONMENT

> *The creature that wins against its environment destroys itself.*
>
> —Gregory Bateson

Why is it that "names" of so many things oftentimes mean exactly the opposite of what they should mean? "Environmental Protection Agency" sounds like a great idea, a father, a god who will protect us. Yet for those who know mythology, we are aware that throughout time the dark side of the father archetype has functioned like Cronus who ate up his children not wanting them to see the light of day. History (and mythology) repeats itself as our governmental representatives try to stop the light of truth from being born.

After the attack on the United States after 9/11, Christine Todd Whitman, the head of the environmental protection agency under President George Bush, told our first responders that the toxins released at the World Trade Center on 9/11 posed no threat. These heroic firefighters and other support personnel learned the hard way about the deadly effects of a deceitful tale, as they suffered through respiratory diseases and cardiac dysfunction.[31] As time has unfolded, it has been revealed that officials kept potentially disturbing data about health risks from the public (DePalma, 2011).

A breach of the social contract took place. Though citizens of the United States expect a "government of the people" to protect and be guardians of their health, unfortunately the story of such an ideal government turns out to be a fairy tale. The real story is that nine years after the 9/11 tragedy, forces aligned with corporate greed (like the U.S. Chamber of Commerce) conspired to attempt to undermine the Congress passing a bill that would help to pay for these first responders (Fang, 2010). The real story in our political world is oftentimes a balancing of opposites, so in spite of much resistance and filibuster threats from the Republican Far Right, a bill finally passed to help these first responders on December of 2010. The bill was weakened through compromise, as compared to what many compassionate people would have liked to see to more fully support our first responders (Foley, 2010).

Two months after the 9/11 attacks I went down to the World Trade Center site. Even after two months, from breathing the air there, the inside of my nose filled with a black sticky substance. So, I can only imagine what the lungs of those who were there at the time of the World Trade Center collapse, and for the ensuing weeks, must have suffered. How could anyone, let alone a head of our environmental protection agency purportedly not know the dangers of such poor air quality, and not take measures to protect our first responders against its effects?

Mythological themes symbolically represented by archetypes from the world behind the world repeat themselves. Cronus, symbol of the established order, throughout the ages tries to swallow up the truth and hide the light (Zeus) to protect the established order. This is particularly dangerous when it comes to the health of our citizens and environment. As a testament to the fact that detrimental archetypal themes are not necessarily limited to one political party, after the Gulf of Mexico oil spill in April 2010, the Obama administration allowed millions of gallons of the chemical dispersant *Corexit* to be dumped into the ocean. Nice sounding name…but we can just picture a corporate board coming up with a name that says that this chemical will "correct it, Corexit." Unfortunately, the truth is quite the contrary. Professor Gary Rodabaugh, professor of Biology Ferris State University, expresses concerns about dispersants used at source of underwater emission of the oil, on the underwater ecosystem.[32] Likewise, Dr. Riki Ott, a marine toxicologist presents alarming data about the bio-hazard of the dispersant used by BP to cover up the Gulf Oil spill (Ott, 2010).[33]

Many wonder whether the use of this dangerous dispersant entailed collusion on the part of the Obama administration with BP to hide the view of the oil from the cameras of our media. Whoever is responsible for not letting the public know about its toxic effects, whether it is the Obama administration or the corporate controlled media, the scenario reminds the mythologist in us of Cronus' attempt to hide his children from the light. The question is whether "light" symbolized by Zeus in Greek mythology can be born. Zeus was hidden in the Dikteon Cave and tended by the Amalthea, until the time was right to bring Zeus to replace the rule of Saturn. The archetypal principle of Zeus is often mythologically associated with the zodiacal symbol of Sagittarius, the sign of wisdom and storytelling. So, it is perhaps through being circumspect about the stories we are told, that liberation from the mouth of false stores occurs.

Speaking of stories hidden from us, it also did not make it into our media sources that the chemical dispersant, which was used in our Gulf, was banned as dangerous in England (the home nation of BP, British Petroleum). Remember those days when the United States shipped DDT to third world countries because we did not want to endanger our citizens? Are we now reaping that karma, as we provide an economic outlet for countries to dump their dangerous chemicals on our country and make a nice profit on their banned chemicals at the expense of our health (Suckling, 2011). The story of the "exceptionalism of the United States" and it being an entitled empire that can do what it wants in pursuit of colonial aims has been turned 180 degrees around. In metaphysical psychology this is called an *enantiodromia*, a reversion into the opposite. As far back as Heraclitus, it has been recognized that life and the psyche have a tendency to turn into its opposite to create balance.

Any good therapist will tell a person that an enantiodromia serves a purpose. A therapist would ask a narcissistic patient, "Does the same thing happening to you, which you have done to others, activate empathy and change you?" Similarly, when a culture values monetary profits over the health of its citizens, and does not listen to the voice of nature, "Do the ensuing troubled times awaken awareness and a change of heart?

Perhaps in order to change our hearts we need to focus on our bellies. It is said that the way to a man's heart is through his stomach, so let's look at what is going on in the stomach of humanity. We are told the story that a new era is awakening and that corporations will provide food for all through genetic engineering of crops. Beautiful advertising comes on to our TVs, but what is the rest of the story. Is the information that we are receiving biased? In psychotherapy informed consent is paramount; in scholarly research giving information about who is the source of the funding is a requirement.

In this light, it is important to realize that mega-farming interests represented by corporations such as Monsanto have been attempting to control the world's grain supply with their "Roundup ready seeds," and they apparently do not care about destroying biodiversity or small farmers' lives.[34] With a little investigation, one finds disturbing research that questions the healthfulness of genetically modified seeds including research that shows a correlation with organ disruption problems in animals including their reproductive organs; and evidence is accumulating about its negative effects on human health.[35] Jeffrey Smith's book, *Seeds of Deception* (2004), and the Cornocopia Institute's report, *Cereal Crimes,* are two sources for examining evidence about the dangers of GMOs.

In contrast to our FDA, which does not seem to be standing up for the American consumer (in spite of the fact that insufficient evidence exists to prove the safety of genetically modified organisms), other countries and agencies are honoring the precautionary principle. For example, the American Academy of Environmental Medicine has called on all physicians to prescribe diets without genetically modified (GM) foods to all patients, and many European countries are not allowing crops from GMO countries to be imported.[36] Most serious for the American consumer is the fact that we are often not allowed to even see information about which of the foods we eat are genetically modified.[37] It is disturbing that President Obama currently has sided with large corporations by not allowing consumers to have labels on our foods to tell us which of our foods contain GMOs (Philpott, 2011; Flock, 2012).

For a broader, and equally alarming look at the world behind world of our food consumers should see the movie *Food, Inc*, and carefully examine the research on what mega-farming practices are doing to the food we eat (Striffler, 2005; Rosenberg, 2012).[38] When we can not even trust the stories that we are told about our food, you know we are living in troubled times.

Lest we think that it was only in the times of Greek mythology that those who were considered to be threatening to the established order, were hidden in caves (as Zeus was), we only need to look at such issues such as GMOs and the food we eat, and wonder whether light (Zeus) will be borne out of the dark caves on such issues.

David Korten speaks about how stories maintain our worldview in his books, *When Corporations Rule the World* (2001) and *The Great Turning: From Empire to Earth Community* (2007). He argues that we are held captive to the ways of Empire by a cultural trance of our own creation maintained by stories that deny the higher possibilities of our human nature—including our capacities for compassion, cooperation, responsible self-direction, and self-organizing partnership. Korten says that changing our future begins with changing our stories.[39] He advocates for changing our stories by shifting from the Old Economy to the New Economy, and to replace the cultural stories told to us by the propagandists of Empire with cultural stories that affirm values of mutual caring and accountability.

The *New Oxford Dictionary* defines a trance as "a half-conscious state characterized by an absence of response to external stimuli." Trance-states are induced by hypnotherapists for healing (Rossi, 1986); however the powers of imagination may also be used to induce a sleep walk into a detrimental "story, mine-field"—a field that can blow up values of integrity no less than a mine-field blows up a body.

David Korten's books point out how the prevailing prosperity-stories of modern societies celebrate the ability of "free" (read "unregulated") markets to bring unlimited prosperity to all, and yet there is hype, and self-serving greed involved in the agenda of those who tell these at best half-truths.[40]

David Korten's viewpoint is relevant to this book's frame story about of the Old Woman in the Cave whose garment was unraveled. Just as I have talked about stories and practices for times in our lives when an unraveling takes place, in Korten's book, *The Great Turning,* he speaks about "the great unraveling" that is taking place in our culture in multiple spheres of life such as: our relationship to hierarchical control, the empire that the United States has been, our capitalistic values, our environment, and so forth. He says that a "great turning" is taking place as a next step to deal with the unraveling—a new era that will be as much of a revolution as was the past agricultural and industrial revolution. He argues that in place of the elitist, imperialistic agenda of multinational corporations has undermined the American experiment, and that a life-centered, egalitarian, sustainable, democratic "Earth Community" can be born from the current blessed state of unrest.

There are many other authors who are calling for action in the quest to reverse the prevailing story of the unraveling of our lives in the area of the environment. Lester Brown, in his 2009 book *Plan B 3.0,* calls for a wartime mobilization, an all-out response proportionate to the threat that global climate change presents to our future."[41] Sean Esbjorn-Hargens, who wrote the book, *Integral Ecology* (2009), is another author who is at the forefront of the mythic battle to save our environment.

Many of these leaders who call for environmental action focus on the ocean, a perfect symbol for the mother of life. Much of the plastic that each of us throws away every day (from plastic bags, product descriptions, bottle caps, videos, and various products) ends up as part of the plastic gyres in our ocean, some of which, like the Pacific Gyre are as big as the State of Texas. Our plastic has become a toxic waste dump in the ocean where unsuspecting fish and birds eat little bits of our plastic and suffer disastrous effects, sometimes choking them to death.[42]

Specific stories about some of our fellow creatures perhaps do the best to awake our sensibilities. For example, Albatross on Midway Island go and travel to get food for their young. Eons of years have taught them to go and eat what is on the surface of the ocean to bring back food for their chicks. Since they have not been prepared for the plastic that is now on the surface of the ocean they eat it, and then fly back to Midway. When they feed their young their regurgitated products, their young die from the bottle caps, plastic cigarette lighters, and other forms of plastic.[43]

What can we all do stop such atrocities committed against our fellow creatures and environment? In our culture, many people have been hypnotized into a worldview that says, "The bountiful earth is there for us to use, or abuse." Luckily there is now another story that is emerging. We all are fellow creatures of the earth in collective partnership." What we do to another (not just another human being), we do to ourselves." The ancient practice of "outward introspection" teaches us that everything outside is a symbol for a part of ourselves. We are the Albatross' children who, like those chicks, suffer the effects of plastic pollution.

Albatrosses have been described as "the most legendary of all birds.[44] An albatross is a central emblem in *The Rime of the Ancient Mariner* by Samuel Taylor Coleridge. It is from the Coleridge poem that the usage of the albatross as a metaphor is derived. Someone with a burden or obstacle is said to have "an albatross around their neck"—the punishment given in the poem to the mariner who killed the albatross. In part, due to the poem, there is a widespread myth that sailors believe it disastrous to shoot or harm an albatross. Can those of us (hopefully more and more of us) whose hearts are moved by stories, actually change our ways? As a small gesture in the this direction, I do my best not to buy plastic bottles of water since I heard this story; and I am doing my best to recycle the remaining plastic bags I have by using the same ones each time I go to the grocery store.

The Predatory Birds That Control Our Lives

While I was writing this section of the book synchronicity was once again alive. I turned on my TV where I saw the B.B.C. documentary called *Life,* which told the story of a water bird called the Frigate. This predator does not have the ability to catch fish on its own. Its feathers have no oil to protect them from the waters of the sea. So they steal from other fish like the Tropicbirds who fly back with the fish they have caught, grabbing the skillfully caught fish that the tropical birds are bringing back to their young. This documentary shows vivid, poignant pictures of these Frigates attacking Tropicbirds on their way back to their young. These Tropicbirds store their catch in their throats, so the Frigates attack their throats unmercifully. The Tropicbirds have found a solution to these "vultures of the sea." They drop the food they want to give to their young back into the ocean. Then the Frigates leave them alive and pick the dead fish off of the surface of the sea without having done the work to capture their daily food.

Metaphors speak well. We have created a culture of vulturing Frigates...our multinational corporations. They steal the food from the working class of America. Politicians who give tax incentives and bend laws in their favor reward them; and due to the current laws of the game (including sadly, our Supreme Court in the January 2010 "Citizens United vs. Federal Election Commission" case) many of our politicians are "owned by" these corporations. This Supreme Court decision now legitimizes the donations of unlimited and undisclosed money to our campaigns by domestic and even foreign corporations, thereby to buy off our politicians without our knowing who is behind the theft (Linkins, 2010).

Now, these bought politicians can revolve back and forth into and out of corporations and regulatory agencies, serving corporate rather than public interests. This process, known as "regulatory capture," involves a federal or state regulatory or other government agency becoming too cozy with those it is charged to oversee.[45] This is, in all probability, one of the main reasons that the Gulf Oil spill happened—due to the collusion between our government's Mineral and Mining Services and various oil companies. Regulatory capture is also happening in many other industries including telecommunications (Rosen & Kushnick, 2011) and with various commodities (Taiibi, 2011c).[46]

In the mythological movie *The Golden Compass* (directed by Chris Weitz) a mythic tale is told of how young children become soulless when they lose connection with their daemon (animal spirit ally). The characters in the movie become evil when they have an evil demon ruling them. Returning to our story, metaphorically speaking, it seems that modern environmental polluters have as their kindred spirits the Frigate birds, who have made many corporate executives, and their cohorts in our government, lose their moral compass. The heart is a human being's moral compass and when the ruling powers of a culture demagnetize and misalign this compass with respect to its institutions, students, and healers…danger looms on the horizon.

War against Students

Following our mythopoetic thread, the "Black Dogs of Predatory Capitalism," have unraveled our students lives. In 2010, the amount of money owed in student loans was greater than the amount owed in all credit card debt, and in 2012 it is likely to top a trillion dollars a year. This is at a time when only 56 percent of graduates were able to find work (Lewin, 2011; Tokarska, 2011). One of the students who I know that graduated with a Master's degree in counseling with over 100,000 dollars of debt put it this way, "I feel like my graduate education put me into indentured servitude for the next two decades."

Contrast our current graduating American students to those in many European countries where free, or relatively inexpensive education, is provided to students…as it used to be in our United States (Bakalian & Maneghello, 2010). When a culture does not support the education of its students, and looks at them as a commodity to exploit, you know we are in troubled times.

One job of the Reluctant Metaphysician is to look at the story behind the story, and to frame the back-story with the power of mythic and symbolic terms. How could our country lose its moral compass in this way? In 2005, Congress modified the bankruptcy code to make it hard to get rid of private student loans. This one of the factors that made it "good business" to feed off the young. To our society's detriment however, a situation has been created that Rebuilding the Dream founder, Van Jones describes metaphorically as, "Kids are graduating school and walking off a cliff."[47] Tragically, suicides have resulted (Johannsen, 2012).

Graduating Student Healers

> *A certain kind of courage is required to follow what truly calls to us;*
> *why else would so many choose to live*
> *within false certainties and pretensions of security?*
> *The truth is that most prefer the safer paths in life*
> *even if they know that their souls are called in another way.*
> *Failing to answer the call means living an unexplored life*
> *and likely means dying without having fully lived.*

—Michael Meade
from *Fate and Destiny*

The future healers of the psyche, graduating mental health professionals, are coming out of school with major debt. These students, who choose a life of service to those in need of psychological healing are living a life that foregoes security in order to follow a path that calls to them. Thus, it is particularly disturbing to me that these students, who have the courage to pursue their calling, are treated by our American culture like the Frigates treat Tropicbirds. I personally know three graduate psychology students of schools where I have taught who have between $100, 000 and $180,000 in debt from their doctoral education; and these are not unusual stories, nor are they extravagant spenders.

The corporate Frigates have conspired to find ways to suck the financial capital out of their lives like vultures breaking eggs and eating the flesh of the young before they have hatched. As one example of an advocate for the "corporate Frigates," the Republican speaker of the House in 2011, John Boehner, "received hundreds of thousands of dollars from for-profit colleges and the private-student-loan industry—and then he sponsored laws that restricted the Department of Education from making less expensive government loans available to students. Then, in a culture where bribery, corruption, and influence peddling are the norm, he unabashedly pushed for federal subsidies for private colleges and trade schools" (Taibbi, 2010, p. 2). It is tragic that our governmental representatives are colluding with those forces that are ripping the American Dream out of the hands of our youth.

Many of these student healers do not realize various real dimensions of the career path into which they are entering. These are some of the upcoming shamans of our modern culture. Yet the wider world into which they are being born does not treat them with due respect. As we have discussed, the macro-environment nowadays consists of overly burdensome student loans, and the parallels of illusory trickle down economics in their teaching careers as well as in their lives as therapists who become part of corporate managed care panels. In addition, the number of hours of internship required in California creates severe economic hardship for these students. So, in addition to the weight of excess debt, they are required to do 1500 hours pre-doc and 1500 post-doc hours. Marketplace dynamics often necessitate students to work in low fee clinics where these student interns work for free or barely make more than it takes to live a life of poverty. How many talented young therapists are we losing to "larceny on the high seas?"

It is well known that medical doctors' characters are damaged by their abusive residency years; it is relatively unknown that psychotherapists suffer their own journey into cultural and systemic abuse from the "War on Healers." President Obama and others suggest that these interns should be allowed to work off their debt by working in an impoverished area for a few years. However, a sufficient compassionate cultural model has not yet been activated to deal with the predatory Frigates of our culture.

Many of the most successful of these students will write books to contribute new understanding and healing methods to our culture. Since internet sales have captured much of the market, and big corporations have forced smaller community oriented bookstores into bankruptcy, some of these students will be selling the books they write in online formats. One of my friends owned one of the best community bookstores (Gaia Books) in Berkeley, which served authors and the community for many years. When the Internet Era began they, and other bookstores, were forced out of business.

When I coach young authors I let them know about the various publishing avenues with which I have experience. There are many advantages nowadays with self-publishing through print-on-demand, where authors can print a small quantity of their own books and then sell them on their own website or through various online venues. Printing a small number of books lowers the expense of inventory; however by printing a larger quantity of the book with offset printing the price per book is lowered. The advantage of selling it through online venues is that a book can get higher exposure and a greater number of sales. However, many are not aware of the costs of doing business with some online vendors; they can take a large percentage, such as fifty-five, of every sale. After printing, shipping and handling costs, and advertising costs are entered into the equation often the profit margin is low unless many books are sold.

If instead these students go to a publishing company to get a book published, nowadays most publishing companies do not give advances other than to the best-known, highest selling authors. Also, regarding author royalties, a very small percentage is given to the author. The bookstore, printer, and publishing company usually make more than does the author. By the time accounting procedures such as percentage of net rather than gross, reserve against returns, and discounts are subtracted from authors' royalties, many young authors feel that they have been "skinned alive," or to continue with the Frigate metaphor the students feel that the little fish that they want to take home to feed their families have been ripped out of their throats by the publishing industry. By the way, publishing companies are also subjected to "Frigates that rip at their throats," which makes it difficult for them to make profits in this era of internet sales.

When these students start rising to the top of their profession and speak at conferences they learn that only the very top tier of presenters is paid. The metaphysician is always on the lookout to see how parallels happen between one level of reality and another, so we cannot help but reluctantly notice that there are some similarities between the cultural macrocosm that has large wage discrepancies between upper management and lower workers, as was pointed out regarding the ratio between workers and CEOs (Mishel, 2006).

At spiritual and psychological conferences most of the presenters are expected to pay their own way for plane fare, hotel, and even conference fees. The storyline is that this is what is needed to do in order to get one's work known; and there is some truth in the "investment line" story of self-sacrifice. At times the conferences themselves are not making sufficient profit to be able to pay presenters, so the comparison between large corporations not adequately compensating workers breaks down here. No problem then exists in not compensating conference presenters. However, when some presenters suggest to some profit making conferences that a shared profit model should be created (so that a win-win atmosphere be created) a kind, but uncomfortable smile often appears on the face of the conference organizers. At times, conference organizers have said, "Don't you know that we live off of this money, and this is the presenter's contribution to our organization?" When presenters reply that everyone could do better if everyone was part of creating an economically viable model, the subject is often changed.

I look forward to those days when economically practical visionaries, and the overarching economic power-holders above, are able to find practical solutions to the economic hardships of the young healers of our culture. The Reluctant Metaphysician's "job" is to transform culturally induced powerlessness into effective actions, and to find attitudes and meanings to transform victimhood into empowerment. So, for example, I encourage people to buy an author's book through the author's website rather than from corporate chains. Likewise, there is a movement toward various e-book formats that may hold promise for young authors. Time will tell how authors will fare on the new high seas.

On the pathway from victimhood to empowerment, in the courses I have taught over the decades, many graduate psychology students have been helped through framing their journey as an initiatory experience. Like the Sun Dance ritual of hanging by a pole with an eagle talon pulling on their heart strings, these students have looked into various of the metaphysical practices I have suggested in this book to deal with their pain about the issues involved in the economics of their career choice.

A distinction can be made here between "a spiritual approach" versus the path of the Reluctant Metaphysician. In Native American culture there is the spiritual practice of "the give-away." Unlike in our culture, where the amount of money that is accumulated is the measure of one's worth, in the Native American culture the measure of ones value is how much one gives away. This heart-centered spiritual philosophy is a way of being from which we can all learn. The spiritual path is one valued pathway in the land of the metaphysician.

If we use the astrological mandala as a centering tool, we might say that "the spiritual path" is symbolized by the symbol of Pisces, a mutable water sign which represents the act of giving and not holding on…like the great sea. The metaphysical view brings in the whole astrological mandala, including the spiritual component. Thus, the metaphysician takes a circumspect view of all facets of the mandala, including economics (the Earth element), because economics are symbols of principles—fairness, practicality, and so forth.

The Reluctant Metaphysician stands in the mythic center of the astrological wheel and chooses actions in each situation based upon the archetypal story that seems most dharmically fruitful. At times, earthy political stances will be appropriate, fiery actions may be most suitable for fire types, or poetic images may be the tool for the air type of person.

The Reluctant Metaphysician who practices the internal martial arts may practice Standing Meditation postures while imagining holding the ball of possibilities in front of his or her heart like a yin/yang symbol. Practicing with a half smile on the face while holding the ball expresses the balancing of opposites and says, "I can be giving like the Native American in me who gives away to the book industry, the universities, and to the corporations that skim off the economic cream from the work I do, as I fulfill my dharma. I do this with love and gratitude for the gift of giving; yet at the same time I reluctantly am aware that an exploitive economic game is being played." Holding the Golden Ball of the Heart posture, while imagining holding this yin/yang ball, allows opposites to be reconciled. Dealing with such negative forces provides an opportunity to do our practice, and perhaps find a way to ward off the dark forces of life by the radiant light of the Golden Ball and the Golden Flowering—not just as an idea, but as a felt experience.

By transposing feelings into images, and traumas into stories, some Reluctant Metaphysicians transform their suffering into teaching tales. Or, we find the powers of the zodiacal wheel of possibilities latent in each of us that can deal with dire circumstances. When some of these students have been in psychotherapy sessions with me, the pathways opened by the teaching stories in this book have been helpful to them. For example, one woman patient (who I agreed to see pro-bono), was homeless in her first year after graduating with her doctoral degree. The tale of the Old Woman in the Cave helped her to see that her life was becoming unraveled by the Black Dogs of predatory capitalism. Listening to this tale she turned her resentment into the stance of equanimity; she was so moved by the homeless people she met while homeless that she ended up doing some counseling for a local homeless shelter.

The Solution: Listening to Stories with Our Hearts

While writing this section of the book I saw a program called *Global Medical Relief Fund: One Child at a Time*. This moving story on *60 Minutes* told the story of Elissa Montani a woman in Staten Island who devotes herself to injured children. One story told was of a child, Wa'ad from Iraq, who was kicking a bottle, which had a bomb in it that shattered his face, tore out his eye, and took away his right arm and left leg. This *60 Minutes* story showed the surgeries and progress made by Wa'ad—thanks to Elissa being moved by his story.

It is wisely said, "An enemy is a person whose story we have not heard." When people go to war rather than finding alternative means of conflict resolution, dire consequences ensue. For example, the effects of war has produced land mines which have crippled many children and many, including the late Princess Diana, have sought to find ways to contribute to healing their horrid effects. If we have ears that truly listen, and hearts that feel, and if we each take action in our unique ways—hope remains.

When it comes to our Earth's environment, the effects of war, the results of predatory capitalists on our economy, and the way we treat the healers of our culture, many, including myself, believe that this is a place for Reluctant Metaphysicians to take a stance.

CHAPTER 22:

Pelican Sinks Its Qi:
A Calling from Nature to Us Humans

A human being is a part of the whole called by us, "the universe,"
a part limited in time and space.
He experiences himself, his thoughts and feelings,
as something separate from the rest—
a kind of optical delusion of consciousness.
This delusion is a kind of prison for us,
restricting us to our personal desires and affection
for a few persons nearest to us.
Our task must be to free ourselves from this prison
by widening the circle of understanding and compassion
to embrace all living creatures
and the whole of nature and its beauty.

—Albert Einstein

A Message from the Wildlife at Esalen Institute

Earlier I told you about my powerful dream after being in an Esalen hot tub on a full moon night in the mid 1970s. During the following years, many times after I published a book or wrote an article that contributed to the human growth and potential movement, I contacted Esalen (without telling them about my dream) to see if I could teach there.

Finally in 2005 after having published three books I was accepted to teach a class there. Then I told the program directors about my dream of Four Shaman, and the role that Esalen played in my destiny. They asked why I had never told them of this dream before in the years when I had applied to teach there. I said I felt that would have been using a sacred visionary experience as a crowbar to pry my way into the door of a temple. It did not seem to be fitting.

I am happy to say that I have taught many workshops at Esalen ever since 2005: a seven day workshop on Bodymind Healing in Psychotherapy, many five-day workshops in Bodymind Healing Qigong, and a weekend workshop in Tai Chi Chuan: Four Dimensions of Purpose. It has been a humbling and awesome experience to be teaching in the same rooms as did the heroes that drew me on my Journey to the West. The first room where I taught at Esalen was named "Huxley," after Aldous who led me to explore the deeper dimensions of the psychedelic revolution and the Perennial Philosophy. The next room I taught in was called "Maslow," named after Abraham Maslow, the writer who was one of the authors who most influenced Humanistic psychology and the school where I received my doctoral degree.

In January of 2010 I was invited to do another workshop at Esalen. I dropped off my books in the Esalen bookstore as I had done each year that I had taught there. Then, I got back into my car and drove back up the hill by the Esalen entry gate to get to my room on the other side of the river near the Big House. Same old ritual...But this time in the middle of the road right in front of my car was a giant pelican, at least waist high to an average human being. Just like the many people who were taking photos, I stopped my car in amazement of this Being, magnificent in its splendor. I was about ten feet away from it, jolted out of my complacency. After a while, I needed to get to my room and communicated my human need to it by moving my car forward a foot.

Figure 28: Pelicans Sinks Its Qi

The pelican jumped onto the hood of my Honda in an awesome gesture of primordial power with its enormous wings outstretched. Many of the bystanders kept taking photos, jolted out of their complacency. After a few minutes of awe, I once again remembered that I needed to get to my room. The pelican was not moving. So, I decided to give it a little nudge to get off my car hood by rolling my car back a foot and pressing on the brake. The pelican didn't move; it was as if it was stuck to the car hood.

Synchronistically, I was on my way to teach my workshop on Tai Chi Chuan: Four Dimensions of Purpose. I was about to transmit to the students an initiatory practice of how to sink one's qi so that the practitioner is so rooted that he or she cannot easily be pushed over or moved by someone much heavier. This is part of the "Earth Initiation" of Tai Chi Chuan pushing hands practice. It is called *sili,* or testing the qi. One of the best ways to learn this practice, I was about to tell my students in the upcoming workshop, was to learn the secret Tai Chi practices of Standing Meditation Qigong. Also, I was about to tell my students that Tai Chi stems from shamanic practices of the animal forms of Qigong.

Hua Tau, a first century Chinese medical doctor and teacher of the animal forms of Qigong, taught the bird form of Qigong which initiated a practitioner into how to sink one's qi and stand on one leg in a rooted manner to develop leg strength, to cultivate lightness of heart, and to become rooted in the earth so that he or she is not "a pushover." However, if I had any illusions of thinking that I was "the teacher" of this practice of "sinking the Qi," the pelican was about to teach me about my limitations.

I needed to get on to my room to unpack, and I really wanted the pelican to move. So, I let the car roll down the hill even further this time, about four feet or so, and I really hit the brake. The pelican did not move. I couldn't imagine the "sinking the qi abilities" that would be necessary to perform such a feat. Finally, when the pelican was good and ready after my next feeble human attempt to dislodge it, this amazing bird Qigong master jumped onto the roof of my car, stayed there for a while, and then jumped back onto the road, landing behind my car.

One message from the bird to me was to be humble about my knowledge of what I thought I knew about the Animal Frolics of Qigong. However, as Carl Jung said, a symbol is expansive in nature and has no one fixed meaning. A general symbolic meaning of the pelican is the "universal giving Great Mother." When food supplies are low the pelican is reported to bite its own chest with its beak and feed its young with its flesh and blood. But, the general symbolic meaning of anything takes on its unique meaning by the way our own life experience fills it out. It is this unique meaning that helps us to expand our personal horizons and be in touch with the wider whole of which we are a part.

My teaching assistant, Elizabeth McAnally, was in the seat next to me during "the pelican visitation." We were not aware that on that very night one of her best friends, Kelleen Nicholson, who lived a few miles north of Esalen in the Bay Area, was to die. The sea took her friend's life in a tragic drowning accident. After Elizabeth got back home to the Bay Area, and found out about her friend's death, she reflected on the pelican experience that we had, and she connected the visitation from the pelican spirit with Kelleen, one of the most giving people she knew. It gave her solace when she read a passage by Ralph Waldo Emerson called "The Present Age." Here it is:

As the wandering seabird which crossing the ocean
lights on some rock or islet to rest for a moment its wings,
and to look back on the wilderness of waves behind,
and onward to the wilderness of waters before,
so stand we perched on this rock or shoal of time,
arrived out of the immensity of the past
and bound and road ready to plunge into immensity again.

So apropos. This poem became a way for Elizabeth and I to discuss how all our lives are like a temporary moment of rest on an islet (or on a car with a 4 Shaman license plate), coming from the ocean of love of the universe and flying back there. And the pelican is a symbol for keeping an open, giving heart through the process.

All of my cars for the last decades have had a 4 Shaman license plate to keep fresh in my memory the calling of that dream I had in the early 1970s when I first visited Esalen. In that dream, which I told you about earlier, I was a Native American shaman whose destiny was to bring knowledge of the surrounding tribes back to Esalen. I told you about how I had a sense at that time that the dream meant that my life's journey had some part to play along with at least three others, to bring knowledge of other traditions back to Esalen.[1]

At Esalen I have met many workshop leaders and incredible students who I believe are the other shaman of my visionary dream. The mystical foursome is a symbol that represents wholeness, whether it is four points of the square, four crows at the time of a significant death, or four people Standing together in the cave of Delphi. Maybe you fellow metaphysicians are one of these four shaman, circling back to Esalen to the place where the various waters of life join. Maybe you are about to bring back to the symbolic center of a world the treasures of your journey to a culture so in need of it?

Can we Hear the Call of Nature and Our Animal Brethren?

I care not for a man's religion
whose dog and cat are not the better for it.

—Abraham Lincoln

What this pelican taught me at this time at Esalen Institute was that the fourth shaman of my dream might be the elements of nature itself—the magical forces that are speaking to us from this special place on the planet where East meets West, and where three types of water join. Perhaps the ocean symbolizes the wisdom of the larger sea of knowledge to which we open when we are at Esalen; the river symbolizes each of our individual lives and how they merge with the sea of all Being; and the sulfur hot springs are the place where we can experience a *dissolutio* into the wider whole of which we are a part—whether we call this dissolving by its the Taoist term, *Wuji,* or use the Kabalistic name, *ain soph.* Most importantly it seems that each of us needs to find the unique meanings that speak to us from nature's wild-life, and from the wild life around us everywhere, as we resacralize the cosmos. Listening to Nature's voice can direct us and redirect us on the path of our life journeys, helping us to find how our individual lives can contribute to the wider whole of which we are a part.

While I was at Esalen during the year of this pelican visitation, some old timers spoke to me about how it was very rare for pelicans to fly inland and land on the grounds of Esalen. When I got back to my home in the Bay Area, I saw an article in the *S.F. Chronicle* that said that pelicans had recently been seen flying and landing inland, eating worms and other atypical substances.[2] It is still a matter of speculation as to why. Some say that it was because their normal food in the ocean was becoming toxic; others say that it was because of global climate change. I do not know if the giant pelican that landed on my Honda with the "4 Shaman" license plate was trying to communicate and get noticed by us humans; maybe it was trying to convey a cross-species message to ask us rectify an environmental danger to them.

I hope that my other fellow shamanic journeyers will explore this further…and that each of us will explore the meanings of Esalen's, and our world's, wildlife where bleeding messages are sent to those of us who listen and can open our sentient senses to receive them.

Figure 29: Brown Pelican's Pain Communicates Its Story to Humanity

Brown Pelican is seen on the beach at East Grand Terre Island along the Louisiana coast on Thursday, June 3, 2010. (AP Photo/Charlie Riedel)

It seems synchronistic to me that just a few months later there was a major oil spill in the gulf of Louisiana. One of the birds that was most discussed and shown on the news was a brown pelican who was just in the process of hatching its young in the waters off the Louisiana coast. I heard various ornithologists on the news say that this was the worst possible time for such an oil spill to occur, because this is was the beginning of the breeding season of the brown pelicans. How tragic must things get in order for our human culture to open our ears and listen? If we were a biblical culture we would see plagues being given by God to get us to rise up and correct the ways that the corporate Pharaoh is enslaving us in our era. How much clearer could it be than to see damage that our human culture has perpetrated upon the very symbol of the Great Mother, the pelican who feeds its young from the flesh of its loving heart?[3]

Figure 30: A bird covered in oil flails in the surf at East Grand Terre Island along the Louisiana coast Thursday Jun 3, 2010 (AP Photo Charlie Riedel).

If our culture still knew how to learn from the symbolic messages contained in the inner and outer stories of our lives, instead of worshiping the gods of Reason and Greed, we would be uncontrollably crying or taking effective, political, and judicious action to stop future environmental slaughter of pelicans and their hatchlings. If we viewed the Earth's story as a family of species and treated the life forms of the Gulf as members of our family we would be behaving differently as a species. Black slaves and women have been given voting rights; many argue that the species of the Earth as well should have voting rights (Kelly, 2010).

Figure 31: A Brown Pelican is mired in heavy oil on the beach at East Grand Terre Island along the Louisiana coast on Thursday, June 3, 2010 (AP Photo Charlie Riedel).

Consciousness and judicial action are called for. And no, I do not mean the kind of judicial action that was taken after Exxon after the Exxon Valdez destroyed the coastline, animals, and people's lives in Alaska. Now twenty years later there are still environmental toxins, loss of livelihood, and physical and mental health effects of the spill. Exxon promised the people of Cordova that they would be made whole, and yet for two decades they fought a battle with the people who were harmed. Eventually our supreme court disturbingly allowed a reduction of fines originally awarded, and the appeal process took twenty years to compensate people for the disaster.[4]

Though corporations are inherently self-serving, they are not inherently destructive of the common good. Like any other entity they need to be regulated. Regulation is symbolized by the archetype of Saturn, which brings limits; and innovation is symbolized by Uranus, which brings an incentivizing and activating of the hero myth. Both are worthy attributes. From a metaphysical perspective, when the wheel of archetypal principles (as symbolized by the astrological zodiac) is out of balance, then troubled times occur. The big picture is that until the 1880s corporations were examined every few years: if they were not serving the public interest they were given death sentences, i.e. their corporate charter would be rescinded and their profits went back into the commons (Hartmann, 2007, 2010). Unfortunately due to the current state of deregulated capitalism this is no longer the case. Corporations often feel entitled to make any profits they can make with no care about the societal consequences of their actions. "We've come a long way baby," as the old saying goes; unfortunately we are still babes in the woods as we deal with the lack of regulations against the forces of corruption that are destroying our American culture and environment. The wheel of life needs to be brought back into balance.

The Solution Lies in Consciousness and the Awareness of Story

Just as my Esalen dream in the mid 1970s spoke of coming full circle, this story of my experience with the pelican brought me full circle. During those years my quest was based on the belief that the answer to the Earth's problems was in consciousness itself. Though at many times I have felt guilty that I did not follow the path of being an environmental lawyer to use my given talents to fight the forces that allow corporations to act wantonly against the environment and people's health, another path has been mine. Though one can always lament "the road not traveled," it is now clearer than ever that it is the light of consciousness that is my contribution to make, along with many others from "my temple." Over the years it has become more and more clear that it is one type of consciousness that produces the destructive forces of greed that separates one person from another's suffering; and it is another type of consciousness that creates the energy and forces that help to make any age, any culture, including ours, to bloom like a golden, generous, radiant flower.

From a holistic perspective it is important to have an openness to hearing all sides of a story: the real story of the corporate executive, the victim of the corporate executives' actions, and the story of the bleeding heart of the pelican that comes to us in images not just words. Real listening to stories not only changes a child's world, it could save our adult world and the planet we inhabit. When we look at the mass extinctions that are currently happening,[5] perhaps one of our purposes as humans is to give voice to our fellow creatures and give them their due place under the sun.

Remember the Truth and Reconciliation Commission in South Africa after years of Apartheid? A pivotal moment in world history would be having such a commission where corporate executives had to own the truth of their "apartheid regime," which separated them from earth-friendly values. The governmental officials that colluded with them to co-create this state of affairs could stand side-by side with their corporate partners explaining their "crimes against humanity." Many psychologists and organizational consultants (some from the organizational development tracks at various psychology programs around the country such as Saybrook University) are now working with those corporate executives and governmental officials and are exploring with them on how they can balance environmental concerns with the profit motive.

As well, a psychologist or organizational consultant in an ideal metaphysically inclined world would help open-minded corporate executives to examine the inner world behind their desire for so much excess profit that it is at the expense of their workers and society. Is it an obsessive-compulsive disorder based in similar dynamics as the "hypertensive executive" case illustration that I discussed earlier? Each individual in time may realize that life's purpose is to be on a path of being true to his or her own Self (purposely spelled with a capital "S," since the Self, in the Jungian metaphysical sense of the word involves the axis that connects individual needs with the wider whole of which they are a part.)

I am grateful that I have had students and patients who have had positions of political power and are in the process of being able to influence our culture in ways that I cannot as a psychologist and Qigong teacher. One was a manager of grocery chain store where my discussions with him about the dangerousness of pesticides and the inadequacies in food labeling have influenced policies in his stores. Likewise my discussions with researchers in the pharmaceutical industry have influenced one or more researchers to be more aware of the detrimental side of effects of pharmaceuticals.

Pelican Practices and Cross-Cultural Stories: A Saving Grace for Our World

What are practices and stories that can help to change our world? It is interesting that a movement that I had been practicing for many years, which I call "Pelican Shares Its Qi with the World," involves imagining that you are a pelican sharing your heart with the world. You can tap on your heart or lung with fingers closed and then outstretch the hands and give; or you can focus on receiving from the world. This is a pelican blessing that anyone so inclined can do as they "shape-shift" into a pelican giving their gift to life, or appreciating what is received from life. This is a powerful practice to do each morning after doing some Standing Meditation to begin our day by coming into alignment with our life's purpose and what we have to offer the world.

Figure 32: Pelican Shares its Qi with the World

Speaking of birds, there is an old story in the East that Vishnu the God of creation every night takes flight as a wild gander. As it flies away into night it takes the breath away, then breathes the world back into existence.[6] Turning this into a mediation practice, we can imagine as we exhale that the metaphysical part of ourselves is taken away on a journey to reconnect ourselves with its divine source, as we inhale a new world comes into existence.

Metaphysics teaches that symbols amplify energy. This is a basic axiom and insight of Jungian psychology and of all those who understand symbolic processes. Stories generate energy as well, even more so, since they are composed of many symbols. In terms of creating change in feelings and creating the impetus to action, symbols and stories are change agents. Just as stories, dreams, and symbols can add actual energy to amplifying the messages of what each of us needs to do on our life's path, so can symbolic vehicles drive humanity to a better place.

Can we hear the pelican's call, the bleeding heart of nature, screaming, crying out its story to us asking us to take action for our fellow creatures and our planet? A hope for humanity during troubled times lies in listening to the pelican's call to each of our individual lives. We are each called to be true to our individual purpose, or as Shakespeare put it, "This above all to thine own Self be true." In doing so, we become part of the moving spokes of the wheel of life.

There are many symbols and stories that can evoke the needed "metaphysical energy" that is needed to turn the wheels of our world by using mythic wisdom. We began this book with the story of Icanchu. He played a drum out of a piece of charcoal made from a devastated world turned to ashes. We can each take inspiration from this story as we find the tune of our inner drummer. Each of us is called to find the rhythm of our unique story to aid in drumming into existence the vibratory frequency of a new world during these difficult times? Will we say that it is too difficult, or say in fear this path will create our being unable to make a lucrative living? Facetiously, I would suggest taking the first letters of Icanchu's name and chant, "I Can." Or, if you want to chant his whole name you say sing, "I can chew, " while meditating on how, "I can chew up the hard things in life, transform them in ways that nourish my spiritual journey; and like the birds who transmute substances to feed their young, so can I feed the world by keeping in mind the youth who will live seven generations from now."

Or, we can follow the way of the Pelican who Sinks Its Qi; and by using the methods from our old teachings such as *The Secret of the Golden Flower* (which teaches how to use the breath of the microcosmic orbit to sink our qi) we each can find our life stance. Can you hear the pelican's call? What is it saying to you about how to give a piece of your heart to the world? Can you find your stance so that the technological forces of life will not uproot you?

What are the stories to which BP corporate executives listen?[7] What mantras are they chanting such as, "Profits are my calling. We each need to take care of our own self-interest. Greed is good?" The threads of these fabricated hypnotic inductions lead back to bought-off, corporate storytellers that are economically motivated for the few; they are not the sacred weavings of initiatory tales that advocate for a balanced perspective that honors "the precautionary principle (Andorno, 2004)," natural life, and the wider whole of which we are a part?

The Reluctant Metaphysician looks for opportunities to illuminate the world behind the world of our environment and our political environment. For example, the Governor of Wisconsin Scott Walker wanted to pass a bill that would destroy the ability of public employees to have collective bargaining rights, and also as a part of this bill, publicly owned utilities could be sold to his large campaign donors such as the Koch brothers. When the *Buffalo Beast* editor-in-chief, Ian Murphy, heard that one intent behind the bill was to pass on lucrative utility contracts to the billionaire Koch brothers, he called up the Governor and pretended to be one of the Koch brothers. This prank enabled Murphy to get vital information about the behind the scenes favors that are given to wealthy donors, and he received national news coverage that exposed how such collusion subverts the interests of the wider public (Linkins, 2011).

Like Icanchu, during a time that the world was destroyed, threw rocks at the branches of the tree of life to let new seeds drop to the ground, so did Murphy use the trickster archetype to throw rocks at destructive branches of government. The hope is that actions like these will bring down to earth new public awareness that hopefully will allow the seeds of new policies to grow that better serve the public good.

Each of us can find our way to contribute to rebirthing the world during troubled times. Tapping on the archetype of the trickster can also be found in the street theater that was done by activists in New York and Baltimore. Their rally was called "Suckers for Suckers," and they passed out lollipops in front of the Bank of America to protest how ordinary citizens pay taxes. They were protesting an unbalanced tax code that allows the Bank of America and many major corporations to avoid paying billions in taxes by stashing huge amounts of profits in offshore tax havens (Shen, 2011). Like Icanchu, Ian Murphy, and the Bank of America protesters, each of us can find our inner drummer during difficult times to create change in the world.

The story of the balance needed between human being's use of nature for survival and the detrimental destruction of nature is the survival tale of humanity's evolution. It is the story of how we have survived, and the story which if not mastered will lead to our demise. Throughout our history, Human Beings pushed back nature to make room for buildings, burned its forests for heat, and diverted its rivers courses for water projects. These activities have given us shelter, warmth, and energy; and we would not want to be without these gifts. However, animals, which also use elements of nature for their survival, do not unnecessarily destroy their habitat. The Native Americans have a name to describe the phenomenon of human beings' destruction of their environment and perhaps the Earth itself—it's called "Wetico Psychosis" (Forbes, 1992).[8] As a psychologist I must say that more focus should be put on the psychological disorders of society. These psychological maladies are a danger to our species not just our individual lives.

After all, the story of the destruction of nature has been there as a teaching story to humanity from our civilization's very first tale. In the *Epic of Gilgamesh,* the oldest tale of our civilization, one of the sub-themes involves the killing of the giant guardian of the forest, Humbaba. After that, Enkido (Gilgamesh's friend) felled the cedars of Lebanon all the way down to their roots as far as the banks of the river Euphrates; and they subsequently killed the Bull of Heaven. (The Bull is symbolic of the astrological sign, Taurus the zodiacal symbol of nature.) One historical interpretation of the tale of Gilgamesh is that an ecological disaster happened, in the form of the subsequent flood, due to unsustainable agricultural practices used in building one of the first human cities, Urek. Could Enkido's resultant punishment and sentence of death by the offended God Enlil be an ecological warning about the problems that arise when our instinctual selves (symbolized by Enkido) operate without due respect for nature? Some scholars think so, and that environmental catastrophes often happen thereby (Lucas, 2004; Pointing, 2007; Hoepper, 2011).

There are those that are part of the ecological consciousness movement today that are putting this awareness into practice. For example, environmental filmmaker and ecological field researcher, John Liu, was part of a project to restore the ecological destruction of the enormous Loess Plateau in Northern China, the home of the Han Chinese culture. He was one of the keynote speakers at the annual 2011 Bioneeers Conference where the audience saw his film, *The Lessons of the Loess Plateau.* The film shows how sustainable agricultural practices could rehabilitate the ecosystem functions that were the result of many years of unsustainable agricultural practices. From John Liu's and the Reluctant Metaphysician's perspective on storytelling, much of the environmental degradation that the world ecosystems are suffering is based upon the false story of our age—that production and consumption are the most important things in life (Liu, 2009).

At the 2011 Bioneers Conference, Karen Brown, creative director of the Center for Ecoliteracy, gave a plenary address about various school programs around the country where school children are learning sustainable agriculture and solar energy practices not only theoretically, but by growing organic food with solar energy right on their school grounds. The Smart by Nature program is part of the new Green Schooling Movement, which is revolutionizing K–12 education with sustainability in mind.

Normally in our culture, particularly if we watch mainstream television, the suffering of everyday life is front and center—"If it bleeds, it leads." The Reluctant Metaphysician looks to the world behind the world to uncover and transform the forms of consciousness that create the dark side of life.

At a recent Bioneers conference, the environmentalist and entrepreneur Paul Hawken (2007) put up a film on the screen. It was a list of names of organizations who are doing inventive things all around the world: with trees, fisheries, rivers, different modalities of communities and economic systems, materials that do not use up scarce resources, the harnessing sea waves to escape from oil dependency, and endless other things. Hawken said that he could let this film roll for weeks and there would be thousands and thousands of names working on what is happening beneath the surface of society. Similarly, other inspiringly good work done by grassroots environmentalists all over the world can be found at the Goldman Environmental Prize website (wwwgoldmanprize.org).

I began this book, and my "quest to the West" talking about how I believed that consciousness was the answer to many of our culture's problems. Stories form consciousness into vessels of our making. Those vessels can pour toxic or healing waters into the body politic.

The *Avatar* Movie, Anima Mundi, and Hope for Our World

It is heartening to see that some of the best movie directors of our age, like James Cameron, tell the stories of our age in ways that weave together metaphysical and environmental themes. In his 2009 movie *Avatar*, we see the story of a paraplegic Marine, Jake Sully, battle the forces of greedy mining interests who want to exploit the extraterrestrial moon Pandora with no regard for the native humanoids (the Na'vi) who live there. Jake is offered the ability to be transformed into a genetically bred human-Na'vi hybrid and have his consciousness transferred into a Na'vi body. The movie viewer, along with Jake, becomes transformed by entering into the new reality. Here we see in vivid 3-D, the mythos of our civilization's colonial exploitation that involves a non-caring attitude toward environmental consequences.

What is most valuable from the metaphysician's point of view is how well the movie depicts, and can induce the audience into, the experience of various metaphysical realities. The experience of *anima mundi*, the world soul (Jung, 1968), is transmitted to the viewer as the moviegoer experiences *Eywa* (the name for the mother Goddess on Pandora, whose consciousness pervades all of life). The scene where Jake plugs his tail into the tail of his bird-horse, and they become one, is a vivid, symbolic representation of the shape-shifting rituals that shamans on our planet Earth used to help members of their tribes to experience a oneness with nature. In a ritual-healing scene, Dr. Grace Augustine (played by Sigourney Weaver) is plugged into the living matrix of tree roots and luminescent threads dangling from trees while the whole Na'vi tribe chant and rock in unison. This scene depicts well the metaphysical altered state of the *unus mundus*—and it may be able to open even the most rational sceptic to the experience of energetic healing whereby a person becomes one with the World Soul, and the Tree of Life.

A picture may be worth a thousand words; and a movie is worth a thousand concepts. Rupert Sheldrake's (1988, 1991) concept of the morphogenetic field is well embodied in this movie, and the experience of entering into oneness with *Eywa* is like the experience of *Wuji* (the mother of qi, the void) in Tai Chi practice where the practitioner enters into an experience of oneness with all of life. The luminescent threads leading to this *Eywa* are analogous to the threads of energy that the Tai Chi practitioner reels from trees and the surrounding environment.

Mythic parallels abound in the subscript of the movie. The term *Na'vi* sounds like the word "navel," which represents the belly center (*tan tien*) in Taoism where the initiate finds the center of the field of the bodymind where divine and human meet. This Taoist concept is like the *omphalos* in the ancient Greek tradition, which represents the center of the world from which a new world is reborn. Another interesting mythic parallel is between the moon's name in the movie, Pandora (meaning "all gifts'), and the name of the Greek mythic figure from whose opening of her jar of gifts the world's evils emerged.

It is fascinating that a Greek myth, derived from an era thousands of years before the advent of modern technology, can tell a tale that speaks to the technological jar that modern society has opened with its gifts that have created such ecological devastation and poisoning of our planet.[9] In the Greek story, the goddess Hope remains after Pandora closed the jar.

True to the archetypal tale of Pandora it is hopeful and heartening to see young people today who are forging in an alchemical jar (vessel) a pro-environmental movement to try to bring "green technologies" to counter the forces in the world that parallel the uncaring mining interests depicted in the *Avatar* movie. "Hope" indeed remains in the efforts of many of the organizations that our younger generation is creating. For example, the activist organization Working Assets, also known as Credo, has a cell phone company that is a competitor to big phone and credit card companies. Credo gives one percent of customers' phone charges, and ten cents of each credit card purchase, to environmental and political action causes. They donated (from 1985 to 2010) over $65 million to groups like Greenpeace and Doctors without Borders; and they were a major contributor to the defeat of Proposition 23 in California, which was an attempt by big Texas oil companies to reverse California's leading-edge environmental policies.

So, ordinary citizens do not need to feel powerless in the midst of the forces of greed. By plugging into our connection to the *anima mundi* we can align ourselves with the forces of Hope stemming from the symbolic navel of our Earth. By finding our visionary symbols from nature we can draw energy from the supernal. We can be like pelicans, and choose empowering ways to use our awareness to take a stance and give from our hearts to feed our young and our planet.

Virgil said, "We make our destinies by our choice of Gods." I hope you now see that our stories are like unto God(s), and that we make our destinies by the stories we listen to, the way we interpret them, and the new stances we take thereby.

CHAPTER 23:

To My Children's, Children's Children

To penetrate into the essence of all being and significance,
and to release the fragrance of that inner attainment
for the guidance and benefit of others
by expressing in the world of forms—truth, love, purity, and beauty ...
This is the sole game, which has any intrinsic and absolute worth.
All other happening, incidents and attainments can,
in themselves, have no lasting importance.

—Meher Baba

Reflections on my Generation's Contribution to Experiential Metaphysics

I started this book with a dedication to my son Joab, my godson Alexander, and to all humanities' children. My generation has left in its wake many contributions to humanity. Among our most well known political contributions are: helping to create the Civil Rights movement and the women's empowerment movement, mounting protests to end the Vietnam War, and fostering a distrust of our country that exploited the resources of the world to pursue its own colonial interests (Perkins, 2005).

My hope is that the contributions we have made to the inner world will be as well remembered. Sometimes the outer and inner contributions are not so easy to separate. Inventions by computer geniuses of my generation like Steve Jobs and Steve Wozniak not only changed the way we "do business," but they have changed the consciousness of the world.

It is my hope that the metaphysical world opened by the generation of the human growth and potential movement will be remembered in its deeper light. So, although the use of psychedelics did lead to overdoses and excesses, it also opened the doors of perception to the world behind the world (Huxley, 1977; Wasson, 2008).

The metaphysical pathways that were opened by the musicians, poets, and songwriters of my generation were often inspired by the use of psychoactive plants, which were used in indigenous cultures for eons to open the doors of perception. Now it is known that the same cannabinoids that the hippies ingested when smoking marijuana are naturally occurring in the brain itself (endocannabinoids). Some cultural anthropologists believe that human beings evolved by using substances that induced altered states, and that these states of consciousness were as important to their inner evolution as was food to their outer survival (McKenna, 1992). One hypothesis is that these substances helped human beings to be better hunters through making our hunting senses more acute to get food and enhance our ability to listen and be present to deal with the dangers of life in survival territory (Furst, 1972).

However, this current book is more about how not only psychedelics, but also spiritual practices and natural inner and outer awakenings evoke an inner hunter whose quest is to give meaning to, and activate the hunt for, the deeper meanings of being a human connected to divine awareness. Those of us who read Aldous Huxley's *Doors of Perception,* listened to the Beatles' *Sgt. Peppers,* and were moved by the opening to the inner world heard a call to open to another reality.

Many spiritual leaders of this era such as Ram Dass (a.k.a. Richard Alpert) and Alan Watts, and political leaders of this era such as Martin Luther King, John F. Kennedy, and Robert Kennedy opened my generation's heart to a life of service to a larger spiritual purpose. These pioneers of the spiritual and political consciousness revolution helped to remind a materialistic culture of the importance of the inner world and inner values.

Since then, perhaps because our materialistic culture is so imbalanced in terms of not honoring the world behind the world that was part of indigenous and spiritually oriented cultures, many have felt a calling to explore the antidote to this dire state of affairs—spiritual and metaphysical traditions. Those like myself who were moved to investigate the world's esoteric literature to find out more about this inner world became psychologists, poets, inventors, and seekers of cross-cultural ancient sacred wisdom traditions.

Some of these seekers experimented with plant medicines that were used to open the doors of perception in ancient initiatory rites (Wasson, 2008; Harner, 1990). However, due to various issues such as the excesses and improper uses of such substances in the hippie era and a rigidity of thought from political reactionary forces, research was shut down. This overlooked the potential benefits and spiritually transforming uses of these plant medicines.

The positive result of making psychedelics illegal was that those who were interested in exploring altered states were moved to explore more natural means of cultivating such awareness. Thus, other people and I journeyed into the spiritual and metaphysical practices explored in this book—such as Tai Chi Chuan and other means of re-enchanting the cosmos.

Currently, a rapprochement is taking place where scientific research has begun again on how psychoactive and psychedelic substances can be integrated into a holistic treatment approach to various conditions. There is research demonstrating the efficacious use of marijuana with reducing chronic pain and acting as a preventative treatment for various chronic diseases (Werner, 2011). Ibogaine, a psychoactive alkaloid naturally occurring the root bark of the West African shrub Iboga is showing promising results in the treatment of opiate and other drug addictions (Brown, 2011). There are various studies on the use of MDMA (Ecstasy) to help in the healing of post traumatic stress disorder under the auspices of the Food and Drug Administration (Baggot, 2001), and other scientific organizations.[1]

Some of this research is taking place at our most prestigious institutions. For example, The McLean Hospital of Harvard Medical School is conducting a study under the supervision of John Halpern, M.D., to determine if MDMA can help terminal cancer patients experiencing end-of-life anxiety. Other studies involve the use of psilocybin and LSD to combat headaches and anxiety, and using MDMA for post traumatic stress disorder in Israel.[2] A circumspect perspective is needed regarding setting, what other chemicals are added into the MDMA when it is taken as a "street drug," intention in using the drug, and various therapeutic cautions need to be honored. As with all drugs and medications, there can be dangers as well as benefits as is well depicted in the TV program *Drugged: High on Ecstasy* on the National Geographic Channel in 2011.[3]

I told you earlier that when I went to the Quebec World's Trade Fair in 1967, I watched (while on a psychedelic) a simulated dying experience in a 360-degree theater there? I hoped that at some point in the future those psychedelics would be used to help facilitate the dying process. Now, many years later, it is heartening to hear about the results of a study by Dr. Charles Grob of U.C.L.A., which was published in the *Archives of General Psychiatry* about the use of psilocybin with terminal cancer patients and how after such experiences, patients measured a significant reduction in anxiety (Grob et. al, 2011). Similar research is also currently also taking place at John Hopkins Medical School and at N.Y.U. (Zaitchik, 2011).

Designing creative rituals to help facilitate the dying process may be part of the job description requirements of the Reluctant Metaphysician of the future. The rituals and metaphysical practices that I have outlined throughout this book are ways to activate such states without psychedelics (see Appendix II).

As I write about the interest that members of my generation and I have had with exploring the depths of the human soul, and the parallels between *The Tibetan Book of the Dead* and the psychedelic experience (Leary, 1987), I wonder. How much has being part of the Pluto in Leo (sign that rules the Sun) generation (born between 1938 and 1957) influenced my path? The sceptic in me would argue with an astrologer who proclaimed this by saying that there are so many in my generation who do not have an interest in bringing light (Leo) to the realm of the underworld (Pluto). Likewise in indigenous cultures throughout the ages many initiatory rituals have used psychedelics even when Pluto in Leo was not occurring. However, the adept astrologer would counter that I have Pluto in my tenth house, which rules one's occupation. Interestingly, I have made bringing light to the underworld my occupation. Adding to the weight of this placement is the fact that Saturn is directly conjunct Pluto and they are the most elevated planets in my chart. So, the astrologer would point out the synchronicity involved in the confluence of aspects related to my occupational fruition in leading people on "underworld journeys."[4]

It is fascinating how this generational configuration of bringing light to the under-world was one of the first impulses that drew me from being an attorney to changing the course of my life mid-stream to wanting to guide people into and out of their depths during their bad acid trips in the early days of the psychedelic revolution. Likewise, the chapters in this book about Greek Caves, my father's death, and my lectures at San Francisco State on topics about the journey into and out of the underworld would add to the astrologer's case about the synchronicity between the celestial sphere and the chosen path of my life. I must reluctantly admit to the astrologer that, as the Buffalo Springfield song says, "There's something happening here; what it is ain't exactly clear…"

Meditative Disciplines

Meditation, one of the key metaphysical tools for accessing the world behind the world, has come a long way on its journey in our culture. The doors to meditative disci-plines that the baby-boomer generation opened with visits to Maharishi and other Eastern masters are now more integrated into the healing practices of our Western culture. In the last decades, yoga studios have proliferated, health practitioners use mindfulness medita-tion as a respected tool, and according to *Time Magazine* ten million Americans now have a meditative practice (Cullin, 2006).

People who meditate correctly and on a regular basis have produced measurable health related changes, according to research done at the Benson-Henry Institute for Mind-Body Medicine. For instance, eighty percent of hypertensive meditation patients were able to lower their blood pressure and they decreased medications; sixteen per cent were able to discontinue using their medication all together. One hundred percent of patients who suffered with insomnia reported improved sleep from meditating, and the majority of them were able to reduce or eliminate sleeping medication. In addition, folks who suffer from chronic pain reduced their physician visits by thirty six percent and open-heart surgery patients had fewer post-operative complications, all due to a regular practice of meditation.[5]

At the beginning of this book I told you that I would share with you the meditative practices I discovered on my journey up "Mount Analogue." Some of the ones I have shared with you are:

- The meditation in movement tradition of Tai Chi Chuan
- Static forms of postural initiation such as Standing Meditation Qigong
- Microcosmic Orbit Breathing
- Chanting in the shower in the morning, prayer and flute playing before you go to sleep
- Outward introspection and the re-enchantment of the cosmos

- Guided meditation methods such as the River of Life
- The imaginal caves of our lives
- An imaginal mourning ritual for rising in a plane with the full moon
- Honoring our departed loved ones with playing a flute, or doing a Levusha Ritual for honoring the departed

Metaphysical Ecology and the Wider Whole of Which We Are a Part

> *It's 3:23 in the morning and I'm awake*
> *Because my great, great grandchildren*
> *Won't let me sleep.*
> *My great, grandchildren ask me in dreams,*
> *What did you do while the planet was plundered?*
> *What did you do when the Earth was unraveling?*
>
> —Drew Dellinger
> *Love Letter to the Milky Way*

There is perhaps no more important area of focus for the Reluctant Metaphysician than our human relationship to the planet that we inhabit. Just like a nightmare can awaken us from a bad dream, so can a story or powerful image awaken us from the nightmare of the pollution of our world. The pathways that we, and our culture, choose can potentially be realigned thereby. From a metaphysical perspective, the ways of this world are a manifestation of archetypal patterns and energies in the world of forms. By changing a story we can change the energy of the world, no less than a line of iron filings are realigned by a shift in a magnet's position. For example, Greed can be demagnetized by a new mental set and new actions can arise that are in alignment with a new archetype such as Service to Humanity. (Remember Parcival's quest was answered when he realized that the Grail Cup was there to serve the Kingdom.)

In the last chapters I spoke of the ill effects that manipulative ego-serving stories can have on the American economy, medical system, environment, and on our healers. The story line of our culture and of corporate philosophy has spilled over to the rest of the world. For example, Western hegemonistic culture spins the tale that the "third world" is ours for the taking. Luckily, we have courageous authors such as John Perkins, an "economic hit man" (Perkins, 2005), who tells us the story behind the story. In the years he spent working for an international consulting firm, his job was to convince underdeveloped countries to accept enormous loans, much bigger than they really needed, for infrastructure development. After the development projects were contracted to U. S. multinational corporations, and these countries were saddled with huge debts, the American government and the international aid agencies allied with them were able, by dictating repayment terms, to essentially control their economies.

Many other authors have added to our awareness of the negative effects of corporations on our world such as award-winning journalist Naomi Klein's (2007) book *Shock Doctrine* which outlines her views on "disaster capitalism;"[6] and investigative reporter Greg Palast's book, *Vultures' Picnic: In Pursuit of Petroleum Pigs, Power Pirates, and High-Finance Carnivores*. He reveals how various environmental disasters like the Gulf oil spill, the Exxon Valdez, and lesser-known tragedies such as Torrey Canyon were caused by corporate corruption, failed legislation, and, most interestingly, veiled connections between the financial industry and energy titans. He shows how the big powers in the financial and oil industries slip the bonds of regulation over and over again, and take advantage of nations and everyday people in the process (Palast, 2011).

Though ravages of destroyed countries and their citizen's lives have taken place due to the nightmare that this has produced, now that these tactics have been exposed there are people and organizations who are trying to change the dream of the modern world, and counter such forces of corporate greed and environmental degradation.

One such organization is the Pachamama Alliance, which was born in response to a request form the Achuar, an indigenous people deep in the Amazon region of Ecuador. After watching the land of neighboring tribal land being destroyed by multinational corporations, one of the Achuar had a dream that they should forge a partnership with people from the industrial world who would work with them in protecting the rainforest. The Pachamama Alliance grew as a partnership with the indigenous people of the West Amazon basin to defend their territories and cultures.

I recently went to a dinner with a few thousand activists that are part of a world wide effort to help native peoples in creating sustainable economic alternatives to help indigenous people to be able to resist the threat from predatory capitalists who want to mine, oil drill, and log these forests without due regard for the consequences to their actions. Through the efforts of organizations like Pachamama that support ecotourism and improving agriculture and aquaculture practices, alternatives are beginning to grow. Pachamama gives training in geographic information systems so that indigenous partners can map their territories and secure communal title to their lands. As well there is a program called Jungle Mamas that empowers indigenous women and their communities through training to ensure safe birthing practices and improved maternal, newborn, and community health.

We have been living in a story that says human beings are the sovereign rulers of this planet and the resources that are on this planet are there for our unmitigated use. Organizations such as Pachamama are building an alliance of experts from around the world to bring forth the universal adaptation and implementation of "the Rights of Nature," and they helped to champion the inclusion of this concept in Ecuador's new constitution in

2008. An organization named Pacha's Pajamas has created books, multimedia, and music to creatively bring the Pachamama philosophy to our youth (Ableman, 2011).

Many organizations are increasingly getting on the new wagon of "going green." While I was writing this section of my book at a local Starbucks, I bought a bottle of Ethos water and saw a note on the water bottle that says that five cents from the profits from each bottle is donated to humanitarian projects in coffee growing communities to provide clean safe water to those in need. So every organization and person can find their ways to contribute on a large and small scale to increasing our consciousness of the welfare and ecology of the planet we all inhabit.[7]

One of the most important areas of focus for the metaphysical ecologist is harnessing the energy of life. Our culture's reliance on fossil and nuclear fuels has put our nation and world in danger. A metaphysician's job is to be aware of the forces of the world behind the world that pull the puppet strings of those on the Earth. Engrained beliefs, grandiosity, and greed are three G-strings that entice the shortsighted to the Land of Danger.

There are many who are involved in presenting various alternative solutions to our planet's energy crises. If we create an energy mandala, each approach on the wheel would be given its due place. One spoke on the wheel is David Bloom's perspective on the use of alcohol as a fuel in his book *Alcohol Can Be a Gas*. He is just one of many authors who advocate for the importance of renewable fuels as an important component of our world's future energy needs. A longsighted view is needed to help those who hold self-serving interests to release their death grip on our world's energy economies, so that we can move away from an excessive dependence upon petroleum products and begin to contribute to lessening the effects of global climate change.[8] Spokes on the wheel of an energy mandala of sustainable solutions can be comprised of a huge variety of feedstocks, including sugar beets and cane, nuts, mesquite, Jerusalem artichokes, algae, and coffee-bean pulp (Bloom, 2007). Likewise wind power, wave power, and solar power can be part of the wave of the future.

A shift to renewable sources of energy is not an unrealistic fantasy as one can see in Brazil's focus on becoming world's first sustainable biofuels economy. As the leader in the biofuel industry, they no longer have any light vehicles running on pure gasoline due to the Brazilian government making it mandatory to blend ethanol with gasoline.[9]

The metaphysician looks with interest on how in the United States we seem to focus on combustibles. Just like the big bang of our ruling cosmology we have pursued the pathway to the big bang of the combustion engine. These are yang sources as compared to yin sources that come from reflective sources of power such as from solar panels. Another apt metaphor: Why do we choose underworld sources like coal and oil rather than sources from the upper world such as light (solar power) and wind? For a power elite that claims it is Christian and honors a God of the heavens, why does it trust mostly in energy from the lower worlds (hell)?

A balanced view would lead to honoring all worlds for our energy needs as the Greeks honored the gods and goddesses of the Earth, the underworld, and heavens. Metaphysical awareness expands avenues of possibilities and mindsets to make a more holistic relationship with the wider whole of which we are a part.

It is poignant that as I am writing this last chapter (during 2010 and 2011) there have been many "eruptions from the underworld" events that are shaking the world stage. In April of 2010, the Gulf oil spill disaster took place, which shot a hole in the underbelly of the United States and in the inflated attitude that believed that a disaster like this could not take place. Then the movie *Gasland* was nominated for an academy aware in award early 2010; it showed the ecological dangers of the hydraulic mining method of *fracking,* which uses high-pressure injections of water into deep underground shale deposits to release natural gas. Then, on March 11, 2011 the Fukushima nuclear disaster took place. The public awareness brought forth by such disasters is beginning to realign public consciousness of the dangers in such technologies.[10]

One does not need to be an astrologer at such times to wonder whether some unseen hand is at work during this time when Pluto (God of the Underworld) is in the zodiacal sign of Capricorn (sign of the Earth, where Pluto is from 2008 to 2024). As these earth changes were taking place in early 2011, Jupiter-Pluto was in square aspect; and Uranus (the planet of sudden eruptions) had just moved into Aries (the zodiacal sign symbolic of being headstrong). The Reluctant Metaphysician is not causal about such synchronicities; but instead we wonder how we can reorganize meaning as we act "as if" a message is coming to us from a visitation from an underworld deity. In Greek mythology Pluto, God of the Underworld was seen to be a counter-veiling force to balance out the hubris of those who followed the path of the sky Gods. Icarus' inflation holding onto the reins of Zeus' (Jupiter's) chariot led him to crash into the sea. Each symbol in the transiting chart of Fukushima can be explored to give meaning (Turnage, 2011). For example, Uranus in Aries, symbolizes headstrong attitudes that may lead to volatile occurrences when one is not sufficiently circumspect.

There are countries that are listening to nature's warning about the dangers of nuclear power, such as Switzerland. After the idealized fantasies of safe nuclear power met the realities of the Fukushima meltdowns and the leakages of radioactive material into our world's oceans, Switzerland suspended their approval process for three new nuclear power stations and will not replace old nuclear reactors (EuroActiv, 2011).

Turning Our Metaphysical Eyes Heavenward:
The Astrological Metaphors Hidden in Current Planetary Changes

While I am writing and reworking this section of the book at the end of 2010 and the beginning of 2011, there is a Jupiter-Uranus conjunction, an apt symbol for the overturning (Uranus) of the social order (Jupiter). Remember that Uranus, symbol of revolution (it revolves in a different way than the other planets), was discovered during the time of the American and French revolutions. It has also been empirically associated with the principle of change, rebellion, freedom, liberation, reform, unexpected breakup of structures, sudden surprises, revelations, lightening-like flashes of insight, intellectual brilliance, cultural innovations, technological invention, creativity, the cosmic trickster, and the imagination. With respect to personal character, the archetype of Uranus is associated with the rebel, the innovator, the awakener, the individualist, and the eccentric.

Mythically oriented astrologers agree that these qualities of the archetype of Uranus most closely correspond to Prometheus, the Titan who rebelled against the Gods and who stole fire from the Gods to it give it to humans (Tarnas, 2007). The archetype of Uranus/Prometheus when it is in conjunction with Jupiter symbolizes a revolution of the social order.

In many spheres there seems to be a revolutionary theme being played out on the national and international stage. In the United States, President Obama has made a few steps to overturn the oppressive corporate forces behind our national healthcare system. On the international stage *WikiLeaks* is bringing to light the behind the scenes forces that are manipulating world events. For example, *WikiLeaks* reported the fact that pressure was put on the Spanish government to stop various members of the Bush administration from being tried for war crimes. When various governments and corporate entities have mounted attacks on *WikiLeaks,* various activist organizations such as Anonymous have launched cyber-attacks on these organizations.

Remember that earlier in the book I said that during difficult times the Reluctant Metaphysician looks up to the sky and wonders why and wherefore. I also told you about how in my early awakening to the metaphysical path I read Herman Hesse's *Glass Bead Game*, which explored how different levels of reality oftentimes seem to be in synchronous relationship to each other, opening the mind to Wonder. Nowadays, I must admit I am so busy with my life that I do not have much time to look up to the astrological heavens; however, the once in a generation social upheavals taking place induced me to reluctantly take the time to blow the dust off of my old astrology ephemeris.

I wanted to explore further what was going on in the heavens that on the day (December 17, 2010) that the Middle East Revolutions began in Tunisia, and the poor fruit vendor Muhamed Bouazizi had his scale confiscated by a municipal official who asked for a bribe for him to continue his vending. For those who do not know the story, Mr. Bouazizi did not have the funds to pay for this bribe, and this was the "straw that broke the camel's back" for Mr. Bouazazi after many other confrontations with corrupt officials. After Mohamed Bouazizi lit himself on fire in protest a peoples' uprising occurred, joining in the protest.

The sceptic in me is still awed with the astrological synchronicities occurring at the time of this occurrence. Saturn was at the central degree of the zodiacal sign (15 degrees of Libra) that symbolizes the scales of justice—an apt symbol for Mr. Bouazizi and other

Tunisians no longer being willing to submit to an unjust, oppressive authority. Adding to the power of the planetary alignments on that day, Saturn (authority) was in square aspect to Pluto (eruption of emotional forces from the underworld) at 4 to 5 degrees of Capricorn—a fitting symbol for the impulse of eruption of anger against Tunisian Dictator Ben Ali who ruled Tunisia with an iron fist for decades. Mars, (the planet that rules iron, and the fires of anger) was in direct conjunction with Pluto (5 degrees of Capricorn) on the date of Mr. Bouazizi's self-emulation that sparked (Mars) the Middle East uprisings. All of these planetary aspects are fitting symbols of the expression of the anger of people-power to overturn oppressive dictatorial powers.

I was even more awestruck when I looked back at my astrological mentor, Dane Rudhyar's book on the symbolic meanings of the specific degrees of this conjunction (in 4 and 5 degrees Capricorn). About 4 degrees of Capricorn, Rudhyar writes "A group of people outfitting a large canoe at the start of a journey…" and, "A social group more strongly than ever reveals its homogeneity and common will when it decides to move away from its familiar habitat." For 5 degrees of Capricorn, the Sabian symbol reads, "Indians on the warpath. While some men row a well-filled canoe, others in it perform a war dance" (Rudhyar, 1973, pp. 231–2). The rational lawyer still in me must reluctantly admit that one could not be much more specific in finding fitting symbols to represent the uprising of the unified Tunisian people?

As the social revolution in the Middle East spread, interestingly, Saturn (the symbol of the ruling order) went stationary retrograde in Libra (symbol of the scales and balance) on Jan. 25, 2011 right at the time that the Egyptian revolution began. Astrologers say that when a planet goes stationary retrograde that it symbolizes an archetypal principle stopping in its tracks, halting its progress in order to engage in a process of reexamination in order to refocus on the purpose of its manifestation. Again, the rational lawyer in me must reluctantly admit that this is an apt synchronistic symbol for how people of Egypt and the Middle East at this time reexamined their relationship to the dictatorial Saturnian powers that had ruled them for centuries, and they revolted to create a new balance in the social order (Libra).

Adding to the meaning of this climate of social change during this time is that the planet Pluto is in the zodiacal sign of Capricorn from 2008 to 2024, which symbolizes the potential for chthonic changes to fundamental social structures. Still another potent configuration that adds to the power of the synchronicity of the revolutionary times of early 2011, is the square aspect of Pluto (emergence of destructive and overturning forces from the underworld) to the Jupiter-Uranus conjunction. It is fascinating that at this time the Egyptian people rose in protest about their government's policies. They used the ability to communicate though social networking media (Jupiter-Uranus). The Egyptian government tried to suppress the revolution through closing down the internet. It is fitting that Uranus being the first planet outside the boundaries of our sight is also a symbol for electricity, and that during this time Saturn has been opposite to Uranus. A metaphysician can't help wondering whether perhaps a "glass bead game (Hesse, 1982)" is being played in the great game that we call "Life," as governmental (Saturnian) forces oppose the release of information to the people of the world exemplified in WikiLeaks, Tunisia, Egypt, and other countries in the Middle East and other places.

As I write this section in February of 2011, tens of thousands of people in Wisconsin are rising up protesting the anti-labor policies of Governor Walker, who is funded by the billionaire Koch brothers (Kroll, 2011). The last time I saw this kind of uprising of popular sentiment was during the uprising of my generation during the Vietnam War. Interestingly, a similar planetary conjunction of Jupiter-Uranus was taking place then in 1968 and 1969 when, syncronistically, a revolution was taking place. Then too, like the current uprising in Egypt, protests filled the streets against an unjust war. And fascinatingly, on the date of the exact conjunction of Jupiter-Uranus, July 20, 1969, was the date that earthlings first walked on the moon (Brand, 2010).[11]

Moving forward in time, on July 13, 2011 Uranus (planet symbolic of revolutionary new ideas and radical action) and Pluto (symbolic of destruction and transformation) were in a close one degree square aspect just as the Occupy Wall Street movement began with a blog post in the Canadian-based publication, *Adbusters*. At this same exact time, in Israel the social protest movement erupted that begun with video editor Daphne Leaf's problems with finding affordable housing. As in other protests at this time, Daphne used the social networking technology (symbolic of the Uranus archetype) of Facebook to publicize her difficulties.

A public tent protest began in Habima square and on Rothchild Boulevard in Tel Aviv, and it spread through Israel during this Uranus-Pluto square aspect. Uranus-Pluto in square formation is symbolic of the sudden eruption of forces from the underworld; and certainly this long lasting astrological aspect seems to represent well the many year time-line that may be needed to implement the changes called for by the protests around the world that began at this time.

It is fascinating that at that time Uranus was in Aries (symbolic of enthusiasm, but at times lacking in sufficient definition as it bursts forth with springtime energy) and Pluto was in Capricorn (astrological sign symbolic of the ruling political order). More specifically, it is interesting that when the Occupy Wall Street movement began there was a T-Square aspect between Saturn and the Uranus-Pluto square.[12] These planets in T-square alignment also took place during other economic downturns, during the Great Depression time of 1929–1933, and during the long depression of the 1873–1879 period. Saturn is known to be symbolically representative of frustration, depression, and lack of opportunity—the catalyzing forces behind the Occupy Wall Street movement. The Occupy Wall Street movement took form in the streets of New York on September 17, 2011, and has spread to a great number of cities around the United States and around the world as Saturn is moving away from its square aspect. It is now called by many names such as "OccupyTogether.org, OccupyEverything.org, and OccupytheWorld.org."

Time will tell if the sudden burst of revolutionary change, symbolic of Uranus in Aries, will set the tone for the movement or whether Pluto in Capricorn (deep transformation of the social order) will hold sway. Once again, the sceptic, the hermeneutic astrologer, and the Reluctant Metaphysician may be brought to wonder in the face of such synchronicities, and reluctantly say, "Something is happening here, what it is ain't exactly clear."[13]

People do not want to take to the streets. But in difficult times, reluctantly, following some calling from the heavenly sphere above and the chthonic forces below, humanity is often impelled to rise to the occasion. All of the world is indeed a stage; and the question arises, "Are metaphysical forces the co-directors in partnership with human beings in co-creating the Mystery Play of life here on Earth?" Only a Being higher than ourselves (which some call Cosmic Consciousness, and others call God) knows.

The question is, what kind of major transformation will take place as the various significant planetary alignments take place in our current era. The Jupiter-Uranus social revolution is one such interesting configuration. The Reluctant Metaphysician is also awakened by the cosmic coincidence of Uranus in the last critical degree of Pisces (water, tsunami) moving into 1 degree of Aries (a cardinal fire sign, aptly symbolic of the fire principle discharging nuclear particles into the atmosphere) right as the earthquake, tsunami, and nuclear disaster happened in Fukushima, Japan on March 11, 2011. If anything could influence a person who was reluctant about believing in cosmic coincidences, this would be an eye-opener!

Whether various celestial events such as a Jupiter-Uranus conjunction, Uranus moving into Aries, or other trans-Saturnian configurations are objectively related to current changes in many spheres of life is not so much the point. The most important issue is how we can use celestial symbols to give meaning to the positive social and environmental changes needed for our culture and world.

We are in an era of potential revolutionary change. Time will tell how these changes will affect our future as the revolutionary changes of the 1960s changed women's rights, interracial relations, the emergence of computers, and so forth. Cycles repeat; spirals emerge. Many astrologers believe that Uranus is related to the archetype of Prometheus who stole fire from the Gods. At this current conjoining of Jupiter-Uranus, and its symbolic resonance with social revolution, we have mobile phones, and social networking tools that create new methods of communication. The archetype of Prometheus (Uranus) is reborn in a 21st century that can create new forms of fire for humanity—these new transformative fires are emerging in the technological, political, biological, and environmental realms.

In the environmental arena for example, we have spoken about how organizations such as Pachamama create positive change in our environment. Another one of the leading-edge organizations that is at the forefront of biological and environmental change is the Bioneers. They have had conferences in Marin California since the early 1990s. At each of these conferences that I have attended I feel hope that Promethean forces are operating to change the storyline of modern civilization. Here social and scientific innovators gather from all walks of life and disciplines. These pioneers have peered deep into the heart of living systems to understand how nature operates—like Prometheus, discovering divine secrets behind the world of matter and sharing them with humanity.

Some presenters such as Janine Benyus (1997) advocate mimicking "nature's operating instructions" to serve human ends without harming the web of life. Her work shows how our world can change the narrative of our relationship to the environment from a story line that advocates conquering nature to one that emphasizes cooperating with nature. Her research shows how nature's principles—kinship, cooperation, diversity, symbiosis, and cycles of continuous creation absent of waste—can serve as metaphoric guideposts for organizing an equitable, compassionate, and democratic society.

A metaphysician looks up to the sky at such times and wonders about the forces from the world behind the world that are synchronous with such changes. One of the biggest cycles that is occurring at this time, is the change (due to the procession of the equinoxes) from the Piscean to the Aquarian Age. Each processional age is approximately 2160 years (Rudhyar, 1969, p.106). Aquarius, ruled by the planet Uranus, is not only is related to revolutionary impulses, but also to humanitarian ideals. At this next turn on the spiral of life, the Aquarian impulse is not just about the connection with our fellow human beings, but also with nature itself. So the Aquarian themes that led my generation on the quest to transform racial, political, sexual, and technological spheres is now spreading to other realms. The archetypes of Uranus and Aquarius relate to higher orders of connectedness between the wider whole of which we are a part and our everyday human existence.

Turning Our Metaphysical Eyes Earthward: Cooperating with Nature

Re-enchantment of the cosmos does not mean some esoteric, otherworldly view. It means reanimating life by cooperating in harmony with the world of nature, and our nature, which is a reflection of life itself. Janine Benyus offers leading edge ideas about how to activate principles of "biomimicry" to follow the ways of nature to revolutionize our products, processes, and lives. A few examples: In one project, researchers found out that termites in Africa have the ability to maintain virtually consistent temperature and humidity in their termite mounds despite widely varying extreme temperatures. Using this knowledge of termite mound design led to a project in the Eastgate Center in Zimbabwe to keep this office complex cool without air conditioning. It uses only 10% of the energy of a conventional building its size. In another project, modeling echolocation in bats led to an Ultracane for the visually impaired from researchers at the University of Lead in the United Kingdom. Another impressive biomimicry application is using spiders' web silk, which is as strong as Kevlar used in bulletproof vests. Finally, mushroom researcher Paul Stamets who speaks at Bioneers conferences tells about the use of mushrooms to absorb the effects of oil spills, and the healing effects of these powerful healing myco-medicinal plants (Stamets, 1999, 2005).

As the technological hubris of our civilization leads to nuclear accidents, like the catastrophic one that happened in Japan in March of 2011, it will be interesting to see how bioremediation efforts using mushrooms and radiation-eating microbes can prove to be one of the Promethean gifts from the natural world that can help to treat the dire effects of nuclear contamination to our Earth (Brim, 1986; Wikipedia/bioremediation, 2011).

It is most important, however, to address the consciousness, arrogance, self-serving interests, and lack of imagination that puts humanity in such danger by allowing nuclear plants to be built near earthquake faults or on them, and in tsunami zones. Certainly all citizens need to become informed of the dangers and realities of nuclear mishaps (Ward, 2011), and finding the sustainable solutions to energy creation is the ecological meta-issue behind such discussions.[14]

The metaphysician looks for the hidden stories behind the surface stories. We are told the myth that nuclear power does not cause pollution or contribute to global climate change; and that it is "clean and green," inexpensive, and safe. Dr. Helen Caldicott, a medical doctor and anti nuclear activist argues that the truth is that nuclear power contributes to global climate change, the real costs of nuclear power are prohibitive (and taxpayers pick up most of the costs), and the potential for a catastrophic accident outweighs the benefits (Caldicott, 2006). The most recent nuclear accident in Fukushima, Japan shows that there has been merit in the anti-nuclear activists position over the years.[15]

Reversing the subsidies given to nuclear and oil industries, and beginning to shift funding to practical alternative energy sources such as solar, wind, geothermal, and wave-power is a key to unlock a doorway to sustainable solutions. The second key is the consciousness that makes this possible. A different story than the hierarchical, conquering of nature myth, is the dream of a modern world that can find harmony and cooperative relationship with nature—and sources of power that will fulfill these goals. An epic challenge is presented to our world, as vested, bribed government officials vote against such basic remedies as reversing oil subsidies. Instead, crony capitalism supports some the most profitable industries that have ever existed to be subsidized with tax breaks, and to be insufficiently regulated (Foley, 2011).

The metaphysician knows that there are various wavelengths of consciousness. The dream of consensual reality (perhaps symbolized by the brain's beta waves) is the favored bandwidth to which modern human beings have become attuned. As humanity has danced to this rhythm it has led us to great leaps and bounds; but we must not forget that this, our favorite "talk radio station," is a trance state that induces human beings' to become separate from nature. The linear, left-brain's waking dream of the ascendancy of human beings over nature is at a point of reaping its karma as climate change and degradation of our environment becomes a reality. It is time to change the channel. A new myth is needed to transform our current era (Kelly, 2010). The metaphysical practices in this book, which lead to the experience of the *unus mundus*, make such a radical change in consciousness possible.

For example, Tai Chi Chuan is a right brain practice for leading to the experience of the *unus mundus;* and studying mythology can awaken the dreamer to change the dream he or she is living. Though the mental sphere has advantages for functioning in everyday life, it contains hubris, unsustainable risk taking, and may lead to ego-serving economic greed. The result is pollution and degradation of the planet we inhabit. We live the effects of our worldview and experience its toxic effects, as childhood asthma rates rise and environmental disease increases (even affecting the well-gated communities of the super wealthy). We all share the Earth, and we are its citizens and potential protectors.

As I go to various events in the Bay Area, I have a sense that indeed the path less traveled that I followed from New Jersey has led me to where a new sun is rising, and now more people are jumping on this vehicle of consciousness on the move. The birth of the environmental movement that I witnessed in New York on the first Earth day in 1970 has certainly taken further steps.

The obstacles of entrenched beliefs and economic interests are formidable, but as I look around me it seems that my vision of 1971 is alive here in 2010, not just for me but also for our culture. In that big dream, after I was in the land where the Sun rose in the West there were dark clouds around me and I almost forgot from where I came (a place of luminous harmony). In that dream when I came to the planet Earth there were dark clouds all around me, and yet through the clouds a light shined from the heavens that filled the top of my head down to my feet. It does indeed seem that now, on the West coast where I stand that dark clouds of greed and environmental degradation cloud our culture. And yet a light is shining down through many of us who are part of the movement to create green technologies, fair labor practices, sustainable practices for our environment and integrative approaches to health.

There are many clouds around us all, particularly in this decade of the 21st century, when the cloud of nuclear emissions is affecting the air, water, plants, fish and wildlife of the whole planet. However, at any time in history the path of the Reluctant Metaphysician is to find how, in our own unique lives, we can find the life stance that is appropriate for bringing the light of our purpose under the heavens to the Earth.

At the time when I finished the first draft of this book, on December 20, 2010 at 12:30 a.m., there was a rare time of a coincidence of both the Winter Solstice and a full moon eclipse. According to NASA, the last total lunar eclipse that happened on the winter solstice was Dec. 21, 1638. The next one will be on Dec. 21, 2094. At this moment in the Bay area it was a dark and cloudy night. Yet right at the moment of this full moon eclipse, with the moon up at its highest point (that astrologers call "mid-heaven"), I looked at this astronomically spectacular expression of nature, and I could not help but reflect upon this moment's synchrony with the time of the summer solstice of 1971, when I was led to California about four decades ago.

I found it interesting that while I was writing about, and reflecting upon, this forty year journey that transiting Uranus was coming into opposition with my natal Neptune, a full moon aspect that symbolizes reflection on my revolutionary spiritual journey.[16] The journey began approximately forty years ago when Uranus and Neptune were conjunct. So, as I reflect back on that time in my life when I had the dream of the Land where the Sun rose in the West that led me to a new life, on that very day on June 21st of 1971, transiting Uranus was in 9 degrees of Libra in exact conjunction with my natal Neptune at that degree—an apt symbol for a revolutionary change (Uranus) that touches off a change in consciousness and opening to non-ordinary states of wider consciousness (Neptune).

In December of 2010, as I did my Qigong practice on my deck in the midst of the woodlands of Orinda, I opened my hands to the heavens in gratitude for the path I have walked, as the soft lunar light of the heavens came down to me. Something about full moon eclipses make an indelible mark in time and eternity. I played my flute, and said my prayers for light to come to humanity during these dark times. Little did I know that within the next three months, anti-dictatorial movements would arise in the Middle East; and the devastation of Japan took place through an earthquake, tsunami, and a nuclear plant catastrophe. Each of us in the world needs to find the light coming through the dark clouds calling for change—each of us need to find stories and practices to guide our souls during such troubled times. The various outgrowths of the Occupy Wall Street movement are one manifestation of a new story emerging.

Energetic Healing

As I have traveled a long way on my journey, so has the tradition of energetic healing come a long way in its journey in our culture? As I pointed out earlier, the pyramid of science has changed since Einstein put out his famous equation about the inter-change-ability of matter and energy. The infusion of the importance of energetic healing and its incorporation into an integrative model is in its early phases.

My hope is that in time that the integrative paradigm that I have put forth in my books (which includes integrative, energetic, astro-poetic, psycho-mythological, body-mind healing, ecological, and metaphysical dimensions), will be further incorporated into the healing methods of our culture. These are each doorways that lead into the treasure-trove of the Reluctant Metaphysician.

The Reluctant Metaphysician Transformed: The Grateful Metaphysician

Why do I call this path I have walked, *The Path of a Reluctant Metaphysician*? From the perspective of the ego, most of us do not want to lose or change the life we have known, whether it is our habits, relationships, political system, or beliefs. However Life, or Time, or some transformative spirit of the universe comes and calls us—often seemingly against our will—and invites us to expand our perspective and change our world.

The fixed and stable part of myself certainly did not want to leave the path of being an attorney, nor did I want to have disabling blocks in my body—nor do any one of us want to be living in a world of political, economic, or ecological troubled times.

The "refusal to answer the call" has been outlined well by Joseph Campbell (Campbell, 1970, pp.59–69), and the resulting wasteland that can derive from the choice to live in the world of complacency. On the other hand, myths and teaching stories also tell about those who reluctantly answer the call from the world behind the world, and the transformative process that takes place, such as in this next tale.

The Streams and the Sands

Once upon a time a stream passed through varied terrain. It fell over cliffs, and twisted and turned, but it enjoyed traveling in its own banks. Then one day it reached the sands of the desert and found that as soon as it ran into the sand, its waters disappeared.

The stream was convinced that its destiny was to cross the desert, and yet there didn't seem to be a way. Then a hidden voice from the sands whispered, "The sands cross the desert and so can the stream. By hurling yourself in your accustomed way you cannot get across. You will either disappear or become a quagmire. You must allow the wind to carry you to your destination by allowing yourself to be absorbed by the wind."

This idea was not acceptable to the stream. It didn't want to lose its individuality. How could it be regained? The sands replied, "The wind performs this function. It takes the water, carries it over the desert sands, and then lets it fall again. Falling as rain, the water again becomes a river."

The stream again resisted and said, "But can I not remain the same stream that I am today?" "You cannot in either case remain so. You are called what you are even today because you do not know which part of you is the essential one."

When it heard this, an echo began to arise. The stream remembered a state in which some part of it had been held in the arms of the wind. With this thought, it let go for a moment and lo-and-behold started to rise. It was scary…as if that which was identified with, for a long time, was evaporating away. But the awe-filled evaporation process did indeed bring an experience of a deep, long forgotten part of this identity.

As it continued to rise with elation, the memories of the stream's long journey alone in his narrow banks began to return. With this realization, it noticed its form change into a dark cloud, and it felt very sad about the time spent in narrow confines. As it journeyed across the sky, tears rolled down its face. It noticed that they fell as rain to the mountains below, filling a new river that would water new seeds and create new plant life. The stream appreciated the cycle of creation and realized that it had learned something from every part of it. At this moment it felt electrified with appreciation for the cycle of narrowness and expansiveness, and of merging and separating. Lighting and thunder filled the heavens as the stream felt the wholeness of its essential nature.

—Paraphrased and revised from
Shah, *Tales of the Dervishes*

And so it is that a Reluctant Metaphysician who answers the call during times of difficulty can be transformed into a Grateful Metaphysician. During troubled times we can look heavenward along with the astro-poet, the Buddha with the sickness demon, and the Stream who met the Sands. During troubled times we can use our wounds from the physical, mental, emotional, political, and ecological spheres of life to become wounded healers. During troubled times we can find our own way to contribute to the great political, economic, ecological, and cultural turnaround. In doing so, then we too may feel grateful that we have been called to walk the path of the Reluctant Metaphysician.

There are many nowadays that are Reluctant and Grateful Metaphysicians who are drawing from the world behind the world to alleviate their own and our culture's suffering. Our culture itself has seemingly hit into the Sands (of the "Stream and the Sands" story) and is waiting to be reborn by letting go of old narrow ways. Many of us have been watching and waiting for such a cultural transformation to take place. It reminds me of one of my favorite songs of the 60s, "Watching and Waiting," from the era that gave birth to my Quest to the West:

WATCHING AND WAITING

Watching and waiting
For a friend to play with
Why have I been alone so long
Mole he is burrowing his way to the sunlight
He knows there's some there so strong

Cos here there's lot of room for doing
The thing you've always been denied
Look and gather all you want to
There's no one here to stop you trying

Soon you will see me
Cos I'll be all around you
But where I come from I can't tell
But don't be alarmed by my fields and my forests
They're here for only you to share

Cos here there's lot of room for doing
The things you've always been denied
So look and gather all you want to
There's no one here to stop you trying

Watching and waiting
For someone to understand me
I hope it won't be very long

—from the album *To My Children's Children*, The Moody Blues, by J. Hayward Thomas

Our personal dreams, visions, and songs are not our own. We are all like canaries in the dark coal mine of our culture. The messages we carry from the world behind the world not only give warnings about the way we are living, but they also give solutions for curing our personal and cultural troubled times.

Joseph was given the insight to interpret the Pharaoh's dream of the seven fat and seven lean cows to prepare for the impending famine to save his culture from starvation. Similarly, many Reluctant Metaphysicians today are getting messages from the world behind the world and bringing those messages to heal our culture.

One example of transformative cultural ritual inspire by despair is the Burning Man annual event. In its origins, Larry Harvey had a broken heart from a love affair and he and his friend, Jerry James, burned a nine foot tall wooden man on Baker's Beach in San Francisco—a death and rebirth ritual that was a spontaneous act of "radical self-expression." Now the ritual has moved to Black Rock Desert, Nevada, and in 2011 over 50,000 people attended. The ritual has expanded, and the effigy of the burned man is now about forty feet tall. The yearly gathering now contains many creative elements: Participants use a gift economy modeled after indigenous *potlatch* ceremonies where the "give away" is the norm. This de-commodifies the event. "Cultural-creatives" of all mediums share their inspirations, inventions, food, films, and provide a place to practice a new way of living. Participants are encouraged to leave no trace, remove their own litter, and minimize impact on the environment. So, out of the suffering that reluctantly comes to our lives, creative drama can be born that can heal a person and a culture—no less than the Eleusinian rituals in ancient Greece healed their culture through a reenactment of the ritual of the rape of Persephone. It is as true today as it was in Greece, and as we saw in the "Buddha and the Sickness Demon" story…if we don't create ritual our melodrama will be all the more painful.

In the San Francisco Bay Area, there are numerous events where those of us who hold the stresses and strains of modern life go to transformative rituals during times of seasonal change or on the weekends. For example, there are Ecstatic Dance rituals every weekend, which grew from such dance celebrations that began in Hawaii in the year 2000. These dance celebrations originally inspired by Gabrielle Roth's Five Rhythms now include the many forms of bodywork. Usually they start with yoga, then free form movement begins. While a variety of music is played many streams of healing movement traditions join. Among the styles of healing movement are contact improvisation, acroyoga, free-form dance, tai chi dance, or any style that moves ones heart and heals the bodymind.[17]

So, the dreams that I have shared with you of my two streams becoming one are not my dreams. Our culture is joining streams of healing traditions to enter into a new world. In the joining of creative movement traditions; integrative medicine; and indigenous, Eastern, and Western traditions a better amalgam is being forged. I am not the only one who has a vision of the sun rising in the West. From the West coast have come rising innovations of technology (born from those like Steve Jobs and Silicon Valley entrepreneurs), dance rituals, integrative medical clinics, and organizations like the Bioneers and Credo that are bringing the light to a culture through the dark clouds of troubled times. I am not the only one who is kissing the eyes of a wounded culture with the knowledge of indigenous cultures, as we can see from the work of such organizations like Pachamama Alliance. Each of our visions is part of the vision of a planetary whole.

Are the fast-paced changes that are coming to our culture synchronistic with the processional movement into the 2nd degree of Aquarius, and are they part of the manifestation of "the water bearer" bringing a new cycle of manifestation of humanitarian ideals to our culture? I do not know, and Time will tell.[18] However, regardless of the reasons, there are political progressives, cultural-creatives, iconolasts, and every day folk who are no longer just watching and waiting. They are "occupying."

The Last Hippie Standing:
Standing Meditation and Finding Your Life's Stance

This book stands as one old hippie's journey on the path that opened during the consciousness revolution movement that began in the 1960s. It seems that there is a resurgence of some of the mythology of, and political actions of, the hippie movement in the Occupy Wall Street movement, that is happening in current times. Though the power-elite in the top one percent of income earners are trying to demean the movement by pointing out the shortcomings of the protesters (and sometimes with some merit),[19] there are many positive elements of the hippie culture that are being reborn in the new vessel of the Occupy Everything Movement. According to author David Goldberg (2011) the well chosen phrase, "We are the 99 percent" was coined by those creative forces of the Occupy Movement in drum circles; and the mixing of their spiritual, democratic, and political values and processes have roots in the hippie era. Bill Maher, the satirist, said in response to those on the far right who have categorized those protesting on the street as "countercultural others," that it is not the counter-culture that is out in the streets it is the culture itself that is now protesting. Or, as one of my favorite local comedian Swami Beyondananda (also known as Steve Bhaerman) says, "There is an 'up-wising' going on."

As the song "Watching and Waiting" says, we are all moles, burrowing our way to the sunlight, each of us finding our way to contribute to healing our culture's unraveling. And, after we each pass away, our essence (our essential gifts) will speak from the fields of knowledge we have incarnated, the Stances that we have taken in the forests of life, and from the land (inner and outer) that we have tilled in various fields of life—psychological, scientific, technological, spiritual, social, political, and ecological.

Each of us has a story of how we have come through the depths of our underworld journeys through the Corycian caves of our lives, up into the "higher planes" of our lives, and into heavenly spheres. The quintessential legacy that each of us leaves behind is contained in our stories—the spiritual bones of our lives.

In closing, Friedrich Nietzsche has said, "Some people are born posthumously." Perhaps the same can be said of cultural and metaphysical movements, as well as of people. From the perspective of a Reluctant Metaphysician, I would say that there are stars out in deep space whose light only reaches Earth after they have died.[20] It is only then that they are seen and their light is appreciated. Blessings to all of those stars, and the stories of their making. May each of your stories reach the Earth with Godspeed. The world needs them before we pass away.

Keep shining like the stars you are!

APPENDIX I:
List of Selected Stories

~ List of Author's Personal Stories ~

Preface:
- My Mother's Tale About Her Poverty and the Kindness of a Teacher
- My Mother's Tale About the Non-economic Factors That Make a Happy Childhood

Chapter 1:
- The Tree of Life: In My Back Yard

Chapter 2:
- My Childhood Energy Blocks

Chapter 3:
- Murdered by Nazis: My Lucid Repetitive Dream

Chapter 4:
- My Life Path: Two Streams Joining

Chapter 5:
- Dandelions Are Not Just Weeds
- Woodstock: Social Forces and Psychedelic Experiences
- A Lawyer Captured by Astrological Forces?
- My First Philosophy Class: An Introduction to Metaphysics

Chapter 6:
- My First Teaching Job—Montclair State
- Dream of the Land Where the Sun Rises in the West
- Don't Worry Dad, I'll Still Be a Lawyer; but I'll be a Lawyer for the Body, Mind, and Spirit
- Dangers in Answering the Hero's Call: My Journey to California

- The Hawaiian Flute Master: A Cross-cultural View on Honoring Your Departed Loved Ones

Chapter 12:
- Dancing with Deer—Not Dancing with Wolves

Chapter 13:
- My Vision of the Origin of Tai Chi

Chapter 14:
- My Visit to the Cave of the Oracle of Delphi

Chapter 15:
- Healing with the Elements: Transpersonal Hypnosis for a Writer's Block

Chapter 16:
- Meeting Dr. Bessel Van de Kolk: Advocating for Qigong Empowerment for Trauma Victims

Chapter 18:
- A Dream of the Energy-Stream, Vacuum Cleaner in Reverse: Empowerment in Relationship to My Inner Foe

Chapter 19:
- Tai Chi Self-defense in a Bar in Hawaii
- Crane Splitting Hands: Weakling Scholar Uses Empty Force to Protect Himself

Chapter 20:
- Four Crows Join When My Father Dies
- A Mourning Ritual: Rising in a Plane with the Full Moon

Chapter 22:
- Pelican Sinks Its Qi on My Car

– Selected Mythic Tales, Quotes, and Cross-Cultural Teaching Stories –

Preface:
- Mount Analogue

Introduction:
- Ali Baba Opens the Cave with the Words "Open Sesame"
- Sheherazade Transforms the Evil King with her Stories
- Apollo: Sun God and God of the Underworld
- Wizard of Oz
- The Road Less Traveled

Chapter 1:
- Icanchu and Chuna: What to Do when the (your) World is Destroyed
- The Ugly Duckling: Appreciating your Uniqueness
- The Coat of Many Colors: The Biblical Story of Joseph
- The Old Woman in the Cave
- Finding your Sacred Note: An Old Jewish Married Couple's Story
- The Rabbi in the Woods

Chapter 4:
- "I Did it my Way," by Frank Sinatra
- "Envy is Ignorance" by Walt Whitman

Chapter 5:
- *Ananke:* Goddess of Necessity

Chapter 6:
- "This Above All to Thine own Self be True," Shakespeare's Hamlet
- The Secret of the Golden Flower
- Parcival's Quest for the Holy Grail

Chapter 7
- The Tale of Indra: Maybe the Beggar you Just Passed on the Street is God
- The Tale of the *Lamed Vav:* Maybe your Tailor is God
- Awakening out of the Daydream and Entering the Greater Dream: Michael Meade quote

Chapter 8:

- The Importance of Having a Calling: Michael Meade
- Bonzi and the Eccentric Swordsman
- Each Life Involves a Divine Errand: Michael Meade
- Opening to the Genii Within
- Shamanic Dismemberment and the Quest to Find our Soul's Purpose
- Mythogems of our Life's Purpose: 1.) A Chip that Comes from the Tree of Life 2.) Mayan Tale of Poder and the Path to Being a Rainmaker
- The Biblical Abraham Sacrifice of Issac
- The Quest for our "True Names"
- Snow White Swallows the Poisoned Apple

Chapter 10:

- "By seeing yourself in all beings and all beings in your self, enlightenment is found…"—*The Upanishads*
- "What is the work of works if not to establish in an by each one of us an absolutely inimitable center in which the universe reflects itself in a unique and inimitable way. And those centers are our selves and personalities."—Teilhard de Chardin
- The Hermeneutic Path
- Story of the Mullah who Lost his Key in the Dark
- Ram Dass and his Guru—What to Do on your Birthday?
- Ram Dass and his Brother—What Does It Mean to Be Crazy?
- The Roots of Psychotherapy in Cross-cultural Mythic Traditions
- Meaning of the Word, "Chuan" in Tai Chi Chuan
- Jewish Renewal—revisioning Yom Kippur, the *tallis,* the derivation of Spock's "Be well and prosper mudra," "at-onement," Jewish healing dance rituals that mirror Chinese Pa Kua
- A Mourning Ritual: Wrapping Yourself with the Threads of your Departed Loved Ones—the *levusha* ritual that synthesizes the Zohar and Tai Chi

Chapter 11:

- The Lost Golden Ball of Western Fairy Tales: Is Standing Meditation Qigong a Path to Discovering the Lost Golden Ball of Energy?
- Taoist Alchemy and Returning to the Origin of Things
- Standing Meditation: What Do You Stand for?
- Four Kabbalistic Levels of Biblical Interpretation

Chapter 13:

- The "True Origin" (in the mythic/metaphysical sense) of Tai Chi

Chapter 14:

- The Mythology of the Oracle of Delphi
- Psycho-historical Dimensions of the Oracle of Delphi
- Cave Creation Myths: Weaving Tales to Create New Ways of Being

Chapter 15:

- The Monkey and the Banana: To let go of attachments
- Odysseus and the Sirens: To center us in relationship to staying true to our live paths even when distractions occur
- Buddha and the Sickness Demons: To listen to the messages from our illnesses
- The Jewish Farmer: To trust in the existence of the divine mystery play of the forces of life when dire and beneficial circumstances arise
- Perseus and Medusa: For transforming blocks to our life paths and creativity
- Healing Trauma: The ritual of Code Red in Israel

Chapter 16:

- Creating a New Origin Myth for Psychotherapy
- Cross-cultural History of Energy Healing

Chapter 17:

- Creation Myth: The Self-healing Secrets Installed in us by the Gods
- Shape-shifting in the Shamanic Cave of Creation
- Aesclepian Holistic Healing
- The Esoteric Dimensions of Playing Chess

Chapter 18:

- Teaching Story: Seeing the Sacred in the Gestures of Everyday Life

Chapter 19:

- Bonzi and the No-sword School
- Bonzi's Training with an Eccentric Teacher
- Abused Child Defends Herself with Verbal Tai Chi

Chapter 21:

- Uranus and Cronus
- The Myopia of the Cyclops
- The Myth and Reality of the Albatross
- The Native American "Give-away"

Chapter 22:

- The Wandering Seabird—Ralph Waldo Emerson
- Vishnu the God of Creation Every Night Takes Flight as a Wild Gander
- The Avatar Movie, Anima Mundi, and Hope for our World

Chapter 23:

- "To penetrate into the essence of all being and significance..."—Meher Baba
- Full Moon Eclipse on the Winter Solstice
- The Stream and the Sands
- Watching and Waiting Song—the Moody Blues

~ Patient Stories/Case Illustrations ~

Chapter 15:

- Case Illustration: A Critical Perfectionist's Mythic Journey Process
- Case Illustration: The Passive-Aggressive Ostrich
- Case Illustration: The Desperately Grasping Parrot

Chapter 17:

- Case Illustration: Carpal Tunnel Syndrome
- Case Illustrations of Hypertension: The "Hyper-tense" Executive

Chapter 18:

- The Case of the Repulsing Monkey
- Case Illustration: Social Phobia Stemming from Physical Abuse

APPENDIX II:
Practices That Change Our Lives

Chapter 4:

- Outward Introspection: Finding Our Deepest Selves in Nature

Chapter 10:

- The *Levusha Ritual* for Honoring the Departed

Chapter 11:

- The Secret of the Golden Flower
- The River of Life
- Standing Meditation Qigong
- Standing Like a Tree
- The Circle That Arises from Stillness
- Holding Golden Balls in the Waters of Life
- Developing the Golden Ball of the Heart and the Sphere of the Self
- The Taoist Practice of Cultivating the Golden Ball
- Dispersing Stagnant Qi and The Golden Flower
- Tai Chi Chuan
- Taoist Immortal Paints the Heavenly Rainbow
- Why Does the Reluctant Metaphysician Practice Tai Chi?
- Outward Introspection
- Creating Your Own Amalgamated Metaphysical Practice System
- Singing in the Shower
- *Aleynu:* "Oh come let us give praise to the source of the light of the world"
- Invocation to the Angelic Archetypes of the Four Directions
- Practicing the Opposite of Your Favorite Metaphysical Practice

Chapter 12:

- Animism and the Animal Forms of Qigong: Rewilding the World

Chapter 13:

- Using the Imaginal in Your Tai Chi Practice
- Bear Pouncing

- Bear Pushes a Tree
- Crane Flying
- *Axis Mundi:* The Investiture Ceremony Hidden in Tai Chi

Chapter 14:

- The Initiatory Dimensions of the Journey into the Cave at Delphi
- The Chant, "Return Again"
- A Ritual for Opening the Imaginal Caves of Our Lives

Chapter 15:

- The Mythic Journey Process: Transforming Your Demons
- It Is Not Stories Alone That Have the Capacity to Change Our Lives: Song, Postures, Stances, and Movements

Chapter 20:

- A Mourning Ritual: Rising in a Plane with the Full Moon

Chapter 22:

- Pelican Shares Its Qi with the World

APPENDIX III:
What Do Qigong and Psychotherapy Give Each Other?

Below is a summary of some of what Qigong and psychotherapy traditions give to each other:

What Psychological Traditions Give to Qigong?

Long before modern psychotherapy existed, "psychological awareness" and mindfulness practice were a part of the static and moving traditions of postural initiation such as Tai Chi and Qigong. However, those who practice these traditions today oftentimes do so without a conscious appreciation of how the tradition can help change their life stance.

As I discussed in my *Secrets to Living Younger Longer* book (2004), according to the research of Tomio (1994) and Goodman (1990), there is a long-lost tradition of postural initiation, which is oriented to facilitate a transformational process—a "shape-shifting" of the a person's life stance. In the Buddhist tradition, according to Tomio (1994), this involves a process whereby the practitioner's *klesas* (unconscious patterns such as envy, greed, and so forth.) are worked on in the process of holding various postures and engaging in various *natas* (physical exercises which utilized sequences of attack and defense). This involves working on the totality of one's life stance (*sthana*), "the totality of a student's perceived and acknowledged mental stance or concurrent position in regard to their self-understanding…[it] was also a term applied to describe an individual's physical condition and health balance" (Tomio, 1994, p. 221). Tomio puts forth the case that the wider tradition called the *Chuan Fa* went through a *diaspora,* but in its earlier form it included healing, self-defense, spiritual unfoldment, and changing the whole of the practitioner's life stance. He defines *"Chuan Fa"* as the associated arts surrounding the *Chuan.* *"Chuan"* usually translates to mean "fist." In my early publications (Mayer, 1996) I suggest the idea that the esoteric meaning of "fist" is the ability to metaphorically hold the five elements —fire, earth, metal, water, and wood—in one's hand. In later publications (Mayer 2004, 2007, 2009) I show how the *Chuan Fa* (associated traditions), as it joins with Western bodymind healing methods, can aid in helping us, as modern people, recover the soulful (Hillman, 1975) aspects of our primordial Selves. I suggest that the Western bodymind healing tradition can aid in the repairing of the broken pieces of the *Chuan Fa* by adding to the internal martial arts Qigong traditions, such as Tai Chi and the *Yi Chuan,* in the following ways:

What Psychotherapy Gives Qigong?

- *Psychotherapy provides Qigong practitioners a psychological framework and clinical methods for transmuting bodymind fixations.* Qigong and Tai Chi aid Western bodymind healing traditions in their ability to create sophisticated state-specific transcendent altered states of consciousness. Conversely, Western psychotherapy aids the traditions of postural initiation by providing a clinical base of knowledge that can give those suffering from various bodymind issues the ability to transmute, not just transcend, the issues that create many bodymind blockages. For example, in the case of Shelly's anxiety (Mayer, 2007, 2009) I showed how relaxation alone, including the induction of trance states, was not sufficient to produce healing. Cognitive restructuring, psychodynamic work, self-soothing and the transformative symbols from her dream life provided some of the necessary ingredients to transmute the psychological patterns rooted in early abandonment and fear of rejection. Likewise in the current book in the case of the hyper-tense executive I showed the importance of the psychotherapeutic "working through" process to create long-term resolution of long-standing issues.

Many concepts and clinical methods of modern psychotherapy are vital in healing the bodymind and activating the core energy of the soul. For example:

- Positive mirroring of the real self (Kohut, 1977, 1981)
- Transmuting introjects (Stolorow, 1987)
- Cognitive restructuring (Beck, 1979)
- Transforming self-identifications (Jacobson, 1964)
- Activating the separation-individuation process (Mahler, 1975)
- Deepening consciousness of psychological meanings. For example, Gendlin's Focusing method can aid a practitioner in becoming conscious of the psychological meanings of body blocks that emerge while holding static postures. As Gendlin has shown, when such new meaning arises, a "felt shift," occurs. From the perspective of *BMHP,* this is a Western embodiment of one aspect of the age-old tradition of shape-shifting.

Listing all of the specific contributions that modern psychotherapy has made to the ability to transmute bodymind fixations and heal the Self would be an overwhelming, extensive, and close to impossible task.

What Qigong Gives to Psychotherapy... (see BMHP, Chapter 21)

- *Qigong facilitates the reintegration of split-off aspects of the Self.* Many have spoken of the issues of self-fragmentation (Stolorow, 1987) and dissociation

(Krippner et al., 1997) commonly arising in the practice of psychotherapy. The psychological inner work necessary to enable one to regain "cohesion of the self" (Horner, 1990) is aided by the Western psychotherapeutic tradition, and I propose that it can be further enhanced by traditions of postural initiation such as Qigong and Tai Chi. (BMHP, Chapter 18)

- *Qigong aids transformation of self-identifications* (Jacobson, 1964) through the process of invoking state-specific states of consciousness that leads to "shape-shifting" (BMHP, Chapter 21).

- *…increases awareness of psychodynamic methods of self-soothing to reverse self-critical internalized messages* (Kohut, 1971, p. 64; Pearlman & McCann, 1992).

- *…imparts awareness of how illness often manifests from mind to energy, then to feelings, and then to bodily structures.*

- *…gives affect containment methods to deal with abreaction* (Gallo, 2002, p. 184) *and impulse control problems* (BMHP, Chapter 15).

- *…aids in healing trauma—reorganizing meaning…helps traumatized patients to regain a safety zone in their bodies.* Qigong traditions, particularly Tai Chi, are especially useful for those who suffer from conditions of sympathetic overload to create somatic safety zones (BMHP, Chapter 8).

- *…employs methods helpful to those who suffer from sympathetic nervous system overload, in cases of fibromyalgia and chronic fatigue* (BMHP, Chapter 13).

- *…contains useful behavioral health applications.* When appropriate, it is natural for such a time-tested method of behavioral healthcare to be applied to many issues that psychologists see in their everyday practices, including insomnia, anxiety, joint problems, energy deficiency, chronic pain, and so forth (see Chapters 6, 7, 13, 19).

- *…helps to heal the healer.* An integrative tradition includes self-healing, spiritual unfoldment, self-defense, and "trance-forming" one's life stance by "shape-shifting."

- *…provides a philosophic framework for how healing often comes from mind, to qi (energy), and then to the body.*

What Qigong Gives Psychotherapy and Behavioral Healthcare

- *Qigong contains useful relaxation methods.* Dr. Herbert Benson (1983) first coined the term "relaxation response," and showed its ability to ameliorate hypertension and cardiac problems. Qigong fits well into the guidelines stated by a National Institute of Health panel (1996) which concluded that integrating behavioral and relaxation therapies with conventional medical treatment is imperative for successfully managing many chronic conditions including chronic pain and insomnia. The panel did not endorse a single technique, but stated that a variety of techniques worked in lowering one's breathing rate, heart rate, and blood pressure as long as they included two features: a repetitive focus of a word, sound, prayer, phrase, or muscular activity, and neither fighting nor focusing on intruding thoughts.

Repetition is a key element in activating healing processes. For example, in energy psychology repeatedly tapping on points while focusing on new constructive beliefs is believed to be related to greater treatment success rates (Andrade & Feinstein, 2003); and in the Eye Movement Desensitization and Reprocessing (EMDR) method the repeated movement of the eyes from side to side while constructive beliefs are being stated is also believed to be integral to positive treatment outcomes. EMDR's originator Dr. Francine Shapiro (1995) suggests that neuronal bursts caused by the eye movements may be equivalent to a low-voltage current and therefore responsible for synaptic changes. She says, "It may be that the repetitive action of any…alternative stimuli—or even repetitive bursts of attention generate such a current. The shifting of the synaptic potential of the neural networks that include the dysfunctional material may cause the information to undergo progressively more processing with each set, until it arrives at an adaptive resolution" (Shapiro, 1995, p. 316).

- For thousands of years, Qigong and Tai Chi traditions have developed sophisticated ways to use whole-body repetition of movement, repetitive movements for isolated body parts, and repetition of sounds to promote healing.
- In addition to Qigong and Tai Chi, Taoist relaxation methods can also be beneficial to enhance the relaxation response. In *BMHP,* I have emphasized those methods that are easy to introduce into the modern healthcare setting, such as *Microcosmic* and *Macrocosmic Orbit Breathing.*

- *Qigong activates state-specific states of consciousness that are both relaxing and energizing.* Qigong does not only activate an altered state that is relaxing, it activates a state-specific state (Rossi, 1986) that is both relaxing and empowering. It resolves the activity-passivity paradox spoken of in the clinical hypnosis literature (Gorton, 1957, 1958). As Sturgis and Coe (1990) showed, whether hypnosis causes arousal or relaxation depends upon the suggestion made (p. 205). Hypnosis is not just about relaxation. Chinese Qigong has known this to be true for thousands of years in its concept called *"fongsung,"* relaxed awakeness. *Fongsung* can be helpful for alleviating symptoms of stress, as well as empowering those who have deficits in the areas of self-assertiveness, those who are stuck in victim roles as result of trauma, and so forth.

- *...contains specific healing and balancing energetic techniques.* For example: (a) static and moving Qigong from Bodymind Healing Qigong (Mayer, 2004, Appendix I) (b) sounds (c) acupressure points (d) Chi Nei Tsang (e) releasing body blocks by dispersing stagnant qi (f) embodying new life stances (Mayer, 2004, 2007).

- *Provides a pathway to develop many of the qualities proved useful by therapists who integrate meditation into psychotherapy* (Bogart, 1991). In conjunction with the psychotherapeutic process, Qigong and Tai Chi can help a person to:

  - Reciprocally inhibit unwanted behaviors (Wolpe, 1958)
  - Establish an observing self (Deikman, 1982)
  - Dissolve into the oneness of life
  - Facilitate ego cohesion in maintaining one's center when meeting the emotional tides of life
  - Develop a compassionate relationship to life issues

- *...enhances development of cohesiveness of self.* Whereas some meditative traditions are oriented to transcendence, for the most part Qigong and Tai Chi are body-oriented traditions that can lead to cultivation of "a cohesiveness of self" (Horner, 1990). Qigong and Tai Chi can facilitate healing the disintegration/reintegration of split-off aspects of Self.

For example, as discussed in Secrets...(Mayer, 2004), in *Yi Chuan Qigong* and Tai Chi practice, initiates are "tested" (*sili*) to see if they can maintain a cohesiveness of self and the sense of the ball of their body when pushed. This is called "maintaining integral force." Various aspects of the ball are tested as to whether one can "bounce," i.e. when pushed does the acolyte fight as he or she is lifted into the air, or is the sphere of the bodily self intact as he or she lands in a new location. (See illustrations of *fajing* with Master Tam in Chapter 19 of this book). From the perspective of BMHP, doing this practice in Tai Chi is not as important as finding the ability to maintain a cohesiveness of self when attacked by the forces of life.

In Chapters 15–18 of *BMHP* (Mayer, 2007) I showed how the interface of Qigong and psychotherapy can help one to practice maintaining self-cohesion and change one's life stance under stress. The way that Tai Chi and Qigong are usually practiced does not specifically focus on psychological issues (such as early emotional wounding and negative beliefs) and maintaining cohesiveness of the self; however, I have put forth the case that oftentimes shifts in a person's psychological stance in life can be a result of this practice. As we saw in the chapters on Bodymind Healing Psychotherapy, an approach that synergistically combines both the psychological dimension and these bodily oriented practices can help one to develop many of the qualities associated with ego strength—such as self-cohesion and a stable attachment style.

- *...helps those with reactive attachment styles to develop a cohesive center when the everyday issues of life assault or impinge upon ones sensibilities, and together with psychotherapy it may provide a bodily base for developing affect modulation skills, and affect tolerance.* (See Mayer, 2007, Chapters 16 and 17.)

- *...adds an energy cultivation practice beneficial to those who are depressed.* (Mayer, 2007, Chapter 12.)

- *...induces an altered state, which is helpful for issues with addiction.* (Mayer, 2007, Chapter 13.)

- *...contributes to the field of clinical hypnosis.* Qigong and Tai Chi are multifaceted traditions that are not only meditative, but they can be seen as forms of hypnosis accompanied by the health benefits known to be related to hypnosis (Rossi, 1986, 1988). They have an empirically time-tested record for enhancing health for a multiplicity of health-related conditions (Sancier, 1996; Pelletier, 2000). Qigong helps to *anchor* (Bandler & Grinder, 1979) state-specific states of awareness (Rossi, 1986) that help the patient to maintain a connection to the somatic ground of new healing pathways.

APPENDIX IV:
Bodymind Healing Psychotherapy (BMHP)
Contributions to the Field of Bodymind Healing

*Chapter numbers refer to BMHP book (Mayer, 2007)
**EP refers to Energy Psychology (Mayer, 2009)

A. **Contributions to Psychotherapy and Behavioral Healthcare:**

  • BMHP offers a ten step holographic, psycho-energetic method that combines traditional psychotherapies (e.g. cognitive/behavioral, psychodynamic/neo-analytic, humanistic/existential, Jungian/archetypal, hypnotherapeutic) with various ancient sacred wisdom traditions (e.g. symbolic process traditions, traditions of postural initiation, cross-cultural self-healing traditions) to contribute towards developing an "integral" transpersonal psychotherapy (Wilbur, 2000, Walsh 2006). {Chapters 2, 4, and 5.}

  • Drawing from ancient esoteric roots, BMHP brings to Western psychotherapy healing methods and perspectives from the Western (e.g. Eliade, 1954, 1958, 1959, 1964, 1965; Neumann, 1954; Needham, 1956; Meier, 1967; Rudhyar, 1970; Campbell, 1978; Jung, Collected Works; Edinger, 1985; Matthews, 1986; Hall, 1962; Goodman, 1990; Kingsley, 1999) and Eastern (e.g. Wilhelm, 1931; Luk, 1964, 1970; Schafer, 1977; Tomio, 1994; Mayer, 2004) mystery and initiatory traditions. {Chapters 2, 4, 5.}

  • Every psychotherapy has its view of what creates "change" in psychotherapy. Generally speaking Freudian and Neo-analytic therapists emphasize the role of transmuting family of origin issues, cognitive behavioral therapies emphasize the importance of belief and the restructuring of cognitions, Jungian Psychotherapy emphasizes the transforming power of symbols of the collective unconscious, Gendlin's "focusing" emphasizes being with the bodymind's "felt sense" and the "felt shift' that arises when new meaning arises from that process. Bodymind Healing Psychotherapy's meta-system perspective values all of these attributes of the process of change; it adds the dimension of drawing from traditions of postural initiation (Goodman, 1990; Tomio, 1994; Mayer, 2004, 2007) as well as the importance of changing one's "life stance" as being a key to creating change in psychotherapy.

- "The origin myth of any thing determines the way it is seen and its destiny, and creates a magical, incantational, hypnotic power" says Mircea Eliade, (1963). In this spirit, BMHP offers a new origin myth for psychotherapy that includes current psychotherapies, but it also adds ancient sacred wisdom traditions (including traditions of postural initiation (such as Qigong and Tai Chi), symbolic process traditions, and so forth. (EP, Mayer, 2009, Chapter 5.)

- BMHP introduces a meta-systematic perspective to offer to the schools of psychotherapy. To transcend the dichotomous, hierarchal, competitive view that leads to arguments about which psychotherapy is best, BMHP suggests using the astrological mandala as a psychotherapeutic meta-system. By looking at which place on the wheel a particular system holds, the contribution made by each system to the whole of psychotherapy can be appreciated (Mayer, 1977, 1983, 2007, 2009.)

- …adds methods from Qigong and other Bodymind Healing Psychotherapy techniques to the growing field of integrative medicine that is attempting to help resolve the current healthcare crisis. {Chapters 1, 2, 5-14.}

- …shows how Qigong in general, and when combined with BMHP in particular, can aid in healing psychological issues in a wide number of areas. The tradition contains useful relaxation methods, activates state-specific states of consciousness that are both relaxing and energizing, provides specific healing and balancing energetic techniques, helps to reciprocally inhibit unwanted behaviors, provides methods to help dissolve mental and somatic fixations, facilitates ego cohesion by helping our central equilibrium when meeting the emotional tides of life, helps develop a compassionate relationship to life's issues, enhances development of cohesiveness of self, enhances stability for those with reactive attachment styles, helps with developing affect modulation skills and affect tolerance, adds energy cultivation practices beneficial to those who are depressed, induces an altered state which is helpful in issues with addiction, aids in transformation of self identifications, adds beneficial methods for those who suffer from syndromes involving sympathetic nervous system overload, and provides tools to allow trauma victims to regain a safety zone in their bodies. {Chapter 21.}

- …reveals specific approaches and methods from the tradition of Qigong to aid treatment of behavioral healthcare patients suffering with specific conditions such as: anxiety, chronic pain, hypertension, insomnia, carpal tunnel syndrome, addictions, joint problems, depression, energy deficiency, and so forth. {Chapters 5–14.}

- ...enhances "subpersonality work" and hypnotherapeutic methods of trance induction by activating state-specific states of consciousness with an expanded view of cross-cultural traditions of shape-shifting. The symbolic process and somatic dimensions of shape-shifting traditions are combined and utilized to help the patient in psycho¬therapy cultivate new life stances. {Chapters 2, 4, 5, and 15.}

- ...contributes to the hypnotherapeutic tradition by coining the term, "transpersonal state-specific state of consciousness" to refer to the orientation of ancient sacred wisdom traditions to provide transpersonal anchors to help connect the person to specific healing altered states. I use the term "transpersonal," as did Dane Rudhyar, one of the first people to use this term in 1930, to refer to the movement of divine energies "beyond" the ego, but also to refer to a descent of spiritual energy "through" the person (Rudhyar, 1975, p. 38). Each Qigong and Tai Chi posture is like a letter in a Rosetta Stone of an ancient language of the bodymind—a link to a long-lost, right brain alphabet. Each letter (posture) represents a transpersonal state-specific state of consciousness that can bring a person into an altered state beyond his or her everyday life stance; as well it can bring specific needed healing states through the person. {Chapter 4, 5.}

- ...adds to the hypnotherapeutic technique of ideomotor signaling the method of "whole body, naturally arising, ideomotor signaling" to help patients harness the primordial pathways of the movement of the life force as it emerges at moments of "felt shift" in psychotherapy. Patients in psychotherapy, particularly at key moments of change, express movements that represent deep, often-unconscious transformative aspects of their psyches. The movements a martial artist uses to confront physical danger are often the same, or similar to, movements which spontaneously arise in a person as he or she deals with emotional dangers. This book, and the practices that lie at its foundation, can help healers learn to become more aware of the body's expression of the primordial Self as it moves toward empowerment and transformation. The ancient art of Qigong, of which Tai Chi is the best know system, contains some of the best and most primordial of these empowering movements. The clinician who is aware of these movements and their multifaceted meanings can help to grease the wheels and facilitate movement in the direction to where the patient's psyche is moving, on the path of its natural healing journey. {Chapter 16.}

- ...delineates a full range of symbolic process methods for psychotherapy by adding the power of somatic processes in general, and Qigong techniques in particular, to ground and further bring out the power of imaginal methodologies. {Chapter 4, 5, and 20.}

- …combines Gendlin's Focusing (1978) with Taoist breathing methods and the use of a mythic storytelling method (the *Mythic Journey Process*) to create important bodymind healing tools for psychotherapists. {Chapter 20.}

- …introduces the term "transcending/transmuting dialectic" to differentiate aspects of psycho-spiritual traditions that can help people rise above versus work through their life issues. BMHP focuses on how specifically Qigong, when integrated with Western psychotherapy, can have both attributes. {Chapter 5.}

- …introduces the *River of Life* practice that combines a Taoist breathing method and visualization techniques to help patients activate a transcendent state-specific altered state and transmute their psychological issues. {Chapter 5.}

- …adds to the Jungian notion of the psychoid nature of archetypes by further integrating the body with Jungian symbolic process methods, as in the *Mythic Journey Process*. {Chapter 4 and 20.}

- …introduces a method of "transpersonal hypnosis"—a directive, storytelling method that adds to the field of hypnosis an emphasis on connecting patients with the elements of the wider whole of which they are a part. {Chapter 19.}

- …provides practices and perspectives from ancient sacred wisdom traditions, including Qigong, to enrich the field of psychotherapists' vision and aid in expanding therapists' repertoire of clinical interventions. {Chapter 23.}

- …provides Qigong practices to aid in the process of "healing the healer" to help mental health professionals "recharge their batteries." {Chapter 24.}

- …extracts the essence of Qigong and Tai Chi to make it a trans-cultural tool, so that a therapist can use key elements of this tradition without practicing Qigong movements or ever mentioning a word about Qigong. {Chapter 5 and 18.}

B. **Bodymind Healing Psychotherapy's (BMHP) Contributions to Energy Psychology:**

Chapter numbers refer to Energy Psychology (Mayer, 2009).

- *BMHP* proposes using phenomenologically based anchoring methods to energy psychology methods, i.e. choosing the patients own movements at the moment of a "felt shift" to anchor new state-specific states of consciousness as a first-choice method. The most common meridian tapping methods are seen as just one of many energy psychology techniques that are part of researchers' differentiated attempts to determine which methods are best for which people at which times in this pre-paradigmatic stage of energy psychology's development. {Chapter 3 and 4.}

- ...advocates for explaining the meaning of acu-points used in treatment. In current energy psychology treatment, often the patient is instructed to tap on various points, but the meaning of those points is not usually discussed in detail. Bodymind Healing Psychotherapy proposes that "meaning" is a key healing agent, and is a significant component of activating "the mind-body trance state." Including the patient's understanding helps create a mindful, connected awareness, which has many positive consequences. {Chapter 3 and 16.}

- ...adds depth psychology methods to energy psychology with a focus on symbolic process methods, including the *Mythic Journey Process.* {Chapter 4 and 20.}

- ...broadens the field of energy psychology by including Qigong. {Chapter 3 and 4.}

- ...expands the foundation of energy psychology by introducing relevant historical foundation material and age-old methods. {Chapter 4.}

- ...adds to the self-touch methods of energy psychology the circle, stop, breathe, and feel method. {Chapter 3.}

For a more complete list of my written and media publications contributing to psychotherapy and the field of bodymind healing please click on this link to my website, http://www.bodymind healing.com/Articles/Contributions-to-Psychotherapy-&-Bodymind-Healing.html

APPENDIX V:
Author's Background, Training in, and Contributions to Tai Chi/Qigong

Training and Bio: My background includes training for over three decades in the internal martial arts at the Integral Chuan Institute with master Fong Ha where I was blessed to have learned Tai Chi Chuan, Xingyi Chuan (also spelled Quan), and Yi Chuan. Some of this training includes Tai Chi sword, saber and staff, the 108 long form of Tai chi Chuan right and left sides, the long form of San Shau. This curriculum has been added to through intensive training with Wuji Qigong master Cai Song Fang, and Yi Chuan Qigong masters Han XingYuan, and Sam Tam. Two-person "joining hands" (pushing hands) practice has been part of the curriculum; and various other aspects of the Chuan Fa (associated arts of the Chuan) have been part of the training including Taoist Alchemy. I have also trained with many other masters of medical Qigong such as Dr. Alex Feng in the Five Animal Forms of Hua Tau. I received a certification in Chinese Health Arts from the Acupressure Institute of Berkeley, CA.

I am grateful to have keynoted the National Qigong Association (2004a) with my presentation on Qigong Ancient Path for Modern Health, and to have been chosen to do a master level workshop at the Eleventh World Qigong Congress in San Francisco (2008). I have presented Qigong workshops at many hospitals (Mt Diablo Hospital; Alta Bates Hospital; University of California, Davis; and UC Medical Center, San Francisco), colleges (John F. Kennedy University, the California Institute of Integral Studies, American College of Traditional Chinese Medicine), and associations such as The American Association for Integrative Medicine. It has been a gift to have had the opportunity to offer many Tai Chi Chuan and Qigong workshops at various national and international locations such as at world-renowned Esalen Institute.

*To see more information on my background, training, publications, and contributions to Tai Chi/ Qigong please click this link, http://www.bodymindhealing.com/Articles/Dr-Mayer-s-Contributions-to-Tai-Chi/Qigong.html

Books and DVD's Which Have Contributed to Tai Chi/ Qigong:

Secrets to Living Younger Longer: The Self-healing Path of Qigong, Standing Meditation and Tai Chi (Mayer, 2004), is based on Qigong, a many thousand-year-old method of cultivating the energy of life (Qi) through movement, breath, touch, sound, imagery, and awareness. Scientific research documents how Qigong can lower blood pressure, increase balance and help with a wide variety of chronic diseases. But this is more than a book on Qigong exercises. Building upon those in the forefront of the mind-body healthcare revolution, this book creates a unique blend, combining Chinese Qigong and Western psychological methods with cross-cultural anthropological research. *Secrets…*is enlivened by mythic tales and imaginative teaching stories from ancient sacred wisdom traditions. *Secrets to Living Younger Longer* contains: A.) Health and longevity practices which are a synthesis of thirty years of my training with some of the most respected Tai Chi and Qigong masters which include practices to simultaneously relax and energize your body , strengthen immunity, reduce hypertension, limber your joints, release computer shoulder tension relieve chronic illnesses, prevent falls, alleviate insomnia and anxiety, find relief from arthritis and fibromyalgia, B.) Building upon the work of Tomio (1994) and Goodman (1990), this book presents intriguing historical research, which includes how Tai Chi and Qigong have roots in Shamanism and a lost, integrative Self-healing lineage that includes self-healing, spiritual unfoldment, self-defense, and changing your life stance. Rediscovering these underpinnings helps to deepen the healing potentials of these arts. C.) Standing Meditation: The key to making Qigong most effective. D.) Transforming your Life Stance: Realizations and examples from a psychologist from his life, and from his patients and students.

Bodymind Healing Qigong DVD. This DVD contains the Qigong and Tai Chi Chuan methods that I learned from 30 years training with some of the most respected masters of these traditions. After 25 years of teaching, I synthesized this knowledge into a single form. It is the experiential illustration of the Secrets...book. Here you can learn practices for: simultaneously relaxing and energizing your body; balancing energies of your internal organs, computer tension in the shoulders, activating your immune system, increasing balance, limbering joints, and more. Dr. Van der Kolk, Medical Director, Trauma Center, Boston University Medical School, uses this DVD in his training of trauma therapists and says, "I liked your Bodymind Healing Qigong DVD so much that in the course I taught we started with two or three sections of it every day."

Bodymind Healing Psychotherapy: Ancient Pathways to Modern Health (Mayer, 2004). Drawing from 30 years of training in Tai Chi and Qigong, I show how to integrate the essence of these practices into psychotherapy and into our healthcare without ever doing a Tai Chi/Qigong movement, and without mentioning a word about Qigong. Using case illustrations from my work in an integrated medical clinic the book shows how ancient and modern, East and West, psychotherapy and mind-body medicine cam be amalgamated to make a stronger integrative medicine. Theory, research, and case illustrations are blended to show how bodymind healing methods can help alleviate hypertension, chronic pain, insomnia, anxiety, depression, trauma, and other common issues plaguing the modern world.

Energy Psychology: Self- Healing Practices for Bodymind Health (Mayer, 2009, North Atlantic/ Random House, 2009). The new field of energy psychology is a leading-edge addition to psychotherapeutic traditions. Research is beginning to accumulate to validate its efficacy in dealing with trauma (Feinstein 2008a) and other psychological issues (Feinstein 2008b). The approach in my book, *Energy Psychology* (2009) expands the field of energy psychology from the well known energy psychology methods such as the Emotional Freedom Techniques by presenting an integral, comprehensive approach (Mayer, 2009b) to healing that combines leading-edge Western bodymind psychological methods with a broad system of ancient, sacred traditions. Incorporating my integral approach called *Bodymind Healing Psychotherapy,* the book *Energy Psychology* draws on Chinese medicine approaches, including Qigong and acupressure self-touch; kabalistic processes; methods drawn from ancient traditions of meditation and postural initiation (Goodman, 1990; Tomio, 1994). This book adds to the field of energy psychology several processes for inducing and anchoring internally generated energy such as Dr. Gendlin's, "focusing" method, psycho-mythological storytelling techniques that involve somatic and symbolic process methods from depth psychology, and naturally arising somatic movements that occur at a moment of "felt shift"(Gendlin, 1978).

Peer Reviewed Articles on Qigong:

My peer reviewed critiques of research methodology (1999, 2003) for examining Qigong's ability to lower hypertension has led to a more careful analysis (Guo, 2008) of potential confounding variables, and research protocols. My approach to alleviating hypertension integrates Qigong, Western behavioral health tools, and psychotherapy (1997b, 2007, 2009, 2010) thereby adding Qigong as a complementary, integrative healthcare method to those Eastern relaxation tools for heart care introduced by Ornish (1993, 1995) and others. My peer reviewed article, *Hypertension: An Integral, Bodymind Healing Approach,* was released in the journal, *Natural Standard: The Authority on Integrative Medicine* (February, 2010); and it more fully includes the importance of the integrating the psychological dimension with Qigong in the treatment of hypertension.

Summary of Author's Contributions to Integrating Tai Chi and Qigong with Western Bodymind Healing:

1. *Bodymind Healing Psychotherapy* (Mayer, 2007) broadens the definition of Qigong to include non-movement, energetic, psychological states that cultivate the universal life force, i.e. the most profound Qigong is following your true life's path. {Chapter 4 and 5}. Also, BMHQ broadens the definition of Qigong by including the use of imagery methods, i.e. *Qigong* is a many-thousand-year-old method of cultivating the energy of life through the use of posture, movement, breath, touch, sound, awareness, and imagery methods. Imagery methods, are not only defined as using images (as most Tai Chi and Qigong teachers do) to facilitate the understanding of and cultivation of Qi; but also "images" include those from the practitioners emotional life that arise while doing the practice that relate to blocks in his or her Qi.

2. BMHP shows how the meaning-making orientation of psychotherapy can add to Qigong by bringing psychological awareness to the postures and movements. For example, by "Focusing" (Gendlin, 1978) on the meaning of sensations, body blocks and postural misalignments while doing Tai Chi and Qigong movements, psychophysiological healing can occur; and this psychological awareness can help Tai Chi and Qigong practitioners to better use their practice to change their life stance. {Mayer, 2007, Chapter 5 and 15.}

3. *Bodymind Healing Psychotherapy* reveals how Qigong and Tai Chi are "soulful traditions" (Hillman, 1975; Moore, 1992). Qigong and Tai Chi have been seen as spiritual traditions. This book is the first to show how Qigong is also a "soulful tradition," following in the path of depth psychologists such as Hillman (1975) and Moore (1992). For example, while one is practicing Tai Chi and Qigong, instead of placing most emphasis on the transcendent, spiritual aspects induced by these practices, one can also focus on the memories, emotions, and images that arise in the practice—making it into a "soulful practice." {Mayer, 2007, Chapter 5.}

4. *In Secrets to Living Younger Longer* (Mayer 2004) it was shown that each Tai Chi posture has four different purposes: healing, spiritual unfoldment, self-defense, and to change the practitioners life stance.

5. *Bodymind Healing Psychotherapy* (BMHP) shows how each Tai Chi/Qigong posture is part of a "healing alphabet" that can form and induce different state-specific states of consciousness (Tart, 1968; Rossi, 1986)) that can be useful to Qigong practitioners and to the psychotherapeutic or behavioral health setting. {Mayer, 2007, Chapter 5 and 16.}

6. Much research shows that Qigong is a useful behavioral health tool due to its relaxing, healing movements (Sancier, 1996 a and b; Cohen, 1997, Pelletier, 2000). I added to the literature in the field that, Qigong does not only activate a relaxed, altered state, it activates a "state-specific state" (Tart, 1968; Rossi, 1986) that is both relaxing and empowering. This state is called *fongsung gong*, a Chinese term for relaxed awakeness. It can be helpful for alleviating symptoms of stress and empowering those who have deficits in the areas of self-assertiveness, those who are victims of trauma, and so forth (Mayer, 2004, 2007, 2009).

7. Qigong not only produces a relaxed state of awareness; but also in its unique way, it provides a pathway to develop qualities seen as useful by therapists who integrate meditation into psychotherapy (Walsh & Shapiro, 2006). Qigong and Tai Chi can reciprocally inhibit unwanted behaviors adding to Wolpe's (1958) behavioral approach; they can aid in developing an "observing self," adding to Deikman's (1982) transpersonal perspective; and they help to cultivate a "cohesiveness of self " adding to Horner's (1990) psychoanalytic methods. Qigong can help to "anchor" that state of awareness that helps to facilitate ego cohesion in maintaining one's center when meeting the emotional tides of life, adding to Bandler and Grinder's (1979) hypnotherapeutic approach to anchoring. Qigong, like many forms of meditation, can help us to develop a compassionate relationship to our life issues.

8. Qigong and Tai Chi are multifaceted traditions that are not only meditative but they can also be seen as forms of hypnosis, and therefore may result in similar health benefits known to be related to hypnosis (Rossi, 1986; Rossi & Cheek, 1988). Both have an empirically time-tested record for enhancing health for a multiplicity of health-related conditions (Sancier, 1996 a and b; Pelletier, 2000).

9. Qigong traditions, particularly Tai Chi, can help traumatized patients regain a safety zone in their bodies (Mayer, 2007, 2009).

10. Qigong adds an energy-cultivation practice beneficial to those who are depressed or suffer from sympathetic nervous system overload, such as in cases of fibromyalgia (Astin et. al., 2003; Fuzhong, 2012), chronic fatigue, and trauma.

11. The well-known relaxation and energizing attributes of Qigong can be effectively applied to many issues that psychologists see in their everyday practices-such as insomnia, anxiety, joint problems, energy deficiency, and chronic pain (Mayer, 2007). As an everyday practice, anyone can tap on these healing benefits, as has been reported in China for thousands of years before Western psychology emerged (Mayer, 2009).

12. Whereas some meditative traditions are oriented to transcendence, Qigong and Tai Chi are, for the most part, body-oriented traditions, which cultivate a cohesiveness of self (Horner, 1990). From an integrative perspective, the way Tai Chi and Qigong are usually practiced, they do not specifically focus on psychological issues, such as early emotional wounding and negative beliefs. However, I put forth the case that oftentimes transformations in a person's psychological stance in life can be a result of this practice. (Mayer, 2007, 2009).

13. Tai Chi and Qigong help those with reactive attachment styles to develop a cohesive center when the everyday issues of life assault or impinge upon one's sensibilities; and together with psychotherapy, these two Eastern disciplines may provide a bodily base for developing centered emotional expression (Mayer, 2007, 2009).

APPENDIX VI:
Quotations About Death

On Death

Those who are dead are never gone;
They are there in the thickening shadow
The dead are not under the earth;
they are in the tree that rustles,
they are in the wood that groans,
they are in the water that sleeps,
they are in the hut, they are in the crowd,
the dead are not dead.

Those who are dead are never gone, they are in the breast of the woman,
they are in the child who is wailing
and in the fireband that flames.
The dead are not under the earth;
they are in the fire that is dying,
they are in the grasses that weep,
they are in the whimpering rocks,
they are in the forest , they are in the house,
the dead are not dead.

—Birago Diop, *Earth Prayers*, p. 29

Do not stand at my grave and weep
I am not there. I do not sleep.
I am a thousand winds that blow.
I am the diamond glint on the snow.
I am the sunlight on ripened grain.
I am the gentle autumn rain.
When you wake in the morning hush
I am the swift, uplifting rush
of quiet bird in circling flight

I am the soft starlight at night
Do not stand at my grave
and weep.
I am not there. I do not sleep.

—Anonymous, *Earth Prayers*, p. 30

In one sense there is no death. The life of a soul on earth lasts beyond its departure. You will always feel that life touching yours, that voice speaking to you, that spirit looking out of other eyes, talking to you in the familiar things he touched, worked with, loved as familiar friends. He lives on in your life and in the lives of all others that knew him.

—Angelo Patri

What is the best way to meet the loss of one we love? By knowing that when we truly love, it is never lost. It is only after death that the depth of a bond is truly felt, and our loved one becomes more a part of us then was possible in life.

—*Kung Fu* series

Everyone dies, but no one is dead.

—Dalai Lama, *Advice on Dying*

I died as a mineral and became a plant; I died as a plant and rose to animal; I died as animal and I was a man. Why should I fear? When was I less by dying? Yet once more I shall die as man to soar with angels blest. But even from an angel I must pass on: all except God must perish. When I have sacrificed my angel soul, I shall become what no mind ever conceived.

—Rumi

To begin depriving death of its greatest advantage over us, let us adopt a way clean contrary to that common one; let us deprive death of is strangeness, let us frequent it, let us get used to it; let us have nothing more often in mind than death…We do not know where death awaits us; so let us wait for it everywhere. To practice death is to practice freedom. A man who has learned how to die has unlearned how to be a slave.

—Michel de Montaigne, *The Essay*

Endnotes

Introduction

1. For the story about the current economy's effects on middle class students see (www.alternet.org/news-andviews/article/513088/in_a_rare_turn_for_msm%2C_%2760_minutes%27_covers_%22the_other_america%22/).
2. For example, one of the best practices for "contending with, and struggling with" an opponent is the practice of Tai Chi Push Hands. Here one learns how to struggle without struggling; how to not collide nor to separate with a force in life. This internal martial arts practice then becomes a metaphor for dealing with other facets of life.
3. I was very moved to see when I was at the Occupy Oakland strike on November 2, 2011 that the protesters from the 99% movement put a sign on the door Oakland City Hall that said, "Occupy your mind." I could not help remembering the John Lennon song, "You say you want a Revolution, you better free your mind instead," in the1968 *White Album*. That song was sung by of those of us in the cultural revolution of that era when Uranus (the higher mind) and Pluto (chthonic revolution) were in conjunction; now in 2011 with Uranus-Pluto in a square aspect it seems synchronistically fitting that the next stage in the struggle of our culture to open and occupy the higher mind is taking place.

Chapter 1

1. I will tell you later about one of my favorite sacred caves in the mountains of Greece near the Oracle of Delphi where many have gone to experience renewal and transformative vision at a time when they have lost their way in life (see Chapter 14).
2. However, when careful research methodology is used, exercise has only moderate effects on deep-seated depression (Mead, 2009).
3. I will tell you more about how Tai Chi and Qigong function as spiritual practices to bring you back to the experience of the Great Goddess of Stillness (called wuji, the mother of Qi) in Chapter 9. Also, you'll hear about how the psycho-spiritual path I developed called Bodymind Healing psychotherapy is a way of finding a new life stance that can bring you to the Cave of New Creation (see Chapters 14 and 15).
4. See Chapter 10 for a discussion of how in the Jewish mystical tradition there is another spiritual garment called the levusha that one imagines as composed of the threads of one's uniquely manifested divine qualities. The practitioner of Jewish mysticism imagines this garment as a protective covering, which enshrouds his or her sacred life, similar to the Eastern concept of one's aura.
5. See Chapter 21 for a more extensive discussion of the student loan crises. To see a documentary on the effects of rapacious lending policies to our students see *Default: The Student Loan Controversy* (www.defaultmovie.com).
6. In this sense, the Reluctant Metaphysician has similarities to "the wooden path" (*Holzwege*) about which Heideggar speaks. Holzwege a way of approaching philosophy that is more akin to open-ended intellectual wandering than to purposeful or goal-oriented thinking (Heideggar, 2003). Another more playful example of iconoclastic interpretations of holidays is the holiday *Festivus,* originally conceived by writer Dan O'Keefe in 1966, and then reaching iconic stature through the *Seinfeld* TV show in 1997 as an alternative to the materialistic fanfare of Christmas.

Chapter 2

1. Later chapters will focus more specifically on how methods of postural initiation and finding a new "life stance" benefited my patients. For example, Chapter 18 contains a case illustration involving a patient who was bullied, and how he found a new life stance.
2. See Chapter 10 for more about the Hatha Yoga practice I do each morning; and Chapter 11 contains a broad range of other practices for Reluctant Metaphysicians.
3. In Chapters 10 and 15, I will tell you about I will tell you about Focusing and Dr. Eugene Gendlin. See Chapters 15–17 for more about Bodymind Healing Psychotherapy.
4. For example, in Chapter 15 I will give you an experience of The Mythic Journey Process (Mayer, 1982, 1993, 2007) that I developed to help my patients ground their life stories by calling forth characters from archetypal myths, while using their bodies' felt sense through Dr. Gendlin's Focusing method.

Chapter 4

1. See Chapter 8 for the story of my Vision Quest.

Chapter 5

1. See Chapter 14.
2. I will tell you more about the evolving story regarding plant medicines in Chapters 21 and 23.
3. The moon's north node refers to the point where the moon's orbit intersects the ecliptic.
4. The Aquarian Revolution refers to the zodiacal ages that are based on the precession of the equinoxes (also called the precession of the earth's rotational axis). It takes approximately 25,868 years for the precession to go fully around all signs of the zodiac; each age is approximately 2160 years. Rudhyar (1969) and Tarnas (2007) outline the symbolic meaning of each of the ages. Many different astrologers disagree when precisely the Aquarian Age begins. Aquarius (an air sign) is ruled by Uranus derives its symbolic meaning from the fact that it exists beyond the seen (Saturn), and revolves around its axis in a different way than the other planets. Thus its symbolism relates to electric technologies, and revolution. Some astrologers believe the Aquarian age began at the time of the Wright Brothers flight in 1903, the beginning of moving from the Piscean Age of water to an age ruled by air power. Towards the end of the time of the first degree of the Aquarian Age (72 years) and the beginning of the second degree was the time of the birth of computers, breakdown of traditional religions, exploration of altered states of consciousness, the birth of the counter cultural hippie movement, and so forth—all apt symbols for the archetype of Uranus (and its mythological association with Prometheus).
5. But perhaps "the universe" has the last laugh because, as I will tell you about more later, Jupiter and Uranus were conjunct at the time that the rebellious forces that ignited the revolution in Tunisia in December 17, 2010.

Chapter 6

1. See Gendlin, E. Focusing, Bantam Books (1978).
2. I will have much more to say in later chapters about how this book, The Secret of the Golden Flower, and the practices of Microcosmic Orbit Breathing, influenced my path in future years.
3. See http://en.wikipedia.org/wiki/Entheogen.
4. Transpersonal psychologist and author Roger Walsh (2009) does a nice job of clarifying Jung's term when he says, "A *Gnostic intermediary* is a person who is able to effectively translate and transmit contemplative wisdom from one culture or community to another. This translation and transmission can be across cultures (e.g. Indian yogic wisdom to Western culture) or across times (from archaic language and concepts into contemporary forms.... What does this require? Well, it seems to require three tasks and three corresponding capacities:

• First, one must imbibe and become the wisdom oneself, since while one can have knowledge, one must be wise. This, of course, is a major task. In fact, when we are talking about profound contemplative wisdom it can take a lifetime. The essence of this step is contemplative practice.

• The second requirement for Gnostic intermediaries is linguistic and conceptual competence. They must master the language and conceptual system of the people and culture to which they wish to communicate. For professionals, this means mastering one's professional conceptual frame-work, e.g., psychology or philosophy.

• The third requirement is translational. Gnostic intermediaries must be able to translate the wisdom from the wisdom bearing culture or tradition into the language and conceptual system of the recipient community. The goal is to make the wisdom understandable, legitimate, and even compelling."

5. If at this point in my life you said to me that this force that was powerful enough to uproot me could have something to do with anything astrological I would have laughed at such a thought, discounting any possibility of such a seemingly irrational claim. As I look back at this time in my life, however, it is fascinating that in my chart transiting Uranus was coming within one degree of conjunction with my natal Neptune (at 6 degrees, 4 minutes of Libra) on the day of my big dream, June 21st 1971.

Many years later I was to find out that this conjunction happens every 172 years; therefore, many people will never have this transit take place in their chart in their lifetimes. Archetypal astrologers consider this meeting of the Uranus (the Promethean archetype) with Neptune (the planet that symbolizes waters of dissolution) to have been synchronistic with the pervasive transformation of our Western culture's underlying vision and with widespread spiritual awakenings that took place during the time between 1985 and 2001. This was when Uranus-Neptune was conjunct within a 15-degree orb (Tarnas, 2010 p. 148).

Though certainly one must be circumspect in conflating astrological synchronicities with multifactorial causes, it is fascinating how symbols can give meaning to external events. The widespread dissolution (Neptune) of old worldviews symbolized by this conjunction goes along well with the heyday of Transpersonal Psychology; at that time behavioral and psychodynamic theories opened to a wider sea of cross-cultural exploration about the nature of the human psyche and the exploration of the psychology of consciousness. Also, many Jungian psychologists see the symbolism of Neptune as related to the collective unconscious, the sea of consciousness that all of us share and which is the home of the archetypes that give birth to our unique selves. However, the meaning of Uranus-Neptune conjunctions is not limited to just psychological domains. In the technological domain, these planetary archetypes played a ubiquitous role during this period of historical time—with electronic communications (Uranus) such as mobile phones and computers having increased the sea of connectedness (Neptune) between us all.

Equally interesting is the information coming from astrological historians, that during the time of this Uranus and Neptune conjunction the Berlin Wall came down in November of 1989, aptly called a "revolution by dissolution," reflecting a Uranus conjunct Neptune theme. Another interesting coincidence is that this same conjunction occurred during the time of 412 B.C.E. to 397 B.C.E., the years of Socrates' most influential teachings, during the final decade and a half of his life, which included the entire period of Plato's study with him. For a more in depth discussion of the symbolism of this conjunction in many spheres of life see Richard Tarnas' writings ((Tarnas, 2007 pp. 355–366; Tarnas, 2010, pp. 150–153).

An interesting historical parallel to this Uranus-Neptune conjunction in my chart, at the time of my once in a lifetime move to the West coast to learn more about the wider consciousness that pervades life, is that the birth of Platonic philosophy and the Western metaphysical tradition took place when one of the earlier Uranus-Neptune conjunctions occurred. The time of my Uranus-Neptune conjunction in 1971 certainly was a time when the walls of my old world dissolved (Neptune), opening the river of my life into a sea of wider cross-cultural experiences, spiritual practices, and metaphysical explorations.

So, is a "glass bead game" (Hesse, 1982) being playing with our life? How much do our dreams and archetypal astrological configurations create resonant fields or align with synchronistic turnings of the cosmic clocks of our lives? One question that arises in the mind of the metaphysically inclined hermeneutician is, "What kind of multi-factorial forces are at play in creating the images that rise within us to guide us to our destinies?"

Chapter 7

1. Two issues can be raised about the approach in Tarnas' epochal work. First, his analysis of the correspondences between cosmos and events rests upon using a 15-degree orb for the planetary aspects to four axial alignments. Since there are four axes and 15 degrees on both sides, of a square, conjunction, and opposition aspect (4 x 30 degrees = 120 degrees out of a 360 degree circle), the chance of a correspondence by chance is one in three. This is not a high enough standard to reach normal scientific probability levels of .05 or .01. Secondly, it can be argued that his extensive and impressive collection of supportive data may be inadvertently "cherry picking" data, i.e. there could be unconscious bias in choosing historical, cultural, and scientific correspondences to fit these axial alignments. To learn more about various "positive confirmation biases" see http://en.wikipedia.org/wiki/Confirmation_bias. One way to further verify the validity of the correspondences would be to survey historians, cultural experts, and scientists who know nothing about astrology, and ask them what they think were the most important dates for various achievements in their disciplines—this could rule out selection bias. These probative questions that I raise show why I prefer to take a "meaning reorganization" point of view rather than a "hidden reality" point of view (Fingarette, 1963) towards astrological correspondences. The meaning reorganization view does not preclude that a hidden reality may exist. In my written works I prefer to put the emphasis on allowing Mystery to live, thus leading a person to their own investigation to find their truth (Mayer, 1977, 1983).

2. I will tell you more about the part that Esalen played in my evolution later in this book (see Chapter 22).

Chapter 8

1. The term "experiential metaphysics" has been used in academic settings to discuss various epistemological and ontological questions such as whether we can ever know a phenomena of experience in itself apart from our own interpretive overlay (Sherover, 1987; Kline, 1989). The term has been associated with naturalistic philosophy by such thinkers as Dewey (Shook, 2000), and with the psychology of religion by prolific philosophers such as William James (Lamberth, 1999). Each different exploration into the territory of experiential metaphysics has its particular focus.

2. See Chapter 16.

3. When I was in college, I developed a system of encapsulating all the significant points in a book, and in every book I have read since then I use this system. I summarize the main points of the book on the inside of the back cover. Then I turn down the corners of all of the most important pages; and I put stars in green magic marker next to the most important concepts and green check marks next to facts. I underline in green magic marker the most important lines of text and underline in yellow magic marker the specific facts. This way I can get to any almost any idea that I have read in the last three decades in a few minutes. Some might call this obsessive; I reframe this as strategic focus in the service of a higher goal. I view this character trait symbolically represented by my Sun conjunct Uranus in Gemini my Eighth House of metaphysics and its relationship to the other configurations there. These aspects represent well my transpersonal excitement about world of ideas and its connection with with my dharma (the dharma point of my chart, the north node of the moon is also in the Eighth House in Gemini). Just like many of us would like to hold on to memories of past lovers, since I have a love affair with metaphysics (Venus in the Eighth House of metaphysics) I like to ground (Venus in Taurus) these ideas by having easy access to the memories. No one symbol does justice to any of our character quirks; but it is an illuminating exercise to look at our traits through the lens of symbols, and make our stories and life meaning from there. This can connect our ways of Being to the wider whole of which we are a part.

4. For a wider discussion the emergence of the metaphysical pluralism of the late twentieth century and its synchronistic relationship to the Uranus-Neptune conjunction and other astrological aspects of this era see cosmologist Rick Tarnas' view (Tarnas, 2010, p. 151).

5. See Chapter 9 for the story about my possible relationship to the Baal Shem Tov.

Chapter 9

1. www.skthoth.com.

2. To see more about the astrology of celebreties see, www.astrotheme.com/celebrities_distribution.php.

3. Further exploration of both sides of the debate between astrologers and sceptics can be found at the following locations: For the sceptics view see www.skepsis.nl/mars.html. For chronologies that put the sceptics critiques into proper perspective see the article, "A Brief Chronology of the 'Mars Effect' Controversy," at www.planetos.info/marchron.html. At this site are references where serious researchers can begin further exploration. For a fascinating on-line discussion with Roger Walsh, Will Keepin, and the public see, Is our fate in the stars? A dialogue on astrology, (2004), *Knowledge Center,* www.kc.mslater.com/~kfi/kc/viewitem.php?id=170&catid=169&kbid=ionsikc.

Chapter 10

1. See Chapters 14 and 15 to see more about the part that the Greek mystery tradition played in my life.

2. See Chapter 16 to see how to use the astrological mandala as a psychotherapeutic meta-system.

3. See Chapters 15-17 for a description of how I extended the terrain of psychology to include various the ancient sacred wisdom traditions.

4. As I mentioned in Chapter 8, my work with Dane Rudhyar led me to write a doctoral dissertation and a book on how astrological metaphor could be used as a language of personality in psychotherapy.

5. See Chapter 5 for a list of the *Mystery…book's* contributions to Astrology.

6. See Chapter 11 for a more extensive discussion on Microcosmic Orbit Breathing.

7. See Chapter 15 for a description of the Mythic Journey Process.

8. Actually, there are transcendent and transmuting elements in both Eastern and Western spiritual traditions.

9. In Chapter 15, I discuss the role of "personification" in the Mythic Journey process.

10. There are other authors as well who have written about the integration of Jungian psychotherapy and the body, for example: Conger, J. (2005). *Jung & Reich: The Body as Shadow* (2nd. Ed.). Berkeley: North Atlantic Books. Sassenfeld, A. (2008). The body in Jung's work: Basic elements to lay the foundation for a theory of technique, *The Journal of Jungian Theory and Practice,* C. G. Jung Institute of new York, Vol. 10. No (1), pp. 1-13, www.junginstitute.org/pdf_files/JungV10N1p1-20.pdf—see Sassenfeld's bibliography at this URL for information about the role of the body in Jung's work, and a bibliography of references about Jung's work as it relates to the body, somatic psychotherapy, movement therapy, and so forth.

11. See Chapter 17 for illustrations of how Tai Chi movements can help to ground symbolic inner work and help to create a new life stance.

12. Building upon Hillman's ideas, in my Mythic Journey Process (MJP) the storyteller personifies the specific "Demons" that arise from the felt sense of a body block or tension in the bodymind. You write down the various ways that you tried to defeat the Demons, and then say "Then one day…" Then one day, what happened? A very amazing thing happens for nearly everyone who does the MJP—an image or story arises that resolves, or "brings soul" to, a life issue. See Chapter 15 for the Mythic Journey Process.

13. In Chapter 17 and 18 I discuss how I discovered, along with my patients, how at a moment of "felt shift" various physical gestures often arise that are similar to Tai Chi Qigong movements When a therapist is aware of their meanings, new archetypal ways of being can be anchored in the bodymind.

14. See an illustration of *fajing* practice in Chapter 19.

15. The book *Acu-Yoga* (1981) was written by my friend Michael Gach, the past owner and director of the acupressure institute of Berkeley, where I enjoyed receiving a Chinese Health Arts certification in 1990.

16. Eliade, M., *The Forge and the Crucible,* University of Chicago, 1956, pp. 79–86. One of the derivations of the word shaman is the Vedic sram, to heat oneself. According to an Eskimo shaman, "Every real shaman has to feel an illumination in his body, in the inside of his head or in his brain, something that gleams like fire..." Evan Wentz says the same thing about Tibetan Yogis who produce a psychic heat that renders them impervious to temperature, even to long-term exposure to snow while wrapped only in sheets dipped in icy water. See Achterberg, J., *Imagery and Healing,* op. cit., p. 34.

17. Regarding my interest in intellectual journeys to foreign cultures, it was fascinating for me to see that in my astrological chart, Mercury (symbol of the mind's interest) is in the ninth house, which astrologers believe rules philosophy and long journeys to foreign cultures. So, according to astrological theory it was understandable that I would be inclined to have an interest in intellectual (Mercury) far journeys to the philosophies of the Far East, and China.

18. From my research in shamanism, I later called this, "a shape-shifting of a person's life stance" (Mayer 2004, 2007, 2009).

19. See Chapter 18 for more about the integration of the traditions of Tai Chi and psychotherapy, and how this integration leads to seeing psychotherapy as a method of changing one's life stance.

20. For more on the integration of psychotherapy and ancient sacred wisdom traditions see Chapters 15–17.

21. The *Ain Sof,* of the Kabbalah, is similar to the meaning of Wuji in the Qigong tradition.

22. I will tell you more about how these songs have become an important part of my life in the next chapter about practices (Chapter 11).

23. In my last books (Mayer, 2007, 2009) there is a more detailed discussion about the connections between Abulafia's methods and my River of Life practice.

CHAPTER 11

1. In Chapters 16–18 I will tell you how, after being initiated into these practices, I brought many of its healing methods to my patients and students.

2. There are quite a few reports of negative results that come from excess practice of Qigong. I have had two patients referred to me over the years who may have developed qi deviations from obsessive practice. When one of these people came to see me, his prior excessive practice may have led to his developing a tumor behind his third eye from overly focusing there; and likewise, another patient may have developed a condition like trigeminal neuralgia from his excessive focus on his belly (tan tien). These were cases of people who did the practice in a compulsive manner for many hours at a time, for many days, and for many years.

3. Earlier I discussed how my name was similar to the name Michael Maier, the alchemist who taught Carl Jung's grandfather about the Western mystery tradition of symbolism (Jung, 1961, p. 233). I spoke about the metaphysical idea that the Kabalistic resonant theory of naming (Suares, 1992) might make me feel an association to him. If there is a part of me that resonates with being "his reincarnation," I wish my ideas would be as well received as his were. Even though Jung talked about the psychoid (physical) dimension of archetypes towards the end of his career, in my opinion, current Jungians for the most part resist the bringing of the archetypes into the somatic and experiential realm. (See my other endnote reference in Chapter 10 to Sassenfeld's article regarding some of the ways that the somatic dimension has been spoken to by some Jungian authors.)

   As Carl Jung was able to survive the rejection by his Freudian colleagues through his faith in his individuation process, so was I. For me, I believe it is partially in the weaving hands of the Goddess of Fate as to whether the unique twists in the garment of my individuation process, and my own life story, will someday bring the experiential elements of the Secret of the Golden Flower and its relationship to Qigong to the Jungian community and to psychology.

Endnotes

Every soul sees a flower in his or her own unique way. Some Jungian scholars have equated the practice of The Golden Flower with the evocation of "consciousness" or the "individuation process" (Beebe, 2006). I believe the practice is much wider and deeper than any one conceptual framework, including mine, can hold. For example, I do not believe it is equatable with the creation of "consciousness" per se, yet aspects of consciousness such as intention (*yi*), heart/mind unity (*xin*), spirit (*shen*) and the void, the mother of qi (*wuji*) are all constellated by the practice.

The same issue about interpretative schemas in my opinion is true of the idea of "individuation" as it is applied to the Secret of the Golden Flower. Some leaders in the field of Jungian psychology look at the end of the out-breath that the text emphasizes and describes "the turning the light around" as related to coming to the place where thought itself arises (Beebe, 2006). Just as each of us projects onto a Rorschach inkblots our unique meanings, we do the same with a flower (including a Golden Flower). From my background with Dr. Gendlin's "focusing method" I see the light turning around as related to the connection between Gendlin's idea about the constellation of felt meaning that arises from "focusing on the felt sense in the body.

In the early 1980s I brought up to Dr. Gendlin that in the *Secret of the Golden Flower* text it speaks of "sinking the plumb line;" and I explained that this helps people to "focus" on their feelings (the Water of Life that waters the inner flowering of our Being). Even at that time in my life I was following the path of my medicine name of *Michael, Two Streams Joining,* and in that spirit I tried to bring together Focusing with Taoist practices. So, I told Dr. Gendlin that I thought he was rediscovering what had been talked about in certain ancient traditions such as the arising of felt meaning after the exhalation in Taoist microcosmic orbit breathing. I suggested to him that he use Taoist breathing from the *Secret of the Golden Flower* in addition to his methods for his clearing a space step, which he liked. (I wrote an article about this in his *Focusing Folio* in 1982.)

I have always been sensitive to being limited by any one story about the meaning of anything, so in the metaphysical/psychological system I was in the process of constructing I did not want to be limited to just these two rivers (of Taoism and Focusing) joining.

As an aside, an astrologer might say that this quality of mine may be based in my natal sun being conjunct Uranus, and therefore like the planet Uranus being outside of the boundaries of Saturnian limits, so do I seek to be outside any limited system. A rationalist would say that there are many other more simple explanations for why I like to be outside of fixed boundaries. For example, another more simple explanation for this quality of mine would be that I come from a Jewish background where in an old shtetl in Europe my ancestors survived by being outside the boundaries of others' ways. The astrologer might answer that my particular Sun-Uranus conjunction is in Gemini in the house (8th house) of metaphysics, which could lead to a propensity to use my outside the box thinking in the arena of metaphysics.

4. In the rest of this chapter I will give you more of a sense of the experiential dimensions of the Golden Flower practice. I will describe how the practice bloomed for me in three decades of practice: (1) How the practice saved my life in the desert in Israel, (2) How it fit into to the wider practice of Qigong, (3) How I discovered deeper dimensions of the practices while scuba diving in Tahiti; (4) How it brought light to my study of psycho-mythology, and (5) How I added my unique twist to it in the River of Life practice I developed so that I could apply it to help my patients and students. See my *Secrets...* (2004) book for further discussion.

5. I discuss more completely the transcending and transmuting dimensions of the River of Life in my last two books (*Bodymind Healing Psychotherapy* and *Energy Psychology*).

6. In my last books I have shared other standing postures, the historical and shamanic origins of this practice, and how it leads to the experience of "the Golden Ball" (Mayer, 2004).

7. Though Basmajian's study shows us that there is evidence that human beings can learn to voluntarily control the electrical activity of a single cell, such power should be used cautiously. Be careful not to focus too much on an area that is in need of healing, because there is already often an excess of energy in that place. It is often time better to focus on the river of qi that moves through that blocked area than on

the spot itself (particularly if the disturbed area is already in a condition of excess). The practice of the Yin-Yang Balancing Method cultivates this awareness (Mayer, 1996, 2009).

8. In other traditions this dissolving experience is called by different names such as oceanic consciousness, dissolutio, Samadhi, or the mystical experience of oneness. It is not the purpose of this book to differentiate between these different traditions other than to say that in the Qigong wuji tradition the emphasis is placed upon the energetic, experiential dimension.

9. Not all Yi Chuan Qigong practitioners call these postures by the same name, or attribute the same intention to them. As in all fields of life, traditionalists debate with iconoclasts.

10. See Chapter 18 to see the story of one of my patients for whom this posture helped him to find a new life stance.

11. To see more information on the correlation between the practices of the Golden Ball in Yi Chuan Qigong and in cross-cultural mythology see my *Secrets...* book (2004).

12. To say that something is "nothing but" a hypnotic induction is a product of reductionistic thinking that belittles and attempts to reduce a phenomena to less than its holistic attributes. It is now well known that imagery (one of the key elements of hypnosis) has much documented science to show its role in healing (Achterberg, 1985; Rossi, 1986, 1988). Just because a phenomena, or practice, has hypnotic elements to it does not invalidate it. In fact it may pave the way to showing the substance behind its efficacy to the Western mind due to the substantial research on clinical hypnosis.

13. In my other books (Mayer, 2004, 2007, 2009) I have discussed the scientific research related to this experience. Also, see Oschman's book, *Energy Medicine, The Scientific Basis* (2000).

14. As you will see in Chapter 18, my work with Standing Meditation became to integrate it with modern psychology. I asked, "What do our postures say about our life stance? What are each of us aware of while Standing?"

15. To support the claim of the extraterrestrial origin of Qigong, Hausdorf cites the book, Po Wu Chih (Record of the Investigation of Things), a third century A.D. text by Chuang Hua (Hausdorf, 1994, p. 73).

16. There are Four Kabalistic Levels of Biblical Interpretation: (1) *Peshat* (lit. "simple"): the direct interpretations of meaning (2) *Remez* (lit. "hint[s]"): the allegoric meanings (through allusion). (3) *Derash* (from Heb. *darash*: "inquire" or "seek"): *midrashic* (Rabbinic) meanings, often with imaginative comparisons with similar words or verses. (4) *Sod* (lit. "secret" or "mystery"): the inner, esoteric (metaphysical) meanings, expressed in Kabbalah. http://en.wikipedia.org/wiki/Midrash.

    Likewise, certain Buddhist Scholars (Tomio, 1994) have spoken of the four purposes of the Chuan Fa (the associated internal martial arts traditions).

17. For a more complete discussion of how each Tai Chi and Qigong movement is an initiation into four dimensions of purpose see my *Secrets...*book (Mayer, 2004).

18. In Chapter 19 you will see some illustrations of various "Push Hands" practice. There are many sources for learning more about Tai Chi Push Hands including my *Secrets...*book that included an exploration of the Tai Chi tradition (Mayer, 2004).

19. For more about a postmodern viewpoint on Tai Chi see Chapter 13.

20. For a summary of the contributions I have made to the Tai Chi and Qigong tradition see Appendix V.

21. By transposing our emotional qualities into elements of nature a psycho-mythological healing can take place. See Chapter 18 for a discussion of how "shape-shifting" relates to psychotherapy and changing one's life stance.

22. The short set of Bodymind Healing Qigong is in the back of my last two books (Mayer 2007, 2009).

23. Specifically, a few of my favorites are: Middle Eastern music—*Eliyahu & the Qadim Ensemble* by Eastern Wind; Australian Didgeridoo music—*Nomad* by Australian Music International; *Afro-Celt Sound System, Volume 1: Sound Magic* by Real World; and music from the *Spirit of the Rainforest* by Terry Oldfield.

24. See *The Journal of the Foundation for Shamanic Studies*, Shamanism Annual, Special Issue Highlighting Mongolian Shamanism, Issue 24, December, 2011.

25. See The Cultural Conservancy, www.sacredland.org.

CHAPTER 12

1. An illustration of the movement Pa Kua Fish can be found in my *Secrets...*book, p. 163, or it is in most other illustrative books on Tai Chi.

CHAPTER 13

1. In Chapter 18 I will tell you about how before I learned of Dr. Goodman's work. I discovered that at moments of change ("felt shift") in psychotherapy that hand movements or gestures would arise that could be anchored in a patient's imagination to create new ways of Being. For example, a patient who was self-critical might spontaneously put a hand on his or her heart. Or, a Tai Chi posture such as Repulse Monkey would naturally emerge for a patient who had never practiced Tai Chi, which expressed some primordial feeling such as, "Stay away from me, I need boundaries."

2. There is increasing awareness about the biases and false claims that have come from peer reviewed "scientific research." An article in *PLoS Med,* has claimed that there is less than a 50% chance that the results of any randomly chosen scientific paper will be true, Ioannidis JPA (2005) Why most published research findings are false. *PLoS Med* 2(8): e124. doi:10.1371/journal.pmed.0020124. Following up on the *60 Minutes* expose' of the false cancer cure claims at prestigious Duke University by Dr. Potti, Dr. Mercola in his article, "Is his Fraud Too Big Even for 60 Minutes," pointed out that such falsification of data is not unusual, and has also taken place with painkillers, autism, and other areas of research, www. mercola.com/sites/articles/archive/2012/03/10/chemotheraphy-is-medical-fraud.aspx?e_cid=20120310_ DNL_art_1.

CHAPTER 14

1. *Indian Folklore Atlas of Hot Springs National Park* by Marcus Phillips and Sandra Long. Copies of the *Folklore Atlas* may be obtained from the Garland County Historical Society, 328 Quapaw Avenue, Hot Springs, AR 71901. 501-321-2159, www.manataka.org/page104.html.

2. For more about the story of the defeat of Medusa by Perseus see Chapter 15.

3. The political, economic, and ecological dimensions of the work of the Reluctant Metaphysician are addressed in the last three chapters of this book.

CHAPTER 15

1. See my last books for more about how to deal with the obstacles that are in the way of allowing the power of a new life story to change our old life story (Mayer, 1993, 2007, 2009). This is the work of works of our lives.

2. You will see this illustrated later in this chapter in the story of a woman whose Mythic Journey process leads her to find her medicine animal name and healing gestures, which creates a transformative practice to deal with her Demon of Passive Aggressiveness.

3. See later in this chapter for more about the story of Perseus, and how it relates to the Mythic Journey process.

4. See Chapter 10 for more about the importance of Dr. Eugene Gendlin's "Focusing" process to my evolution as a psychotherapist. His use of body's felt sense as a guide to new meanings and fresh perspectives on life's problems was an invaluable contribution to my work. From his influence, I sought to make storytelling into a embodied healing journey.

5. I spoke more about James Hillman's influence on my life in Chapter 10.

6. If you are so inclined, I invite you to practice the movements that I have outlined in many of my books and in my Bodymind Healing Qigong DVD. Or, practice the movements from another Tai Chi or Qigong teacher.

7. In Chapter 11, I discuss how music, movements, and songs, have been important to the holistic healing paradigm that I have created for Reluctant Metaphysicians. Such practices are not only useful in everyday civilized life, but are also helpful using for dealing with the difficulties of living in a war zone.

8. To see a video of the use of healing rituals with children of Israel who are suffering from post-traumatic stress in a war zone see www.youtube.com/watch?v=34GYNxhn7SU&feature=player_embedded).

CHAPTER 16

1. Appendix IV outlines various contributions I have put forth to bring together the streams of Qigong and psychotherapy.

2. Focusing is a method of body-oriented psychotherapy that pays attention to the felt sense in the body in such a way that the felt meaning of body blocks emerges and a felt shift of energy happens thereby. As I told you about in Chapter 10, when I came out to California I become Dr. Gendlin's Focusing training coordinator of the San Francisco East Bay area for ten years. Following the path of "two streams becoming one" I integrated Focusing with Qigong, microcosmic orbit breathing, and psycho-mythology.

3. In Chapter 9, I discussed how I co-founded and taught at the Transpersonal Psychology Department at John F. Kennedy University from 1978-1990. I was delighted to have been able to teach the first program in the United States to master's level counseling students on the integration of Tai Chi, Qigong, and psychotherapy there.

   Later, I was grateful that the California Institute of Integral Studies invited me to teach the first two classes ever offered on the integration of Qigong and psychotherapy to doctoral students. Then I taught courses in Eastern perspectives on healing at San Francisco State University for three years, bringing this knowledge base to undergraduates—just as I would have liked to have happened for me in my early years.

4. In the last chapter, for example, I told you about how I joined symbolic and somatic approaches in the story telling method, the Mythic Journey Process.

5. More specifically, in Chapter 18 I will discuss how I hope to contribute to the field, a view of psychotherapy as changing one's life stance.

6. This metaphysical viewpoint does not preclude an examination of which approaches are most efficacious for which psychological conditions…rather it complements it. The interface between experimental psychology and a metaphysical, mandalic view becomes a hermeneutic. Questions arise: For example how was a given approach chosen to study, which approaches were excluded (for what reasons), and so forth.

7. Even though I received a very positive review from the major *APA Journal PsycCritiques* for my *Bodymind Healing Psychotherapy* book (2007), Time and the turns of the wheel of Fate will tell whether this way of looking at psychotherapy will gain greater acceptance.

8. Though, at this point, my continuing education courses that include energy psychology are among some of the only energy psychology classes that are accepted for continuing education units by the California Mandatory Continuing Education for Psychologists, many of my traditional psychology colleagues still have not accepted the value of integrating Qigong and psychotherapy.

9. This rejection of workshops for continuing education units for psychologists based on the title "Energy Psychology" may be changing. My first workshop that had Energy Psychology in the main title was accepted for May of 2012 at Kripalu Center in Massachusetts.

10. In the following chapters you will see how this new life path involves, what I call "finding a new life stance" (Goodman, 1990; Mayer, 2004).

11. See Chapter 13 for a discussion of the "soulful" and "spiritual" dimensions of Tai Chi.

12. Some of the schools where I have presented my integrative approach are: The California Institute of Integral Studies, John F. Kennedy University, The Institute of Transpersonal Psychology, and Bryn Mawr college. Also, I did presentations at many hospitals such as Mt. Diablo Hospital and Alta Bates Hospital to my colleagues. As well, many workshop venues were open to this integrative approach, such as Esalen

Institute, The Community Institute of Psychotherapy, Kripalu Center, the Wright Institute, and various Qigong and Energy Psychology conferences.

Amongst the leaders in the field who kindly gave me endorsements for my books are: a past American Psychological division president, Dr. Stanley Krippner; a past president of the Jungian Institute Dr. John Beebe; Dr. Ken Pelletier, author of *The Best Alternative Medicine: What Works, What Does Not?:* Jim Gordon, M.D., former chairperson of the White House Commission on Complementary Medicine, and others.

13. Dr. van der Kolk is a co-principal investigator of the field trials for the DSM IV and V study of trauma and the director of Boston University School of Medicine's Trauma Center.

14. I give some case illustrations of how Tai Chi and Qigong, in combination with psychotherapy, can help to create a somatic safety zone in Chapter 18.

15. I discuss in detail, the case of a patient with a panic disorder in Chapter 6 my book Bodymind Healing Psychotherapy.

16. Various ways that the integration of Qigong and psychotherapy can be helpful to psychotherapy patients can be seen in Appendix III of this book.

17. For more on somatic psychotherapy, there was a symposium of various somatic psychotherapies sponsored by Meridian University in December, 2011, www.bodymindhealing.com/index2.php?option=com_ jcalpro&Itemid=43&extmode=view&extid=49.

18. For example, see Chapter 18 for case illustrations

19. You saw a specific example of how merging of the streams of Tai Chi, mythology, and psychology can create a healing, "soulful" practice in the case illustration of the Passive Aggressive Ostrich in the Mythic Journey Process chapter. For a more complete view of how I addressed the integration of Qigong and psychotherapy and behavioral healthcare see Appendixes IV.

20. *Bodymind Healing Qigong* * includes exercises from:

Set 1: Raising & Lowering Qi with Heavenly Palms

Set 2: Tai Chi Ruler

Set 3: Standing Meditation: Wuji and Yi Chuan Qigong

Set 4: Exercises after Standing to Disperse Stagnant Chi

Set 5: Ancient Taoist Healing the Internal Organ Exercises

Set 6: Boddhidharma's changing muscles, sinews & bone marrow

Set 7: Ancient Animal Qigong

Set 8: Spiritual Qigong Practices

Set 9: Walking Meditation

Set 10: Yang Style Taiji Chuan

*An explanation of each set can be found in my book, *Secrets to Living Younger Longer: The Self-healing Path of Qigong, Standing Meditation and Tai Chi.* As well all of the movements are illustrated in my Bodymind Healing Qigong DVD. See: www.bodymindhealing.com.

Chapter 17

1. See Chapter 2 for more about the healing, energetic experiences of my childhood.

2. This common movement can be found in almost any illustrated Tai Chi book, or in my *Secrets…*book (Mayer, 2004, p. 158).

3. Some of the venues where I have presented my integrative approach are Alta Bates Summit Medical Center, Mt. Diablo Hospital Medical Center, Bryn Mawr College, Institute of Imaginal Studies, Saybrook Institute, the National Institute for the Clinical Application of Behavioral Medicine, American Institute of Integrative Medicine, and Esalen Institute.

4. I have discussed many of these cases in my last books (Mayer, 2007, 2009). I have also addressed the research methodology issues involving therapeutic claims and have written about them in various peer-reviewed articles (Mayer, 1999, 2003, 2010).

CHAPTER 18

1. This imaginal tale metaphorically expresses what had become my path. Once again the Reluctant Metaphysician's eyes open to wonder about the synchronicity between this tale about the transcendent meaning of gestures and the rising degree of my astrological chart of 25-degrees of Libra, which according to Rudhyar's Sabian symbols book means, "To see the transcendent cosmic meaning of every particular experience." Also, as I told you earlier, the planet that rules my rising sign (Libra) is Venus in Taurus (an earth sign) on the cusp of the Eighth House of metaphysics. So, another interesting synchronicity is that I indeed found a love for how the physical body (Taurus) expressed metaphysical realties in every day life.
2. In the broadest sense, I believe that the answer to what creates change in psychotherapy can be answered by use of the astrological mandala as a psychotherapeutic meta-system to organize different therapeutic systems, including ancient sacred wisdom traditions (Mayer, 1984, 2007).
3. See Chapter 13 for more on the animal forms of Qigong. Also see my book, *Secrets...* (Mayer 2004).
4. Speaking of how unactualized careers fantasized about in our youth may reemerge and bloom later in life: Though I never became an adult tournament chess player, when I became a Tai Chi teacher later in my life I trained my students in how take stances and make movements while doing Tai Chi push hands so that this two person practice becomes like a game of Taoist interpersonal chess, and an opportunity to cultivate the psychological elements of ourselves (Mayer, 1994, p. 172–180).
5. In my last two books I gave numerous examples of cases where this happened in key moments of psychotherapy (Mayer 2007, 2009).
6. Usually I keep my Qigong students and my psychotherapy patients separate. I have discussed why and when I make exceptions to this (Mayer 2007).
7. For more extensive examples of psychotherapy as changing one's life stance see my last two books, *Bodymind Healing Psychotherapy* (2007) and *Energy Psychology* (2009).

CHAPTER 19

1. See Chapter 11 for a discussion of the Golden Ball in the *Secret of the Golden Flower* book, and in cross-cultural mythology.
2. You can see these Crane postures illustrated in my book, *Secrets...*2004, p. 131.

CHAPTER 21

1. I have discussed the history of modern medicine's attempt to undermine ancient traditions of healing in my last books (Mayer, 2004, 2007, 2009). See also, *A Return to Healing* (Saputo, 2009).
2. An article on the mental health insurance health parity law, by Robert Pear, can be found at www.nytimes.com/2010/05/10/health/policy/10health.html).
3. See these links to learn more about the importance of mental health parity: http://www.case.edu/med/epidbio/mphp439/Mental_Health.htm#_edn4#_edn4; www.calendow.org/uploadedfiles/publications/by_topic/access/mental_health/mental health and universal coverage.pdf; www.surgeongeneral.gov/library/mentalhealth/summary.html
4. See http://en.wikipedia.org/wiki/Precautionary_principle.
5. For more on the control of our culture by corporate giants see, www.pbs.org/wgbh/pages/frontline/shows/cool/giants.

6. Many of the tea party followers have distorted the original story of the tea party, which was an anti-corporate thrust by the people against the British East India Company about their unfair tax advantages. It is rare to hear any Tea Party spokesperson advocate for an anti-corporate agenda since unbeknownst to many tea party advocates they are funded by major corporations, such as the Koch brothers, who actually advocate for the opposite of the original anti-corporate tea party colonist's principles. The Koch brothers are pro-corporate libertarians who generally are for anti-government regulations. So, the original tea party story has been turned around 180 degrees, now meaning the opposite of what our founders intended. To see more about this important issue see: "Unequal Protection": The Boston Tea Party Revealed, Tuesday 12 April 2011 by: Thom Hartmann, Berrett-Koehler Publishers, www.truth-out.org/unequal-protection-boston-tea-party-revealed/1301986800. Also see the New Yorker article (2010) by reporter Jane Mayer www.newyorker.com/reporting/2010/08/30/100830fa_fact_mayer; and Robert Greenwald's video can be found at www.kochbrothersexposed.com.

7. From Thom Hartmann's blog, May 22, 2010.

8. See www.scholastic.com.

9. Demand never dropped in the German economy, because workers always had a good paycheck and so their economy continued to be robust. From Thom Hartmann's blog August 13, 2010; Schmitt, 2011.

10. www.chron.com/disp/story.mpl/business/steffy/4318193.html.

11. The crisis of middle-class America, FT.com (Financial Times). By Edward Luce, Published: July 30, 2010 17:04 | Last updated: July 30, 2010 17:04. See Thom Hartmann's blog August 2, 2010.

12. www.nytimes.com/2010/08/01/opinion/01stockman.html?pagewanted=1&_r=1.

13. http://blogs.wsj.com/deals/2010/08/12/hold-the-pabst-blue-ribbon-gm-is-not-hiring/, www.alternet.org/story/147886/michael_moore%3A_profits_are_way_up_at_general_motors_..._so_why_aren%27t_they_hiring.

14. According to Senator Bernie Sanders on the Thom Hartmann show 10/24/2010.

15. After intense pressure President Obama added a Signing Statement proclaiming that his administration would not apply the NDAA against American citizens. But a signed statement does not have the force of law, and this gives no assurances of how future presidents could act in denying American citizens their constitutional rights to due process and *habeus corpus*. For more information about the current controversial interpretations of the National Defense Act Amendment 1031 see, http://blog.amnestyusa.org/us/can-us-citizens-now-be-detained-indefinitely/, http://rt.com/usa/news/obama-hedges-ndaa-sued-933/ and http://en.wikipedia.org/wiki/National_Defense_Authorization_Act_for_Fiscal_Year_2012.

    It is difficult for any of us to attribute definitive meanings to President Obama's initial support of this amendment. Attribution Theory (Kelley, 1980) says that the closer one gets to the source of information the more our attributes change from personal to situational. In the case of this situation with habeas corpus and President Obama, we do not know if, for example, he knows that suspension of *habeas corpus* might be necessisary due to some advance with biological warfare weapons. However, even in such a case there seemingly would be no reason why a judge's prior or subsequent order should not be required to protect an individual's privacy rights.

16. According to Senator Bernie Sanders as stated in his Friday, Lunch with Bernie Hour, on 9/24/10, with radio host Thom Hartmann.

17. In addition, the top one percent of people in our country now earn over 23 percent of all income, more than the bottom 50 percent of all people. All these statistics were reported in the independent Senator Bernie Sanders' newsletter December 28, 2010. Multiple respected sources are making the public aware of such important statistics. Robert Reich, who was the secretary of labor under President Bill Clinton, says that "almost a quarter of total income generated in the United States is going to the top 1 % of Americans; and the top one-tenth of one percent of American now earn as much as the bottom 120 million of us." The Perfect Storm that Threaten American Democracy, *Alternet*. Retrieved on October 20, 2010, www.alternet.org/story/148558/the_perfect_storm_that_threatens_american_democracy.

18. Michael Snyder, "The Economic Collapse: 15 Shocking Facts Show that the Middle Class is Being Wiped Out," *Alternet,* retrieved Sept 24, 2009.

19. One of the important petitions to consider signing addresses corporate personhood, which is at the root of the corporatocracy that was given legitimacy by the Supreme Court ruling in Citizens United vs. Federal Election Commission. See www.movetoamend.org.

20. Many of the Yes Men pranks can be seen in the movie, *The Yes Men Fix the World* (2009).

21. See Thom Hartmann's blog March 23, 2012 by Louise Hartmann, www.thomhartmann.com/blog/2012/03/brazil-arrests-17-chevron-oil-executives-environmental-crimes.

22. For the economic realities behind why companies such as Apple outsource labor see, Duhigg, C. & Bradsher, K. (2012), "How the U.S. Lost Out on iphone Work," *The New York Times,* Jan 21. To see an article critical of and exposing of the results of Apple's foreign labor contracts see, Gupta, A. (2012). Iempire: Apple's sordid business practices are even worse than you think, *Alternet,* February 7. Also see, Mike Daisey's theater piece, *The Agony and Ecstasy of Steve Jobs;* and the article about it by Rampell, C. (2011) A trip to China can make a guy hate his I phone, *New York Times,* September 29. A good video about the issues involved at the Foxconn Factory can be viewed on *Democracy Now,* Apple, accustomed to profits and praise, faces outcry for labor practices at Chinese factories, February 2, www.democracynow.org/2012/2/10/apple_accustomed_to_profits_and_praise.

    For those who feel disempowered when they listen to such news: When hearing about the conditions at Foxconn, Apple customer Mark Shields wanted to write a letter to Apple, but then he thought, why not start a petition instead? 250,000 signatures later, his petition was part of Foxconn being influenced to make promised changes in their policies. Anyone can initiate a petition campaign on www.change.org., April 1, 2012.

23. See, www.nytimes.com/2010/01/23/business/23labor.html, www.u-s-history.com/pages/h1678.html.

24. See http://en.wikipedia.org/wiki/Single-payer_health_care.

25. See www.pnhp.org.

26. See www.gazette.net/stories/051106/businew210548_31954.shtml, or www.fiercehealthpayer.com/story/unitedhealth-ceo-stephen-hemsley-took-home-102-million-2009/2010-07-06. It has been hypothesized that the reason that companies like Blue Cross arbitrarily reduce psychologists rates to lower than the rates charged by auto body shops, electricians, and plumbers and the number of psychologists accepted onto their panels is that fewer psychologists will be available for patients on managed care panels; and this will reduce utilization and increase profits. Ragusea, S. "BCBS of Florida Takes Dangerous 'New Directions,'" *The National Psychologist,* Vol. 21 (3) 2012.

27. Beginning in 2011, the new law requires insurance companies in the individual and small group markets to spend at least 80 percent of the premium dollars they collect on medical care and quality improvement activities. Insurance companies in the large group market must spend at least 85 percent of premium dollars on medical care and quality improvement activities, www.healthcare.gov/news/factsheets/2010/11/medical-loss-ratio.html.

28. For comparison rates between MRI's in Japan and the U.S. see, www.npr.org/templates/story/story.php?storyId=120545569.

29. For example, I told you the story in Chapter 12 about how one of my nature rituals was to go out to the woods backpacking and imbibe a psychedelic once a year as part of a renewal ritual.

30. More information on the rebirth of research on the use of psychoactive drugs research will be discussed in Chapter 23.

31. For an article on our 9/11 responders see, www.examiner.com/x-38569-Atlanta-Health-News-Examiner~y2010m3d18-911-first-responders-suffering-from-dangerous-heart-problems-scientists-announce-in-Atlanta.

32. www.youtube.com/watch?v=lGBvAskEF_U&feature=email, retrieved from You Tube, December 2010.

33. Dr. Ott's video about the effects of the chemical Corexit is available at, www.democraticunderground.com/discuss/duboard.php?az=view_all&address=385x482059.

34. For the political and economic issues that underlie Monsanto's attempt to capture our food supply with genetically modified seeds see: Mercola's article, "This Company May Be the Biggest Threat to Your Future Health," May 1, 2008 www.articles.mercola.com/sites/articles/archive/2008/05/01/this-company-may-be-the-biggest-threat-to-your-future-health.aspx. For an overarching perspective on the insidious nature of the change to our agriculture due to corporate influence see, *The Future of Food* at, www.youtube.com/watch?v=jNezTsrCY0Q. For the way that Monsanto's corporate policies are affecting farmers and increasing suicide rates in India see, "Could Monsanto Be Responsible for One Indian Farmer's Death Every Thirty Minutes?" www.articles.mercola.com/sites/articles/archive/2009/05/05/Could-Monsanto-Be-Responsible-for-One-Indian-Farmers-Death-Every-Thirty-Minutes.aspx. The story of Monsanto's battle against small farmer Percy Schmeiser can be found at, www.percyschmeiser.com/

35. For the specific research on the health related research on GMO seeds see Smith, J. (2004) *Seeds of Deception.* Also See, Dean, A., and Jennifer Armstrong, M.D. (2009) statement of warning to medical doctors about Genetically Modified Food that was reviewed and approved by the Executive Committee of the American Academy of Environmental Medicine, May 8th, www.aaemonline.org/gmopost.html. To see the Cornocopea Institute's report on "Cereal Crimes." see, www.cornucopia.org/cereal-scorecard/docs/Cornucopia_Cereal_Report.pdf. For specific health related problems and potential dangers associated with GMOs see, www.articles.mercola.com/sites/articles/archive/2011/04/27/19-studies-link-gmo-foods-to-organ-disruption.aspx, and also on the Mercola site see the article, "Doctors Warn: Avoid Genetically Modified Foods," www.articles.mercola.com/sites/articles/archive/2010/03/25/doctors-warn-avoid-genetically-modified-food.aspx.

36. To learn more about the attempt of many European Unions to ban GMOs see, Bloom, J. (2011, March 23) "Is Europe's Ban on Monsanto's GMO Crops Illegal?," www.redgreenandblue.org/2011/03/23/is-europes-ban-on-monsantos-gmo-crops-illegal/. Also see the Reuter's report, "EU Upholds Austria, Hungary Right to Ban," www.uk.reuters.com/article/2009/03/02/eu-gmo-bans-idUKBRU00731420090302. Philpott, T. (2011), "Obama's Broken Promise on GMO Food Labeling," *Mother Jones,* Oct 6.

37. For a list of genetically modified foods that may be at your grocery story see, Genetically Modified Food - GM Foods List and Information, http://www.disabled-world.com/fitness/gm-foods.php#ixzz1nAOXjO7Z www.disabled-world.com/fitness/gm-foods.php. Dr. Mercola's article tells how labels cannot always be trusted, www.articles.mercola.com/sites/articles/archive/2012/02/29/new-vermont-gmo-labeling-policy-officially-introduced.aspx?e_cid=20120229_DNL_art_1. To sign the petition to give consumers the right to know whether GMOs are in their foods go to, www.labelgmos.org. The petition to stop FDA ties to Monsanto and to protest President Obama's appointment of Michael Taylor (the former Monsanto VP) to the number two job at the FDA, and the story about it at the *Washington Post* can be found at, www.washingtonpost.com/blogs/blogpost/post/monsanto-petition-tells-obama-cease-fda-ties-to-monsanto/2012/01/30/gIQAA9dZcQ_blog.html. There is now an iphone app that a person can take to the grocery store that will give you a better idea about which foods contain GMOs, www.itunes.apple.com/app/true-food/id379459607?mt=8.

   Finally, the Cornucopia Institute discovered that Martek Bioscience Corporation bypassed federal organic labeling standards to allow toxic chemicals and GMOs into our food including infant formula. For more information see, www.cornucopia.org/NOSB_DHAletter.pdf, www.articles.mercola.com/sites/articles/archive/2012/04/01/gmo-infant-formula.aspx?e_cid=20120401_SNL_Art_1, Why is this Organic Food Stuffed With Toxic Solvents? April 1, 2012.

38. For a discussion about the *Food, Inc.* movie by Robert Kenner and Eric Schlosser see, www.youtube.com/watch?v=6cb6HwzCkEs. The dialogue about the need for sustainable approaches to feeding our population requires circumspect exploration, with the consumers' health in the forefront. Likewise, researching the court cases and abuses that Tyson Foods (one of the biggest food manufacturers in the United States) reveals the dangers of inadequate regulations and the consequences we pay for insufficient care of consumers' health, see, Rosenberg, M. (2012) The scary danger of meat, *Alternet,* January 30, www.alternet.org/food/153908/the_scary_danger_of_meat_(even_for_those_who_don't_eat_it)_?page=3. Or see

Striffler, S. (2005). *Chicken: The Dangerous Transformation of America's Favorite Food* (also available as Google e-Book), Yale University Press. To see one perspective on how the food we eat can be part of re-empowering ourselves see the movie *Food Matters*, www.articles.mercola.com/sites/articles/archive/2011/10/02/food-matters-the-movie.aspx.

In the current controversy about "pink slime" it has been discovered that ammonium hydroxide has put into our food to "decontaminate it" as well as parts of animals that are not normally considered to be 100% ground beef (such as trimmings that once were relegated to pet foods). Regardless of the outcome of the research on whether these "additives" are harmful, consumers are upset that there has not been truth in labeling and wants the U.S.D.A to serve as a better watchdog of the process. There certainly is a need to eliminate harmful bacteria like E. Coli from meat; however the issue is that these harmful bacteria are more likely to be in the cheap filler meat, and the question is how much oversight is there in monitoring the amount of chemical residue left in meat after treatment. From the Reluctant Metaphysician's perspective we want to know what is in the world behind the world of food, so that proper hermeneutic exploration of the advantages and disadvantages of such practices can be examined in the light of science rather than in the dark boardrooms of corporate decision making. See, Moss, M. (2009). Moss, M. (2009). "Safety of Beef Processing Method Is Questioned," December 30 www.nytimes.com/2009/12/31/us/31meat.html?_r=1 .

For those who feel powerless as a single individual to do anything about such things: An ordinary mom and food blogger, Bettina Elias Siegel, was part of the solution of keeping "pink slime" out of school cafeterias. She was upset to learn that USDA was arranging to offer school districts ground beef containing 7 million pounds of 'lean, finely textured beef,' more commonly known as "pink slime... In just 9 days, nearly 250,000 signed people her petition on wwwchange.org, leading the USDA to change its policy and offer districts, for the first time ever, ground beef without this cheap filler." You can go to www.change.org and start your own petition on an issue about which you are concerned.

39. www.davidkorten.org/which-story.

40. www.davidkorten.org/content/prosperity-stories.

41. For more information on Lester Brown's perspective on global climate change see, www.time.com/time/health/article/0,8599,1700189,00.html#ixzz0wKC30liM.

42. www.plasticpollutioncoalition.org.

43. Horrifying pictures (which should be required viewing for corporate polluters and policy makers), can be seen on the website. www.midwayjourney.com/ or www.chrisjordan.com/gallery/midway/ – pile CF000719a 24x32.

44. For more about the albatross see, http://en.wikipedia.org/wiki/Albatross.

45. See, http://en.wikipedia.org/wiki/Regulatory_capture.

46. www.alternet.org/story/149437/how_at%26t%2C_verizon_and_the_telecom_giants_have_captured_the_regulator_supposed_to_control_them), www.rollingstone.com/politics/blogs/taibblog/revolving-door-from-top-futures-regulator-to-top-futures-lobbyist-20120111 – ixzz1jH9hcgqP

47. In the past five years, tuition and fees at public universities have risen by 57% (40% after adjusting for inflation). Over the past decade, debt levels for graduating seniors with student loans more than doubled from $9,250 to $19,200—a 108% increase (58% after accounting for inflation). At public universities, debt levels for graduating seniors with student loans more than doubled from $8,014 to $17,250 over the past decade—a 116% increase (65% after accounting for inflation). At private universities, debt levels for graduating seniors with student loans nearly doubled. Since 1995 Sallie Mae's stock has returned over 1,900%, trouncing the S&P 500's 228% gain (Jaffe, 2011). These issues are poignantly portrayed in, *Default: The Student Loan Controversy* (www.defaultmovie.com). Macro-economic issues about student loans are discussed in the article, by Jaffe, S., $422,320 for a College Degree? With Tuition Skyrocketing, It is Time to Rethink Higher Education?, *Alternet,* Jan16, 2012.

Finally, according to the National Association of Independent Colleges and Universities, just 56% of students who embark on a bachelor's degree program finish within six years, according to a 2011

Harvard study titled Pathway's to Prosperity. Just 29% of those who seek an associates degree obtain it within three years. According to the Organization for Economic Co-operation and Development, just 46% of Americans complete college once they start, worst among the 18 countries it tracks. We're behind Slovakia. The Harvard study pins the low graduation rate on raising college prices that have sextupled since 1985—driving outstanding student loan debt to over one trillion dollars for the first time in the history of the world, See, www.naicu.edu/news_room/sessionID.884633777/news_byTopic_list.asp, and www.thomhartmann.com/forum/2012/03/america's-students-are-still-screwed.

Chapter 22

1. See Chapter 7 about how in my Four Shaman dream, I was a Native American living many centuries ago at Esalen. The eldest shaman of the tribe asked four younger shaman, including myself, to travel North and then make a circle East back to Esalen gathering the knowledge of all surrounding tribes to bring it back to Esalen. I went on that journey, and when I got around the circle ¾ of the way I was killed by an arrow shot into in my neck.

2. http://articles.sfgate.com/2010-02-17/news/17892346_1_ill-pelicans-bird-rescue-center-brown-pelicans.

3. To see moving pictures of the brown pelicans tortured by oil as a result of criminal neglect and corporate greed see: www.boston.com/bigpicture/2010/06/caught_in_the_oil.html.

4. See Ott, 2008; also see http://en.wikipedia.org/wiki/Exxon_Valdez_oil_spill.

5. www.well.com/~davidu/extinction.html.

6. For further information on the mythology of the Wild Gander see Campbell, 1970; Meade, 2008, p.140.

7. A balanced view says that some corporations are making attempts to be responsible citizens. See www.thedailybeast.com/newsweek/2009/09/20/the-greenest-big-companies-in-america.html. However, one must be circumspect and be aware that some large corporations "Greenwash" their unsustainable actions with a pretense of environmentally conscious actions, http://en.wikipedia.org/wiki/Greenwashing.

8. Wetico Psychosis also involves consuming and co-opting the life force of another, as happened when the United States attempted to break Native Americans' connection to their culture. This is not limited to the United States; it also happened in a wide variety of other cultures (According to the Thom Hartmann Radio Program, January, 17th, 2012).

9. A recent revelation about the Stuxnet computer virus is another example of the modern incarnation of the Pandora myth. This virus was presumably created by some governmental agency to sabotage the Iranian nuclear program, and it may now be able to be turned back on other countries including the United States. Now that "Pandora's Box" has been opened, danger looms regarding cyber warfare of the worlds' nuclear power plants, water plants, and everything run by its computerized electrical infrastructure. See the *60 Minutes* show on March 4, 2012, www.cbsnews.com/8301-18560_162-57390124/stuxnet-computer-worm-opens-new-era-of-warfare/?tag=currentVideoInfo;videoMetaInfo.

Chapter 23

1. References for these studies can by found through the Multidisciplinary Association for Psychedelic Studies (MAPS, 2008; Otalora, 1984). Updated research on the affects of MDMA on the brain can be found at www.maps.org/mdma/litupdate3/clinical.html.

2. www.suite101.com/content/a-review-of-psychedelic-research-a94051.

3. For an extensive library that documents the complex relationship between humans and various psychoactive drugs see www.erowid.com, and www.maps.org.

4. Many other astrological configurations in my chart could also be synchronistic with my interest in depth psychology and "journeys to the underworld" – in particular my Sun, Uranus, Venus, and Moon's north node in the 8th house. However, in keeping with Fingarette's (1963) meaning reorganization viewpoint I am not making a case for having discovered a hidden reality about the causative nature of my interests.

5. www.helium.com/items/660939-evidence-based-facts-on-meditation

6. Naomi Klein is an award-winning journalist who has introduced the theory of "disaster capitalism", i.e., that introducing radical changes in terms of economic and government policy when a country is in shock allows the rise of unchecked multi-national corporations to take advantage of and damage those societies in the process. Klein draws her theory from early electro-shock therapy when it was found that patients who were shocked were more susceptible to suggestion in the period after the shock. She then shows how the CIA uses the same tactic on prisoners to get compliance after shocking them. Finally, Klein says that governments use a similar manipulative strategy on the larger populations of their countries to introduce radical changes when a crises or disaster strikes, for example implementing curtailing of liberties after the 9/11 disaster. Klein also critiques the Milton Friedman, "Chicago Boy's laissez-faire" approach to economics, business, and government, where business is largely unregulated running itself and government is little more than a bare bones system (Klein, 2007).

7. In the last chapter the issue of "Greenwashing," was addressed, whereby a company covers their unsustainable actions with a pretense of environmentally conscious actions. See, http://en.wikipedia.org/wiki/Greenwashing. Each corporation should be evaluated on the basis of their actions.

8. For a review of some of the literature and debate on climate change see the Stern Review, www.en.wikipedia.org/wiki/Stern_Review. Among the many organizations that are addressing the dangers of global climate change is 350.org. See, www.350.org/en/mission.

9. See http://en.wikipedia.org/wiki/Biofuel.

10. See www.beyondnuclear.org/ for a discussion of the dangers and alternatives to nuclear power. To learn more about the potential dangers of fracking see, www.propublica.org/article/buried-secrets-is-natural-gas-drilling-endangering-us-water-supplies-1113, Bateman, C. (2012). "A Colossal Fracking Mess: The Dirty Truth behind the New Natural Gas," *Vanity Fair,* June 21, http://www.vanityfair.com/business/features/2010/06/fracking-in-pennsylvania-201006.

11. For a more extensive discussion of the symbolic relations between cosmic cycles and political events see the book *Cosmos and Psyche* and other writings by Rick Tarnas. He goes in depth into the Uranus-Pluto and other trans-Saturnian planetary configurations and how they relate to current and past historical events (Tarnas, 2007, 2010).

    It should be noted that many other astrologically significant trans-Saturnian configurations at that time (such as a Uranus-Pluto conjunction) also symbolize the volatility of the 1960–1972 period and "the eruption of revolutionary and emancipatory impulses, and accelerated historical change, social and political turmoil, and heightened creativity and innovation in all spheres of human activity that has shaped the global zeitgeist ever since" (Tarnas, 2010, p. 149).

12. A T-square alignment involves a triangular like structure with two planets in opposition, and another planet in square aspect to each. The T-square of 2010 involved a Saturn-Uranus opposition, both of which were square to Pluto in Capricorn. Astrologers believe that this adds power to the aspects between the three planets and a focus of energy on the planet at the tip of the triangle, like an arrow being shot by a bow. In this case, the T-square configuration does symbolize well the Plutonic arrow shot at the ruling elite (Capricorn) of many countries during this time.

13. See www.adbusters.org/blogs/adbusters-blog/occupywallstreet.html. The call to action to Occupy Wall Street took place on July 13, 2011 when there was a Uranus-Pluto square. Also see, http://blog.beliefnet.com/astrologicalmusings, and Harris, C., "The Occupy Wall Street Movement, An Archetypal Perspective," Blog Posting, www.facebook.com/notes/chad-harris/the-occupy-wall-street-movement-an-archetypal-perspective/180168702062898. For a more scholarly discussion of the Uranus-Pluto square aspect with historical correlations see Tarnas, 2007, 2010.

14. See, www.beyondnuclear.org.

15. Solar energy may be able to be part of a multifaceted energy solution. Some sources say that Germany's solar panels produce more power than Japan's entire Fukushima complex (Mims, 2011), other sources say that the quantity of energy produced by solar compared to nuclear is not yet sufficiently productive

(Massur & Swezey, 2011). Even if currently the math does not add up for substituting solar power for nuclear, as solar cell technology develops and government subsidies are equalized, safer energy sources will likely provide viable alternatives (Caldicott, 2006).

16. An opposition is like a full moon aspect, where the meaning of the planetary alignment (that began at the time of the conjunction) is brought to fruition (Rael & Rudhyar, 1980. It is equally interesting that while I have been intensely writing this book, transiting Pluto (intensity) is in opposition to my natal Mercury (activities of the mind, such as writing). Could the astrologer Caroline Casey be on to something when she says, "We are the agents of synchronicity, through which the big story of life talks to itself?"

17. "Contact Improvisation" is a form of dance improvisation where physical contact provides the starting point for explorations through movement improvisation, http://en.wikipedia.org/wiki/Contact_improvisation. "Acroyoga" is a physical practice that combines yoga, acrobatics and other healing arts. It cultivates trust, connection and playfulness between partners, http://en.wikipedia.org/wiki/Acroyoga.

18. No one can say with certainty when the Aquarian age begins. In a previous endnote, I explained how it takes approximately 25,868 years for the precession to go fully around all signs of the zodiac. Each age is approximately 2160 years. Some astrologers believe the Aquarian age began at the time of the Wright Brothers flight in 1903, the beginning of moving from the Piscean Age of water to an age ruled by air power. Towards the end of the time of the movement from 0 degrees to 1 degree of Aquarius Age (72 years) was the birth of the hippie movement, and the cultural revolution of that time. Some astrologers say we are now in the 2nd degree of Aquarius, symbolic of manifestation (the numerology of number 2) of Aquarian humanitarian ideals—pictured as "the water bearer" who brings the waters of life to humanity.

19. For example, questions can be raised about episodes of violence. The lack of cohesive leadership, in attempt to foster democratic values, has the disadvantage of leading to infiltration by some that do not represent the essential transforming message of the movement. As I have said in a previous endnote, the Aries phase of a movement activates a vital energy, which in time needs to be conscientiously formed.

20. I first heard this metaphor in a temple in a talk by Rabbi Zalman Schachter-Shalomi.

References

Ableman, A. (2011). *Pacha's pajamas: A story written by nature*. Amazon Digital Services, www.pachaspajamas.com.

Achterberg, J. (1985). *Imagery in healing: Shamanism and modern medicine*. Boston: New Science Library.

Adams, M. (2007). Corporate greed, corruption, and the coming collapse of America as we know it. *Natural Health News,* June 22, www.naturalnews.com/021911.html#ixzz1h6vQuT20.

Ader, R., & Felton, D. (1991). *Psychoneuroimmunology.* San Diego, CA: Academic Press.

Ader, R. (2000). The placebo effect: If it's all in your head, does that mean you only think you feel better? *Advances in Mind-Body Medicine, 16,* 7–46.

Adler, A. (1982). *Pattern of life.* Alfred Adler Institute of Chicago.

Alpert, R. (also known as Ram Dass) (1971). *Be here now.* San Cristobal, NM: Lama Foundation.

Anderson, U.S. (1954, 1980). *Three magic words.* Wilshire.

Andorno, R. (2004). "The Precautionary Principle: A New Legal Standard for a Technological Age" (PDF). *Journal of International Biotechnology Law* 1: 11–19.

Andrade, J., & Feinstein, D. (2003). Energy psychology: Theory, indications, evidence. In D. Feinstein, *Energy psychology interactive.* Ashland, OR: Innersource.

Aposhyan, S. (2004). *Bodymind Psychotherapy: Principles, techniques and practical applications.* New York: W.W. Norton.

Arguelles, J. (1972, 1990). *Mandala.* Shambhala.

Assagioli, R. (1965). *Psychosynthesis: A collection of basic writings.* Viking.

Arthur, J. (2000). *Mushrooms and mankind.* Book Tree, 2000.

Astin, J. A., Berman, B. M., Bausell, B., Lee, W. L., Hochberg, M., & Forys, K. L. (2003, October). The efficacy of mindfulness meditation plus Qigong movement therapy in the treatment of fibromyalgia: A randomized controlled trial. *Journal of Rheumatology, 30*(10), 2257–62.

Bach, R. (1977) *Illusions: The adventures of a reluctant messiah.* New York: Dell Co.

Baggott, M., Jerome, I. & Stuart, R. 2001. 3, 4-methylenedioxymethamphetamine (MDMA)—a review of the English-language scientific and medical literature. Submitted to FDA as part of IND # 63,384. *MAPS,* www.maps.org ; www.maps.org/mdma/litupdate3/clinical.html.

Bakalian, S., & Menaghello, A., *Default: The Student Loan Documentary.* www.defaultmovie.com.

Bandler, R. & Grinder J. (1981). *Trance-formations: Nerurolinguistic programming and the structure of hypnosis.* Moab UT: Real People Press.

Barkeline, J. (2011). *Ford looks to dandelions for natural rubber.* Retrieved May13, www.GreenBiz.com.

Beck, A. T. (1979). *Cognitive therapy of depression.* New York: Guilford Press.

Beebe, J. (2006). *Individuation in the light of Chinese philosophy.* A paper presented at the Third Conference of Analytical Psychology & Chinese Culture, September 22-24, 2006 Guangzhou, China, with the theme "Ethics and Wisdom: East and West."

Benson, H. (1975). *The relaxation response.* New York: Avon.

Benyus, J. (1997). *Biomimicry: Inside the revolutionary new science that is rediscovering life's best ideas-and changing the world.* New York: William Morrow.

Bergier and Pauwels, (1973). *The eternal man.* New York: Avon Books

Basmajian, J. (1963, August). Control and training of individual motor units. *Science Magazine, 2,* 440–441.

Bivens, J. (2011). CEOs distance themselves from the average worker. *Economic Policy Institute,* November, 9.

Blanck, G.. & R. (1974). *Ego psychology: Theory and practice.* Columbia University Press.

Blanck G & R. (1979). *Ego psychology II: Psychoanalytic developmental psychology.* Columbia University Press.

Bloom, D. (2007). *Alcohol can be a gas: Fueling an ethanol revolution for the 21st century.* International Institute for Ecological Agriculture.

Blount, A. (1998). *Integrated primary care: The future of medical & mental health collaboration.* New York: W.W. Norton.

Bogart, G. (1991). Meditation and psychotherapy: A review of the literature. *The American Journal of Psychotherapy,* XLV(3), 383.

Bohm, D. (1989). *Quantum theory.* Dover Publications.

Boorstein, S. (Ed.) (1996) *Transpersonal psychotherapy (2nd ed).* Albany: SUNY.

Boothby, R. (2001). *Freud as philosopher: Metapsychology after Lacan.* London: Routledge.

Brand, G. (2010). The 2010-2011 Jupiter-Uranus Conjunctions & the Jupiter-Uranus cycle. *Echo Newsletter,* May 17. http://garybrandastrology.com/articles/echo/Jupiter-Uranus_Conjunctions_5-17-2010.html.

Brim H, et al (1986). Engineering deioncoccus radiodurans for metal remediation in radioactive mixed waste environments. *Nature Biotechnology 18,* (1), 85–90. Also see Wikipedia for research on bioremediation.

Brommage, T. (2008). *Three Wittgensteins: Interpreting the tractus logico-philosophicus.* Dissertation: University of South Florida, Scholar commons @ USF.

Brown, L. (2009). *Plan B 4.0: Mobilizing to save civilization.* W.W. Norton.

Brown, T. (2011). Ibogaine Research in Opiate Addicts. Presentation at annual M.A.P.S. conference, Oakland CA.

Bucke, R. (1901). *Cosmic Consciousness: A study in the evolution of the human mind.* Innes & Sons.

Byrne, R. (2006). *The secret.* Atria Books.

Caldicott, H. (2006). *Nuclear power is not the answer.* The New Press.

Cassirer, E., (1953). *Language and myth.* New York: Dover Publications.

References

Castaneda, C. (1968), *The teachings of Don Juan: A Yaqui way of knowledge.* University of California Press.

Casteneda, C. (1971), *A separate reality: Further conversations with Don Juan.* New York: Pocket Books.

Campbell, J. (1970). *The hero with a thousand faces.* World Publishing Company.

Campbell, J. (1970). *Flight of the wild gander: 1st Gateway Edition.* Henry Regnery Company.

Campbell, J. (1978). *The mysteries: Papers from the Eranos yearbooks* (Bollingen Series XXX). Princeton, NJ: Princeton University Press.

Christiensen, M. (2010). *Acid Christ: Ken Kesey, LSD, and the politics of ecstasy.* Schaffner Press.

Chopra, D. (1990). *Quantum healing: Exploring the frontiers of mind/body medicine.* Bantam.

Chopra, D. (2005). *SynchroDestinty.* Random House.

Chuen, L. (1991). *The way of energy.* London England: Gaia Books Limited.

Church, D. (2007). *The genie in your genes: Epigenetic medicine and the new biology of intention.* Santa Rosa, CA: Elite Publication.

Colliver, V., (2010). State regulators fine 7 insurers $4.85 Million. *San Francisco Chronicle,* November 30th, p. D. 1 & 5.

Cohen, K. (1997). *The way of Qigong.* New York: Ballentine Books.

Cohen, K. (1994). Native American healing touch. Goldco, CO: *Newsmagazine of ISSSEEM,* Vol. 5, No. 1, Spring.

Cool, L. (2012). Can LSD cure alcoholism? *Day in Health,* March 12, www.health.yahoo.net/experts/dayinhealth/can-lsd-cure-alcoholism.

Cook, B. (2009). United settles SEC backdating investigation. *American Medical News,* January 14, www.ama-assn.org/amednews/2009/01/12/bisc0114.htm.

Cook, C. (2012). I'm on food stamps: My shame and pride in signing up for the most stigmatized benefit. *Alternet,* Feb 8th.

Craig, G., & Fowlie, A. (1995; 1997). *Emotional freedom techniques: The manual.* Sea Ranch, CA: Author.

Cipriani, A., Barbui, C, Gaddes, H. (2005). Suicide, depression, and antidepressants. *BMJ,* 330: 373. www.bmj.com/content/330/7488/373.full?ehom.

Cullin, L. (2006). How to get smarter one breath at a time. *Time Magazine,* www.time.com/time/magazine/article/0,9171,1147167-2,00.html. Retrieved December 20, 2010.

Daniels, M.(2009). Perspectives and vectors in transpersonal development. *Transpersonal Psychology Review,* 13 (1), 87–89.

Darwin, C.(1890, 2009). *The expression of the emotions in man and animals.* Cambridge University Press.

Daumal, R. (1952, 1992). *Mount analogue.* Shambhala.

Deadman. P., Al-Khafami, Baker, K., (2005) *A manual of acupuncture.* Eastland Press.

De Graw, D. (2010). The richest 1% have captured America's wealth: What's it going to take to get it back? *Alternet,* Feb 17, Part II, p. 1.

DeGraw, D. (2011). Middle class deathwatch: 33 frightening economic developments. *Alternet*, September 18, 2011, www.alternet.org/story/152457/middle_class_death_watch_33_frightening _economic_developments?page=1.

Deikman, A. (1982). *The observing self*. Boston, MA: Beacon Press.

Denvir, D. (2011). Ayn Rand U? Rich Conservatives—Not Just the Kochs—Buying Up Professors and Influence on Campus. *AlterNet*, May 24.

DePalma, A. (2011). New docs detail how feds downplayed ground zero health risks. *ProPublica: Journalism in the Public Interest*, September, 8.

Deressiewicz, W. (2011). Faulty Towers: The Crisis in higher education. *The Nation*, May 4, www. thenation.com/article/160410/faulty-towers-crisis-higher-education?page=full.

Diepersloot, J. (1997). *Warriors of stillness Vol. I: Meditative traditions in the Chinese martial arts*. Walnut Creek: CA: Center for Healing and the Arts.

Djen, l. & Needham J. (1980). *Celestial lancets: A history and rationale of acupuncture and moxa*. Cambridge University Press.

Doblin R and Kleiman M. (1990). Marijuana as Antiemetic Medicine: A Survey of Oncologists' Experiences and Attitudes. *American Society of Clinical Oncology Survey*.

Dossey, L.(2000). *Reinventing medicine: Beyond mind-body to a new era of healing*. Harper One.

Dossey, L. (1992). But is it energy? Reflections on consciousness, healing and the new paradigm. *Subtle Energies*, 3(3), 69–81.

Dossey, L. (1993). *Healing words: The power of prayer and the practice of medicine*. New York: Harper San Francisco.

Dossey, L. (1994). Healing Energy and consciousness: Into the future or a retreat to the past? *Subtle Energies*, 5(1).

Douglas N., & Singer, P. (1999). *Sexual Secrets*. New York: Destiny Books.

Duhigg, C. & Bradsher, K. (2012) How the U.S. lost out on iphone work. *The New York Times*, Jan 21, www.nytimes.com/2012/01/22/business/apple-america-and-a-squeezed-middle-class.html? pagewanted=all.

Dychwald, K. (1983). *Bodymind*. Jove.

Edinger, E. F. (1985). *Anatomy of the psyche: Alchemical symbolism in psychotherapy*. LaSalle, IL: Open Court.

Eichler, A. (2011). Middle-class Americans often fall down economic ladder: study. *The Huffington Post*, Sept 7, 2011.

Ellerbe, H. (1995). *The dark side of Christian history*. Morningstar Books

Eliade, M., & Trask, W. (1954). *The myth of the eternal return*. Princeton, NJ: Princeton University Press, Bollinger Foundation.

Eliade, M. (1963). *Patterns in comparative religion*. New York: World Publishing Company.

Eliade, M. (1963b). *Myth and reality*. Harper & Row.

Eliade, M. (1964). *Shamanism: Archaic techniques of ecstacy*. Bollingen Foundation: Princeton University Press.

References

Eliade, M. (1958). *Rites and symbols of initiation.* New York: Harper & Row.

Edinger, E. F. (1985). *Anatomy of the psyche: Alchemical symbolism in psychotherapy.* LaSalle, IL: Open Court.

Esbjorn-Hargens, S., Zimmerman, M. & Bekoff, M. (2009). *Integral ecology: Uniting multiple perspectives on the natural world.* Integral Books.

EurActiv (2011). Switzerland bins nuclear reactor plans, May 26, www.euractiv.com/climate-environment/switzerland-bins-nuclear-reactor-plans-news-505150.

Fadiman, J. & Frager, R. (2001). *Personality and personal growth.* Prentice Hall.

Faux, Z. (2011). Moody's, S&P Caved In to Ratings Pressure From Goldman, UBS Over Mortgages. *Bloomberg,* April 13, www.bloomberg.com/news/2011-04-13/moody-s-s-p-caved-to-mortgage-pressure-by-goldman-ubs-levin-report-says.html.

Feinstein, D. (2009). Facts, Paradigms, and Anomalies in the Acceptance of Energy Psychology: A Rejoinder to McCaslin's (2009) and Pignotti and Thyer's (2009) Comments on Feinstein (2008a). *Psychotherapy: Theory, Research, Practice, Training,* 46(2): 262–269.

Feinstein, D. (2008). Energy psychology in disaster relief. *Traumatology.* 14(1), 124–137.

Feinstein, D. (2008). Energy psychology: A review of the preliminary evidence. *Psychotherapy: Theory, Research, Practice,* pp. 199–213.

Feldenkrais, M. (1991). *Awareness through movement: Easy-to-do health exercises to improve your posture, vision, imagination, and personal awareness.* Harper One.

Feng, A. (2003). *The five animals play Qigong.* Oakland, CA: The Taoist Center.

Fang, L. (2010). U.S. Chamber of Commerce lobbied to help GOP kill bill to provide health care to 9/11 first responders. *Think Progress.Org,* December, 17.

Fang, L. (2012). Why can't you smoke pot? Because lobbyists are getting rich off of the war on drugs. *Alternet,* March 7, www.alternet.org/story/154448/why_can't_you_smoke_pot_because_lobbyists_are_getting_rich_off_of_the_war_on_drugs?page=2

Ferguson, C. (2012). *Predator nation: Corporate criminals, political corruption, and the hijacking of America.* Crown Business. See www.alternet.org/story/155643/charles_ferguson%27s_%27predator_nation%3A_corporate_criminals%2C_political_corruption%2C_and_the_hijacking_of_america%27?akid=8862.222058.CMkJIG&rd=1&t=2.

Ferrer, J. Romero, M., & Albareda R. (2005). Integral transformative education: A participatory proposal. *The Journal of Transformative Education,* 3, (4), 306-330.

Ferrer, J. (2011). Participatory spirituality and transpersonal theory: A ten-year retrospective. *Journal of Transpersonal Psychology,* Vol. 43, (1), 2011.

Fikes, C. (1993). *Carlos Castaneda: Academic opportunism and the psychedelic sixties.* Millenia Press.

Fingarette, H. (1963). *The self in transformation.* New York: Harper & Row.

Flock, E. (2012), Monsanto petition tells Obama: 'Cease FDA ties to Monsanto.' *Washington Post,* Blog Post, Jan 30th, www.washingtonpost.com/blogs/blogpost/post/monsanto-petition-tells-obama-cease-fda-ties-to-monsanto/2012/01/30/gIQAA9dZcQ_blog.html.

Foley, E. (2010). 9/11 First responders health care bill passed by house & senate, December 22, www.huffingtonpost.com/2010/12/22/911-first-responders-heal_1_n_800326.html.

Foley, E.(2011). Senate GOP votes down bill to end big oil subsidies. *The Huffington Post*, www.huffingtonpost.com/2011/05/17/oil-subsidies-senate-gop_n_863308.html, May 19.

Fontenrose, J. (1959, 1980). *Python: A Study of the Delphic myth and its origins.* Berkeley: University of California Press.

Forbes, J. (1992). *Columbus and other cannibals: The Wetiko disease of exploitation, imperialism and terrorism.* Automedia.

Ford, K. (2005). *The quantum world: Quantum physics for everyone.* Harvard University Press.

Jay C. Fournier, et al., (2010). Antidepressant drug effects and depression severity, *JAMA,* 303(1):47–53. http://jama.ama-assn.org/content/303/1/47.abstract?maxtoshow=&HITS=10&hits=10&RESULTFORMAT=&fulltext=2010+depression&searchid=1&FIRSTINDEX=0&resourcetype=HWCIT.

Frankl, V. (1967). *Psychotherapy and existentialism: Selected papers on logotherapy.* New York: Simon and Schuster.

Fraser, C. (2010). *Rewilding the world: Dispatches from the conservation revolution.* Picador.

Frenier, C., & Hogan, L. S. (n.d.). *Engaging the imaginal realm: Doorway to collective wisdom.* Retrieved July 5, 2006, from www.collectivewisdominitiative.org papers/frenier_imaginal.htm#imaginal.

Freud, S. (1899, 1965). *The interpretation of dreams.* New York: Avon Books.

Freud, S. (1923). *The ego and the id.* London: Hopgarthe Press.

Freud, S. (1933; 1990). *New introductory lectures on psychoanalysis.* New York: Norton.

Frost, R. (1920) The road not taken, poem, www.bartleby.com/119/1.html.

Fuchs, W. (1976). *Phenomenology and the metaphysics of presence: An essay in the philosophy of Edmund Husserl.* The Hague: Martinus Nijhoff.

Fukuyama, M. & Sevig, T. (1999) *Integrating spirituality into multicultural counseling.* Sage Publications.

Furst, P. (1972). *Flesh of the Gods: The ritual use of hallucinogens.* London: George Allen and Unwin LTD.

Li, F., Harmer, P., Fitzgerald, K., & Eckstrom, E., et. al. (2012), Tai Chi and Postural Stability in Patients with Parkinson's Disease. *New England Jour. Med.,* 366:511–519.

Gach, M. (1990). *Acupressure potent points.* New York: Bantam.

Gach, M. (2004). *Emotional healing with acupressure.* New York: Bantam.

Gach, M., & Marco, C. (1981). *Acu-yoga: Self help techniques to relieve tension.* New York: Japan Publications, Inc.

Garlinkle, M. S., et al. (1998, November 11). Yoga-based interventional for carpal tunnel syndrome. *Journal of the American Medical Association,* 280(18), 1601–1603.

Gatchel, R. J., & Blanchard, E. B. (1993, 1998). *Psychophysiological disorders: Research and clinical applications.* Washington, DC: American Psychiatric Association.

Gendlin, E. (1962). *Experiencing and the creation of meaning.* Toronto, Ontario: Free Press of Glencoe.

Gendlin, E. (1978). *Focusing.* New York: Bantam Books.

Gendlin, E. (1986). *Let your body interpret your dreams.* Wilmette, IL: Chiron Publications.

Gendlin, E. (1980). Imagery is more powerful with focusing: Theory and practice. In J.E. Shorr, G.E. Sobel, P. Robin, J.A. Connella (Eds.), *Imagery. Its many dimensions and applications,* pp. 65–73. New York/London: Plenum Press.

Geoghegan, T. (2010). *Were you born on the wrong continent?* The New Press.

George, D. (1986). *Asteroid goddesses: The mythology, psychology and astrology of the reemerging feminine.* San Diego: ACS Publications.

Gerber, R. (1996). *Vibrational medicine.* Santa Fe, NM: Bear & Co.

Goldberg, D. (2011). Don't diss the drum circles: Why hippie culture is still important to our protests. *Dissent Magazine,* Retrieved from *Alternet,* October 25, www.alternet.org/vision/152863/don't_diss_the_drum_circles%3A_why_hippie_culture_is_still_important_to_our_protests/?page=1.

Goodman, F. (1990). *Where the spirits ride the wind: Trance journeys and other ecstatic experiences.* Indiana University Press.

Goodman, P. (2010). Corporate profits hit new record, U.S. Workers still struggling. *The Huffington Post,* November 23, www.huffingtonpost.com/2010/11/23/corporate-profits-q3-2010-_n_787573.html.

Gordon, J. (1996). *Manifesto for a new medicine: Your guide to healing partnerships and the wise us of alternative therapies.* Reading, Mass.: Perseus Books.

Gore, B. (1995). *Ecstatic body postures.* Santa Fe, NM: Bear & Co.

Gorton, B. (1957). The physiology of hypnosis. *Journal of the American Society of Psychosomatic Dentistry,* 4(3), 86–103.

Graves, R. (1955). *The Greek myths, I and II.* New York: Penguin.

Greenberg, G. (2007). *Jesus brief: Who really killed Jesus?* Continuum Press.

Grim, R. (2011). Read the never-before published letter from LSD-inventor Albert Hoffman to Apple CEO Steve Jobs. *The Huffington Post,* October 11, www.huffingtonpost.com/ryan-grim/read-the-never-before-pub_b_227887.html

Grob, C., Danforth, A., Chopra G., Hagerty M., McKay C., Halberstadt A., Greer, G. (2011) Pilot Study of Psilocybin Treatment for Anxiety in Patients With Advanced-Stage Cancer. *Arch Gen Psychiatry.* 2011 Jan;68(1):71-8. www.heffter.org/news/psilocybin-treatment-for-cancer-anxiety-study-published-in-archives-of-general-psychiatry.

Grof, S. (2006). *When the impossible happens.* Sounds True Catalogue.

Guo, X., Zhou, B., Nishimura, T., Teramukai, M., & Fukushima, M. (2008). Clinical effect of Qigong practice on essential hypertension: A meta-analysis of randomized clinical trials. *Journal of Alternative and Complementary Medicine,* Vol. 14, No 1, pp. 27–37.

Gupta, A. (2112). Iempire: Apple's sordid business practices are even worse than you think. *Alternet,* February 7, www.alternet.org/story/154043/iempire%3A_apple%27s_sordid_business_practices_are_even_worse_than_you_think?akid=8234.222058.dRTGgR&rd=1&t=2.

Ha, F., & Diepersloot, J., (1991), A discussion of the realities of empty force. *Tai Chi: The Leading International Magazine of Tai Chi Chuan,* August, pp. 8–11.

Ha, F. (1995). *Stillness in movement: The practice of Tai Chi Chuan* (Video/DVD). San Francisco, CA: Vision Arts.

Ha, F., & Olsen, E. (1996). *Yiquan and the nature of energy.* Berkeley, CA: Summerhouse Publications.

Hall, M. (1962). *The secret teachings of all ages.* Los Angeles: The Philosophical Research Society.

Hanna, T. (1988). *Somatics: Reawakening the mind's control of movement, flexibility, and health.* Da Capo Press.

Harner, M. (1990). *The way of the shaman.* New York: Harper & Row.

Halifax, J. (1988) *Shaman: The wounded healer.* Thames & Hudson.

Halifax, J. (1979). *Shamanic voices.* New York: Dutton.

Hartmann, T.(2004). *The last hours of ancient sunlight: Revised and updated: The fate of the world and what we can do before it's too late.* Broadway.

Hartmann, T. (2007, 2010). *Unequal protection: How corporations became "people"—And how you can fight back.* Berrett-Koehler Publishers.

Hartmann, T. (2007). *Cracking the code: How to win hearts, change minds and restore American' original vision.* Berett-Koehler.

Hartmann, T. (2010). *Rebooting the American dream: 11 ways to rebuild your country.* Berrett-Koehler Publishers.

Hawken, P. (2007). *Blessed unrest: How the largest movement in the world came into being and why no one saw it coming,* New York: Viking Press.

Heidegger, M. & Fried, G., Polt, R. (2000). *Introduction to metaphysics.* Yale University Press.

Heidegger, M. (2003). *Holzwege.* A collection of essays. Germany: Klostermann.

Heinlein, R. (1987). *Stranger in a strange land.* Ace Paperback.

Hesse, H. (1943, 1982, 2002). *The glass bead game* (Magister Ludi). Picador.

Hesse, H. (1969). *Journey to the East.* Noonday Press.

Hickman, L. (1998). *Reading Dewey: Interpretations for a postmodern generation.* Indiana University Press.

Hillman, J. (1972). *The myth of analysis.* Evanston, IL: Northwestern.

Hillman, J. (1975). *Re-visioning psychology.* New York: Harper and Row.

Hillman, J. (1979). *Dreams and the underworld.* New York: Harper & Row.

Hoepper, B. (2011). Journeys of desperation: Environmental refugees across the ages. *The National Centre for History Education,* retrieved May 13 2011, www.hyperhistory.org/index.php?option=displaypage&Itemid=725&op=page.

Hollick, M.(2006). *The science of oneness: A worldview for the twenty-first century.* New York, NY.: Maple Vail Press.

Horner, A. (1984). *Object relations and the developing ego in therapy.* New York: Jason Aronson.

Horner, A. (1990). *The primacy of structure: Psychotherapy of underlying character pathology.* Northvale, NJ: Jason Aronson, Inc.

Houston, J. (1992). *The hero and the goddess: The odyssey as mystery and initiation.* New York: Ballentine Books.

Huasdorf, H. (1998). *The Chinese Roswell: UFO encounters in the far east from ancient times to the present.* Boca Raton, FL: New Paradigm Books.

Huffington Post (2011). U.S. poverty: Census finds nearly half of Americans are poor or low-income. *The Huffington Post* reporting on census data, posted 12/15, www.huffingtonpost.com/2011/12/15/census-shows-1-in-2-peopl_1_n_1150128.html.

Hui K.S., et. al. (2000). Acupuncture modulates the limbic system and subcortical gray structures of the human brain. Evidence from MRI studies in normal subjects. *Human Brain Mapping,* 9(1), 13–25.

Hunter, J. (1992). *Culture wars: The struggle to control the family, art, education, law, and politics in America.* Basic Books.

Huxley, A. (1977). *The Doors of perception: Heaven and hell.* New York: Harper Collins.

Huxley, A. (1944, 1990). *The perennial philosophy.* Harper Perennial.

Ioannidis J. (2005). Why most published research findings are false. *PLoS Med* 2(8): e124. doi:10.1371/journal.pmed.0020124.

Irwin M., Pike, J., Cole, J., & Oxman, M. (2003). Effects of a behavioral intervention, Tai Chi Chih, on varicella-zoster virus specific immunity and health functioning in older adults. *Psychosomatic Medicine,* 65: 824–30.

Irwin, M., Olmstead, R., & Motivala, S., (2008). Improving sleep quality in older adults with moderate sleep complains: A randomized controlled trial of Tai Chi Chih. *Sleep,* Vol. 31, No 7.

Irwin, M., Olmstead, R., and Oxman M., (2007). Augmenting immune responses to Varicella Zorster Virus in older adults: A randomized, controlled trial of Tai Chi. *Journal of the American Geriatrics Society,* 55(4):511-517.

Irwin, M., Pike, J., & Oxman, M. (2004). *Shingles immunity and health functioning in the elderly: Tai Chih as a behavioral treatment. eCAM,* 1:223–32.

Jacobs, T., Epel, E., Lin, J., Blackburn, E., Wolkowitz, O., et al. Intensive meditation training, immune cell telomerase activity, and psychological mediators. *Psychoneuroendocrinology,* 2010; DOI: www.sciencedirect.com/science/article/pii/S030645301000243X.

Jacobson, E. (1964). *The self and object world.* New York: International University Press.

Jaffe, S. (2011). The next bubble is about to Burst: College grads Face dwindling jobs and mounting loans. *Alternet,* June 1, www.alternet.org/story/151149/the_next_bubble_is_about_to_burst%3A_college_grads_face_dwindling_jobs_and_mounting_loans_?akid=7039.222058.AiCtOK&rd=1&t=2.

Jenny, H. (1974). *Cymatics*. Switzerland:Basilius Press.

Jensen, B. (2005). *Science and practice of iridology, vol. 1: A system of analyzing and caring for the body through the use of drugless and nature-cure methods*. Whitman Publications.

JNC 7, (2003) Seventh report of the Joint National Committee on the Prevention, Detection, Evaluation and Treatment of High Blood Pressure released in 1997. *U.S. Department of Health and Human Services*, NIH Publication No 03-5233, December.

Johannsen, C. (2012). The ones we've lost: The student loan debt suicides. *Alternet*, July 4, 2012, *Huffington Post*, July 2, 2012.

Jung, C. G. (1961). *Memories, dreams, and reflections*. New York: Random House.

Jung, C. G. (1966). *Spirit in man, art and literature. Collected works of C.G. Jung*, Vol. 15. Princeton, NJ: Princeton University Press.

Jung, C. G. (1977). *Mysterium coniunctionis*. Princeton University Press.

Jung, C. G. (1957–1970). *The collected works of C. G. Jung, Vols. 1–19*, Bollinger Series. Princeton, NJ: Princeton University Press.

Jung, C. G. (1960). *The structure and dynamics of the psyche, Vol. VIII*, Bollinger Series, Princeton, NJ: Princeton University Press.

Jung, C. G. (1968). *Psychology and alchemy*. London: Routledge.

Kalsched, V.(1996). *The inner world of trauma: Archetypal defenses of the personal spirit*. London: Routledge.

Katz, R. (1993). The Kung approach to healing. *Parabola Magazine*, Spring.

Keen, S. & Fox, A. (1974). *Telling your story: A guide to who you are and who you can be*. Signet.

Keen, S. & Fox, A. (1989). *Your mythic journey: Finding meaning in your life through writing and storytelling*. Tarcher.

Keleman, S. (1981). *Your body speaks its mind*. Center Press.

Keleman, S. (1986). *Emotional anatomy: The structure of experience*. Westlake Village, CA: Center Press.

Kelley, H., & Michela, J. (1980). Attribution theory and research. *Annual Review of Psychology*, Vol. 31: 457–501, February.

Kelly, S. (1993). *Individuation and the absolute: Hegel, Jung, and the path toward wholeness*. Paulist Press.

Kelly, S. (2010). *Coming home: The birth and transformation of the planetary era*. Lindisfarne Books.

Kerenyi, K. (1976), *Hermes: Guide of souls*. Zurich, Switzerland: Spring Publications.

Ketcham, C. (2011). The reign of the one percenters: How income inequality is destroying our culture. *Orion Magazine*, Oct 7, this article can also be found on *Alternet*, www.alternet.org/story/152652/the_reign_of_the_one_percenters%3A_how_income_inequality_is_destroying_our_culture?page=1.

Kingsley, P. (1999). *In the dark places of wisdom*. Inverness, CA: Golden Sufi Center.

References

Kirsch, I. (2010). Antidepressants: The emperor's new drugs? *Alternet,* January 29. www.huffington post.com/irving-kirsch-phd/antidepressants-the-emper_b_442205.html.

Klein, N. (2007). *The shock doctrine: The rise of disaster capitalism.* New York: Metropolitan Books.

Kline, G. (1989) *Alfred North Whitehead: Essays on his philosophy.* University Press of America.

Kohut, H. (1971). *The analysis of the self.* New York: International Press.

Korten, D. (2001). *When corporations rule the world.* Berrett-Koehler Publishers.

Korten, D. (2007). *The great turning: From empire to earth community.* Berrett-Koehler Publishers.

Krassen, M. & Aharon, M. (2011) *Chayyey Sarah.* Retrieved February 8, 2011, http://rainofblessings .org/messages_archives/ChayyeySarah.html, p. 1.

Krebs, T. & Johansen. (2012). Lysergic acid diethylamide (LSD) for alcoholism: Meta-analysis of randomized controlled trials. *Journal of Psychopharmacology,* March 8.

Kripal, J. (2007). *Esalen: America and the religion of no-religion.* University of Chicago Press.

Krippner, S. (1994). Energy medicine in Native American healing practices. Goldco, CO: *Newsmagazine of ISSSEEM,*Vol. 5, No. 1.

Krippner, S. et. al. (1997). Broken images, broken selves: Dissociative narratives in clinical practice. Routledge.

Krippner, S., Cardena, E. (Editor), & Lynn, S. (Editor). (2000). *Varieties of anomalous experience: Examining the scientific evidence.* Washington D.C.: American Psychological Association.

Kroll, A. (2011). Wisconsin Gov. Scott Walker: Funded by the Koch Bros. *Mother Jones,* Feb 18, http://motherjones.com/mojo/2011/02/wisconsin-scott-walker-koch-brothers.

Kunz, B & K (2003). *Reflexology: Health at your fingertips.* DK Adult.

Lachman, (2007). *Rudolf Steiner: An Introduction to his life and work.* Tarcher.

Laing, R. (1983). *The politics of experience.* New York: Pantheon.

Lakoff, G. & Johnson, M. (1999). *Philosophy in the flesh: The embodied mind and its challenge to western thought.* Basic Books.

Lakoff, G. (2005). The brain's concepts: the role of the sensory-motor system in conceptual knowledge. *Psychology Press,* Cognitive Neuro-psychology, 22 (3/4), 455–479.

Lamberth, D. (1999). *William James and the metaphysics of experience.* Cambridge University Press.

Larsen, D. (2003). The psychedelic secrets of Santa Claus. *Cannibis Culture Magazine,* Dec 18th.

Larsen, S. & R. (1981) The healing mask. In *Parabola, Myth and the Quest for Meaning,* Vol. VI No. 3, pp. 81.

Laszio, E., Grof, S., and Russel, P. (2003) *The consciousness revolution.* Elf Rock.

Lazlo, E. (2006). *Science and the reenchantment of the cosmos: The rise of the integral vision of reality.* Inner Traditions.

Leary, T., Metzner, R., & Alpert, R. (1987). *The psychedelic experience: A manual based on the Tibetan book of the dead.* Citadel Press.

Lefebvre, A. (2011). Transpersonal psychology: A bibliography. *eRenlai Magazine,* www.erenlai. com/media/downloads/ALefebvre_Transpersonal_r.pdf.

Lerner, M. (1994). *Jewish renewal: A path to healing and transformation.* New York: Putnam.

Levine, B. (2010). Are antidepressants a Scam? 5 myths about how to treat depression. *Alternet,* Dec 5, www.alternet.org/story/149084/are_antidepressants_a_scam_5_myths_about_how_to_treat _depression_.

Levine, P. (1997). *Waking the tiger: Healing trauma.* North Atlantic Books.

Lewin, T. (2011). Burden of College loans on graduate grows. *The New York Times,* April 11. www. nytimes.com/2011/04/12/education/12college.html?_r=1.

Lewis, M. (2011). When Irish eyes are crying. *Vanity Fair,* March, www.vanityfair.com/business/ features/2011/03/michael-lewis-ireland-201103.

Lichtblau, E. (2011) Common cause asks court about Thomas speech. *New York Times,* February 4, http://www.nytimes.com/2011/02/15/us/politics/15thomas.html.

Linkins, J. (2010). The supreme court *Citizen's United* decision is terrifying. *The Huffington Post,* Jan 21, www.huffingtonpost.com/2010/01/21/the-supreme-courts-citize_n_432127.html.

Linkins, J. (2011). Scott Walker gets punked by journalist pretending to be David Koch. *The Huffington Post,* February 23.

Lipton, B. (2005). *The biology of belief.* Santa Rosa, CA: Elite Books.

Lipton, B. (2006). From keynote address at Association for Comprehensive Energy Psychology Conference, May 4, Santa Clara, CA.

Liu, J. (2009). *Hope in a Changing Climate.* The film, www.hopeinachangingclimate.org/watch-the-film/index.html.

Liu, T & Chen, K. (2010). *Chinese medical Qigong.* London: Jessica Kingsley Pub.

Lowen, A. 1958. *Language of the body.* New York: Collier Macmillan.

Lowen, A. (1994). *Bioenergetics: The revolutionary therapy that uses the language of the body to heal the problems of the mind.* Penguin.

Lucas, F. (2004). *Ecological themes in Gilgamesh, The humanities index.* Blog, August 26, www. humx.org/movement/ancient/ecological-themes-gilgamesh.

Ludemann, B. (1999). *The great deception: And what Jesus really said and did.* Prometheus Books.

Luk, C. (1964, 1972). *The secrets of Chinese meditation: Self-cultivation by mind control as taught in the Ch'an, Mahayana and Taoist schools in China.* New York: Weiser Books.

Luk, C. (1970). *Taoist Yoga: Alchemy & immortality.* Red Wheel/Weiser.

Lyall, S. (2008). Stunned Icelanders struggle after economy's fall. *New York Times,* November, 8. www.nytimes.com/2008/11/09/world/europe/09iceland.html?_r=1&oref=slogin.

Mahler, M., Pine, F., & Bergman, S. (1975). *The psychological birth of the human infant.* New York: Basic Books.

Maier, M. (1989) *Atalanta fugiens: An edition of the fugues, emblems and epigrams.* Translated and edited by Joscelyn Godwin, Phanes Press.

Managed Care Matters, (2011). *Pigs get fat and hogs get slaughtered.* Retrieved March 27, 2011, www.joepaduda.com/archives/000542.html.

References

MAPS, Winter, 2009, Multidisciplinary Association for Psychedelic Research, http://inderdisciplinaryscience.suite101.com/article.cfm/a_review_of_psychedelic_research.

Markoff, J. (2005). *What the doormouse said: How the 60s counterculture shaped the personal computer.* Viking Adult.

Maslow, A. (1962) *Toward a psychology of being.* NY: Van Nostrand.

Maslow, A. (1971). *The farther reaches of human nature.* NY: Viking, Books.

Masur, S and Swezy, D (2011)l. *Doing the math: Comparing Germany's solar industry to Japan's Fukushima reactors.* Breakthrough Institute, retrieved March 24, 2011, http://theenergycollective.com/breakthroughinstitut/54322/doing-math-comparing-germanys-solar-industry-japans-fukushima-reactors.

Matt, D. (1996). *The essential Kabbalah: The heart of Jewish mysticism.* New York Harper One.

Matt, D. (2003). *The Zohar: Pritzker Edition.* Stanford University Press.

Matt, D. (2004). *The Zohar: Pritzker Edition: Volume Two,* Stanford University Press.

Matt, D. (2007). *The Zohar: The Pritzker Edition, Volume Four,* Stanford University Press.

Matthews, C. and J. (1988). *The Western way: A practical guide to the Western mystery tradition – the native tradition.* (1), Penguin.

Matthews, C. and J. (1986). *The western way: A practical guide to the western mystery tradition: The hermetic tradition* (2), Arkana Paperbacks, Imprint of Routledge, Kagan, Paul.

Mayer, M. (1977). *A holistic perspective on meaning and identity: Astrological metaphor as a language of personality in psychotherapy.* San Francisco, CA: Saybrook Institute, Ph.D. Dissertation submitted in partial fulfillment for the degree of Doctor of Philosophy in Clinical Psychology.

Mayer, M. (1982). The mythic journey process. *The Focusing Folio,* 2(2).

Mayer, M. (1984). *The mystery of personal identity.* San Diego, CA: ACS Publications.

Mayer, M. (1993). *Trials of the heart: Healing the wounds of intimacy.* Berkeley, CA: Celestial Arts.

Mayer, M. (1996). Qigong and behavioral medicine: An integrated approach to chronic pain. *Qi: The Journal of Eastern Health and Fitness,* 6(4), 20-31.

Mayer, M. (1997a). *Psychotherapy and Qigong: Partners in healing anxiety.* Berkeley, CA: The Psychotherapy & Healing Center.

Mayer, M. (1997b). Combining behavioral healthcare and Qigong with one chronic hypertensive adult. Mt. Diablo Hospital-Health Medicine Forum. Unpublished study.(Video available from Health Medicine Forum, Walnut Creek, CA, www.alternativehealth.com).

Mayer, M. (1999). Qigong and hypertension: A critique of research. *Journal of Alternative and Complementary Medicine,* 5(4), 371-382. (Peer-reviewed).

Mayer, M. (2000). Bodymind healing Qigong (DVD). Orinda, CA: Bodymind Healing Center.

Mayer, M. (2001a). Find your hidden reservoir of healing energy: A guided meditation for cancer (Audio cassette). Orinda, CA: Bodymind Healing Publications.

Mayer, M. (2001b). Find your hidden reservoir of healing energy: A guided meditation for chronic disease (Audio cassette). Orinda, CA: Bodymind Healing Publications.

Mayer, M. (2001c). The River of Life: A Guided Meditation (CD). Orinda, CA: Bodymind Healing Publications.

Mayer, M. (2003). Qigong clinical studies, in W. B. Jonas (Ed.), *Healing, intention, and energy medicine* (pp. 121-137). England: Churchill Livingston. (Peer-reviewed.)

Mayer, M. (2004). *Secrets to living younger longer: The self-healing path of Qigong, standing meditation and Tai Chi.* Orinda, CA: Bodymind Healing Publications.

Mayer, M. (2004b). Qigong: Ancient path to modern health (DVD of keynote address to National Qigong Association). Orinda, CA: Bodymind Healing Publications.

Mayer, M. (2004c). What do you stand for? *The Journal of Qigong in America,* Vol. 1, Summer.

Mayer, M. (2004d). Walking meditation: Yi Chuan Qigong. *The Empty Vessel: A Journal of Contemporary Taoism.* Summer.

Mayer, M. (2005). Qigong: An age-old foundation of energy psychology. *The Energy Field, Association for Comprehensive Energy Psychology,* Vol. 6, (4), Winter.

Mayer, M. (2007). *Bodymind healing psychotherapy: Ancient pathways to modern health.* Orinda, CA: Bodymind Healing Publications.

Mayer, M., (2008). Mind-body treatment for anxiety and panic disorders. *California State Journal of Oriental Medicine,* Summer.

Mayer, M. (2009). *Energy psychology: Self-healing practices for bodymind health.* North Atlantic/Random House, 2009.

Mayer, M. (2009b). Bodymind Healing in Psychotherapy: Towards an integral, comprehensive energy psychology. *The Energy Field: The International; Energy Psychology News and Articles,* Winter, p. 13. Available free online: www.bodymindhealing.com/Articles/An-Integral-Comprehensive-Energy-Psychotherapy.html.

Mayer, M. (2009c). Bodymind healing and Qigong in psychotherapy. Alliant International University, on-line course, www.ce-psychology.com/product210.html.

Mayer, M. (2010). Hypertension: An integral bodymind healing approach. *Natural Standard,* February, (Peer Reviewed).

Mayer, M. (2010b). Bodymind healing in psychotherapy and behavioral healthcare. *Smart Life Forum Newsletter,* 2010.

McCabe, J. (2010). *Hemp: What the world needs now.* Carmania Books.

McDougall, W. (1911). *Body and Mind.* New York: Beacon Press.

McKenna, T. (2008). *The alchemical dream: Rebirth of the great work.* Mystic Fire Productions, http://video.google.com/videoplay?docid=-1594923458222660515.

McKenna, T. (1992). *Food of the Gods: The search for the original tree of knowledge.* Bantam Books.

McKinley, J. (2010).Texas conservatives win curriculum change. *New York Times,* March 12.

McNally, T. (2010) Why Germany has it so good—and why America is going down the drain, *Alternet* (October 14), www.alternet.org/story/148501/why_germany_has_it_so_good_and_why_america_is_going_down_the_drain?page=1.

References

Mead, G., et al. Exercise for depression. Cochrane Database Syst. Rev. 2009 Jul 8;(3):CD004366, www.ncbi.nlm.nih.gov/pubmed/19588354.

Meade, M. (2006). *The water of life: Initiation and the tempering of the soul.* GreenFire Press.

Meade, M. (2008). *The world behind the world: Living at the ends of time.* Green Fire Press.

Meade, M. (2010). *Fate and destiny: The two agreements of the soul.* Greenfire Press.

Meier, C. A. (1967). *Ancient incubation and modern psychotherapy.* Evanston, IL: Northwestern University Press.

Merleau-Ponty, M. (1964). The metaphysical in man. In *Sense and Non-Sense,* Trans. Dreyfus, H. and Dreyfus, P., Northwestern University Press.

Michel, L. (2006). CEO-to-worker pay imbalance grows. Economic Policy Institute, June 21, www.epi.org/publication/webfeatures_snapshots_20060621/.

Mims, C. (2011). Germany's solar panels produce more power than Japan's entire Fukushima complex. *Gristlist,* www.grist.org/list/2011-03-22-germanys-solar-panels-produce-more-power-than-japans-entire-fuku.

Mithoefer, M. et al, (2010, September). 80% of Post traumatic stress sufferers lost symptoms after taking ecstasy. *Journal of Psychopharmacology,* www.alternet.org/drugs/147624.

Mooney, C. (2006). *The republican war on science.* Basic Books.

Mooney, C. (2009). *Unscientific America: How scientific illiteracy threatens our future.* Basic Books.

Mooney, C. (2012). *The republican brain: The science of why they deny science—and reality.* Basic Books.

Mooney, C. (2012b). The republican brain: Why even educated conservatives deny science—and reality. *Alternet,* February 22, www.alternet.org/story/154252/the_republican_brain:_why_even_educated_conservatives_deny_science_and_reality/?page=entire.

Moncrieff J, Kirsch I. (2005). Efficacy of antidepressants in adults—Efficacy of antidepressants in adults. *British Medical Journal,* 331(7509):155–7.

Moore, T. (1992). *Care of the soul: A guide for cultivating depth and sacredness in everyday life.* New York: Harper Collins.

Needham, J. (1956). *Science and civilization in China, Vol. 2.* Cambridge University Press.

Neumann, E. (1954). *The origins and history of consciousness* (Bollinger Series). Princeton, NJ: Princeton University Press.

Norml, (2010). National Organization for the Reform of marijuana laws. Retrieved Sept 5, 2010, http://norml.org/index.cfm?Group_ID=7002.

Ogilvy, J (2010). *An actual man: Michael Murphy and the human potential movement.* Perfect Paperback.

Orman, S. (2011). *The money class: Learn to create your new American dream.* Spiegal and Grau, www.time.com/time/business/article/0,8599,2058086,00.html.

Oschman, J. (2000). *Energy medicine: The scientific basis.* New York: Churchill Livingston.

Osho, (2002). *Tao: The pathless path.* Renaissance Books.

Otalora M. 1984. MDMA and LSD therapy in the treatment of posttraumatic stress disorder in a case of sexual abuse. MAPS website, www.maps.org/research/mdma/marcela.html.

Ott, R. (2008). *Not one drop: Betrayal and courage in the wake of the Exxon Valdez oil spill.* Chelsea Green Publishing.

Ott, R. (2010). Bio-remediation or biohazard: Dispersants, bacteria and illness in the gulf. *The Huffington Post,* September 17.

Pacher, P., Batkai, Kunos, G. (2006). The endocannabinoid system as an emerging target of pharma-cotherapy. *Pharmacological Reviews,* September, Vol. 58, No. 3, pp. 389–462.

Pagel, E. (1989). *The Gnostic gospels,* Vintage Books.

Palast, G. (2011). *Vultures' picnic: In pursuit of petroleum pigs, power pirates, and high-finance carni-vores.* Dutton.

Papadakis, T. (1988). *Epidauros: The sanctuary of Asclepius.* Zurich & Athens: Verlag Schnell and Steiner Munchen.

Paracelsus, Jacobi, (editor) (1995). *Paracelsus: Selected writings.* Princeton University Press.

Pasnau, R. (2011). *Metaphysical themes.* Oxford University Press.

Pedraza, R. (1977). *Hermes and his children.* Zurich: Spring Publications.

Perlman, O. L., & McCann, L. O. (1992). Constructivist self-development theory. In D. K. Sakheim & S. K. Devine (Eds.), *Out of darkness.* New York: Lexington.

Perkins, J. (2005). *Confessions of an economic hit man.* Plume.

Pertschuk, M. (2010). *The DeMarco factor: Transforming public will into political power.* Vanderbilt University Press.

Pert, C. (1997). *Molecules of emotion: The science behind mind-body medicine.* New York: Touch-stone.

Peters, C (2011). Overrule the supreme court on campaign finance reform. *The Baltimore Sun,* July 5, http://articles.baltimoresun.com/2011-07-05/news/bs-ed-campaign-finance-20110705_1_arizona-free-enterprise-campaign-laws-campaign-finance-reform.

Philpott, T. (2011). Obama's broken promise on GMO food labeling. *Mother Jones,* Oct 6.

Pignotti, M., and Thyer, B. (2009). Some comments on "Energy Psychology: A Review of the Evi-dence": Premature conclusions, incomplete evidence? *Psychotherapy: Research, Practice, Training,* 49, 257–261.

Pointing, C. (2007). *A new green history of the world: The environment and the collapse of great civilizations.* New York: Penguin.

Potter, W. (2010). *Deadly spin: An insurance company insider speaks out on how corporate PR is kill-ing health care and deceiving Americans.* Bloomsbury Press, www.wendellpotter.com.

Province, M., Hadley, E., Hornbrook, M., Lipsitz, A., Miller, P., Mulrow, C., Ory, M., Rael, L. & Rudhyar, D. (1980). *Astrological aspects: A process oriented approach.* New York: ASI Publishers.

Reich, R. (2009). Robert Reich: Glass-Steagall Act, bring it back. *Reviewer Magazine,* November 15, http://reviewermag.com/press/?p=1524.

References

Reich, W. (1970). *Character analysis*. Farrar, Straus, & Giroux.

Reid, T. (2009). *The healing of America: A global quest for better cheaper and fairer health care*. New York: Penguin Press.

Reinhardt, U. (1996). A social contract for 21st century health care: Three-tier health care with bounty hunting. *Health Economics*, Vol. 5, (6), pp. 479–499.

Rigoglioso, M. (2009). *The cult of divine birth in ancient Greece*. Palgrave Macmillan.

Rinpoche, S. (1993). *The Tibetan book of living and dying*. San Francisco: Harper Collins.

Robbins, J. (1996). *Reclaiming our health: Exploding the medical myth and embracing the source of true healing*. Tiburon, CA: HJ Kramer.

Rosen, D., & Kushnick, B. (2011). How AT&T, Verizon and the Telecom giants have captured the regulator supposed to control them. *Alternet,* January 8.

Rosenberg, M. (2010). 15 dirty big pharma tricks that rip you off and risk your health for profit. *Alternet,* December, 22. www.alternet.org/story/149282/15_dirty_big_pharma_tricks_that_rip_you_off_and_risk_your_health_for_profit?utm_source=feedblitz&utm_medium=FeedBlitzRss&utm_campaign=alternet.

Rosenberg, M. (2012). The scary danger of meat. *Alternet,* January 30, www.alternet.org/food/153908/the_scary_danger_of_meat_(even_for_those_who_don't_eat_it)_?page=3.

Rossi, E. (1986). *The psychobiology of mind-body healing: New concepts of therapeutic hypnosis*. New York: Norton.

Rossi, E., & Cheek, D. (1988). *Mind-body therapy: Methods of ideodynamic healing in hypnosis*. New York: Norton.

Rossi, E. (2002). *The psychobiology of gene expression: Neuroscience and neurogenesis in hypnosis and the healing arts*. New York: W.W. Norton & Co.

Roszak, T. (1995). *The making of a counter culture: Reflections on the technocratic society and its youthful opposition*. Berkeley: University of California Press.

Rowan, John (2005). *The transpersonal: Spirituality in psychotherapy and counseling (2nd edition)*. London: Routledge.

Rubik, B. (2002). The biofield hypothesis: It's biophysical basis and its role in medicine, *Journal of Alternative and Complementary Medicine, 8,* 703–717.

Rudhyar, D. (1969). *Astrological timing: The transition to the new age*. New York: Harper & Row.

Rudhyar, D. (1970). *The astrology of personality*. New York: Doubleday.

Rudhyar, D. (1970). *The planetarization of consciousness*. New York: Harper and Row.

Rudhyar, D. (1973). *The astrological mandala: The cycle of transformations and its 360 symbolic phases*. New York: Random House.

Rudhyar, D. (1975). *From humanistic to transpersonal astrology,* Palo Alto: The Seed Center.

Sabhava, P (1993). *The Tibetan book of the dead (the great book of natural liberation through understanding in the between)*. New York: Bantam.

Sancier, K. (1996a). Anti-aging benefits of Qigong. *Journal of the International Society of Life Information Science,* 14(1), 12–21.

Sancier, K. (1996b). Medical applications of Qigong. *Alternative Therapies, 2*(1), 40–46.

Sancier, K. M., & Holman, D. (2004). Multifaceted health benefits of medical Qigong. *Journal of Alternative and Complementary Medicine, 10*(1), 163–166.

Saputo, L, (2009). *A return to healing: Radical health reform and the future of medicine.* Origin Press.

Sassenfeld, A. (2008). The body in Jung's work: Basic elements to lay the foundation for a theory of technique. *The Journal of Jungian Theory and Practice,* C. G. Jung Institute of New York, Vol. 10, No. 1, 1–13.

Sattin, R., Tinetti, M., & Wolf, S. (1995, May 3). The effects of exercise on falls in elderly patients: A pre-planned meta-analysis of the FICSIT trials, *Journal of the American Medical Association (JAMA), 272*(17), 1341–1347.

Savage, M. (2005). *Liberalism is a mental disorder.* Thomas Nelson Publisher.

Schafer, E. (1977). *Pacing the void: T'ang approaches to the stars.* Berkeley, CA: University of California Press.

Schiller, F. (1993). *Fredrich Schiller: Essays.* Continuum.

Schmitt, J. (2011). There's a right way and a wrong way to deal with a jobs crisis—Why is Germany doing it so well? *Alternet,* May, 30.

Schneider, M. (1994). *A beginner's guide to constructing the universe: The mathematical archetypes of nature, art, and science.* New York: Harper Collins.

Schore, A. N. (2003). *Affect regulation and the repair of the self.* New York: W.W. Norton & Company.

Schultz, E. (2011). *Retirement heist: How companies plunder and profit from the nest effects of American workers.* Portfolio Books, and *Alternet,* September 27, www.alternet.org/story/152549/how_companies_plunder_and_profit_from_the_nest_eggs_of_american_workers?page=1.

Schure, E. (1977). *The great initiates.* New York: Steiner Books.

Scotton, B., W, Chinen, A., & Battista, J. (eds) (1996). *Textbook of transpersonal psychiatry and psychology.* New York: Basic Books.

Shanor, K. (2010). *Bats sing, mice giggle: The surprising science of animals' inner lives.* Totem Books.

Shapiro, F. (1995). *Eye movement desensitization and reprocessing.* New York: Guilford Press.

Sheldrake, R. (1988). *The presence of the past: Morphic resonance and the habits of nature.* New York, NY: Times Books.

Sheldrake R. (1991). *The rebirth of nature: The greening of science and God.* New York, NY: Bantam Books.

Shen, F. (2011). Local activists protest tax havens for corporations. *Baltimore Brew,* April 19.

Sherover, C. 1987). Toward experiential metaphysics: Radical temporalism. In ED Neville, R. *New Essays in Metaphysics,* State University of New York Albany.

Shook, J. (2000). *Dewey's empirical theory of knowledge and reality,* Vanderbilt University Press.

Sifers, S. (2011). Soul loss or diminishment? A re-examination of the foundation for Shamanic Studies Tibetan Living Treasures' Lha Kuck Ceremony, *Journal of the Foundation for Shamanic Studies,* Issue 24, December.

Smith, J. (2004). *Seeds of deception*. Green Books Ltd.

Smith, R. (2002). *Pa-Kua: Chinese boxing for fitness & self-defense*. Berkeley: North Atlantic.

Smith, S. (2012). Disposable professors? How the labor crisis in higher education is compromising your child's education, *Alternet*, April 3.

Snyder, G. (1990). *The practice of the wild*. Read how you Want Press.

Stametz, P. (2005). *Mycelium running: How mushrooms can help save the world*. Berkeley: Ten Speed Press.

Stamets, P. (1999). *MycoMedicinals: An informational treatise on mushrooms*. MycoMedia.

Starfield, B. (2000). Is U.S. health really the best in the world? *Journal of the American Medical Association, 284*(4), pp.483–485.

Steiner, R. (2010). *From the history and contents of the first section of the esoteric school 1904–1914, letters, documents, and lectures*. Steiner Books.

Storm, H. (1972). *Seven arrows*. New York: Harper & Row.

Striffler, S. (2005). *Chicken: the dangerous transformation of America's favorite food*. (Also available as Google eBook), Yale University Press.

Sturgis, L., & Coe, W. (1990). Psychological responsiveness during hypnosis. *International Journal of Clinical Hypnosis, 38*(3), 196–207.

Suares, C.. (1992). *The cipher of genesis*. New York: Weiser Books.

Suckling, K. (2010). Kierán Suckling on the Gulf oil disaster, one year later: Democracy NOW!—April 20, 2011. www.biologicaldiversity.org/news/center/audio_video/kieran-s-demnow-04-20-2011.html.

Taibbi, M. (2011). The crying shame of John Boehner. *Rolling Stone Magazine,* January 5, www.rollingstone.com/politics/news/matt-taibbi-the-crying-shame-of-john-boehner-20110105?page=2.

Taibbi, M. (2011b). Why isn't Wall Street in jail? *Rolling Stone,* February 16.

Taibbi, M. (2011c). Revolving door: From top futures regulator to top futures lobbyist. *Alternet,* Jan 11.

Tarnas, R., (1993). *Passion of the Western mind: Understanding the ideas that have shaped our world view*. Ballentine Books.

Tarnas, R. (2010). World transits 2000–2020. *Archai: The Journal of Archetypal Cosmology,* www.archaijournal.org/Tarnas_World_Transits_2000-2020_An_Overview.pdf.

Tarnas, R. (2007). *Cosmos and psyche: Intimations of a new world view*. Plume.

Tart, C. (1969). *Altered states of consciousness*. New York: John Wiley & Sons.

Taruskin, R. (2005). *Oxford history of classical music*. Oxford University Press.

Tokarska, K. (2011). Congress proposes relief for student loan borrowers. *Equal Justice Works,* August 11, www.usnews.com/education/blogs/student-loan-ranger/2011/06/22/congress-proposes-relief-for-student-loan-borrowers.

Tomio, N. (1994). *The Bodhisattva warriors*. New York: Samuel Weiser.

Tonya, L. et. al., Intensive meditation training, immune cell telomerase activity, and psychological mediators. *Psychoneuroendocrinology,* 2010; DOI: www.sciencedirect.com/science/article/pii/S030645301000243X.

Tsanoff, R. (1942). *The moral ideals of our civilization.* E. P. Dutton & Co.

Turnage, B. (2011). The Astrology of disasters—The Fukishima power plant explosion. *Astrology Media Press Blog,* March 12, 2011, http://astrologyexplored.net/home/?p=2040.

Turner, K. (2011). A revival of Mongolian shamanism. *The Journal of the Foundation for Shamanic Studies,* Issue 24, December.

Turner, K. (2011). A revival of Mongolian shamanism. *Shamanism Annual: The Journal for the Foundation for Shamanic Studies,* Issue 24, December, 2011.

van der Kolk, B. (1987). *Psychological trauma.* Washington, DC: American Psychiatric Press.

van der Kolk, B. (1994). The body keeps the score: Memory and the evolving psychobiology of post-traumatic stress. *Harvard Review of Psychiatry,* I, 253–265.

van der Kolk, B.(2002). Beyond the talking cure: Somatic experience and subcortical imprints in the treatment of trauma. In F. Shapiro (Ed.), *EMDR, Promises for a paradigm shift,* APA Press.

van der Kolk, B., et. al. (1996). *Traumatic stress: The effects of overwhelming experience on mind, body, and society.* New York: Guilford Press.

van der Kolk, B., & Fisler, R. (1995). Dissociation and the fragmentary nature of traumatic memories: Overview and exploratory study. *Journal of Traumatic Stress,* 8, 505–525.

Verghese, H., et. al. (2003). Leisure activities and the risk of dementia in the elderly. *New England Journal of Medicine,* 348:2508-2516, June 19. www.nejm.org/doi/full/10.1056/NEJMoa022252.

Von Franz, M. (2001). *Creation myths.* Shambhala.

Vestal, C. (2010). As economy takes toll, mental health budgets shrink. *Stateline,* July 19, www.stateline.org/live/details/story?contentId=499181.

Waite, A. (1894). *The hermetic and alchemical writings of Paracelsus.* Two Volumes, translated by Arthur Edward Waite, London: Google Books.

Wallas, L. (1985). *Stories for the third ear.* New York: W.W. Norton.

Waley, A. (1943). *Monkey: Folk novel of China.* New York: Grove Press.

Walsh R. and Keepin, W. (2004). Is our fate in the stars? A dialogue on astrology. Knowledge Center, May 14, www.kc.mslater.com/~kfi/kc/viewitem.php?id=170&catid=169&kbid=ionsikc.

Walsh, R., & Shapiro, S. (2006, April). The meeting of meditative disciplines and Western psychology. *American Psychologist,* 61(3), 227-239.

Walsh, R. (2009). The transmission of wisdom: The task of Gnostic intermediaries. *Journal of Transpersonal Research,* 2009, Vol. 1, pp. 114–117.

Ward, C. (2011). The nuclear myth melts down: How the "peaceful atom" became a serial killer. Common Dream.org, March 24, www.commondreams.org/view/2011/03/24-7. Also see www.beyondnuclear.org.

References

Ware, M., Wang, T., Shapiro, S., Robinson, A., Ducruet, T., Huynh, T., Gamsa, A., Bennett, G., Collet, J., (2010). Smoked cannabis for chronic neuropathic pain: A randomized controlled trial. *CMAJ.* 10.1503/cmaj.091414. August, www.cmaj.ca/content/182/14/E694.

Wasson, R. (2008) *The Road to Eleusis: Unveiling the secret of the mysteries.* Berkeley: North Atlantic Books.

Watts, A. W. (1961). *Psychotherapy East and West.* New York: Ballentine.

Watts, A. (1966). *The Book: On the taboo against knowing who you are.* New York: vintage Books.

Wayne, P. & Kaptchuk, T. (2008). Challenges inherent to Tai Chi research: Part I–Tai chi as a complex multicomponent intervention. *Journal of Alternative and Complementary Medicine,* Vol. 14, No 1, pp. 95–102, www.treeoflifetaichi.com/TC_Theory1.pdf.

Weber, M., Fichoff, E., and Swidler, A. (1993). *The sociology of religion.* Beacon Press.

Weil, A. (2000). *Spontaneous healing : How to discover and embrace your body's natural ability to maintain and heal itself.* Ballentine Books.

Werner, C. (2011). *Marijuana gateway to health: How Cannabis protects us from cancer and Alzheimer's disease.* Dachstar Press.

Whitaker, R. (2010). *Anatomy of an epidemic: Magic bullets, psychiatric drugs, and the astonishing rise of mental illness in America.* New York: Crown.

Whitman, D. (1977). Africa and the word. *Parabola Magazine,* Vol. II, (2), New York: Tamarak Press.

Wilber, K. (2006). *Integral spirituality: A startling new role for religion in the modern and postmodern world.* Boston: Integral Books.

Wilber, K. (2007). *Up from Eden: A transpersonal guide to human evolution.* Quest Books.

Wilber, K. (2001). *Grace and grit: Spirituality and healing in the life and death of Treya Killam Wilber.* Boston: Shambhala.

Wilber, K. (2000). *Sex, ecology, spirituality.* Shambhala Publications. www.praetrans.com/en/ptf.html.

Wile, D. (1999). *Tai Chi's ancestors.* New York: Sweet Chi Press.

Wilford, J. & Goodstein, L. (2006). 'Gospel of Judas' surfaces after 1,700 years, *The New York Times,* April 6.

Wilhelm, R. (1931, 1963). *The secret of the golden flower.* New York: Harcourt, Brace & Jonovich.

Winkler, G. (2003). *Magic of the ordinary: Recovering the shamanic in Judaism.* Berkeley: North Atlantic Books.

Winter, C. (2008). Is there satanic symbolism in the GOP's logo? *Mother Jones,* March 14, http://motherjones.com/mojo/2008/03/there-satanic-symbolism-gops-logo.

Wolfe, T. (2008). *The electric kool-aid acid test.* Picador Press.

Wolfe, N. (2012). NDAA: Congress signed its own arrest warrants. Naomi Wolf's Blog, January 12, http://readersupportednews.org/opinion2/275-42/9236-focus-naomi-wolf-ndaa-congress-signed-its-own-arrest-warrants.

Wollam, G., & Hall, W. (Eds.). (1988). *Hypertension management: Clinical practice and therapeutic dilemmas.* Chicago: Yearbook Publishers. Quoted by R. Rosen, E. Brondolo, & J. Kostis (1998). Non-pharmacological treatment of essential hypertension: Research and clinical applications. In Gatchel, R. & E. Blanchard (Eds.), *Psychophysiological disorders: Research and clinical applications* (pp. 63–100). Washington, D.C.: American Psychological Association.

Wolpe, J. (1958). *Psychotherapy by reciprocal inhibition.* Stanford, CA: Stanford University Press.

Wu, W., Bandilla, E., Ciccone, D. S., Yang, J., Cheng, S., Carner, N., Wu, Y., & Shen, R. (1999). Effects of Qigong on late-stage complex regional pain syndrome, *Alternative Therapies,* 5(1), January, Peer reviewed.

Zaitchik, A. How Christopher Hitchens could help his fellow cancer patients by promoting psychedelic end of life therapy. *Alternet,* May 17, http://beta.alternet.org/media/150980/how_christopher _hitchens_could_help_his_fellow_cancer_patients_by_promoting_psychedelic_end-of-life_ therapy.

Zinn, H. (1980). *A people's history of the United States.* Harper and Row.

Index

extremism, 49
    literalistic fallacy, 136
LSD, and creativity, 334

M

Mahler, Gustov, 131
Maier, Michael (alchemist),
    121, 221
Managed care, 332
Marijuana, 335, 361
Martial arts, 146
    life-saving training, 198
    purpose, 207
Maslow, Abraham, 97
Matt, Hana, 157
May, Rollo, 133
MDMA, ecstacy research, 363
Meade, Michael
    quote on dreams, 85, 98
    quote, on our true calling, 99,
        105, 108
    story, our lot in life, 112
Meaning and light (*numen* and
    lumen), 273
Medicine animal name, 112, 256,
    267, 272
Medicine, modern history, 314,
    315
Medicine name groups, 125
Medicine wheel, 261
Meditation traditions, 364
Meditation traditions, and
    Qigong, 271
Medusa, 225, 238
Meher Baba, 96
Meier, C. A., 106
Memories, superior, 84
Mental health system
    creative approaches, 126
    politics and economics of, 330
Metaphors, use in healing, 234
Metaphysical
    ailments of our times, 111
    experiences, my early,
        70–71
    philosophy, 258
    unique path, 43, 67, 101,
        117, 154

Metaphysical concepts,
    genii, 105
Metaphysical pluralism, 103
Metaphysical versus spiritual
    path, 43, 306, 345
Metaphysical versus spiritual
    view of astrology, 345
Metaphysicians
    cross-cultural traditions, 103
    varieties of, 102, 276
Meta-physicians, 102
Metaphysics
    and animals, 144
    and astrology, 130, 373
    and beliefs, 254, 259
    and destiny, 123
    and ecology, 367, 374
    and energy, 265
    and healing the bodymind,
        102, 276, 320
    and synchronicity, , 307
    definition, 70, 102
    experiential, 70, 272, 361
    Hall, Manly, 131, 132
    hidden reality vs. meaning
        reorganization, 135
    of the body, 130
    variety of approaches to, 303
Metapsychology, and Freud, 258
Meyer, Jon, 194
Microcosmic orbit breathing, 81,
    164, 179, 242, 280, 356
    and Focusing, 138
    visualizations, 163, 224
Middle East, uprising, 371
Millman, Dan, 93
Mind body problem, 187
Mindfulness meditation,
    contrasted with Qigong, 169
Ming men (lower back), 184
Mithras, initiation ceremony, 210
Model mugging, and trauma, 267
Moirae (weaver of destiny), 45,
    53, 130, 223
Monsanto, 337
Moon landing, 371
Morphogenetic field, 359
Mount Analogue, xxxi
Mushrooms, healing effects, 373

Myth, definition, 204
Mythic Journey Process, 138
    and Focusing, 240
    development of, 237
    integrative dimensions of, 141
    method, 242
    transforming inner demons,
        237
Mythological themes, hero's
    call, 88
Mythology
    and interpretation, 214, 220
    and intimate relationships,
        128
Myths. *See* Greek myths

N

Names
    resonant frequency of, 121
    symbolic, 124
Naming
    African, 113
    ancient tradition of, 76, 117
    Egyptian mystery tradition,
        113
    healing power of, 121, 125,
        244, 250, 253
    in ancient traditions of per-
        sonality description, 113
    medicine animal, 112, 256,
        267, 272
    name groups, 125
    Native American, 64, 110,
        112, 253, 256
    search for our true names, 99,
        113, 121, 221, 251
    true name's power, 113,
        115, 117
Native American give away, 344
Native American naming rituals,
    110, 253
Nature spots, to rebirth the soul,
    203, 213, 227
Nature versus Environment
    debate, 259
Necessity, goddess, 104, 219, 276
Neck tension, healing
    principles, 55

Index

Other Books by the Author

Books:

Energy Psychology: Self-healing Practices for Bodymind Health (North Atlantic/Random House, 2009).

Bodymind Healing Psychotherapy: Ancient Pathways to Modern Health (Bodymind Healing Publications, 2007).

Secrets to Living Younger Longer: The Self-Healing Path of Qigong, Standing Meditation and Tai Chi (Bodymind Healing Publications, 2004).

Trials of the Heart: Healing the Wounds of Intimacy. (Celestial Arts, 1993).

The Mystery of Personal Identity (ACS Publications, 1984).

Selected Media Resources:

Bodymind Healing Qigong (DVD).

The River of Life: A Guided Meditation (CD).

Bodymind Healing and Qigong in Psychotherapy, Alliant International University, on-line course, www.ce-psychology.com/product210.html.

For a more complete listing of Dr. Mayer's media publications, articles,
and books, and for information about his workshops, book signings,
and private sessions in person or through the internet, see:
www.ReluctantMetaphysician.com or
www.bodymindhealing.com

ABOUT THE AUTHOR: Michael Mayer is a reluctant metaphysician and storyteller who uses ancient sacred wisdom traditions to help people find a healing pathway through troubled times. Michael, "Deer Kissing Eyes," (following the medicine animal name that came to him through his forty night vision quest), helps individuals and groups to open to their inner vision and transform their lives thereby. As a Tai Chi and Qigong teacher, Michael uses traditions of postural initiation to facilitate a person's discovering self-healing abilities and to discover new life stances. As an astro-mythologist (who doesn't believe in predictive astrology), he won the astrology prize from the Astrological Association of Great Britain for the most valuable contribution to astrology in 1979.

Dr. Michael Mayer is a psychologist in private practice, author of twenty publications, including five books and various peer-reviewed articles on bodymind healing. He does workshops on his integrative approach at professional conferences, universities, hospitals, and various workshop locations. He co-founded the Transpersonal Psychology Department at John F. Kennedy University where he trained therapists for twelve years; and he co-founded an integrative medical clinic where he specializes in giving his patients self-healing methods for physical and mental health problems. Dr. Mayer is a Fellow of the American Association of Integrative Medicine.

Michael is inspired by special places in nature where he plays his flute, practices Tai Chi and Qigong, and develops rites of renewal for his community.

Made in the USA
Charleston, SC
10 January 2014